Return of the Peregrine

A North American Saga of Tenacity and Teamwork

The Peregrine Fund
World Center for Birds of Prey
5668 West Flying Hawk Lane
Boise, Idaho 83709
United States of America

(208) 362-3716

www.peregrinefund.org

Working to Conserve Birds of Prey in Nature

Founded 1970

Officers of The Peregrine Fund • October 2003

Return of the Peregrine

A North American Saga of Tenacity and Teamwork

Editors: Tom J. Cade and William Burnham

Associate Editor: Patricia Burnham

Art Director: Amy Siedenstrang

Acknowledgments

The production of this book is reflective of the Peregrine restoration program, involving a large number of people with diverse backgrounds who have contributed in many different ways to a single objective—so many people it is impossible to list them all individually. The authors for chapters and sidebars deserve acknowledgment for their contributions as do the larger number of people who have donated the use of their photographs, and all for no financial compensation. The same is true for the artists who have provided the use of their work and those individuals and companies who control the reproduction rights of art work we used. Others assisted by providing information and advice on many production aspects, including the publication and printing. We especially thank Cornell University Press and its science editor, Peter Prescott, for expert advice. Professional copy editor Elizabeth Pierson improved the manuscript with her very thorough review. Brenda Ruckdashel helped importantly with the literature cited section and appendices while Sherri Haley assisted with proof reading and Amy Sandfort in scanning and sizing photographs. Global Information System specialist Rob Rose helped importantly with maps.

Making this book possible through their critical financial contributions were Russell R. Wasendorf, Sr., Chairman and CEO, Peregrine Financial Group, Inc., the Richard King Mellon Foundation, Samuel C. Johnson, Imogene Powers Johnson, and The Ahmanson Foundation.

ISBN: 0-9619839-3-0
Library of Congress Control Number: 2003111126
Published by The Peregrine Fund
©2003 The Peregrine Fund

A nonprofit, tax-exempt organization.
Boise, Idaho, U.S.A.

Printing: Joslyn & Morris
Boise, Idaho

Contents

*T*his book documents the single largest effort ever accomplished to prevent the predicted extinction and to restore viable populations of a species—the Peregrine Falcon in North America. The book was written by those individuals with key roles in this effort. Although it is not a complete account, as it is impossible to include all the events and details, 68 authors tell their own particular stories and report some of the results. As much as possible, names of those who assisted, and in few cases opposed, the recovery program are mentioned, along with photographs of people, places, events, and of course, Peregrines. Most chapters also include sidebars with personal accounts by those who did the work.

The early chapters are arranged chronologically, topically, and geographically (United States, Canada, and Greenland) as the events occurred and activities expanded, beginning with the 1965 International Peregrine Conference. Derek Ratcliffe discusses his discovery of the cause of the Peregrine's decline, followed by personal accounts of individuals searching for breeding Peregrines and who documented the falcon's disappearance throughout much of North America. The ensuing chapters focus on recovery efforts in Canada and the United States (Eastern, Midwest, Rocky Mountains, Northwest, and California). Several other chapters document the involvement and contribution of groups of individuals such as the hack site attendants, falconers, and state wildlife biologists. Also included are chapters explaining the role of the U.S. federal government in the restoration, and another focusing on the involvement of the U.S. Fish and Wildlife Service and the influence of the Endangered Species Act. The penultimate chapter is written by Ian Newton, who reviews the contribution of the restoration effort and related research to the current knowledge of the Peregrine Falcon.

We thank the authors who contributed to this book without any financial reward or encouragement and apologize to those many individuals who were not asked to contribute to the publication but who were involved with Peregrine restoration. It was not possible to include everyone because of the sheer number of people and organizations. We encourage those not mentioned here to tell their stories elsewhere, as everyone's contribution to the welfare of the Peregrine is unique and important.

William Burnham

Tom J. Cade

Editors

Prologue

Life History Traits of the Peregrine in Relation to Recovery

Tom J. Cade

Much has been written about the Peregrine in the past 40 years, with a literature now exceeding 2,000 primary scientific references (White et al. 2002), and most readers of this book are likely to be familiar with at least the general features of the falcon's biology and natural history. Even so, certain aspects of its lifestyle are worth summarizing here as a necessary biological and ecological background against which to view the effort to restore the Peregrine. In some ways the particular characteristics of the Peregrine constrained what could be done to help the species, but in other ways they provided unique opportunities that led to successful recovery. The following sections consider some of the advantages and disadvantages of the Peregrine's biological traits for hands-on restoration.

Life in the Air

The Peregrine is foremost a bird of the air—a perfect flying machine designed for high speed and aerobatic maneuvers that allow it to capture a wide variety of other birds, from warblers to geese, in full flight. Falconers and naturalists alike have often exclaimed about the Peregrine's speed and the sheer beauty of its performance in the stoop or in ringing flights after high-flying prey.

Indeed, it is the aerial contest between a consummate hunter and its equally accomplished quarry that has always made watching a Peregrine so thrilling.

Many authors have written about these hunting episodes, but it is hard to find better descriptions of the flights of trained Peregrines than those of Major Charles Hawkins Fisher (1901), an English gentleman who hawked with an assortment of interesting companions in The Old Hawking Club in the latter part of the 19th Century. For hunts by wild Peregrines, none surpass the accounts by the two most indefatigable, life-time Peregrine observers, Dick Treleaven (1977, 1998) in Cornwall and Dick Dekker (1984, 1999) in Alberta. These two have each seen and described hundreds of Peregrine hunts and tabulated their rates of success under a wide range of circumstances, in fair weather and foul.

One of the most persistent questions about the Peregrine is how fast it can fly. It depends, of course, on whether one is talking about horizontal flapping flight or the speed the falcon can achieve in the "stoop"—the sometimes perpendicular dive by which the falcon uses the force of gravity to attack its prey. The Peregrine has often been referred to as the world's fastest flying bird, or fastest animal, but

the assertion is probably not quite true either for horizontal flapping flight or a stoop.

A Peregrine's normal cruising speed is about 64 to 88 km (White et al. 2002), comparable to that of many other birds. The maximum measured horizontal speed of a wild Peregrine was 113 kph recorded during a low ground hunt over arctic tundra while being followed by a helicopter (White and Nelson 1991). Ken Franklin (1999) mentioned a trained Peregrine that kept up with an airplane flying at an indicated airspeed of 120 kph, under the unusual circumstance of flight at 3,659 m while following the aircraft. Although a Peregrine is capable of catching very fast flying birds such as swifts, pigeons, sandgrouse, and shorebirds in direct pursuit using its own muscle power, it can seldom catch up to a good homing pigeon, and 112 to 120 kph is likely near the top speed of a hunting falcon in this mode of flight. Thus, a flapping Peregrine is not much faster than a cheetah running flat out.

The stoop is another matter, and past estimates of its speed range from under 160 to more than 480 kph (White et al. 2002). Theoretically a bird the size and shape of a stooping Peregrine should achieve a terminal velocity in a vertical dive of about 365 to 381 kph (Orton 1975), but the speed depends partly on mass and partly on drag, which is influenced by shape. With minimum drag, a 500-g tiercel could achieve about 90 m per second, or 300 kph, whereas a 1,000-g falcon would reach more than 100 m per second, or more than 360 kph (Tucker et al. 1998). Optical tracking measurements of three-dimensional paths of stooping Peregrines at an eyrie in Colorado are consistent with these theoretical calculations (Tucker 1995, V. A. Tucker pers. comm.), as are Ken Franklin's (1999) remarkable observations of trained Peregrines stooping with skydivers from an airplane at 3,659 m.

Remember, however, that a Peregrine seldom or never hunts from an altitude of 3,600 m above ground level, and it must drop vertically more than 1,000 m to achieve speeds near terminal velocity. Furthermore, a falcon usually stoops at an angle of less than 90 degrees to the ground; therefore, the stooping speeds actually achieved during hunts are more in the range of 128 to 240 kph, more than enough to overtake the fastest birds in flapping flight. Consider also that a Golden Eagle weighing 4,000 to 5,000 g probably can stoop even faster than a Peregrine, although I am unaware that any measurements have been made.

It is the combination of speed and maneuverability that makes the Peregrine such an accomplished hunter of flying birds (birds being the most difficult quarry for a raptor to catch) and one of the most awesome creatures to observe in nature. These attributes also carry over into another aspect of its life—courtship and territorial behavior. As Dick Treleaven (1998) noted, the stoop and other aerobatics are often more exaggerated and spectacular in expression during courtship and territorial advertisement around the eyrie than in hunting. The tiercel in particular engages in a variety of power dives (some passing close over the head of the perched female), loop-the-loops, roller-coaster-like undulating maneuvers (in which he rolls 180 degrees from side to side), and various "cliff-racing" or figure-eight flights back and forth in front of the nesting cliff, often ending with a sudden pitch onto the nesting ledge.

Later, the mates fly together in mutual high soaring, during which one may stoop in mock attack on the other. The attacked bird rolls over and presents its talons to the on-comer; they may lock talons together briefly, touch breasts, and engage in billing—the so-called "aerial kiss" as authors of an older period described it. Some of these behaviors may be ritualized forms of courtship-feeding, as the male sometimes does beak-to-beak food exchange with the female in the air, whereas at other times she flies under him, rolls over, and grabs the prey from his feet, or he simply drops the prey to her as she comes in under him.

Perhaps no observer has described these behaviors and the emotions they evoke in the viewer more eloquently than Archie Hagar, the state ornithologist of Massachusetts, who studied Duck Hawks there in the 1930s to 1950s (see Chapter 3):

"The culmination of these flight displays depends much on the weather, but the patient watcher will see an exhibition of flying that is literally breath-taking . . . again and again the tiercel started well to leeward and came along the cliff against the wind, diving, plunging, saw-toothing, rolling over and over, darting hither and yon like an autumn leaf until finally he would swoop up into the full current of air and be borne off on the gale to do it all over again . . . . Nosing over suddenly, he flicked his wings rapidly 15 to 20 times and fell like a thunderbolt. Wings half-closed now, he shot down past the north end of the cliff, described three successive vertical loop-the-loops across the face, turning completely upside down at the top of each loop, and roared out over our heads with the wind rushing through his wings like ripping canvas. Against the background of the cliff his terrific speed was much more apparent than it would have been in the open sky. The sheer excitement of watching such a performance was tremendous; we felt a strong impulse to stand and cheer" (in Bent 1938).

The exact functions of all these intense and sometimes frenzied actions, carried out through hundreds of meters of air space, remain somewhat speculative and inferential. (How does one carry out a controlled experiment to study such behavior?) Likely territorial advertisement and defense are part of the answer, particularly in regard to the tiercel's activities early in the breeding season. Another likely function is mate attraction, in which both males and females engage. Finally, the protracted interactions and displays between the male and female prior to egg-laying probably serve to solidify the pair-bond and possibly also to stimulate and synchronize the reproductive systems of the two, so that the male has viable sperm available to fertilize the female when she comes into egg-laying condition.

Life in a Cage

When the captive propagation of Peregrines began to be seriously considered in the 1960s, one of the big questions was how much cage space would be required to accommodate the needs of a breeding pair. Some naturalists familiar with the aerial courtship displays of the Peregrine argued that any practicable confinement would be too small to allow for such movements and, therefore, the likelihood of successful breeding would be remote.

Fortunately, it turned out that the more dramatic and space-consuming forms of aerial display are not essential in order for many pairs of Peregrines to breed in confinement. A cage on the order of 10 x 20 ft in area and 15 ft high provides sufficient space for a pair to carry out their most important "close-up" interactions with each other (Wrege and Cade 1977). These activities consist of nest-scraping behavior by both male and female separately; single ledge display, in which one bird

The sheer excitement of watching such a performance was tremendous; we felt a strong impulse to stand and cheer.

stands over the nest scrape with head low and tail up, accompanied by "eechiping" vocalizations; mutual ledge display, with both birds facing each other at the scrape, bowing and "eechiping"; frequent courtship-feeding of the female by the male; the precopulatory, slow-landing, and hitched-wing display of the male; female solicitation with head lowered and tail up; and copulatory mounting, which may or may not be accompanied by coitus (see White et al. 2002 for further details). All these behaviors, which also occur in the wild, can be accommodated by a suitable arrangement of shelf and branch perches and one or more pebble-filled nesting ledges inside a breeding chamber.

These displays, which in the wild are mostly performed in a relatively small area close to the nesting site, are the minimum behavioral stimuli that will bring many Peregrines into full breeding condition. It should be noted, however, that some Peregrines do not reproduce successfully in captivity on their own, and this fact may indicate that the aerial displays are necessary for some individuals. There is enough redundancy in the Peregrine's breeding system so that about half of all birds brought into captivity have been able to mate and reproduce naturally. Artificial insemination has been used for other birds that became reproductively competent but would not mate.

Another advantage of the Peregrine in confinement is that it has an unusually calm and equable disposition compared with other birds of prey, such as accipiters, and even with other falcons such as Prairie and Aplomado Falcons. Although it can be a demon of action in the air, the Peregrine actually leads a rather phlegmatic existence, spending much of its time perched and calmly surveying its world or sleeping. Dick Treleaven (1998) has commented on how the Peregrine's dual personality presents difficulties to the observer: after watching a Peregrine sitting and doing nothing for two or three hours, it is just when one drops ones binoculars for a quick rest of the eyes that the bird is likely to be off in a flash doing something interesting. The Peregrine tames readily and adjusts rather easily to human handling and training, and this behavioral equanimity is one of the main reasons why the Peregrine has always been the favored bird for falconry—it is predisposed to domesticated life.

One can assume, therefore, that the Peregrine is less physiologically stressed by captivity than many other birds and that stress-related cortical steroid hormones are less likely to interfere with the function of the sex steroid hormones in repro-

duction. Even so, one of the hard lessons early propagators had to learn was that wild Peregrines trapped in fall passage or as adults almost never breed in captivity and usually maintain regressed gonads in the breeding season, even after years in confinement. By contrast, many young birds taken as nestlings or recent fledglings breed when they become sexually mature, usually at two or more years of age. This striking difference is almost certainly related to the greater stress of captivity imposed on the reproductive system of the wild-caught adults.

Distribution and Abundance

An intriguing combination of facts about the Peregrine is that although it is the most widely distributed, naturally occurring species of bird in the world, breeding on all continents except Antarctica and on many oceanic islands, nowhere is it really common, even for a raptor, except in a few localized circumstances. Over much of its range it is distinctly rare. The name Peregrine means wanderer or migrator, and so great are the dispersive capabilities of this bird that it seems likely there are few places on earth where a Peregrine has not occurred at some time or other. Arctic migrants annually make round-trip movements from Greenland to South America of 24,000 to 26,000 km, and wandering Peregrines have often come aboard ships hundreds of kilometers from land in both the Pacific and Atlantic Oceans (White et al. 2002).

Historically in North America breeding Peregrines were widely but patchily distributed over the entire continent from the High Arctic of Greenland (up to more than 77°N latitude; Burnham 2001) and the Canadian Arctic Islands south through the tundras and boreal forests of Canada and Alaska, and temperate regions of the United States to Baja California and the Sierras of Mexico, to about 24°N latitude. It was never a common bird of prey on a continental scale, being one of the three or four least numerous raptors north of Mexico, excluding some Neotropical species that reach the northern limit of their distributions in the southern United States.

The abundance of Peregrines in North America was never as precisely known as it was in Europe, where falconers and naturalists have for centuries

Table P.1. Historical Peregrine Numbers in North America.

Region	No. known eyries	Estimated total pairs
East temperate forest (Canada & United States)	315	450–500
West montane & inter-mts. (S. Br. Columbia into Mexico)	258–296	500–1000
Pacific Coast (Washington into Baja California)	332–417	350–500
Pacific Northwest Coast & Aleutian Islands	370	700–1000
Arctic & Boreal N. America & Greenland above 55°N latitude	400–450	8600–9000
Total	1675–1858	10600–12000

kept records of the occupancy of eyries. A few local or regional surveys to determine the number and location of eyries were carried out in North America before the DDT period of decline in the 1950s and 1960s. The two summaries by J. J. Hickey (1942) for eastern North America and by Richard M. Bond (1946) for western North America were the starting points for most of the subsequent work that has been done to determine the number of known eyries for particular regions—often states or provinces—and from those numbers to estimate actual population size (e.g., Cade 1960 for Alaska).

It is always important to keep in mind the distinction between the number of known or occupied eyries, the actual data, and the estimate of total population size, which is an inference or extrapolation of known local densities to a larger region, usually stated in the case of the Peregrine without any statistical estimate of error. Generally the accuracy of an estimate of total population size is inversely related to the size of the region under consideration and is directly related to sample size. For example, Hickey (1942, 1969) obtained information on a total of 205 "valid" and "probably valid" nesting sites in the Appalachian region from Maine to Alabama, and he offered a "tentative estimate" of 350 nesting pairs as the total breeding population of this region. Because falconers, egg-collectors, and naturalists had worked this region fairly thoroughly in earlier decades and the known locations were well distributed throughout the region, most students of the Peregrine have continued to accept 350 pairs as about right for the size of the historical population. In contrast, Bond (1946) offered a range of estimates for all of western North America from Alaska to Mexico of 750 to 1,500 breeding pairs based on 78 eyries known to him in Alaska, 67 in Canada, 136 in the continental United States, and 47 in Mexico, totaling 328. Even his upper estimate was way off, because his sample size was too small for the huge region under consideration and greatly under represented the large arctic and boreal populations of Alaska and Canada.

Additional historical eyries became known as researchers scoured through old records in museums, obscure publications, private egg collections, and the field notes and memories of aging falconers and naturalists. Table P.1 shows the number of known and probable eyries and estimates of actual population size based on them for five regions of North America. The number of eyries is sometimes shown as a range, because there is often disagreement among researchers as to whether or not a particular record should be considered valid, or because two or more observers may have reported the same eyrie by a different name or location or because two or more eyries may have belonged to the same territory (all this work was done before Global Positioning Systems). In summary, there are between 1,675 and 1,858 known and probable historical Peregrine eyries in North America, and the breeding population before the onset of the pesticides-induced decline can be estimated at somewhere between 10,600 and 12,000 pairs, of which 8,600 to 9,000 occurred in the boreal and arctic regions north of 55°N latitude. See White et al. (2002) for details and sources.

It is interesting to compare these figures with information for Europe (Glutz et al. 1971, Ratcliffe 1993, Rochenbauch 1998). In a region of some 3.2 million sq km, excluding Russia and associated republics to the west and south, there were an estimated 9,320 to 12,470 pairs of Peregrines, approximately the same as for all of North America, with more than 12.5 million sq km. The disparity in density is even greater today; for example, the British Isles, France, and Spain alone have close to 5,000 breeding pairs, nearly half the total estimated population of North America. The Peregrine has always been much rarer in North America than in Europe, for reasons that are not clear. Some think it is because there is a greater supply of prey species in Europe.

In North America, as elsewhere in the world, the density of nesting pairs in various habitats ranges from exceptionally sparse (one pair per 1,000 to more than 10,000 sq km) to more usual densities of one pair per 100 to 300 sq km, to exceptionally and locally common (one pair per 10 sq km or less, see White et al. 2002 for specific examples). The highest known concentration of nesting Peregrines was on Langara Island in the Queen Charlotte Islands off the northern coast of British Columbia. There a superabundance of colonial nesting alcids (food) and numerous cliff nesting sites reduced spatial requirements for nesting, allowing some 20 or more pairs to breed along the 42-km perimeter of the island; at one locality, Cloak Bay, with a shoreline of some 1.7 km and an area of about 520 ha, five to eight pairs nested between 1952 and 1958 (Beebe 1960).

Densities on the order of one pair per 10 to 20 sq km occur, or occurred, in some local tundra-nesting Peregrines (e.g., Colville River, Alaska; Rankin Inlet, Northwest Territories) and on some islands off the coast of California (Anacapa) and Baja California (Natividad). Similar densities occur today in Grand Canyon National Park, Dinosaur National Monument, and elsewhere on the Colorado Plateau. Otherwise, densities in arctic tundra typically ranged from one pair per 50 sq km in optimum habitat to one pair per 250 sq km in areas where nesting sites were limiting (Fyfe 1969). In taiga and boreal forests, densities varied greatly depending on the occurrence of cliffs for nesting, from about one pair per 100 to 200 sq km in interior Alaska with many cliffs in mountains and along rivers to about one pair per 500 to 2,000 sq km or more in portions of the eastern Canadian boreal forest where few cliffs occur. In the eastern deciduous forest and mountain zones, densities were about one pair per 850 to 2,600 sq km. In western interior regions, excluding the southern Great Plains, densities ranged from one known pair per 6,000 plus sq km in Colorado (but current density is now at least four times higher) to about one pair per 3,000 sq km in the northern Sierra Nevada of California. In most of the southern Great Plains, arid parts of the Great Basin, and southwestern deserts, densities were on the order of one pair per 10,000 to 20,000 sq km or lower.

The fact that the Peregrine was always a naturally rare bird in North America with more or less discrete, localized breeding populations, even before its pesticide-induced decline, made the goal of restoring the species in regions where it had been extirpated or greatly reduced in numbers easier than it would have been if the species had been more numerous and more uniformly distributed over the landscape during the breeding season. Particularly where biologists adopted reintroduction or restocking with captive-produced falcons as the strategy for recovery, it was easy to be optimistic about statewide or regional goals that could be defined in the dozens of reestablished pairs rather than in the hundreds. The recovery goal for the entire "eastern region" of the United States (including the Midwest) was half of the originally estimated population of 350 to 400 pairs, or 175 to 200 pairs, with at least 20 to 25 pairs in each of five recovery areas. The recovery goal for the Rocky Mountain/Southwest region was 185 pairs, and for the Pacific Coast states 183 pairs. All of these goals had easily been exceeded by 1999 when the *anatum* subspecies was finally delisted by the U.S. Fish and Wildlife Service. In retrospect these goals were too modest, but their achievement set the Peregrine on the road to attaining whatever population sizes the present-day carrying capacities of the various eco-regions in North America will allow.

. . . the breeding population before the onset of the pesticides-induced decline can be estimated at somewhere between 10,600 and 12,000 pairs . . .

Ted Swem

… *one of the mysteries of Peregrine biology is what makes a particular cliff or other location acceptable while a similar site is never used.*

The Eyrie and Nesting Habitat

Another aspect of the Peregrine's life history that has always attracted falcon enthusiasts is that the bird often nests in some spectacular and challenging setting, so that the falcon and its habitat become inseparable dimensions of the observer's esthetic experience. A set of Peregrine eggs has a certain beauty of its own, as any egg-collector will tell you, but how much more beautiful those eggs are when viewed in their scrape on some commanding cliff-face high above a rushing river or surging sea, set amongst the grasses, flowers, and shrubs that compose the special flora of Peregrine nesting sites. Derek Ratcliffe (1993) in his book on British Peregrines paints some lovely verbal pictures of falcon eyries.

Although worldwide the Peregrine has adopted a variety of different nest sites, from flat ground to trees, and a variety of manmade structures to boot, a cliff of some sort is by far the most common nesting site. Such eyries range in location and character from high, rocky crags and tors in mountains to river and lake fronting cliffs and bluffs, coastal and insular sea cliffs and offshore stacks. Thus, the Peregrine's breeding distribution and density are very much determined by the distribution and occurrence of suitable nesting cliffs (or other structures that individual pairs deem

usable); only in areas where cliffs are abundant does the spacing of pairs assume a more regular pattern that appears to be regulated by a combination of food supply and territorial behavior (Ratcliffe 1993).

Not all cliffs are suitable eyries, however, and one of the mysteries of Peregrine biology is what makes a particular cliff or other location acceptable while a similar site is never used. Of course the cliff must have a nest site protected from weather and predators, and access to a food supply; but many unoccupied cliffs qualify in these particulars. Also, since Peregrines find tree and ground nests serviceable in some parts of the range, why not in other similar landscapes?

Despite the fact that the Peregrine is a great traveler and disperser, when it comes to occupancy of an eyrie it is a real homebody, seldom switching nesting locations once it becomes an established breeder. Moreover, these favored eyries are passed on from generation to generation, so that histories of occupancy spanning decades and even centuries are the rule rather than the exception, especially for the highly superior sites where reproduction is nearly always successful. Although tradition is no doubt a part of continued occupancy over generations, there is more to it than one bird simply adopting a pattern of use from other birds, because eyries that were abandoned for a decade or more during the DDT era were reoccupied when populations began to recover. Not only were the same cliffs reoccupied but in many cases the exact same ledges and potholes that had served as nest sites before. This behavior indicates that there are special habitat features that Peregrines recognize and respond to innately and that place them in the best situation for nesting. Could some of the aerial displays, the scraping and ledge displays, or just sitting on a rock and surveying the surroundings be part of how a Peregrine assesses the suitability of a nesting location? We human observers have yet to see clearly what it is that the Peregrine's genes are directing it to discern when it seeks out a nesting place.

As Joe Hickey (1942) and other early students of the Peregrine realized, the consistent occupancy of the same nesting cliffs year after year offers researchers some unique possibilities for studying the dynamics of Peregrine populations over time. Although direct observations at a cliff nest are difficult, or even dangerous, and usually requiring rope-climbing, cliffs themselves are conspicuous on the landscape and make regional—even national— surveys or censuses rather straightforward. Population changes over a period of years can be noted by recording the annual occupancy by Peregrines of these traditional nesting locations, as the British have demonstrated most thoroughly with their series of national Peregrine surveys conducted at 10-year intervals since 1961 (Ratcliffe 1993). It was by this simple method of recording annual occupancy of known eyries that naturalists first established the fact that under normal circumstances breeding Peregrine populations remain remarkably stable at about 80 to 90% occupancy of all eyries per year, even in the face of considerable juvenile mortality and human persecution around the eyries. Following World War II the same kind of observations revealed the drastic and unprecedented reduction in occupancy of historical eyries that coincided with the use of organochlorine pesticides in the 1950s and 1960s, and also the equally dramatic reoccupancy of eyries following

restrictions and bans on use of these chemicals in the 1970s and 1980s. By the 1990s, many new cliffs that had never been known to house Peregrines in the past were also occupied, but that is another story.

In a similar way, the tenacity of Peregrines to hold to the same nesting territories year after year and the tendency of many young Peregrines to return as adults to breed in the neighborhood of their natal nesting sites (philopatry) were helpful in the reintroduction and restocking programs. The strong philopatry meant that when young falcons were released in a given area, there was a strong likelihood that many of the young that survived to breeding age would settle in that area to nest. This phenomenon was demonstrated over and over in the eastern U.S. reintroduction region, particularly in coastal areas where we used artificial hack towers in marshes with abundant bird life. Of some 25 towers used for hacking, all but two or three were later adopted as nesting sites, most of which have been in continual use for 20 or more years. Some released falcons did disperse long distances to nest (see Chapters 10 and 20), but most settled within 80 k of where they were hacked. If natal dispersal had been highly dispersive and unpredictable, with most individuals moving well beyond their release or natal areas, as is the case with some bird species, the establishment of new breeding populations by reintroduction in vacated range would have been much more difficult, if not impossible.

Just as numerical increase in a recovering population is an indicator of population viability and normalcy, so is the site tenacity of breeding Peregrines. If our reestablished Peregrines had shown a tendency to nest here and there and to abandon sites frequently, that would have been worrisome. But that did not happen. In 95% of cases, once a pair established itself on a particular nesting structure, whether natural or manmade, that site has remained an active eyrie, just as was the case in historical times before the species was extirpated in the eastern states.

Critics who earlier claimed it would be impossible to breed the Peregrine in captivity and reestablish it successfully in the wild simply failed to understand the nature of the bird.

When considering aspects of life history that influence population dynamics and structure of a species, biologists sometimes find it convenient to categorize species as K- selected or r-selected, terms referring respectively to carrying capacity (K) and intrinsic rate of increase (r). K-selected species tend to be large in body size, slow maturing with delayed sexual development, and long-lived with high survival rates, low rate of reproduction, small total population size, stable populations through time (as long as environmental conditions do not change drastically), and usually with a significant component of nonbreeding adults ("floaters"). Their populations tend to be limited by a restricted number of nesting sites or by territorial spacing of breeders and other forms of intraspecific aggression, often giving rise to "over-dispersed" densities that appear lower than the available food supply might permit (see Wynne-Edwards 1962 for discussion of over-dispersion). The California Condor and Wandering Albatross are examples of extreme K-selection.

In contrast, r-selected species tend to be small in body size, rapidly developing, sexually mature in one year or less, and short-lived. They have a high rate of reproduction, however, so that annual population size may vary by a factor of 5 to 10 or more, total population size tends to be large, year-to-year trends may vary greatly, and there are usually few nonbreeding individuals in the population. Their populations tend to be limited by factors that affect recruitment into the breeding population, such as food supply and bad weather or other lethal factors (predators, parasites, diseases). Such populations usually do not remain long at the carrying capacity of their habitats but rather depend for long-term viability on vigorous population growth to counterbalance high mortality. Examples of r-selected bird species range from the African Quelea and Australian Zebra Finch (both of which can breed when only a few months old, have multiple broods in a season and reach huge numbers under favorable conditions—true boom and bust populations) to less extreme species such as various blackbirds and other passerines.

Between these extremes, other bird species show a continuum of variation in life-history traits. The Peregrine, for example, tends toward K-selection but not to the extreme degree of a condor or Golden Eagle. It is a medium-sized bird, develops fairly slowly (32 days incubation, 42 or more days from hatch to fledging), can reach sexual maturity in one year but usually delays to the second or third year (or longer where breeders are at the limit of carrying capacity), has a modest rate of reproduction (one to two young per territorial pair per year), and exists in small numbers but with highly stable and buffered breeding populations with a significant number of floaters (see Chapter 20 for further details).

Biologists generally consider K-selected species to be more difficult to conserve and restore than r-selected species, particularly when conventional methods of habitat preservation or restoration and legal protection from human persecution are the main methods used. Newton (1998) has an interesting discussion of the reasons for this view in his book *Population Limitation in Birds.* By contrast, when "hands-on" methods such as captive propagation and reintroduction/restocking are the methods used for restoring populations to vacant or depleted ranges, K-selected species have certain advantages. One only needs to compare programs such as those for the r-selected Atwater's Prairie-Chicken and Masked Bobwhite Quail with those for the Whooping Crane, Bald Eagle, Peregrine Falcon, and Mauritius Kestrel to see how much better K-selected species have fared under hands-on management.

For one thing, as previously noted, populations of K-selected species are usually small, making it easier to achieve reasonable restoration goals; r-selected species may require thousands of reestablished individuals to achieve reasonable prospects of long-term population viability. Regional Peregrine populations are just about optimal in this regard. Although K-selected species are slow to develop and have delayed sexual maturity, their greater longevity more than compensates for these delaying traits—both in captive propagation and in reestablishing birds in the wild. One has to wait seven years for a condor to reach breeding age, but once it starts to breed it keeps going for 40 years or so. Again, the Peregrine offers a convenient compromise, first breeding at two to three years and continuing for 15 to 16 years. K-selected species are generally less subject to predation and some other causes of death than the smaller r-selected species, so that a high percentage of released birds is likely to survive to breeding age; the Peregrine is intermediate with a first-year mortality of about 50% and an adult rate of 10 to 20%. A disadvantage of a K-selected species is its lower rate of reproduction. The Peregrine usually lays three to four eggs, and successful pairs fledge one to four young, usually two to three in the wild; but in captivity, by taking eggs away from breeders and incubating them artificially, the production of fertile eggs can easily be increased to eight or more per season, so that the disadvantage of low reproduction can be offset when the species is an indeterminate layer.

Other population characteristics that make the Peregrine easier to reestablish than some other species seem related to its adaptations for small population size and wide dispersion of individuals and nesting pairs. Peregrines have an uncanny ability to find nesting partners over vast distances, as isolated nests hundreds of kilometers from their nearest neighbor attest. Traditional nesting at fixed, easily identifiable locations no doubt makes pairing easier than would be the case if falcons shifted nest sites (territories) frequently, especially so for released Peregrines during the early stages of reintroduction when there are only a few individuals in the population. Also, the long-term use of traditional nesting areas makes any needed habitat management for the Peregrine easier than for a species that shifts its nesting locations from year to year (e.g., some harriers, kites, and buzzards). Thus, the management of a viable Peregrine population largely revolves around maintaining the permanent eyries through preservation of local habitats and, in some instances, by habitat improvements to the nesting sites (Cade et al. 1996). Finally, the presence of floaters (nonbreeding adults) in falcon populations at or near carrying capacity provides a comforting buffer against sudden or extreme losses among the breeders and, as in the case of the effects of DDT on reproduction, allows managers some extra time to discover the problem and correct it before a population decreases to the point of no return.

Conclusion and Summary

Critics who earlier claimed it would be impossible to breed the Peregrine in captivity and reestablish it successfully in the wild simply failed to understand the nature of the bird. Although master of the sky and a denizen of wild and haunting landscapes, the Peregrine has also for centuries been a bird of the gauntlet and the lure—a bird that by its gentle and placid disposition comes readily to the hand to do man's bidding in the hunt. As Frank Beebe (1964) once remarked, it is difficult to understand how the Peregrine escaped complete domestication considering its long history of intimate association with human beings. In short, the falcon was behaviorally predisposed to propagation in captivity, so much so that eventually some 7,000 Peregrines were bred and released in North America, not to mention many more in Europe and

hundreds of others that have been produced for falconry.

Falconers understood that just as a wild Peregrine can be captured, tamed, and trained to hunt cooperatively with man and dog, so a domestically produced falcon can be weaned from captivity and encouraged to assume a fully wild existence. The history of falconry is replete with instances of successful return to the wild both in the case of passage and haggard falcons that were lost during the hunt and also of eyasses that were left too long at hack until they became independent of their keepers.

The successes in reintroduction and restocking were further abetted by several life-history and population traits of the Peregrine. Foremost of these characteristics is the fact that Peregrines exist in small population units of a few dozen to a few hundred pairs, making regional recovery efforts feasible in terms of time and money expended. It was natural, therefore, that several regional breeding and release programs sprang up across the continent. The habit of breeding at the same locations for decades and centuries provides biologists with an opportunity for long-term studies of population dynamics and trends in Peregrines, makes reestablishing and monitoring of populations easier, and simplifies any needed preservation or restoration of nesting habitat. The fact that the Peregrine is a moderately K-selected species means that many of its life-history traits favor population restoration by reintroduction or restocking, as do some other population characteristics such as the ability of individuals to find mates over vast distances (over 1,000 km in some cases). Lastly, the existence of floaters, which are ready and able to replace dead or moribund breeders quickly, maintains the stability and fitness of the breeding population through time.

It would perhaps be too much to say that restoration of the Peregrine was a foregone conclusion for all the reasons outlined here. Still, those who knew the Peregrine well could see, from the very beginning, a rather complete picture of how this falcons's unique traits could be used to recover the species by hands-on methods.

Biographical information for Tom Cade can be found at the end of Chapter 5.

Robert Bateman 1988©

Chapter 1

Introduction:
The Madison Peregrine Conference and the Struggle to Ban DDT

Tom J. Cade and William Burnham

The effort to restore the Peregrine in North America extended over virtually the entire continent.

This book highlights the people who were involved and summarizes work carried out as far away as western Greenland, the vast Canadian barren grounds, northern and interior Alaska, and south along the western coasts, mountain chains, and interior prairies into Mexico; and in the Midwestern Great Lakes region eastward to the Maritimes, and south from Maine to Georgia. It was truly a phenomenal scale of work involving the monitoring of breeding populations, habitat analysis, banding of nestlings and migrants, analysis of chemical contaminants, release of captive-bred falcons on a scale most of us could not imagine 40 years ago, and incalculable numbers of meetings in the offices of state and federal bureaucrats, conservation organizations, individual contributors and foundations, and corporations.

We like to date the beginning of the Peregrine recovery effort in 1965, the year when Professor Joe Hickey (Figure 1.2) at the University of Wisconsin convened the first International Peregrine Conference. At that conference biologists learned the full extent of the Peregrine's difficulties— unprecedented population crashes had occurred since the 1950s in both Europe and North America, coincident with the widespread use of DDT and other organochlorine pesticides. Full proof of the involvement of DDT and dieldrin in the disappearance of Peregrines came several years later, but the circumstantial evidence presented at the Madison Conference and later published in *Peregrine Falcon Populations: Their Biology and Decline* (Hickey 1969) was convincing to most of us.

At the end of that conference a group of attending biologists and falconers got together to discuss what could be done to save the Peregrine from possible extinction in North America. Obviously, as Rachel Carson (1962) had already made clear in *Silent Spring,* elimination or reduction in the use of harmful pesticides was essential, but in 1965

◀ **Figure 1.1** *Peregrine Falcon* ©Robert Bateman. Reproduction rights courtesy Boshkung Inc. and Mill Pond Press.

such action seemed politically unrealistic in the face of strong agro-chemical interests touting the virtues of synthetic pesticides. One of President Lyndon Johnson's scientific advisers at the Madison conference said categorically that restrictions on the use of DDT would never happen. That declaration became a challenge for many of us.

Another idea, especially championed by the falconers, was to breed Peregrines in captivity as a way to keep some birds alive, should the wild ones disappear entirely. Explicit also was the idea that should chemical contamination of the environment lessen in the future, the progeny of captive birds could be used to replenish vacant

Figure 1.2 Joe Hickey, ca 1967, ▶ ex-Golden Gloves boxer and Professor at the University of Wisconsin, organized the Madison conference in 1965 where the role of pesticides in the decline of the Peregrine came to the limelight. He courageously defended the data implicating DDT in the face of personal insult on the witness stand.

Courtesy Jim Enderson

J. K. Cleaver, courtesy Archives of American Falconry

▲ **Figure 1.3** The late Don Hunter, founder of The Raptor Research Foundation.

The Madison Conference

Grainger Hunt

My world view abruptly changed at the 1965 Peregrine conference. Participant after participant told the same story about the demise of age-old populations, clear evidence that this wonderful species was in trouble worldwide. Prior explanations had ranged from a rash of raccoons to the loss of the Passenger Pigeon to a newly acquired taste Peregrines had for their own eggs. Earlier that summer I had studied the works of Tom Cade and Derek Ratcliffe, and here they were! I listened to talks about Peregrines in the Adirondacks and Finnish bogs and the cliffs of England and France. I was particularly concerned about the Peregrines that nested on the arctic rivers and that visited the Texas coast in fall, and I wondered whether they might stop coming. The high point of the meeting began when Ratcliffe and Ian Prestt superimposed a slide of the distribution of Peregrine disappearance in Great Britain upon that of cereal farming. A perfect fit! Prestt removed the Peregrine slide and dropped in ones pertaining to the Merlin and Sparrowhawk. Again, clear agreement. He then substituted a slide of the European Buzzard, a mammal predator, and got no fit at all until the cereal farming slide was replaced with the distribution of gamekeepers. The scientific case against pesticides had dropped on the table like a stone, and all who returned home from the meeting knew they had things to do.

> *The scientific case against pesticides had dropped on the table like a stone...*

For biographical information see sidebar, A Pile of Prey Remains, Chapter 4.

habitats. Thus, the concept of combining the techniques of captive breeding and reintroduction was born at that meeting, which Don Hunter chaired (Figure 1.3).

Under Don's leadership, a new organization called The Raptor Research Foundation came into existence in 1966 to promote both these activities. The foundation functioned importantly in the early years to disseminate information on propagation techniques quickly among the growing community of private and institutional raptor breeders and also in obtaining wild falcons for the breeding projects. All four of the main institutional breeding and release programs—The Peregrine Fund, the Canadian Wildlife Service program at Wainwright, Alberta, the Santa Cruz Predatory Bird Research Group in California, and The Raptor Center at the University of Minnesota—trace their origins directly or indirectly to this seminal meeting in 1965.

After the Wisconsin Conference the U.S. Fish and Wildlife Service (FWS) became concerned about the legal status of the Peregrine in the United States. At that time there was no federal protection for the species. Some FWS officials began considering the possibility of listing the Peregrine as an "endangered species" under one of the earlier versions of endangered species protection. A technical problem arose, however, because prior to the 1973 Endangered Species Act the law provided that only full species or "recognized" subspecies could be listed, and all continental Peregrines from the Arctic to Mexico were considered to be the same subspecies, *Falco peregrinus anatum*, the Duck Hawk. Although a clear case could be made for the endangered status of Peregrines in southern Canada and the coterminous United States, experts thought at that time that no serious losses had occurred among the large populations of Peregrines nesting in the Far North.

This problem was solved in 1968 when our good colleague and Arctic-traveling companion Clayton White (Figure 1.4) described the arctic falcons as a separate subspecies, *F. p. tundrius* (Figure 1.5). Clay had been studying the biosystematics of North American Peregrines for his doctoral degree at the University of Utah, and when John Aldrich, Chief Scientist for FWS's Division of Migratory Birds, learned that Clay had found significant morphological differences between the tundra-inhabiting falcons and those nesting south of the tree line, he encouraged him to describe the former as a new subspecies, clearing the way to consider the threatened status of the southern

▲ **Figure 1.4** Clayton White banding nestling Rough-legged Hawks in Alaska.

▼ **Figure 1.5** Immature specimens of Peregrine Falcon subspecies occurring in North America.

Falco peregrinus anatum   *Falco peregrinus tundrius*

Falco peregrinus pealei

▲ **Figure 1.6** Leslie Glasgow holding a Peregrine on Assateague Island, 1969.

Robert Berry

birds. Still, FWS was slow to take action on the redefined *anatum* subspecies.

Meanwhile, renewed field surveys in Alaska and northern Canada revealed that these arctic Peregrines were showing symptoms of the same pesticide-induced disease as the southern birds—abnormally thin-shelled eggs, high DDE residues in body tissues and eggs, and reduced reproductive output, although reduction in the number of breeding pairs had not yet occurred. It was predicted to occur and did occur in the 1970s (Cade et al. 1968).

In November 1969, a group of concerned scientists held a second Peregrine meeting at Cornell University. They reviewed all the laboratory and field data that had been collected since the Madison conference and decided to send a petition to the governments of the United States, Canada, and Mexico asking them to do whatever was in their power to provide legal protection to the remaining populations of Peregrine Falcons. Amazingly all three governments responded sympathetically, but neither Canada nor Mexico had authority to do anything.

Then, one of the unsung heroes of the Peregrine saga entered the arena—Assistant Secretary of the Interior for Fish and Wildlife and Parks, Leslie Glasgow (Figure 1.6), a quiet but effective man from the bayous of Louisiana. He liked our letter, understood the urgency, and took the bureaucratic bull by the horns. He must have been a disciple of the Truman doctrine that "the buck stops here," because in 1970, only a few months after our petition arrived on his desk from Interior Secretary Walter Hickel, both the *anatum*

Beating the Bureaucracy

F. Prescott Ward

I was effectively barred in 1969 by local Interior officials from conducting studies on migrating falcons at Assateague Island in Maryland and Virginia. After personally approving my research program, Secretary Glasgow, sensing that local administrators still might not cooperate fully, asked if he could accompany me when the fall migration got underway on Assateague.

The island was famous for large concentrations of migrating Peregrines, but falconers' (and my research) access was shut off in 1969 with passage of the Assateague Island National Seashore Act. The northern two-thirds of the island is in Maryland and comprises Assateague Island National Seashore, administered by the National Park Service. The southern third is in Virginia, where the Chincoteague National Wildlife Refuge under the Fish and Wildlife Service is located.

The refuge manager in 1970, the year of Glasgow's personal involvement, was a tall man with a booming voice and expansive vocabulary, J. C. Appel.

My research associates and I were headquartered on the northern, Maryland sector of Assateague. For the visit, Glas-

> *An exuberant Leslie Glasgow banded and released the bird, then turned and said, "Damn, that was fun. Let's get some more!"*

gow flew into a small airstrip on Wallop's Island, close to the nearby Chincoteague Refuge, where Appel picked him up. It was prearranged that Appel would drive Glasgow north through the refuge and meet my crew and me at noon on Maryland's Fox Hill Levels.

Just before Glasgow's arrival, I captured a passage tiercel. An exuberant Leslie Glasgow banded and released the bird, then turned and said, "Damn, that was fun. Let's get some more!" I drove while Glasgow sat next to me in the front seat. In the back of the small, four-wheel-drive vehicle were Earl Baysinger, Chief of the Bird Banding Lab, a good friend and supporter, and J. C. Appel.

The vehicle bumped south on the Maryland front beach for several miles to the state line. Here, a sturdy cable fence on pilings ran from the bay eastward across the dunes and directly into the ocean, precluding any vehicular access to the refuge. I stopped, scanned the refuge beach with binoculars, then threw the vehicle in gear and started north again.

"Wait a minute," said Glasgow. "Why aren't we going down there?" he asked, pointing south toward the refuge beach.

F. Prescott Ward with a newly captured adult Peregrine. ▶

Wendy Paulson

"That's Chincoteague National Wildlife Refuge, Sir," I replied. "We aren't authorized access."

Glasgow was quick and assertive with his response. "You told me when you visited my office that you had records from falconers who caught birds there from the 1930s through the early 1950s. You also told me that they traveled the full length of Assateague. Doesn't it make sense that if you want your sighting and capture data to be comparable, you need to have access to the entire length of Assateague as well?"

Before his political appointment, Leslie Glasgow was a professor at Louisiana State University. Early in his career, he had conducted extensive field research on woodcock, and his scientific bent was being fully expressed now.

"Yes, Sir," I replied. "Our results would be far more meaningful if we had access to Virginia."

"Well, let's go then!" said Glasgow.

Just then the basso profundo voice of J. C. Appel resonated from the rear of the vehicle. "I don't wish to presume to suggest an alternate course of action for the Secretary, but I wish he would consider the following factors before making an irrevocable decision. First, Chincoteague is the third most visited refuge in the system, and many of our thousands of visitors are drawn by the wild character of our trackless sands, by the … "

Glasgow cut him off mid-sentence. "I know, J. C., but this is October, and visitation is down to a dribble."

"Ah, excellent point, Mr. Secretary," replied Appel. "However, please also consider that my technical staff has not had an adequate opportunity to peruse the applicant's proposal, to insure that it fits well with other approved research use of the refuge, to dovetail it … "

Glasgow shot back, "J. C., these boys submitted proposal after proposal to you and Bert Roberts up north starting more than a year ago. How much time do you all need? Besides, I made the decision on behalf of Interior that this study should proceed, should proceed now, and should encompass all of Assateague."

Appel would not quit, and point/counterpoint continued for a few more rounds until Glasgow finally opened the door of the Jeep, stepped onto the sand, and said, "God damn it, J. C., come out here!"

Appel and Glasgow walked about 100 ft away from the vehicle with Glasgow gesturing emphatically. Baysinger in the back seat needled me unmercifully. "Man, if you thought you were causing trouble before, look what you've done now. These refuge boys are gonna put a contract out on you. Your goose is so cooked … . "

In a state of increasing anxiety, I said, "Jesus, Earl—shut up." Baysinger laughed heartily, obviously enjoying the surreal theater occurring on the beach just outside of earshot.

Finally, after a few minutes of animated argument between Glasgow and Appel, Glasgow firmly extended his hand, palm up. Appel slowly and ceremoniously reached for his key caddy on his belt, extended the spring-loaded chain, peeled off a key to the refuge gate, and dropped it into Glasgow's open hand.

Appel silently resumed his position in the back seat and did not say a word the rest of the afternoon. A flushed Leslie Glasgow handed me the key saying, "Here. Now conduct your research like we discussed, and please send me a copy of your report at the end of the season."

F. Prescott Ward, *a falconer and raptor researcher, received a veterinary doctorate from the University of Pennsylvania in 1965 and a Ph.D. in pathobiology from The John Hopkins University in 1979. He initiated autumn banding surveys on Assateague Island, Maryland/Virginia, in 1967 that have continued without interruption today and initiated similar spring/fall surveys on Dry Tortugas, Florida, and spring raptor banding surveys on Padre Island, Texas, in the early 1980s. During his distinguished career (1966–1998) as a civilian employee of the U.S. Army and specialist in defense against chemical and biological warfare agents, he funded many migration and breeding surveys on Peregrine Falcons throughout their range. He was also responsible for developing colored/numbered tarsal bands for raptors and sponsored research into satellite telemetry that now enables researchers to follow daily movements of birds of prey remotely virtually anywhere in the world. He is presently Vice President for National Defense Programs, Midwest Research Institute, and among other things, was responsible for establishing a large laboratory in Washington, D.C., that process air samples collected for biological agents in the National Capitol Region for extraction and bioforensic work on biological agents.*

and *tundrius* subspecies were officially listed as endangered. Today such actions typically require four or five years or more.

Unfortunately, Secretary Glasgow did not last long in office, having to resign when Hickel was forced to step down, but we have always had great admiration for him. He is the only assistant secretary we have known who could get the career employees working under him to do what he wanted done. One example has to do with a locked gate on Assateague Island and how researcher Scott Ward obtained the key to open it so he and his crew could continue beach-trapping and banding migrant Peregrines (see sidebar, Beating the Bureaucracy, this chapter).

It was one thing to get the Peregrine declared an endangered species and to produce the convincing scientific evidence linking persistent DDE residues in the environment to population declines of Peregrines, and quite something else to secure the political decisions to control the use of registered pesticides that turned out to have harmful side effects. But that too was accomplished, thanks in no small measure to the activism of a fledgling organization called the Environmental Defense Fund,

▲ **Figure 1.7** William Ruckelshaus, EPA Administrator who stopped the use of DDT.

Photo provided by William Ruckelshaus

established by Professor Charles F. Wurster at Stony Brook in New York (see sidebar, The Environmental Defense Fund and the Bannng of DDT, this chapter). Charlie teamed a group of young environmental lawyers with some scientists—Joe Hickey, Bob Risebrough, FWS researchers at Patuxent Wildlife Research Center, Maryland, and others who were willing to serve as expert witnesses in order to secure changes in the laws and regulations governing the use of organochlorine pesticides. The first victory came in Suffolk County, New York, on Long Island, followed by a law banning the use of DDT in Wisconsin in 1969. That same year the Canadians withdrew the registration of DDT for use in their country. The final act came in the United States when the first Environmental Protection Agency (EPA) Administrator, William Ruckelshaus, withdrew the use of DDT for nearly all purposes nationwide.

Ruckelshaus is another of our heroes, because he made his decision against tremendous political

pressure from the agro-chemical and farming interests and against the finding of his own hearing examiner. It would have been easier politically for him to let the registration of DDT stand, but he heard the evidence, understood it, and made the right decision. Let there be no doubt: the banning of DDT in 1972 was the single most important action taken to ensure the survival and recovery of the Peregrine Falcon in North America. Without it, we would not have celebrated the delisting of the American Peregrine in 1999, for it made possible everything good that happened to the Peregrine in the last decades of the 20th Century.

With the banning of DDT, the breeding and release programs could move forward with confidence that their falcons would be able to survive and breed in the wild. Since 1974 biologists have released about 7,000 young falcons in southern Canada and the United States. At the same time, remaining wild falcons have been reproducing better and probably surviving longer. The number of nesting pairs began to increase from the late 1970s on, first in the north and then in the south. By the early 1990s there were again several thousand pairs of arctic Peregrines, and the subspecies *tundrius* was officially removed from the list of endangered species in 1994. In the range of the *anatum* subspecies there were more than 1,600 active nest sites known in 1998, up from only 159 in 1975. Most breeding populations continued to increase at rates of 5% or more per year.

Always a rare bird even in the best of times, the Peregrine now occurs throughout nearly all of its historical range in North America, as well as in areas where it never was before. The Peregrine is indeed back, and we now have an opportunity to see it in action in the centers of our largest metropolitan areas as well as in the remotest wilderness reaches of our western and northern landscapes. How much better can it get?

One other aspect of the Peregrine story needs mention—and that is the role of the storytellers themselves in creating a sympathetic public appreciation for the bird, because without the widespread public support the Peregrine has enjoyed, the effort to restore the species would

Ruckelshaus is another of our heroes, because he made his decision against tremendous political pressure from the agro-chemical and farming interests and against the finding of his own hearing examiner.

The Environmental Defense Fund and the Banning of DDT

Charles F. Wurster

By early 1966 it was clear that DDT was causing widespread damage to ecosystems, birds, fish, and other wildlife and that the controversy following publication of Rachel Carson's *Silent Spring* in 1962 would not bring about a ban on DDT. DDT was still being widely used.

In April 1966 a group of scientists and other conservationists, impatient with traditional and ineffective approaches to environmental protection, filed a lawsuit against a Long Island mosquito commission, seeking to halt its use of DDT on local marshes. Two weeks later a temporary injunction halted use of DDT for the rest of the season, and the case went to trial in December. DDT was never used again on Long Island. It marked the beginning of what we now call environmental law.

Impressed with the success of marrying science and law where other approaches had failed, 10 of us, mostly scientists, incorporated the Environmental Defense Fund (EDF, now named Environmental Defense) in October 1967. EDF was to be a national organization, and the idea was to protect the environment by taking scientific information into the courtroom. At that point, however, there was nothing resembling an organization—only 10 people with a shared idea.

Within two weeks EDF filed suit in Federal Court in Michigan against both dieldrin and DDT, eventually obtaining court orders prohibiting DDT use by more than 50 cities in the state. In Wisconsin, a petition to the Department of Natural Resources led to a hearing in Madison involving 27 days of testimony from 32 witnesses, notably including Senator Gaylord Nelson and Professor Joe Hickey, and in 1970 DDT was banned throughout the state.

With more than 100 scientists prepared to testify to the damaging effects of DDT, EDF then sought a national ban by filing legal petitions with the U.S. Departments of Agriculture and Health, Education, and Welfare in October 1969. When the agencies ignored the petitions, EDF filed suit in the U.S. Court of Appeals for D.C., and the agencies three times attempted to have EDF dismissed from court for lack of standing to bring such actions. But three times EDF was granted standing, decisions that became vital to the developing new field of environmental law.

In 1970 pesticide regulation became the responsibility of the newly created U.S. Environmental Protection Agency (EPA), and one of EPA's first items of business, under court order, was to hold hearings on DDT. The most exhaustive examination of the DDT issue to date, the hearings began in August 1971 and lasted eight months, with 125 witnesses filling 10,000 pages of testimony. Finally on 14 June 1972, DDT was banned nationally by William D. Ruckelshaus, Administrator of EPA. Following an industry appeal, the EPA decision was upheld by the U.S. Supreme Court on the basis of substantial evidence.

Central to this decision was the testimony of many scientists documenting the disastrous effects of DDT on reproduction in predatory birds, particularly the Peregrine, Osprey, Bald Eagle, and Brown Pelican. Eggshell thinning caused by DDE, with resulting population collapses, left the DDT industry with evidence they were completely unable to refute, try mightily though they did.

This six-year litigation campaign by EDF not only led to the banning of DDT, permitting recovery of these birds in the decades that followed, but it also produced important, beneficial changes in pest-control practices and pesticide regulation. EDF litigation against dieldrin and aldrin led to a national ban in 1974 on these destructive pesticides. And finally, these DDT decisions set legal precedents in the development of environmental law that became the foundation of this crucial tool for environmental protection.

... three times EDF was granted standing, decisions that became vital to the developing new field of environmental law.

Photo provided by Charles Wurster

Charles Wurster *is Professor Emeritus of Environmental Sciences, State University of New York at Stony Brook, and has been a member of the Board of Trustees of Environmental Defense since its inception.*

19

The Making of *Varda, the Peregrine Falcon*

(Excerpts from 20 August 1999 speech at North American Peregrine Falcon Celebration)

Roy E. Disney

▲ Varda, from the Walt Disney Productions film.

At The Walt Disney Company, there is a common element in everything we do … namely, that we tell stories. Back in 1967, I found a story that seemed to me to be particularly worth telling. It was about the epic journey of a Peregrine Falcon named Varda and her struggle to survive.

When we first decided to make this film, I had learned that the Peregrine was in trouble, but I had no idea how much trouble. So, I figured that all we had to do was write a script, find some birds and some falconers, and start filming. I immediately discovered that it was not going to be so easy. The Peregrine was already being considered for inclusion on the endangered species list. We would need to get permits … and this brought us to Tom Cade and Cornell University.

Tom had to be convinced that we were not just another one of those Hollywood-type operations that might not grasp the importance of taking really good care of the birds. So, he lectured us and made us pretty much sign our lives away. Only then were we allowed to proceed.

Thus began not only the film but also our real education. Tom made us aware of how man's carelessness had brought the Peregrine to the brink of extinction, and we became determined to make some small contribution toward making the public aware of these magnificent creatures. I seem to remember that he also insisted that we all read Rachel Carson's *Silent Spring*, which had come out only a few years before.

We were no longer just making a film … now we were on something of a mission as we put together the story of Varda's extraordinary migration from Alaska to Florida. Of course, Disney is known for telling happy, upbeat stories; but we were also determined to include an unmistakable message about the dark and unhappy environmental threat to the Peregrine's survival.

So, early in the film, we put in a scene that clearly showed how the shells of the Peregrine's eggs had been made too thin from DDT residues. This effect was particularly shocking because it was occurring in the pristine Alaskan wilderness, far from the farms where DDT was in widespread use. Long before *The Lion King*, this scene provided a powerful message about our planet's delicate circle of life.

After we had put the film together, we found an unexpected problem. In those days we always ran the completed Sunday night shows for our sponsors, who had some capacity to edit material they saw as contradictory to their message. Well, it happened that year that one of our sponsors was a certain petroleum company—one which shall remain nameless—and when its representatives saw *Varda*, I got an urgent call from our representative in the projection room, strongly urging me to drop the scene about the weakened eggshells. Needless to say, I strongly disagreed, and there ensued some rather heated negotiations about the nature of truth.

And so, we reached a compromise. The oil company agreed to leave the scene in as long as we didn't use the word "pesticide." We smiled, shook hands … and headed for our dictionaries. We spent a whole day searching for just the right synonym for "pesticides." Finally, we came up with the phrase "chemical sprays and powders." Sounds awful, doesn't it?

It turned out that the imagery summoned up by this phrase had far more impact than simply saying "pesticides." If anything, the message had been strengthened, thanks to the oil company!

So, there were very mixed feelings when our petroleum sponsor saw that *Varda* went on to become our highest rated show of the year, with around 60 million viewers—nearly one-third of the entire American population. Our beautiful winged star clearly made quite an impression in her television debut.

Naturally, we do not take credit for it—we were just one among many voices—but, coincidentally or not, within a year the first actions to restrict the use of DDT in North America took place. The national bans in Canada (1969) and the United States (1972) made it possible for The Peregrine Fund to pursue its path of species survival … a path that was still steep and challenging but no longer hopeless. In August of 1999 with the delisting of the Peregrine, we arrived at the summit, from which the Peregrine can fly high and free.

Roy Disney *is Vice Chairman, The Walt Disney Company, Chairman of the Board, Shamrock Holdings, Inc., and Chairman of the Board Emeritus and a board member of The Peregrine Fund. He continues to influence conservation of nature through The Walt Disney Company and his other personal endeavors.*

Figure 1.8 Marlin Perkins (left) and Tom Cade at Mt. Tom, Massachusetts, preparing to film a segment of a program for *Wild Kingdom*.

have been much more difficult, perhaps impossible. It is no exaggeration to say that the Peregrine became a glamour bird—the epitome of the "charismatic species"—after it was declared endangered, the darling of journalists and newsmakers. Numerous newspaper and magazine articles appeared, and many TV programs featured the Peregrine—*Wild Kingdom*, the BBC documentary *In the Shadow of the Falcon* on PBS, the Johnny Carson Show, and news reports by Walter Cronkite, Dan Rather, Peter Jennings, and Tom Brokaw. Several popular books were written—*To Save a Bird in Peril* by David Zimmerman (1975), one of the earliest and best; Richard Treleaven's *Peregrine: The Private Life of the Peregrine Falcon* (1977), used as a manual to sharpen the eyes of many hack site attendants; Candice Savage's *Peregrine Falcons* (1992) and Emma Ford's *Peregrine* (1993); and children's books such as Alice Schick's *The Peregrine Falcons* (1975) and Priscilla Jenkins's *Falcons Nest on Skyscrapers* (1996). Hack site attendants and other field personnel of the Peregrine projects wrote at least five books: John Kaufman and Heinz Meng's *Falcons Return* (1975), Dan O'Brien's *The Rites of Autumn* (1988), P. H. Liotta's *Learning to Fly* (1989), Marey Houle's *Wings for My Flight* (1991), and Saul Frank's *City Peregrines: A Ten Year Saga of New York City Falcons* (1994).

There has also been one motion picture by Walt Disney Productions, *Varda, the Peregrine Falcon*. Directed by Roy Disney (see sidebar, The Making of *Varda the Peregrine Falcon*, this chapter), it appeared just before the Peregrine was placed on the endangered list and probably did more to call the public's attention to the plight of the Peregrine and to engender public sympathy for the falcon than any other story that has been told about the bird.

The beginning of Varda's story was filmed on location at an eyrie on the Tanana River, Alaska, with Dennis Grisco's field assistance. By 1975 only two known pairs remained on the Tanana, but by the late 1990s there were 27 nesting pairs, more than had been known before the population crash, mirroring on a local scale the phenomenal return of the Peregrine to the North American continent.

Biographical information for Tom Cade can be found at the end of Chapter 5 and for Bill Burnham at the end of Chapter 8.

Chapter 2

Discovering the Causes
of Peregrine Decline

Derek Ratcliffe

*The crash in the British Peregrine
population was recorded by good fortune.*

The Peregrine Enquiry 1961–1962

Pigeon fanciers had petitioned the government for removal of legal protection from the Peregrine, and the British Trust for Ornithology (BTO) was asked to conduct a fact-finding enquiry on numbers and distribution of breeders, their nesting performance, and food habits. I was appointed organizer of the Peregrine Enquiry in 1960, and after preliminary gathering of existing information on Peregrine breeding distribution from interested parties, the full survey across Britain and Northern Ireland was launched in 1961.

After almost complete recovery of the Peregrine in mainly southern areas depleted by war-time control (against risks to service carrier pigeons), by 1960 the bird showed signs of decline again in southern England and Wales. The 1961 results confirmed this decline, showing that the whole of southern England had only 33% of normal population, whereas in Wales the figure was 38%. Farther north, numbers were 70% of normal in

northern England and 75% in southern Scotland. Only in the Scottish Highlands and Islands, the remotest and most northerly part of Britain, was the Peregrine population apparently close to normal, with levels ranging from 80% in some districts to 97% in the inland central and eastern district. The total for Great Britain was estimated, on the basis of 60% coverage of known territories, as 554 occupied territories which (counting these optimistically as all "pairs") represented 68% of the pre-war (normal) population of 820 pairs (Ratcliffe 1963).

As well as territory desertion, there was a characteristic syndrome of breeding failure in the territories still occupied: many were held by unpaired birds, some pairs evidently did not lay, and many clearly failed after laying. Broken and disappearing eggs were frequent in nests that were inspected; and among the pairs which reared young, mean brood size was less than the customary figure of 2.5 fledged eyasses. Coastal populations were also more seriously affected than those inland.

I reported these initial survey results, pointing to a decline quite unprecedented in the history of the Peregrine in Britain, to Stanley Cramp at the BTO. He said the most obvious cause was the new

◀ **Figure 2.1** *Peregrine Falcon Family* © Alan Hunt. Reproduction courtesy of The Peregrine Fund.

and highly toxic organochlorine seed-dressings introduced to British agriculture around 1956–1957—the cyclodiene group of dieldrin, aldrin, endrin, and heptachlor. Ornithologists had rapidly become aware that use of these seed-dressings, especially on spring-sown cereal crops, was followed by the catastrophic deaths of granivorous wild birds on the same fields. Smaller birds, such as finches, sparrows, and buntings, often died virtually on the spot, whereas bigger birds such as Wood Pigeons frequently struggled away and were found flapping helplessly in adjoining areas. Stanley Cramp and others had been assembling the evidence on these bird "kills" and published two important reports (Cramp and Conder 1961, Cramp et al. 1962).

Besides the grain-eating birds that were directly poisoned, the corpses of predatory birds were being found in the vicinity of these bird kills—Sparrowhawks, Kestrels, and Barn and Tawny Owls. Clearly, these species had not fed on dressed grain, but they had eaten the bodies of birds that had, and they suffered secondary poisoning as a result.

Things began to fall into place for the Peregrine. The first link in the chain of argument was that through random factors affecting exposure to seed-dressings, together with individual differences in sensitivity to them, many birds would live and move away from the crop fields having ingested amounts of the cyclodienes insufficient to kill them but still active chemically. Some of these birds, especially pigeons, would move into areas with Peregrines and be taken by them. If a Peregrine ate just one bird with a low dosage of organochlorine residues, the chances of it suffering toxic effects would be small; but if it continued to eat contaminated prey, these chances would increase in due proportion. The probability of Peregrines suffering ill effects from the seed-dressings would increase according to the extent of treated cropland, its proximity, and the degree of sublethal contamination of the prey populations.

It thus became very believable that the decline in the Peregrine population reflected a gradient of organochlorine exposure, highest in the south of England, with the largest extent of arable farmland, and decreasing northward as arable farming became steadily less important. The pattern of breeding failure, from nonbreeding to reduced brood size, was also understandable, as a gradient of contamination within a local Peregrine population, reflecting random variations in exposure to toxic residues and in individual response to them. This became the working hypothesis, and the search for supporting evidence gathered pace. No other explanation seemed credible. As an unprecedented event in Peregrine biology in Britain, this wholesale southern decline had to have an unprecedented cause.

The BTO Peregrine Enquiry continued through the spring and summer of 1962, and the results showed an appreciable deterioration from 1961. In southern England numbers were down to only 10% of normal level, in Wales to 25%, in northern England to 49%, and in southern Scotland to 61%. Even Peregrines in the Scottish Highlands were affected by then: in five districts the breeding strength was down to 70-75% of normal, and only in the central inland and far northeast coastal districts (including Orkney and Shetland), with 92% and 96%, were levels unchanged. The total British breeding population, estimated from a territory

▲ **Figure 2.2** The now-extinct Eastern ("Rock") Peregrine observes a chick hatching.

Charles A. Proctor, courtesy of the Audubon Society of New Hampshire

coverage of 68%, was 456 occupied territories (= "pairs"), representing 56% of pre-war level. Further overall decline was 12% since 1961 (Ratcliffe 1963).

Although the BTO enquiry ended in 1962, I continued to monitor the situation with annual sample surveys. In 1963 in southern England only three pairs were reported, all in the southwest, and a Welsh sample of territories gave only 13% occupation. Northern England was down to 43% occupation, but the sample from southern Scotland was too small for a meaningful conclusion. In the Highlands, the east coast Peregrines were now in decline, but in the central inland district the population remained normal, and in the northwest district it held steady at 75%. When corrections were made for geographical bias in the samples, the national population was estimated at 361 "pairs," or 44% of normal level, a decrease of another 12% since 1962. In each year 1961–1963, the counting of territories held by single birds as pairs almost certainly underestimated the true scale of decline, and by 1963 numbers may well have been only 40% of normal level (Ratcliffe 1965).

Monks Wood Experimental Station

In 1960, Norman Moore in the British Nature Conservancy was appointed head of a new Toxic Chemicals and Wildlife Team which he had planned from his concern about the dangers posed by the new synthetic insecticides and herbicides of agriculture. I joined them in 1963 at Monks Wood in Cambridgeshire, to continue my Peregrine work, as did Ian Prestt (working on the smaller birds of prey and fish-eating birds) and Don Jefferies (experimental toxicologist working on captive birds).

Norman realized that the highly persistent and fat-soluble organochlorine compounds were likely to cause the biggest problems for wildlife, and his program concentrated on them. When Rachel Carson published her devastating polemic *Silent Spring* in 1962, Norman's team was already well into studies of the effects of DDT and the new cyclodiene compounds. The BTO-Royal Society for Protection of Birds (RSPB) surveys of seed-dressing bird incidents had used chemical analysis to obtain toxic residue data, but only when gas-liquid chromatography became available in 1963 did accurate measurement of minute amounts of organochlorines become possible. Ian Prestt set up a monitoring program for residues in birds found dead and appealed for corpses to be sent to him. These were analyzed by independent scientists in the Laboratory of the Government Chemist or the Department of Agriculture for Scotland.

In 1961, I took the addled egg from a Peregrine hill eyrie in Perthshire, in the southern Scottish Highlands. It was found to contain small amounts of DDE (the metabolite of DDT), dieldrin, heptachlor, and gamma-BHC (lindane) (Moore and Ratcliffe 1962). This was the first direct evidence that Peregrines could pick up organochlorine residues from their prey—not just one compound, but an entire cocktail of them. The amounts were probably too small to cause serious damage to the adult Peregrine but could have caused death of the embryo. But if a Peregrine living in hill country 10 km away from the nearest farmland could collect these residues, how much greater must be the exposure for individuals living close to extensive areas of cereal croplands? Many sea-cliff breeding haunts of Peregrines in southern England and the east coast of Scotland backed onto large arable farms where organochlorine seed-dressings were much used.

The Perthshire Peregrine egg was also the first time a wild bird's egg was used to demonstrate the presence of chemical residues in a parent bird. I followed up by taking annually up to 12 fresh Peregrine eggs and any available addled eggs for analysis of organochlorine content. The method does not sample the whole population, because it is limited to females still able to lay eggs, but within this segment it shows sublethal levels of contamination and possible associated reproductive pathology. It also compares geographical differences in contamination levels. During 1963–1966, 22 eggs from 13 different female Peregrines in northern England and southern Scotland all contained DDE—(mean 15.7 ppm), dieldrin (0.7 ppm), and heptachlor epoxide (0.9 ppm), and 18 contained isomers of BHC. Combined organochlorines were 17.8 ppm (mean). Six eggs from the central Scottish Highlands had mean combined organochlorine residues of 6.9 ppm, matching the healthier state of the Peregrine there than in the other two regions.

▲ **Figure 2.3** Dented, thin-shelled Peregrine eggs, a frequent result during incubation.

File photo

This was the first direct evidence that Peregrines could pick up organochlorine residues from their prey—not just one compound, but an entire cocktail of them.

▲ **Figure 2.4** Joe Hickey, ca. 1950, trapping Peregrines on Assateague Island. He is using the "dig-in" method where the trapper lies on his back and is covered with sand except for head and hands. A camouflaged cover is placed over the head so the person can see out while holding a pigeon in the hands. When the Peregrine grabs the pigeon, the trapper grabs the falcon by the legs.

Obtaining evidence on lethal doses of residues for Peregrines was more difficult and rested on analysis of tissues in birds found dead without trauma or disease. Only a few bodies were obtained, together with two trained Lanner Falcons which had died after being fed wild pigeons. Jefferies and Prestt (1966) concluded that a combined dieldrin and heptachlor epoxide level of 5.2 to 9.3 ppm in the liver indicated an acute lethal dose for both Peregrines and Lanners. They also calculated that eating a few of the more heavily contaminated larger prey individuals, such as pigeons, was sufficient to build up this residue level in a falcon's vital organs.

The Peregrine was not the only affected raptor. Ian Prestt conducted an enquiry into the status of the smaller birds of prey, through a countrywide appeal for information from ornithologists. He also used sample study areas for monitoring Sparrowhawk populations in different parts of England and Wales. The results showed quite clearly that the Sparrowhawk and Kestrel had undergone serious declines, becoming scarce or even absent in heavily arable districts and reduced in numbers even where farming was mainly pastoral and stock-rearing (Prestt 1965).

Restrictions on Organochlorine Pesticide Use

The outcry over the frequency and scale of farmland bird kills caused the government's Advisory Committee on Pesticides to consider the evidence and its implications. In July 1961, the Committee recommended a voluntary ban on the use of dieldrin, aldrin, and heptachlor for dressing spring-sown cereals, and use for autumn sowings only where the risks from wheat bulb fly were high. The ban came into force the next spring, and there was a marked decrease in bird death incidents, but the Peregrine continued its headlong decline, probably because the adverse effects had mounted through the preceding autumn and winter.

To our great relief, the 1964 sample survey of Peregrine populations indicated that numbers had stabilized nationally at around the 1963 level. The Advisory Committee was pressed for a further review, and Monks Wood submitted evidence on the damaging effects of organochlorines on certain birds. The outcome, in 1964, was a recommendation for additional restrictions on cyclodienes, with complete withdrawal of fertilizer formulations, horticultural uses, and sheep dips. Although the much less acutely toxic DDT and lindane were not included in these restrictions, their residues began to show a decline in avian tissues within a few years, as the message to farmers sank in.

Derek Ratcliffe

Joe Hickey

I met Joe Hickey in Edinburgh in 1964, and we had a long discussion of the problems. Joe had read my report on the BTO Peregrine Enquiry (Ratcliffe 1963) and knew our views about the causes of the crash. He had that spring arranged for a repeat of the extensive survey he made of eastern U.S. Peregrines in the 1930s (Hickey 1942). Dan Berger and Charles Sindelar were the survey team, and they drove over 22,526 km in 14 states and one Canadian province, checking 133 known eyries in the nesting season, all of which they found deserted (see sidebar, The 1964 Survey of Peregrine Eyries in the Eastern United States, Chapter 3). The crash of Peregrine populations there was complete, and nobody had noticed it happening, so its onset could not be dated. The last eastern eyries on record as occupied were in the late 1950s (Hickey 1969). With reports of declines from various parts of Europe, Peregrines were clearly in trouble on both sides of the Atlantic. Joe returned to Madison to plan a conference

to hear evidence on the status of Peregrine populations in the United States, Canada, and various parts of Europe. Just before this was convened, he was back in Britain to attend another conference, organized by Norman Moore at Monks Wood with NATO funds, in mid-1965. This brought together 71 scientists from 11 countries for a 12-day symposium entitled "Pesticides in the Environment and Their Effects on Wildlife." A final public statement argued for monitoring both pesticide residues and populations of animals that might be affected, for standardizing techniques of chemical analysis, for experimental research on the dynamics of pesticides, for long-term studies in the field, and for better control. Above all it identified the persistent pesticides in general and the organochlorines in particular as the main problem for wildlife (Moore 1987).

The Madison Peregrine Conference

I spoke at the Madison Peregrine Conference about the British Peregrine situation and the work on organochlorine pesticides. Ian Prestt

▲ **Figure 2.5** The chalk cliffs of southeast England, where the Peregrine decline began in Britain and became most severe, and where recovery was long in taking place. View is of the Seven Sisters from Seaford Head, Sussex.

Settling the Matter Beyond Doubt

David Peakall

Egg contents readied to be analyzed for chlomated hydro-carbons.

My formal involvement with the Peregrine saga started in 1968 when I accepted an invitation from Tom Cade to come to Cornell University. It was an invitation that a birdwatching chemist could not refuse. The evidence presented at the Madison meeting clearly implicated organochlorines in the decline of the Peregrine, but it was then necessary to make actual measurements of residue levels to back up the circumstantial evidence. The phenomenon of eggshell thinning had been discovered by Derek Ratcliffe and the results published in *Nature* in 1967. Now it was important to see if this thinning could be related to the concentration of DDE in the contents of eggs. We were able to do so for a series of eggs collected in Alaska, and the relationship between eggshell thickness and DDE levels was published in *Science* (Cade et al.1971).

Although this relationship was important to establish, it was a correlation rather than a clear demonstration of cause and effect. The latter was provided by the work of one of the graduate students in the Cornell group, Jeff Lincer (1975). Using captive American Kestrels he was able to show a dose response between dietary levels of DDE and the thickness of eggshells. Further, he collected kestrel eggs from the wild and showed that the levels in these eggs fit onto the same curve relating DDE levels to eggshell thickness.

There was a feeling within the environmental camp that the issue was essentially settled. However, D. L. Gunn in his Presidential Address to the Association of Applied Biologists in 1972 claimed that eggshell thinning had occurred before DDT was widely used and concluded that "the thinning must have some other cause, for an effect occurring before its cause is utterly unacceptable."

Looking at the relationship between DDE levels and eggshell thickness, one can see a reason for this rapid onset as only a comparatively small amount of DDE is needed to cause significant thinning. Although this fact answered Gunn's criticism to some extent, there was truth in his statement, "Ratcliffe's work was done ten to twenty years later, so all sorts of tests were excluded and the whole story had to be based on coincidences in the past."

While I was standing in our laboratory at Cornell watching a graduate student open eggs and remove their contents for analysis, it occurred to me that it might be possible to measure the amount of DDE in the membranes that remain with the shell. I phoned Joe Hickey and explained what I wanted to do. He, in turn, called the

Western Foundation of Vertebrate Zoology and obtained the loan of eggs collected in 1946 and 1947. With great care I filled the eggs with hexane through the small hole through which the egg collector had extracted the contents. I waited impatiently for the next day when I was able to show that DDE was present in those eggs which had spent 25 years in a museum collection. Subsequently, I was able to extend these observations to a much larger series of eggs collected in the United Kingdom and demonstrate a relationship between levels of DDE in the membranes and the thickness of the shell (Peakall et al.1976). Derek Ratcliffe, in his book *The Peregrine Falcon* (1980) was kind enough to say, "David Peakall set the matter beyond doubt by analyzing the rinsings from a series of British Peregrine clutches taken over the critical period and held in private collection."

David Peakall *was born in Purley, Surrey, England, in 1931. As a boy he had a keen interest in ornithology and chemistry. He completed his Ph.D. in physical chemistry in 1956 at the University of London and was later awarded a D.Sc. for his thesis on the ecological effects of pollutants. In 1968 he moved to Cornell University and became a research affiliate of the Laboratory of Ornithology and senior research associate to Tom Cade working on DDE in Peregrine Falcon eggs. In 1975 he became Chief of Wildlife Toxicology for the Canadian Wildlife Service and was instrumental in building an effective team and accomplishing a great deal of research and many projects. He retired in 1991 and relocated to Wimbledon, England, near his childhood home. During his career he wrote more than 250 scientific papers and book chapters and four books. He died unexpectedly in August 2001 and is survived by his wife, Margaret, four children, and two grandchildren. "We are all poorer for losing him, and trust his spirit soars with the Peregrines he so loved," (Burger and Fox 2002).*

came also to talk on the crash in Sparrowhawk and Kestrel populations, closely paralleling that in Peregrines. There were European contributors from France, West and East Germany, Finland, and Switzerland, with brief reports also from Ireland, Sweden, Estonia, Latvia, Lithuania, and Spain. Of these countries, serious Peregrine declines were reported everywhere but in Spain. The North American contingent dealt with nine different regions of the United States, including Alaska; Mexico; British Columbia; and the Arctic region of Canada. Reports ranged from total disappearance of Peregrines from the eastern United States to some degree of decline, and the only stable populations appeared to be the nonmigratory Peale's Falcon of the Canadian Pacific seaboard and the Aleutians and the highly migratory arctic nesters, although the latter were soon to show symptoms of organochlorine poisoning and decline.

Many contributors had expressed views on the causes of Peregrine decline, and the conference now discussed these in depth. Although Joe Hickey had himself worked on organochlorine pesticides since 1958, and knew well the weight of evidence against them, he was determined that the conference should be properly scientific in considering all the conceivable factors that could have caused decline. He had invited biologists to represent other viewpoints, notably the role of avian disease, and skeptics from agriculture, the agro-chemical industry, and even the federal government. Several university animal population ecologists were present, along with elder statesmen, American ornithologists, falconers, and assorted Peregrine enthusiasts.

The conference went with a great swing under Joe's ringmastership and was certainly the most exciting of the many scientific meetings I have ever attended. With so many Peregrine devotees gathered together, there was great stimulation, and discussions continued far into each night. A highlight was when a long theoretical discourse on how disease could have produced all the symptoms of Peregrine decline—but without a shred of evidence—was demolished by falconer James Rice with a few well-chosen words. In discussing pesticides, some of the American delegates found the presence of White House adviser John L. Buckley intimidating, but others argued their case vigorously. The conference ended with a strong consensus that the organochlorine pesticides were by far the most serious problem for the Peregrine and other raptors, and delegates went away full of determination to take action over their favorite bird.

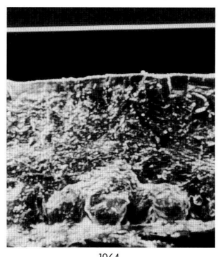

File photo

| 1896 | 1964 | 1969 |

▲ **Figure 2.6** Microscopic views of Peregrine eggshells reveal significant thinning in the 1960s.

Tom Cade, Jim Enderson, Clayton White, and Richard Fyfe decided that monitoring of regional Peregrine populations and residue levels had to be a priority, but in view of the extinction of the Eastern U.S. and Canadian population of the race *anatum*, they and others also determined to embark on a captive-breeding program to restore numbers by hands-on management. Some of the Europeans also inclined toward this two-pronged strategy, but in Britain we decided to keep monitoring and to pin our hopes on the fact that a substantial number of Peregrines remained in Scotland, and that there had been no further decline through 1964 and 1965.

Thin Eggshells

Back home, I continued to puzzle over the high frequency of broken eggs in Peregrine eyries, a phenomenon I was convinced was an integral part of the pesticide syndrome, though predating introduction of the cyclodiene insecticides that we regarded as the particular problem in Britain. I found the first broken egg in 1949, and in 1957 I reported that 13 out of 59 eyries examined with eggs between 1951 and 1956 contained at least one broken egg, compared with only the one instance in 35 eyries between 1945 and 1950 (Ratcliffe 1958). I had early insight into the immediate cause of breakage by watching a female Peregrine eating its own egg at a Lakeland eyrie in 1951. Sometimes eggs disappeared without trace, one by one, and occasionally I found eaten eggs lying on the adjoining hillsides. Broken eggs were also appearing frequently in Sparrowhawk and Golden Eagle nests that I examined, so something new and mysterious was afoot.

I assembled my thoughts on egg-breaking in a draft paper and sent it to several people for com-ment. In it, I suggested that eggshells might have become thinner, to explain the phenomenon. Joe Hickey took me up on this, saying I should examine this possibility by comparing shell thickness in an older and more recent series of blown Peregrine eggs. Desmond Nethersole-Thompson made the same suggestion, but added that weighing the shells would be sufficient, since shell weight obviously depended on thickness. This I did, measuring the size of the eggs as well, because relative weight was the crucial parameter. The simple measurement of length and breadth of the shell with Vernier calipers gave a quickly obtained figure for size which, set against shell weight, was an indirect measure of shell thickness. This eggshell index

$$\frac{\text{weight of shell (mg)}}{\text{length (mm) x breadth (mm) of shell}}$$

proved remarkably robust for the purpose and later became widely adopted in studies of eggshell thinning in wild birds.

The first measurements suggested that older Peregrine eggshells were indeed heavier and thicker than those laid since 1950, but I needed a much larger sample. There were plenty of pre-1940 eggshells in museum collections, but most eggshells from the 1940s and 1950s were in private collections, and illegally taken, but I had no trouble gaining access to as many as I needed. A tour of the country with my calipers and weighing machine provided a mass of data leaving no doubt that Peregrine eggshells had suddenly become markedly thinner from 1947 onward: 371 shells from various districts of Britain and Ireland from 1900 to 1946 had a mean index of thickness of 1.84 mm, whereas 158 from England and Scotland after 1946 had a mean index of 1.47 mm, a decrease of 20%. Sparrowhawk eggshells I had examined showed a decrease in index of 16%, and those of Golden Eagle from the west of Scotland a decrease of 9%, but those from the east of Scotland showed no significant change.

In a short paper in *Nature* giving the results, I claimed a causal correlation between eggshell thinning and egg-breaking in these three raptors (Ratcliffe 1967). I also ventured to say that eggshell thinning followed some pervasive environmental change around 1947, and that the introduction of DDT into general use around 1945 to 1946 coincided closely with the onset of the phenomenon.

Learning of events, Joe Hickey said, "This is a real break-through," and two weeks later his assistant, Dan Anderson, began a tour of U.S. egg collections, also armed with calipers and scale. The result was the finding that North American Peregrines and 22 other raptorial and fish-eating birds had also suffered a substantial decrease in eggshell thickness, dating from exactly the same time (Hickey and Anderson 1968).

Eggshell thinning at once provided a feasible explanation of how a Peregrine population could fade away to nothing through adverse effects on reproduction alone.

The Experimentalists

So far, the evidence for damaging effects of organochlorine pesticides on birds of prey was largely circumstantial. The geographical and temporal correlations between organochlorine use and raptor decline, the pattern of decline in populations and of residue levels in sampled individuals, and the known toxicological data on the same residues in other captive species were highly suggestive but not enough to convince determined skeptics. There had to be experimental work under controlled conditions, preferably using the affected species, to obtain acceptable proof.

At the Patuxent Wildlife Research Center of the U.S. Fish and Wildlife Service in Maryland, Lucille and Bill Stickel had been working on the effects of organochlorines on nonraptorial species, and had also set up a captive-breeding colony of American Kestrels for such experimentation. This work was later handled by Richard Porter and Stanley Wiemeyer. Because concern in the United States was about the massive scale of DDT use and the evidence for its dire effects on other bird species, experimental work there tended to focus primarily on this chemical. DDT and its metabolite DDE had a fairly low avian acute toxicity, so that high tissue levels were needed to kill experimental birds. Porter and Wiemeyer (1972) nevertheless found that low dietary levels of DDE could kill captive kestrels. Much work was done on the effects of DDT on reproduction, and when the eggshell thinning story emerged, effort at once focused on that aspect.

Several studies soon reported that DDT and DDE were potent agents of eggshell thinning in birds (Porter and Wiemeyer 1969). The most convincing work, as regards wild raptors, was by Lincer (1975) who showed that the levels of DDE that produced eggshell thinning in American Kestrels experimentally were the same as those found in a sample of a wild population. Of the other organochlorines examined, dieldrin had no significant effect on eggshell thickness.

Photos courtesy of USGS Patuxent Wildlife Research Center

▲ **Figures 2.7 and 2.8** Bill and Lucille Stickel.

31

Much work also went into investigations of the precise biochemical mechanisms involved in DDT/DDE-induced eggshell thinning. Experimental poisoning of a captive Peregrine population with the acutely toxic cyclodienes was too much for anyone to contemplate, and it was never attempted. The evidence that dieldrin had been a major factor in Peregrine decline thus continued to rest on data for acute toxicity to other captive birds, such as pigeons, quail, and finches, which may have had different physiological tolerances than the raptors.

The discovery of the adverse effects of polychlorinated biphenyls on wild birds (Jensen 1966) was an additional complicating factor. A good deal of research by Bob Risebrough and others went into studying the effects of these industrial pollutants. Their role in Peregrine problems has never been clear, but at high tissue levels they may well have had an additive effect to the insecticide residues. In Sweden, the persistent organomercury fungicides were shown to be a major hazard to birds of prey, and could well have had an additive effect to the organochlorines in Britain, but their role here was never investigated in depth.

The Arguments and Decisions

The wildlife ecologists arguing for removal of pesticides damaging to wildlife met stonewall opposition from the agro-chemical and agricultural lobbies. Van den Bosch (1980) has given a chilling portrayal of what this hostility amounted to in the United States. In Britain, besides the pesticide manufacturers, we had the government's Ministry of Agriculture, Fisheries and Food (and the Scottish and Welsh equivalents) ranged against us in their self-adopted role of friends to farmers and agribusiness. Leading figures in the Agricultural Research Council were also a major source of opposition.

We were dealing with scientists turned lawyers, and making our case against an interest heavy with commercial implications, i.e., conservation politics. Every trick in the courtroom book was invoked by the opposition, including smear technique. There were tedious arguments about the nature of proof and the validity of circumstantial evidence. Pesticide chemists read the odd book on animal population dynamics and proceeded to lecture us on the many other possible causes of raptor decline. Obscurantism appeared to be the opposition's game. In Britain, disciples of the eminent insect physiologist Vincent Wigglesworth, (who had himself warned against the

dangers of profligate use of DDT) were especially hostile. In his accompanying essay (see sidebar, Settling the Matter Beyond Doubt, this chapter), David Peakall shows how D. L. Gunn (1972) made a fool of himself by trying to be clever. Another influential scientist in the same camp simply denied the evidence that DDT had caused eggshell thinning. Some of these adversaries had worked in the tropics, on locust and malaria control, and were so convinced that DDT was an unqualified blessing to humankind that their emotions overrode their science.

With tactics such as these, it was heavy going even to obtain a fair hearing. In the United States the Environmental Defense Fund, led by Charles Wurster, conducted a major campaign for the control of organochlorine pesticides, leading to the hearings on DDT in 1968 (see sidebar, The Environmental Defense Fund and the Banning of DDT, Chapter 1). There was great rejoicing in the environmental camp in 1972, when William Ruckelshaus, the first administrator of the Environmental Protection Agency, courageously banned the use of DDT throughout the United States. In Britain, it was more difficult to convince a somewhat skeptical Advisory Committee on Pesticides (biased toward agricultural interests) of the need for drastic action. Instead we had a series of "voluntary bans" (the British urge not to coerce farmers and landowners) in 1962, 1964, and 1969, which increasingly restricted the use of organochlorines. Dieldrin was banned as a cereal seed-dressing in 1975, but only when the European Union brought in a mandatory ban in 1979 were most organochlorines phased out here. Yet even now, there are in Britain several permitted uses of lindane and one emergency use of DDT. Most other European countries banned the organochlorines by the early 1970s.

The organochlorine problem was solved, and a major wildlife conservation victory won, through the efforts of the 1960s and early 1970s. The final proof of the rightness of our case has been the recovery of the affected populations of birds, especially the Peregrine, and thickness of their eggshells. In the United States this was boosted by the captive-breeding programs that others report on, but these could hardly have achieved such success had there still been a significant environmental problem with DDT and other organochlorines. The British Peregrine population is now at a higher level than ever known before, and most European countries report substantial recovery.

A great deal of further research has rightly continued into pesticide-wildlife effects. Any lingering doubts among the skeptics about the scientific validity of the earlier evidence should have been dispelled by such studies as Ian Newton's comprehensive research on British Sparrowhawks and other raptors and pesticides (Newton 1986). There are valuable reviews which guide interested readers through the now vast literature and present a coherent view of the extremely complex story (Newton 1979, Sheail 1985, Moore 1987).

A rather fruitless debate developed over the relative contributions of DDT and cyclodienes to the crash of Peregrine populations in the United States and Britain (Cade et al.1988). The balance of evidence is that DDT was the main agent of decline in the United States, through causing widespread reproductive failure, whereas in Britain dieldrin brought numbers down rapidly by causing much enhanced adult mortality. There were no doubt local variations in the contributions of various pesticides according to differences in scale and manner of use.

The delisting of the Peregrine as an endangered species in the United States, celebrated in Boise in 1999, is a rare wildlife conservation success story, and one that represents the efforts of a great many people. At the risk of being invidious, I single out the following names for particular acknowledgement for influencing my perspective: Dan Berger, Tom Cade, Jim Enderson, Richard Fyfe, Chuck Henny, Joe Hickey, Don Jefferies, Norman Moore, Morley Nelson, the late David Peakall, Richard Porter, the late Ian Prestt, Bob Risebrough, Lucille and Bill Stickel, Jim Weaver, Clayton White, Stanley Wiemeyer, and Charles Wurster.

Photo provided by Derek Ratcliffe

Derek Ratcliffe *began looking at nesting Peregrines in the English Lake District and southern Scotland while he was a schoolboy, and by searching for eyries every year, gradually worked out their breeding distribution in these regions. After university he joined the staff of the British Government's Nature Conservancy in 1956 and a few years later was asked to organize the national Peregrine census for the British Trust for Ornithology in 1961–1962. This led to annual monitoring of population samples and to involvement in organochlorine pesticide studies, which identified these chemicals as the cause of Peregrine decline in the United Kingdom. He organized subsequent national surveys in 1971 and 1981, and as Chief Scientist of the Nature Conservancy (from 1973) was able to sponsor further raptor-pesticide studies. Since retiring in 1989 he has remained involved in Peregrine surveys and published a revised edition of his book* The Peregrine Falcon, *incorporating data from the last national census, in 1991.*

Chapter 3

History and Extinction
of the Appalachian Peregrine

Robert B. Berry

While driving to and from Penn State in the mid-1950s, I always pulled over at the Dauphin Narrows on the Susquehanna River, just north of Harrisburg, to glass for resident Duck Hawks. In the 1930s, the now famous Craighead brothers had discovered the birds nesting in an alternate site atop an abandoned bridge piling in the river channel. They theorized that the falcons moved from the towering cliff because "they were constantly being shot at and often robbed" (Craighead and Craighead 1939). Despite the unique nesting location, only three young had been recorded since 1939, one fledging in 1946 and two taken by falconers in 1949 (J. Rice pers. comm.). In the early and mid-1950s, one or both adults could be found perched on the pilings, and I had seen them many times before.

On a morning in early May of 1955, the resident female was perched on the second piling from the south shore riverbank. Suddenly her mate appeared with a prey item in his feet and flew directly to the closest piling, vanishing into the dense brush and small trees that grew out of the crumbling downstream portion of the pier. An instant later he emerged and flew directly upriver from whence he had come. Soon he reappeared with another prey item and repeated his performance. I was witness either to a resident pair of Duck Hawks that had young or to an overachieving provider caching food items for future use. Quickly rejecting the rainy day scenario, I headed straight for the home of my friend and mentor Jim Rice, the leading authority on the Duck Hawk in the central Appalachians. The news appeared plausible but unlikely. My previous success in falconry helped convince Rice not only to approve of my taking an eyass for falconry but to help in the endeavor as well.

The next morning Rice and I were standing on the bank of a rain-swollen, murky Susquehanna River, weighing our options about how to get to the pier. We were unaware that two decades earlier, a Craighead brothers' photo excursion to this very same pier, in a rented canoe with an incompetent boatman, nearly ended in disaster. As John Craighead inched his way up the pier's 30-foot wall, two young falcons prematurely fledged and flew out over the river, one reaching the far bank, the other fluttering to the tenuous security of a large rock protruding in midchannel. Determined photographers, the twins paddled into the

◀ **Figure 3.1** Painting by E.L. Poole. Reproduction rights courtesy Frank Bond.
Earl Poole was a lifelong champion of the Duck Hawk.

swirling rapids, reaching the rock only to frighten the young falcon into the river. Pandemonium ensued. The boatman dropped his paddle, the canoe careened sideways and was swamped, but the buoyant eyass was quickly rescued and returned to the piling for photographs (Craighead and Craighead 1939).

Undaunted by fear of failure, or worse, in reaching and then climbing the piling, we decided I should take the plunge and swim to the pier. In our favor, Rice and I were both strong competition swimmers in the prime of life. Our plan was for me to swim to a point far upriver, where the current was relatively slow, and simply drift downstream to the piling, thus avoiding the rapids below. We both assumed I could buck the current on the return trip, albeit with an eyass Duck Hawk lashed to my head, turban style. Rice would stay on shore and go for help if necessary. The first lap proved uneventful, as did climbing the piling, which was aided by a profusion of encroaching vegetation.

Upon reaching the top, I was transfixed at the sight of a strikingly beautiful, nearly fledged eyass Duck Hawk standing calmly amid a carpet of Blue Jay feathers, alongside the carcass of a completely intact Great Crested Flycatcher. The image of this perfect-feathered jewel, nearly the last of its population, as the epicenter of this immense riverine panorama is among my most cherished and haunting memories. I recall wanting to possess that young falcon more than anything else in the world.

Moments later, I departed upriver with only my memories. I had been thoroughly indoctrinated with Rice's version of the falconer's ethic to leave an eyass in every nest.

None of Rice's half-dozen active central Appalachian eyries were productive that year, and only two other pairs were in residence. Several weeks later, we miraculously located a fledgling female at Jump Mountain in western Virginia, a productive and popular Duck Hawk eyrie of the past, long felt to be permanently abandoned. As a pioneer falcon breeder and research collaborator with The Peregrine Fund, I have often fantasized and agonized about the lost opportunity and what might have been. Four more Duck Hawks were known to fledge from the central Appalachians, the last bearers of this population's genes (Rice 1960).

A Candidate Subspecies

Known as the Great Footed Hawk in Audubon's time, the Appalachian Peregrine throughout the Appalachian corridor, and the

▲ **Figure 3.2** Aerial view from cliffs overlooking the Dauphin Narrows on the Susquehanna River. Duck Hawks perched and nested on one of the three pilings closest to the south (right) shoreline, a highly unusual nest site.

▲ **Figure 3.3** John and Frank Craighead at the Dauphin Narrows, holding a fledged Duck Hawk after rescue from the river, 1939.

▲ **Figure 3.5** Released captive-bred Peregrines occupied the Dauphin Narrows bridge pilings, 1977.

Rock Peregrine or Inland Peregrine to a small group of falconer aficionados, *Falco peregrinus anatum* bore the common name of Duck Hawk throughout the first half of the 20th Century. It was considered to occupy nearly all of North America at that time, the exception being the Pacific Northwest, where Peale's Peregrines (*F. p. pealei*) occurred (White 1968).

The eastern *anatum* was large and dark compared with Peregrine populations throughout the world (White 1968), with extensive dark marking and a rufous suffusion on its breast. In a 1946 exchange of correspondence with Ernst Mayr, Curator of Birds at the American Museum of Natural History, Walter R. Spofford, neuroanatomist, naturalist, and a falconer for much of his life, proposed that the Appalachian population be reclassified as a separate race of Peregrine, rather than continue to be considered a geographic population of *F. p. anatum* (correspondence *in* Archives of American Falconry). Mayr agreed that the local specimens available to him from Pennsylvania and New Jersey were "strikingly different" from the highly migratory arctic specimens. He described the adults as having a very black head with a mustache so broad as to merge with the side of the hind neck, completely eliminating the white cheek area. Black marks on the lower back and rump were broad, and the breast was much more heavily marked. Mayr concluded, however, that the occasional specimen did not fit this pro-

file and that more museum specimens were needed. Spofford argued in vain that a valid character of a separate race need only be in a large majority of individuals, especially in a species where breeding and migratory populations overlap. Owing in part to the expressed need for additional museum specimens, Spofford's initiative was apparently dropped. Earlier, Philadelphia Academy of Natural Sciences curator John Cassin (1813-1869) recognized that the western *anatum* falcons were smaller than those of the eastern forest and attempted to separate the races by naming the western subspecies *F. p. nigriceps* (Grinnell 1932). Donald G. Spencer also felt that the Appalachian birds' significantly large size (compared with other Peregrines), distinctive coloration, and less-defined migratory habit all pointed to a separate race (Hickey 1969).

No one thought to enlist the aid of falconers, who were in a unique position to supplement the available museum data with live or deceased Appalachian Duck Hawks for a direct comparison with other populations. Falconers weighed their birds daily as an integral part of the training and hunting process. A wealth of Duck Hawk weights and photos exist in recorded interviews with prominent early falconers and in their personal correspondence (Brian McDonald, Sidney Sigwald, Steve Gatti, and Morley Nelson pers. comm., Archives of American Falconry Interview Series), and I supplemented these with personal

. . . I was transfixed at the sight of a strikingly beautiful, nearly fledged eyass Duck Hawk standing calmly amid a carpet of Blue Jay feathers . . .

▲ **Figure3.6** A Duck Hawk feeds its young at a New Hampshire eyrie, circa 1947.

trapped at 709 g (25 oz); two passage females trapped in their first fall at 1,105 g (39 oz) and 1,191 g (42 oz); and two haggard (adult) females, one weighing 1,190 g (42 oz), the second trapped in the city of Falls Church, Virginia, by Al Nye in 1945, weighing 1,531 g (54 oz).

In his doctoral dissertation, "Biosystematics of the North American Peregrine Falcons," Clayton White (1968) acknowledged that weight is often used as an index of size, but in the Peregrine weight is not a satisfactory criterion for distinguishing a subspecies, and weights were seldom available for the museum specimens he examined. He determined as well that comparison by size, determined by measuring various physical characters such as length of wing, tail, tarsus, and toes, was not uniformly diagnostic. Acknowledging that the average eastern *anatum* adult Peregrine was larger and darker than the smaller and more rufous western *anatum*, White also found that the immature specimens of the two populations were essentially the same color. Nonetheless, he affirmed that the largest eastern forest Peregrines were from the Appalachians in Pennsylvania and New York (and presumably throughout the Appalachian range), compared with a smaller Midwestern *anatum* in Minnesota, Wisconsin, and Michigan. White examined 77 eastern Peregrine specimens, collected throughout the year from Labrador and Ontario south to Florida and west to Minnesota, Wisconsin, and Kansas. He did not separate the populations, even though the Appalachian Mountain chain contained the core eastern forest population, concluding that *F. p. anatum* is "rather variable" (White 1968).

It is puzzling to me that with 20-some taxonomic races recognized worldwide, most of which are not distinct enough to be easily recognizable from their neighbors (Cade 1982), one of the most distinctly large and dark populations of Peregrines was not recognized as a subspecies. To the small number of us still living who had contact with the last few individuals of this population, there is little doubt that the Appalachian Peregrine was a recognizable race. To have exterminated an entire race is a catastrophe.

Geographic Distribution

The eastern population of *F. p. anatum* inhabited a vast area east of the Mississippi River, north to the Canadian Shield, and south into some of the Gulf States. Hickey and Anderson (1969) opined that the eastern population was far in excess of Hickey's (1942) previous estimates. Hickey (1942) had tentatively placed the number of breeding pairs in the eastern states at 350, but

interviews. Table 3.1 provides both the mean and range of weights for captive Appalachian *F. p. anatum*, Pacific Northwest (Queen Charlotte and Aleutian Islands) *F. p. pealei* adults, Peregrines collected for museum specimens during the breeding season (White et al. 2002), captive adult individuals of *F. p. anatum* from the Rocky Mountains (C. Sandfort pers. comm.), and falcons of Greenland origin (*F. p. tundrius*) trapped during the breeding season (White et al. 2002).

The mean weights presented in Table 3.1 of Appalachian Duck Hawks, captured in the central Appalachians and in northern tier states of the southern Appalachians, are comparable to the weights of Peale's Peregrines, considered to be the largest Peregrine subspecies (White et al. 2002), and are considerably larger than the mean weights of western *anatum* individuals (716/616 g, or 116% for males; 1,190/993 g, or 120% for females), as well as of boreal forest *anatum* (716/652 g, or 101% for males; 1,190/977 g, or 122% for females), and Greenland *tundrius* (716/598 g, or 120% for males; 1,190/959 g, or 124% for females). White et al. (2002) noted that body mass varied with age, time of year, and timing of a bird's last meal. Therefore, comparisons of breeding to nonbreeding birds would likely skew the results to the high side for breeding females and to the low side for males providing food to the family. Most of the Appalachian birds were eyasses (young taken from the eyrie), presumably weighed in training and therefore not as robust as wild birds. Included as well in the Appalachian samples were five wild-trapped "inland birds," all originating from the Maryland/Virginia region, including an adult male

Table 3.1 Mean (and range) of weights of Peregrine Falcons of Appalachian, Rocky Mountain, Pacific Northwest, and Greenland origin.

F. p. anatum (Appalachian)		F. p. pealei (Pacific Northwest)		F. p. anatum (Rocky Mountain)		F. p. tundrius (Greenland)	
Male (n = 7)	716 (652–765) g (25 [23–27] oz)	Male (n = 10)	732 (629–908) g (26 [22–32] oz)	Male (n = 7)	616 (556–669) g (22 [20–24] oz)	Male (n = 23)	598 (528–650) g (21 [19–23] oz)
Female (n = 14)	1,190 (1,020–1,531) g (42 [36–54] oz)	Female (n = 10)	1,159 (995–1,304) g (41 [35–46] oz)	Female (n = 7)	993 (953–1,034) g (35 [34–36] oz)	Female (n = 87)	959 (494–1,130) g (34 [28–40] oz)

the amount of unexplored country rendered his estimate as much a guess as a statement of fact. It is reasonable to assume that the Duck Hawk once exploited nearly all of its available nesting habitat in the East, from cut banks and river bluffs to the superior high and wide escarpments that Hickey called "ecological magnets." Duck Hawks were in fact so relatively abundant that some were forced to seek atypical, and in some cases marginal, nesting sites, including low-cut banks and slopes, nests of other raptors, trees, and even bridges and buildings in a few instances. It was widely accepted that breeding densities of the Peregrine were severely restricted by the limited availability of suitable nesting habitat (Hickey and Anderson 1969), although it is becoming increasingly clear that acceptable nesting locations are in part determined by population pressure as numbers increase.

The Appalachian Mountains stretch southward for 1,500 miles from the Gaspe Peninsula to central Alabama, forming the divide between rivers that flow into the Atlantic Ocean and those that drain into the Gulf of Mexico. The chief ranges in the northern Appalachians that served as core habitat for the Duck Hawk included the Green Mountains in Vermont, White Mountains in New Hampshire, and Adirondack Mountains in New York. The Allegheny Mountains in Pennsylvania, Maryland, West Virginia, and Virginia, along with the northern portion of the Blue Ridge Mountains, were the species' major range in the central Appalachians. Less is known about the southern Appalachian population, but eyrie records extend into the southern Blue Ridge, Black, and Great Smokey Mountains into Alabama. Over the mil-

lennia, the Appalachian rivers draining into the Atlantic cut countless valleys with steep sides called "wind" or "water" gaps. Crawford Notch in New Hampshire, the Hudson Valley in New York, and the Delaware Water Gap in Pennsylvania and New Jersey, among many others, created prime habitat for the Duck Hawk. The species' greatest number—fully two-thirds of the estimated eastern population of 350 pairs—inhabited the mountains from Maine to Georgia, with more than 100 pairs in the central Appalachians alone (Hickey 1942). Another geographical concentration of about 60 pairs occurred along the upper Mississippi River and its tributaries (Hickey 1942).

Charles A. Proctor, courtesy of the Audubon Society of New Hampshire

▲ **Figure 3.7** A panting Duck Hawk attempts to shelter its young from the sun.

Inexplicably, few Peregrines are known to have inhabited eastern Maritime Canada. Fyfe (1969) reported seeing no Peregrines along the St. Lawrence Seaway in 1965, and confirmed only a single record in the region in the previous 20 years. Densities of the more northern arctic birds increased into northern Labrador and Quebec.

A small tree-nesting population was recorded in Audubon's time (first half of the 19th Century) along the middle and lower Mississippi River, the Ohio River, and the great prodigious bald cypress swamps of Tennessee (Ganier 1932, Bellrose 1938, Spofford 1942, 1943, 1945, 1947). A few records extended south to northeast Louisiana (Peterson 1948) and north into Illinois (Ridgeway 1889), Indiana (Butler 1878), and Kansas (Goss 1891). Wind-sheared tree trunks and branches from cypress, sycamore, beech, and cottonwood behemoths of the primeval forest created enormous cavities not dissimilar to the ledges and potholes in cliff-site habitat.

continued on page 42

To the small number of us still living who had contact with ... this population, there is little doubt that the Appalachian Peregrine was a recognizable race.

The 1964 Survey of Peregrine Eyries in the Eastern United States

Daniel D. Berger

With heavy hearts, we headed westward at the end of June, knowing we had no more sites to check.

I will never forget the excitement I experienced that weekend in late May 1952 when Ken Kuhn and I made our first trip from Milwaukee to the upper Mississippi River in the hope of locating nesting Peregrines. Within 50 miles of driving upstream from Prairie du Chien, Wisconsin, there it was—a breeding Peregrine silhouetted against the sky, perched on a dead cedar snag jutting out from the cliff face and reminiscent of that famous photograph of Taughannock Falls in New York. We were ecstatic. We located only one more pair that year, but that trip set the stage for my destiny. Annual surveys and banding trips continued for the next 13 years, during which time we came to realize that the birds were disappearing along the river.

The late Professor Joseph Hickey at the University of Wisconsin in Madison became a regular collaborator and followed our survey results with keen interest. In the fall of 1963 Hickey broached the idea of rerunning his survey of Peregrine eyries in the eastern states, work he had carried out 24 years earlier. By this time only one upper Midwest site remained occupied by adults, but they raised no young.

Hickey would be willing to launch the project if I would be willing to conduct the field survey. Would I? It was that proverbial "no brainer." Joe initiated the funding effort and letter-writing to past field workers while his graduate student, Ken Gamble, worked on identifying the U.S. Geological Survey topographic maps we would need to conduct the fieldwork. Much additional assistance was provided by the late Fred and Fran Hamerstrom, with whom I had been working on their long-running prairie chicken research project for the Wisconsin Department of Natural Resources. For my field assistant I selected Chuck Sindelar who had been a volunteer on the prairie chicken project while a student at the University of Wisconsin in nearby Stevens Point. I had to make arrangements to be away for a three-month period, which meant not working on the prairie chickens that spring and having someone run my businesses in Milwaukee.

The survey began on 1 April 1964 in northern Alabama and concluded three months and 14,000 miles later. Previous correspondence with cooperators had not been encouraging. Nevertheless, we were dispirited and discouraged to end up in southeastern Canada without having seen even one *Falco peregrinus*. To be sure, we had not expected much when checking the southern part of the range, which seemed to have been abandoned first. Yet by the time we had reached the hotbeds of eyrie concentration in Pennsylvania, New York, Vermont, and New Hampshire, our expectations had intensified.

Enough cannot be said about the cooperation we received from ornithologists, falconers, friends, and oologists. Falconers in particular were most helpful, especially since they had been most recently involved in monitoring their own local populations. Notable among these were Bob Berry, Al Nye, Brian and Joanne McDonald, Walter Spofford, Heinz Meng, Jim Rice, and William L. Rhein. Others providing assistance were Robert Lyle, Earl L. Poole, Albert F. Ganier, L. N. Wight, Roger Barbour, Bernard and Audrey Kaiman, C. J. Robertson, Joe Hagar, and Helen Flint. Some of these wonderful people provided warm hospitality while we surveyed sites in their areas or provided logistical support. Most important was the financial backing generously provided by Mrs. Kath-

File photo

leen Green Skelton Herbert, whose late husband Richard had conducted intensive studies of the Hudson River Peregrines in the 1940s. Our survey became the first project of the Richard A. Herbert Memorial Fund and was administered by the U. S. Section of the International Council for Bird Preservation. The project provided a fitting legacy to his memory.

Sindelar and I had outfitted my early 1960s Volkswagen microbus with a full-sized luggage rack on top and a shelf inside to store our 250 topographic maps. We were fully loaded by the time we embarked from Milwaukee, Wisconsin, on 1 April equipped with sleeping bags, a new tent, camp stove and lantern, ropes and climbing gear, binoculars, spotting scopes and tripods, cameras, rain gear, and all correspondence relating to the project. We also carried a cage full of pigeons, starlings, and mice along with bal chatris for random raptor trapping and banding along the way. Mail would be forwarded to several preselected locations based on our projected arrival dates. Amazingly, that arrangement worked quite well—even where in some places we used General Delivery as our address.

We traced quite a circuitous route through Tennessee while visiting some 19 reported sites in addition to a number of other promising areas. At one point we stumbled on an abandoned still operation in what was locally called a "rock house." The large open cave, or rock shelter, contained some aged corn mash and various distillery paraphernalia.

Even though the VW bus had had a thorough engine overhaul two months before

departure, by the time we reached Tennessee we were already experiencing engine problems. On top of that we had learned early on that although our new tent had been advertised as waterproof, such was not the case. Repeated applications of waterproofing alleviated the problem, but only to a degree. Somehow we managed to keep the balky microbus going until we reached Washington, D.C., 45 days later. At that point, a complete engine overhaul had again become essential. By 18 May, after having spent nine or 10 days with Brian McDonald checking sites in the Washington, D.C., and southern Pennsylvania region, we continued north in our newly refurbished bus to survey sites in the rest of Pennsylvania and New York. We were perplexed and surprised by the unimpressiveness of many of the Pennsylvania eyrie sites in view of the high density of Peregrines that had existed there in past years. We might have ignored many of these cliffs had we encountered them along the upper Mississippi River. Perhaps the greatest density of old historical Peregrine breeding sites was in the state of Vermont, where we checked 27 of the 33 reported sites. Charles A. Proctor had intensively monitored many of these eyrie sites in the 1930s.

All hope of finding an active Peregrine eyrie in the United States had pretty much evaporated by the time we reached Maine. So on 3 June we bought passage on the ferry *Bluenose* that plied between Bar Harbour and Yarmouth, Nova Scotia. As long as we had come this far, surely we could still find Peregrines in Canada. Some 300

vehicles were lined up at the *Bluenose* for the trip to Nova Scotia. One of them was repeatedly bypassed in favor of others farther back in the line. Finally, when no others remained, that lone vehicle, apparently suffering from engine trouble, was pushed onto the loading ramp, which had been lowered to the bottom deck. Alas, it was not our long suffering VW bus, but rather a Rolls Royce whose embarrassed owner managed to keep a low profile during the six-hour crossing. We spent the next 10 days visiting likely sites in Nova Scotia and eastern New Brunswick with nary a trace of Peregrines. They were gone.

As it turned out, our nearest miss probably came in early May when visiting a site that had been reported by Bob Mengel. According to Bob, young had fledged there as recently as 1952. The site was in Breaks Interstate Park, where the Russell fork of the Big Sandy River cuts a gap through the Cumberland Mountain Ridge between Kentucky and Virginia. We observed a lot of fresh-looking whitewash that we felt could well have been from earlier that year. The presence of heavy construction equipment alongside the railroad tracks below the cliffs and evidence of recent dynamiting

across the river may have been responsible for desertion that season. This could well have been one of the last active sites in the eastern United States.

With heavy hearts, we headed westward at the end of June, knowing we had no more sites to check. Engine trouble again plagued us. In Ashtabula, Ohio, we got the bad news that the bus had lost compression in two of the four cylinders. The starter had conked out earlier, and the generator had been acting up, causing us to limit our driving to daylight hours and forcing us to use our hand crank for starting. So it was with some trepidation that we continued. Nevertheless, we managed to limp the rest of the way back to Wisconsin at reduced speeds. Three months and a day after we set out, we arrived back in Milwaukee.

On our return, Joe Hickey immediately set out to organize the Madison International Peregrine Conference that subsequently convened in late August 1965. Ornithologists quickly came to the realization that Peregrine Falcons had been extirpated in the eastern United States and markedly reduced in many areas throughout the world. The rest is history.

Dan Berger *was born in Milwaukee, Wisconsin, in 1931. With Helmut Mueller, he founded what is now the Cedar Grove Ornithological Station and after 51 years is still active in it. He has worked extensively on Peregrine recovery in Colorado with Jim Enderson and Jerry Craig. He surveyed Peregrines in the western Canadian Arctic with Jim Enderson in 1966 and in the Ungava region in 1967 and 1970 with Jim Weaver and Bob Risebrough. He currently resides in South Pasadena, California.*

Courtesy of Dan Berger

41

Walter Spofford, courtesy Archives of American Falconry

▲ **Figure 3.8** Two eyasses are protected inside a cavity in a 60-foot-high cypress stump at Reelfoot Lake Swamps, Tennessee, April 1942.

Figure 3.9 Richard Herbert clings to the base of the Peregrines' nest tree. ▶

Walter Spofford, courtesy Archives of American Falconry

Surveys

Bent's (1938) life history of the Duck Hawk was the first comprehensive treatise on the species in North America. It provided a wealth of information on natural history and behavior. Later, Professor Joseph J. Hickey (1942) began to organize the definitive survey of the entire eastern population of the Duck Hawk east of the Rocky Mountains. Bond (1946) had already started a similar survey on the Pacific Coast and agreed to enlarge his investigations to cover the entire region west of the Rocky Mountains. Two years were required to gather data and enlist observations on the history of previously published and unpublished nesting sites. Hickey discovered that no other North American bird was surrounded by so much jealousy and suspicion. It was Hickey's great patience, genuine love for the bird, and in my opinion, scholarly, unbiased, non-falconer approach that enabled him to succeed. The actual survey took another two years of field investigations in 1939–1940 to complete, mostly in New York and surrounding states. It had become a cooperative effort to which 147 people generously contributed information. Joe Hickey had assembled half a continent's nesting data that served as a baseline for continued surveys, documenting the eastern Duck Hawk's struggle for survival. His Herculean efforts played a major role in the salvation of the species, not only in North America but in Europe as well. Hickey's major contributors were Joseph A. Hagar, Richard A. and Kathleen G. Herbert, Walter R. Spofford, Daniel D. Berger, and James N. Rice, whose individual observations and data are summarized in this chapter out of a deep respect for these harbingers of the environmental movement.

Hickey assembled the historical records and gathered emerging data into a cogent picture of the chronology of the Duck Hawk's decline. He had recorded 275 historical nesting territories in the United States east of the Rocky Mountains in 1940. He estimated that between 10 and 18% might have been permanently abandoned. In 1964, in preparation for his landmark International Peregrine Conference to be held in Madison, Wisconsin, the following year, Hickey organized a field survey of the previously recorded eyries. His updated list of 236 reported sites in the eastern United States and Canada was reduced to the most valid 209 sites along the Appalachian chain from Nova Scotia to Alabama. Daniel Berger's (Berger et al. 1969) survey team checked 146, or 70% of these (see sidebar, The 1964 Survey of Peregrine Eyries in the Eastern United States,this chapter). None were found to be active, nor could Berger's team obtain a report of an active nest. Of 186 prime formerly occupied eyries, 43 were located in the southern Appalachians, 80 in the central Appalachians, and 50 in the northern Appalachians in New England and northern New York.

Tree-nesting Populations

A largely unknown lower Mississippi tree-nesting population inhabited the extensive cypress swamps of western Tennessee and northern Louisiana, with isolated records, in bottomland forest where cliffs were absent, extending north to Indiana, Illinois, and Kansas. Hickey and Anderson (1969) compiled evidence of 10 definite records of tree-nesting Peregrines: three in Kansas, three in the vicinity of Mt. Carmel, Illinois, and four in Tennessee and Louisiana. Goss (1891) reported that the species was not uncommon in eastern Kansas, nesting in both trees and cliffs. In addition, F. M. Jones (1946) reported two pairs of Duck Hawks nesting in Osprey nests in Virginia in 1946.

The lower Mississippi River population was probably functionally extinct by the beginning of the 20th Century, along with the tree-nesting locations to the north. Not more than a few pairs of Duck Hawks survived in inaccessible regions of the Reelfoot swamps of Tennessee into the 1940s (Spofford 1942), and it took an earthquake to

flood and save the virgin timber and the Duck Hawk of the Reelfoot from the lumber industry (Ganier 1932). Along with the Ivory-billed Woodpecker, a signature species of the great swamp wilderness, the small recorded tree-nesting population of Duck Hawks may have been a remnant of a larger population in Audubon's time that disappeared before being recorded (Hickey 1942).

Southern Appalachians

The southern Appalachian regions of Virginia, the Carolinas, Kentucky, Tennessee, Georgia, and Alabama were the southern limit of the Duck Hawk's prime range. Walter Spofford was perhaps the most active of the Peregrine researchers in the southern Appalachians, but he conducted only sporadic isolated checks, mostly in the 1940s. He reported several active eyries in North Carolina and Tennessee, with a single active site in Tennessee in 1951 (Spofford 1969b). Prior to their 1964 survey, Berger et al. (1969) identified 43 of the most valid historical sites in the region. Some were inactive in the 1800s, and about half were abandoned by 1941. Tennessee had the largest number of verified eyries in the region, with all 16 sites abandoned by the early 1950s. Kentucky had only one reported eyrie, and it was active in 1952. All seven sites in West Virginia and Maryland may have been heavily exploited by falconers and egg-collectors and were abandoned in the 1930s and 1940s. Virginia had eight historical eyries, and one may have been active as late as 1964, a speculative observation based on the appearance of fresh excreta on the cliff (Berger et al. 1969). Curiously, Berger was advised in a letter of an isolated cliff in Alabama that was occupied in 1962.

Rice and I visited a well-known and heavily exploited eyrie at Jump Mountain in the western part of Virginia in 1955. The eyrie was active and successfully fledged a single female, the last verified record of a Duck Hawk fledging from the southern Appalachians.

Jim Rice

▲ **Figure 3.10** Bob Berry, ready to climb the old fashioned way at Jump Mountain, 1955.

Bob Berry

Central Appalachians

The eyries in the central Appalachians, comprising the states of New Jersey, Pennsylvania, and New York, were much more thoroughly documented by Hickey and his major contributors than the southern population. Hickey had identified 80 recorded sites in this region. Jim Rice, as one of Hickey's primary cooperators, had conducted extensive surveys of 24 active nesting territories in New Jersey and Pennsylvania from 1939 to 1960. Richard and Kathleen Herbert had conducted intensive observations of eight eyries along the lower Hudson River Valley in New York State.

Rice's study area encompassed over 22,000 sq mi in Pennsylvania and western New Jersey, the very heart of the Appalachian Peregrine country. Most of Rice's 24 eyries were located along the Susquehanna and Delaware Rivers, or their branches and tributaries. Rice was an insurance agent by profession and traveled throughout the Mid-Atlantic states, often in prime Duck Hawk nesting habitat. He was a naturalist, upland bird hunter, ardent falconer, Boy Scout leader, and

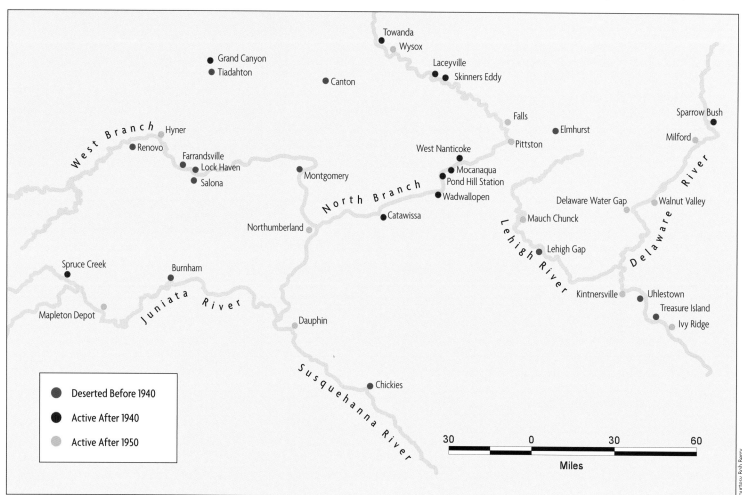

Courtesy Bob Berry

▲ **Figure 3.11** Jim Rice surveys the world of the Appalachian Duck Hawk above Wysox, Pennsylvania, 1953.

▲ **Figure 3.12** Jim Rice's map of Peregrine eyries in the Appalachians.

conservationist who campaigned tirelessly against the shooting of hawks. As a member of the Delaware Valley Ornithology Club, an elite Philadelphia birding organization, Rice was the repository of Peregrine observations from the birding community. His knowledge of falconry and ornithology commanded respect, and his friendly, cheerful, and gracious personality won the confidence and admiration of such bitter antagonists as egg-collectors, falconers, and birders alike. Rice's contribution to the final chapter of the eastern Duck Hawk is not from the viewpoint of a trained scientist but from the perspective of a respected and trusted insider.

Throughout my youth, Jim Rice was my closest friend, my mentor, and frequent companion. It was because of Jim that I was witness to the Appalachian Peregrine's losing struggle for survival, and I owe my lifelong interest in falconry, raptor propagation, and conservation to him.

Each spring, the ritual of "eyrie trips" unfolded anew with renewed enthusiasm. Rice surveyed an eyrie only long enough to determine its status and to band its young. Of the 39 historical locations he knew of (Hickey knew of others), he felt that 16 were permanently abandoned by 1940 (Rice 1969). All of the abandoned sites were on cliffs Rice considered inferior, offering only marginal protection from human and natural disturbances. None were known to be reoccupied, although desertion and reoccupancy of superior sites was not uncommon. The most critical element of a superior cliff in Rice's population was its remoteness from human disturbance.

Although Rice's surveys were incomplete, with Joe Hickey's help he interpolated a chronology of desertion, which described a linear rate of decrease for the 24 active sites identified in 1939, to extirpation in 1960. By 1940, the number of active sites reported was down to 21, by 1943 to 14, by 1946 to 11, declining to only six in 1952, four in 1955–1957, three in 1958, and one in 1959.

Philip Street, a local Peregrine aficionado and birder, reported seeing a Duck Hawk on 4 May 1961 at Shawnee, Pennsylvania, a few miles from the Delaware Water Gap, Rice's last occupied eyrie (pers. comm.). After a 44-year absence, Peregrines once again occupy Mount Minsi on the southwest side of the Delaware Water Gap. Dan Brauning, former Peregrine Fund hack site attendant and wildlife biologist in charge of the Peregrine recovery program for the Pennsylvania Game Commission, reports that along with a second eyrie near Williamsport, Pennsylvania, which successfully fledged a single youngster, 2003 marks the first

year Peregrines have occupied historical Peregrine eyries in Pennsylvania.

Of the 65 active eyries Rice surveyed from 1939 to 1946 (the pre-DDT period), 35 (54%) were successful, producing 81 young, with a productivity rate of 1.25 per active eyrie. Rice surveyed a greater proportion of his known sites in the eight-year DDT period of 1947–1954, yielding 64 active eyries. Of these, only 16 (25%) were successful, rearing 25 young at a reproductive rate of 0.4 per active eyrie, a 69% reduction in productivity for the DDT period. Fledging rates in both periods would have been significantly higher without the activities of falconers, who collected at least 29 young Duck Hawks of 134 produced from the survey area from 1940 to 1951. During the final years of the survey, from 1955 to1959, the number of pairs fluctuated from three in 1955-1956, to four in 1957, three in 1958, and one in 1959, and they fledged a total of five young. Significantly, despite the lack of known disturbance at the most superior cliffs, the three remaining pairs in 1958 and one in 1959 were unable to rear a single youngster. Rice and others banded 46 eyasses; six were subsequently recovered, but none of them were observed as banded adults at his eyries.

The plight of the Appalachian Peregrine, although partially obscured by the seemingly endless numbers of arctic migrant Peregrines along Atlantic beaches, was well known at the time to falconers. The number taken by falconers declined sharply after 1941. Egg-collecting appeared to be a minor factor in Rice's population after the 1920s and 1930s, with only two occurrences known to him, one in 1939 and the second in 1950. Falconers did not molest Rice's population beyond 1951, and only six eyasses were harvested after 1946, perhaps the result of diminishing returns, or a readily available source of arctic migrants from the Atlantic seaboard, combined with a deep respect for the wishes of one man, James Nelson Rice.

Rice felt that the adult birds in his study population were dying out or becoming infertile, without adequate replacements because of egg-collecting in the 1920s and 1930s and the activities of falconers in the 1930s and 1940s.

Richard Herbert's study area included eight active Duck Hawk nesting territories in a 55-mile stretch along the lower Hudson River Valley, from New York City to Storm King Mountain, where a total of 11 different territories had been used at one time or another (Herbert and Herbert 1969). Five sites were heavily exploited in the late 19th and early 20th Centuries, usually by egg-collectors, although specimens of all ages from these

Rice's contribution to the final chapter of the eastern Duck Hawk is not from the viewpoint of a trained scientist but from the perspective of a respected and trusted insider.

Spofford Collection, courtesy Archives of American Falconry

▲ **Figure 3.13** From left: Bill Sargent, Dick Herbert, and Alex Klots (a noted and well-published entomologist) at a Duck Hawk eyrie in May, 1939.

. . . the Herberts felt at the time that human pressures on these birds were such that extirpation was inevitable.

eyries were supplied to museums and private collections. For example, Herbert's Eyrie No. 1 was referenced at least 16 times in the literature, most of which documented collections. Herbert monitored each nesting territory intensively with observations on behavior and natural history from 1930 to 1960, the year of his death. In many cases he could identify individual adult birds by a unique plumage characteristic—a white feather, a color extreme—or by behavior. Three birds in his population attained ages between 17 and 19 years. Kathleen Green Skelton, who later married Richard Herbert, joined the study in 1949, and with Hickey's help, published the results after her husband's death (Herbert and Herbert 1969).

The Herberts' treatise is a bitter and compelling diatribe on what they considered an ignorant, unfeeling and uncaring, greedy and prejudiced society, which had expanded in the United States from 75 million people in 1900 to 179 million in 1960. For a spell in the 1930s, Duck Hawks appeared to be adapting to human pressures, with their spectacular appearance in abandoned quarries and on New York City skyscrapers, bridges, and other manmade structures. But reproductive success was dismal. Duck Hawks were unpopular in the city and suffered from unfavorable newspaper publicity, in part because of their raids on flocks of domestic pigeons. One New York City pair hatched 11 young from 1943 to 1948, but never fledged a single young. Three were killed by the Society for the Prevention of Cruelty to Animals, three were taken by falconers, five (two of which later died) were turned over to falconers by conservation officials for rehabilitation, one was released (fate unknown), and two others were subsequently shot after release. Despite unrelenting human

pressures and increasing persecution for over half a century, the Hudson River population showed a remarkably stable pattern of occupancy through the 1930s, although reproductive failure began to appear. Productivity was 1.1 to 1.2 young reared per active site, the same as Hickey's (1942) calculated productivity of 1.1 young for 19 eyries in the entire New York City region. In the following decade of the 1940s, Hudson River productivity decreased to 0.75 fledged young per active site. Egg-collecting was on the wane by 1940, but falconers had an increasing appetite for birds. In a six-year period, 1943 to 1948, falconers harvested 18 of the 33 young hatched from three of the most productive and popular sites. Without this take, which amounted to 54% of the nestling population, the reproductive rate might have been 1.25 young per active site in the 1940s. Herbert (and possibly others) banded 24 lower Hudson fledglings. Of the 13 birds included on Herbert's 1938 to 1944 banding schedules I examined, two were recovered—one found near starvation and the other dead. As in Jim Rice's survey population, none were observed at Hudson River eyries as adults, despite the Herberts' intensive observations, suggesting a heavy postfledging mortality on the young birds or dispersal to distant nesting territories.

The 1950s were marked by catastrophic reproductive failure and gradual abandonment, exacerbated by highway construction and blasting for the Palisades Parkway (1950 to 1956), which completely destroyed one nest and caused repeated desertion of eggs at several others. Newly constructed picnic grounds above and below the eyries along with hordes of workers and picnickers disrupted some birds. Illegal shooting of the wintering population played a role throughout the New York and New Jersey area. Two adults were shot and found dead beneath their eyries in 1950; a park policeman with responsibility to protect the Duck Hawk was implicated. Not a single young hatched from the eight active lower Hudson River eyries in 1950, and the last two juveniles old enough to fledge were seen by the Herberts in 1951; one fledged, the other was taken by a Brooklyn falconer. Thereafter, only nonproductive pairs were in residence, including two juvenile females, and by the 1959 season only the occasional adult remained. In June of 1961, the last bird was seen on the highest peak on the Hudson, and it subsequently disappeared.

Although they could not gauge the possible effects of pesticides, the Herberts felt at the time that human pressures on these birds were such that extirpation was inevitable.

Northern Appalachians

In 1934, Massachusetts granted full protection to the Duck Hawk, along with all but four species of hawks and owls. Joseph A. Hagar, Massachusetts State Ornithologist and passionate Duck Hawk devotee, was assigned to coordinate and enforce this protection. New York and New Jersey also protected most hawks, including the Peregrine, but had little law enforcement commensurate with that in Massachusetts. From 1935 to 1942, and again in 1947, Hagar conducted intensive observations of 14 Duck Hawk eyries in western Massachusetts, with sporadic coverage from 1948 to 1957 (Hagar 1969). Each of Hagar's cliffs was rated relative to the others based on criteria similar to those of Rice, such as height, human disturbance, and number and suitability of nesting ledges. Hagar had what he considered six superior sites and eight inferior sites. From mid-March until June, he guarded the eyries with the help of up to four wardens. After the first year, there was only one indication of a clutch taken by egg-collectors, so his study population was virtually undisturbed.

During the period 1935 to 1942, productivity from 91 active eyries was 107 young, or 1.2 young fledged per active site. The six superior sites provided 71% of the young. Two of the inferior sites were deserted from 1935 to 1941, and by 1942 four of them were deserted. The eyries were seldom checked during the war years of 1943 to 1946 and were therefore subject to possible molestation, as indicated by the illegal egg-collecting from an eyrie in 1947. Three of the four eyries deserted by 1942 were reoccupied in 1947, but reproduction declined dramatically with only four of the 13 active eyries fledging a total of six young. Although seven of the eight inferior sites were occupied, they fledged but a single bird in 1947 and none thereafter. One pair included a juvenile female, reinforcing Hagar's fears about a declining residual population. He also noted broken eggs in one of the eyries in 1947 and in three more eyries in 1951, losses he attributed to raccoons at the time.

▲ **Figure 3.14** Joseph Hagar, a key figure in Peregrine studies, holding a young Peregrine released at Mt. Tom in 1976.

From a normally reproducing, relatively stable adult population through 1942, the DDT period of 1947–1951 showed a marked decline in both active nest sites and reproduction. The last year that young fledged from two sites in Hagar's population was 1951. By 1955–1957, only an occasional bird remained. Of 88 juveniles Hagar banded, 14 were recovered in later years for a known mortality rate for this population of at least 16%, but as in the experiences of Jim Rice and the Herberts, not a single banded bird was seen at Hagar's eyries. Ten died before reaching reproductive maturity, and four lived from between 3.5 to 13.5 years of age. All of the recoveries were from surrounding states with dense human populations.

Hagar's photographic observations over the four-year period 1947–1950 at a single isolated eyrie on the Quabbin Reservoir (T. Cade pers. comm.) suggest classic reproductive failure from chlorinated hydrocarbon poisoning, including broken eggs, disappearing eggs, and deserted eggs. Hagar also noted that raccoon sign was more in evidence than ever before, including scat and tracks in the eyrie in 1950. Nevertheless, Hagar concluded that raccoons could not have been the whole story.

Walter Spofford conducted extensive, miscellaneous observations of 29 Duck Hawk eyries located in northern New England (Vermont and New Hampshire) and New York (the Adirondack Mountains) (Spofford 1969a). The eyries were checked casually and not every year from 1952 through 1965. As in the populations to the south, the birds in Spofford's study had already declined by as much as 60% before the survey began, but there are no data documenting this decline. From 1952 to 1957, the number of active eyries as a percent of eyries checked remained stable, with 14 to 19 active sites checked, including 11 pairs with the appearance of eggs or young each year. Spofford recorded 31 apparently successful nesting pairs during the six-year period ending in 1957 with an undetermined number of young and another five

Three of the four eyries deserted by 1942 were reoccupied in 1947, but reproduction declined dramatically . . .

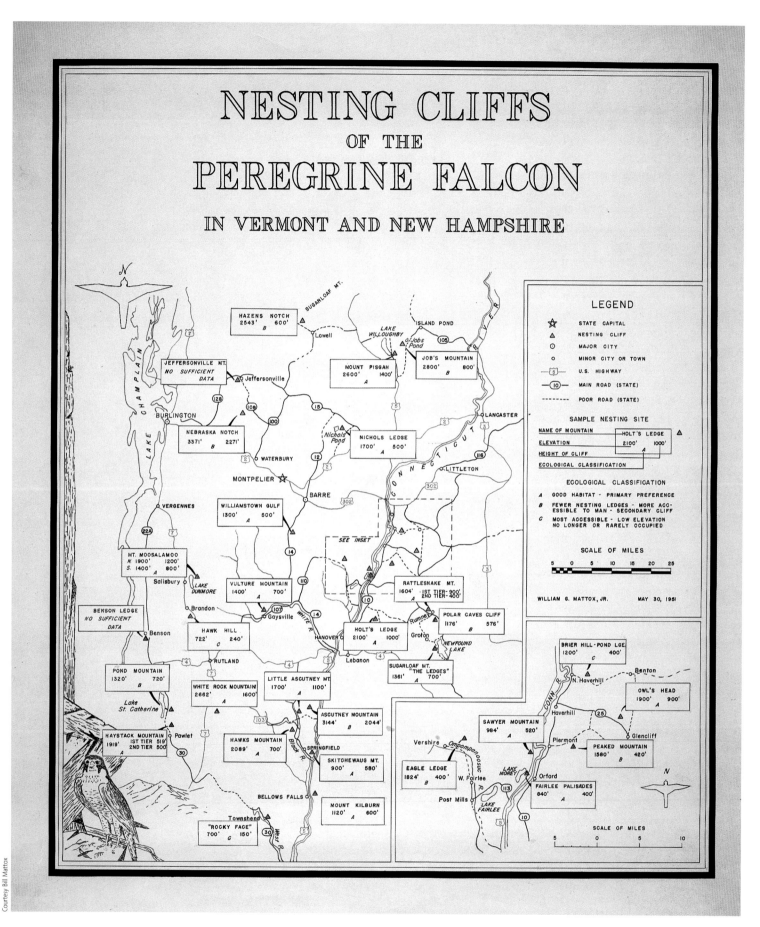

▲ **Figure 3.15** Bill Mattox completed an intensive survey of Vermont and New Hampshire Peregrine nest sites in 1951.

pairs with eggs. Mysteriously, all of the eyries were abandoned the next year, with the exception of a single adult, although fresh excreta were observed at three of the sites. Spofford and Jim Enderson reported an adult male in June 1970 at Willoughby Lake, Vermont, probably the last credible observation of an eastern Duck Hawk south of the St. Lawrence Seaway (Fyfe 1975).

That Spofford's adult population collapsed so quickly is shocking, suggesting adult mortality as opposed to gradual desertion and reproductive failure, which marked other survey areas. However, more than half the known eyries had been permanently abandoned at the beginning of the study, indicating that a chronology of reproductive failure may have been underway earlier. Spofford summarized his survey as follows: "Falconers may have had a substantial although undetermined impact on the birds in Vermont and New Hampshire, but the Adirondack eyries were so high and inaccessible that they were little bothered, but declined simultaneously with the molested sites."

Daniel D. Berger and Helmut C. Mueller studied 14 Peregrine eyries in late May and early June from 1952 to 1965 along 320 km in the gorge of the upper Mississippi River from Red Wing, Minnesota, to Dubuque, Iowa (Berger and Mueller 1969). As with Spofford's study, Joe Hickey inspired Berger's survey, and like the New England study, much of Berger's study population had already crashed prior to the survey. Historical records of nesting Peregrines in the upper Mississippi territory are fragmentary but suggest that more than 50 active eyries existed beyond 1900 in the entire Great Lakes Region (Hickey 1942). The U.S. Fish and Wildlife Service (FWS) estimated the Peregrine population in its upper Mississippi National Wildlife Refuge, composing 84% of Berger's study area, at 20 birds in 1949. Abandonment of sites appeared to begin in the southern part of the study area and spread northward, as Berger was unable to locate a single active site in the southern quarter of his study area, despite reports of birds present before 1941 and as late as 1949. Berger's population of 14 reported eyries was incompletely studied in 1952–1953 but was stable at 11 active sites in 1954–1955. Thereafter, the number of active sites declined steadily, from eight in 1956 to four in 1957–1958. Three pairs persisted in 1960–1961; thereafter only two pairs remained, raising young in 1962. Only a single adult was seen in 1963–1964. Reproduction was highly variable because of the small sample size and was not calculated by Berger because his team did little climbing unless they were certain the eyrie contained young. Nonetheless, 29 fledglings

Walter Spofford, courtesy Archives of American Falconry

were banded and two were recovered, at one and three years of age, 72 and 825 km, respectively, from their nest sites. Like the other observers, Berger observed no banded falcons at his eyries. The 57 annual occupancies of eyries identified in Berger's data produced at least 29 young for a minimum reproductive rate of 0.51 per active eyrie. He learned of another local eyrie on an upper Mississippi River tributary that successfully raised young in 1963 but was abandoned in 1965.

Berger reported four more eyries along the Niagra Escarpment in upper Michigan and northeastern Wisconsin. All were abandoned by 1958, seven years before those along the upper Mississippi. Half a dozen or more records document Peregrines nesting along the Wisconsin River as early as 1886. Compared with the upper Mississippi population, they occupied inferior cliffs along a narrow river corridor and were subject to heavy disturbance by collectors, picnickers, and rock climbers and pre-

▲ **Figure 3.16** Alpine Lookout, one of the Herberts' eight intensively monitored eyries on the lower Hudson River.

Figure 3.17 Walter Spofford, renowned raptor enthusiast. ▶

▼ **Figure 3.18** Peregrine eggs inside a tree nest cavity at Reelfoot Lake, Tennessee, in 1947.

sumably were more susceptible to shooting. By 1940, most of the recorded eyries were abandoned, but at least one site produced young in 1953.

Berger postulated that although falconers took a few young birds, there was little other increase in human activity that could account for the extirpation of the upper Mississippi population. He concluded that human disturbance alone could not be the sole cause of desertion and that the south-to-north progression of the Peregrine's disappearance in his population correlated well with a similar phenomenon he noted in the entire eastern United States.

Pattern of Abandonment and Reproduction

The pattern of abandonment did not appear to be a clear-cut south-to-north progression, because a few eyries persisted throughout the Appalachians into the 1950s. Functional extinction and cessation of reproduction did, however, appear to progress from south to north. That all of the populations had undergone considerable unrecorded declines before the studies is clear. Hickey (1942) calculated the abandonment of known eyries at 10 to 18% for the entire eastern region by 1940. The smaller, intensively studied populations on the Hudson River (eight territories) and in western Massachusetts (14 territories) were exceptions, where eyrie occupancy remained relatively stable from the 1930s until the 1950s. The small population of tree-nesters on the middle Mississippi and Ohio Rivers disappeared before 1900, and the lower Mississippi tree-nesters were functionally extinct sometime in the early 20th Century, with a few pairs persisting in the cypress swamps of Tennessee into the 1940s. Berger calculated that half of the 14 sites in the Appalachian Mountains of Tennessee, representing the core of southern Appalachia's 43 most valid recorded sites, were permanently abandoned by 1941, with the last confirmed occupancy in 1948.

A few isolated, widely separated pairs or single birds lingered into the 1950s: 1957 in North Carolina, 1954 in Kentucky, and 1955 in Virginia (Berger et al. 1969). Only a single young is recorded as having fledged from the southern Appalachians (Virginia) in the 1950s. There were, however, no coordinated studies in the region. Nonetheless, falconers confirmed the harvest of three eyasses from West Virginia and Virginia eyries in 1950 (B. McDonald, S. Gatti, and S. Sigwald pers. comm.).

Rice's central Appalachian population declined steadily from 24 active sites in 1939 to only 10 in 1950, having undergone a 40% reduction before

1939. However, Rice documented 38 annual occupancies of eyries in the 1950s, rearing 14 young. Spofford's northern Appalachian population had declined by as much as 60% before 1952, but he noted 31 apparently successful nesting attempts from 1952 to 1957.

Berger's population in the Great Lakes region had declined to only 14 pairs by 1952. From 1952 through 1959, Berger noted 22 active eyries that produced at least 22 young. He recorded 10 successful pairs rearing 11 young, five in 1960 and six in 1962. Furthermore, Berger had a report of an eyrie on a tributary outside his study area that was successful in 1963 and active in 1964 but abandoned thereafter. Berger's upper Mississippi gorge pairs were unique as the only population to reproduce successfully in the 1960s, several years longer than all of the eyries in the eastern states, as well as those in the surrounding area along the Niagra Escarpment and Wisconsin River system.

Despite relatively stable occupancy in the 1940s, reproduction in Hagar's and Herberts' populations declined from an average of 1.2 young reared per active site in the 1930s and early 1940s to 0.40 and 0.75 young reared, respectively, in the mid- to late 1940s. All reproduction ceased in central Massachusetts and on the Hudson River in 1951–1952. Rice's Pennsylvania and New Jersey population successfully reproduced a few years longer, to 1957. His pre-DDT reproductive rate was 1.25 young, declining to 0.40 in the active DDT years and to 0.30 in the last five successful years with only four active pairs remaining. Spofford's northern Appalachian population had viable reproduction through 1957 as well, with 11 active pairs that appeared to be reproducing normally. That all but a single pair failed to return the following year is not easily explained.

In summary, the tree-nesting population along the lower and middle Mississippi and some of its tributaries was largely exterminated by 1900 with the loss of the great trees. By 1950, all known reproduction had ceased in the southern Appalachians, with a single exception, and all but a few isolated pairs, mostly in the southern Allegheny and northern Blue Ridge Mountains, had been extirpated. In the central and northern Appalachians, including the Great Lakes Region to the west, about two-thirds of the most valid recorded eyries had been permanently abandoned as well. Successful reproduction persisted until 1957 in the central and northern Appalachians, and Berger's upper Mississippi gorge population reproduced five years longer than all of the Appalachian populations.

Postsettlement Exploitation

To explain fully the Duck Hawk's inexorable century-long decline, it is instructive to revisit briefly the cultural and social mores of our pioneer forefathers. Deforestation and overexploitation of North America's fauna and flora began in earnest as soon as the first white settlers arrived in the 1600s. In just a few centuries, humans essentially reconfigured the American landscape. So thorough were the settlers and timber companies that almost every acre of virgin forest from Maine to south Florida and west to the Great Plains fell to the ax or saw. The cutting coincided with an era of unregulated hunting and trapping that peaked in the latter half of the 19th Century, including the commercial exploitation of wild game, furbearers, and plumed birds for the fashion trade. Bounties, poisons, and government hunters assisted the systematic eradication of predators as competitors of man. A population that values livestock and poultry above all else, that avidly consumes wild game with no knowledge of ecology, shows little tolerance for wild predators (Wilcove 1999).

Hawks and owls are predators that were considered "vermin" by the farmer and market hunter and "targets" by sportsmen. Collectively, hawks were known as "chicken hawks" or "hen hawks" whether or not they consumed poultry or game. Slogans such as "the only good hawk is a dead hawk" spread the conventional wisdom. State fish and game departments offered bounties on all hawks and owls as early as 1885 and helped the sporting goods stores drum up business with predator drives through the 1930s. In 1931–1932, my home state of Pennsylvania paid a $5 bounty on Goshawks. Only 22 Goshawks were recovered—but so were 199 other hawks, including five Duck Hawks, considered a rare bird at the time (Edge and Lumley 1940).

Even some scientific authorities characterized the Duck Hawk as a ruthless and wanton killer. Bent's (1938) treatise contains several emotional references taken from the journals of well-known professionals such as Alexander Wetmore and Joseph Hagar. Bent commented that "few of its intended victims can escape." In his *History of the Birds of Kansas,* Goss (1891) described the antipathy toward the species as follows: "The fear of man is not without cause, for our hunters never loose (sic.) an opportunity to shoot at them, knowing how destructive they are to the water fowl (sic.) found in the sloughs along the river bottoms." A decade earlier, in *The Birds of Indiana,* Butler (1878) depicted the Duck Hawk as one of the distinctively harmful species. He went on to

Bounties, poisons, and government hunters assisted the systematic eradication of predators as competitors of man.

▲ **Figure 3.19** Bob Berry supervising the Peregrine release at the Dauphin Narrows on the Susquehanna River on a cold and drizzling day in 1977 (see photos on previous pages).

say that if it were more common, it could do great injury, as its principal food is waterfowl, sand-pipers, plover, and snipe (considered game birds at the time). He also noted that it was destructive to domestic poultry and pigeons, citing the U.S Department of Agriculture as his source.

Hawk shooting as a "sport" peaked in the early 1930s along all the major migration corridors, including innumerable locations along the Appalachian Mountains, Great Lakes, and Eastern Seaboard. Perhaps the most notorious location was a rocky outcrop along the Blue Ridge Mountains near Drehersville, Pennsylvania, known to the hawk shooters as Hawk Mountain. In 1934, Rosalie Edge leased Hawk Mountain and put a stop to the wanton slaughter, but more importantly she focused nationwide public attention on the atrocities of a so-called sport that left dead or dying hawks for other predators (Edge and Lumley 1940). Despite the negative publicity, hawk shooting continued, albeit in a somewhat less blatant fashion, owing to the advocacy of the National Audubon Society and noted conservationists such as Richard Pough, Roger Tory Peterson, and John B. May.

As a young teenager in the late 1940s, I remember well the trips to Kittatinny Ridge, just north of Hawk Mountain Sanctuary, with Jim Rice and his scout troop to "heckle" the hawk shooters. Like many other states, Pennsylvania protected "beneficial" rodent-eating, as opposed to "harmful" bird-eating, hawks. The Duck Hawk was an anomaly, a "protected" bird eater that was protected only because it was considered too rare to be a threat to game or poultry. Mostly we found dead or dying Broad-winged and Sharp-shinned Hawks, but one autumn afternoon at Bake Oven Knob I came upon an adult male Peregrine that appeared to have starved to death as a result of a broken wing.

It was not until 1940 that the U.S. Bureau of Biological Survey published the results of an ongoing survey of thousands of raptor stomach contents, including 77 Duck Hawks—only 11 of which had consumed duck for their last meal. It was not until 1972 that all raptors were added to the Migratory Bird Treaty Act with Mexico, thereby extending federal protection to all birds of prey, but too late for the Duck Hawk.

Peregrines were vulnerable to shooting throughout their life cycle. In addition to concentrations of the species along migration corridors and leading lines created by waterways, the Appalachian Duck Hawk was particularly vulnerable in defense of eggs or young at its eyrie. In a taped interview for the Archives of American Fal-

conry, Al Nye (1986) recalled that a pair of Duck Hawks nesting high on the cliffs overlooking the Potomac River in the 1930s were so aggressive they would attack people canoeing on the river hundreds of feet below. Tree-nesters were even more vulnerable and just as aggressive. The highest cavities were little more than a stone's throw from the ground, inaccessible to a naive climber but an easy shot for the marksmen. Ganier (1932) located a pair of tree-nesting Duck Hawks at Reelfoot Lake, Tennessee, that were so vociferous in their protests that their nest was easily located in the hollow top of a nearby cypress. Wintering Duck Hawks were largely nonmigratory, spending the winter months in the heavily populated eastern states among concentrations of abundant prey species, such as the pigeons in New York City or waterfowl in inland duck marshes and riverine estuaries, where they were especially vulnerable to shooting (Bird Banding Laboratory Records 1928–1956). Today, wild Peregrines in Mexico congregate to feed on the wintering ducks and have learned to follow duck-hunting boats on their way to or from blinds, stooping on the flushing ducks much like a trained falcon (Enderson et al. 1991, P. Widener pers. comm.). It is likely that the Duck Hawk behaved in a similar fashion, with potential lethal results. Enderson (1969) found that 44% of 65 North American Peregrine band recoveries for birds banded prior to 1953 were reported as shot. Also, it appears that underreporting of recoveries of a protected bird such as the Duck Hawk is likely, based on investigations by Geis and Atwood (1961) and Tomilson (1968), who found that less than half the legally shot ducks and doves were reported under ordinary conditions.

Raccoons and Great Horned Owls have long been recognized as major predators of raptors and especially their young. Of Hickey's primary contributors, only Hagar mentioned raccoons as a potential predator at one of his nests. Rice dismissed both raccoons and snakes as insignificant predators of his falcons, although I recall him lamenting the amount of raccoon sign at the Dauphin cliffs, indicating activity that may have contributed to the falcons' emigration to a safer site on the river pilings.

Great Horned Owls had a bounty on their heads in Pennsylvania and perhaps in other states in the early 20th Century, and they were relatively uncommon in the 1930s and 1940s, compared with their presence in virtually every woodlot several decades later. I recall hearing my first "hooting" owl as a young teenager while camping beneath a temporarily deserted eyrie near Hyner,

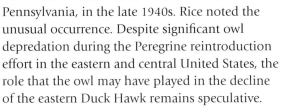

Pennsylvania, in the late 1940s. Rice noted the unusual occurrence. Despite significant owl depredation during the Peregrine reintroduction effort in the eastern and central United States, the role that the owl may have played in the decline of the eastern Duck Hawk remains speculative.

Oologists and Falconers

The combined deleterious effect of egg-collecting and harvesting by falconers is complicated, difficult to measure, and controversial. In the 1930s, ornithologist Ernst Mayr, then at the American Museum of Natural History, felt there was little doubt that commercial egg-collecting was at the present time the worst enemy of our rare hawks and suggested that licensing be required to track collections (Lumley 1937). Most present-day experts consider the negative effects of both egg-collecting and falconry to have been local and transitory in nature with a minimal impact on the pre-DDT population. Egg-collectors claimed that egg-collecting caused less damage than the harvest of fledglings because the birds would lay another clutch. True enough for experienced adults, if the clutch was taken early in incubation, although the second clutch of three eggs was nearly always one egg shy of the first clutch and some eyries were harvested several times in a season. The eyrie failed if eggs were taken later in incubation as the birds did not recycle. William Sargent (1941), professor of biology at The College of the City of New York, described the status of egg-collecting in the *Journal of the American Falconers' Association*. He cautioned that while egg-collecting was on the

wane by 1941, it was a real threat to certain local eyries. In Connecticut, Vermont, and New Hampshire, the Duck Hawk was not protected and was vulnerable to a small group of collectors operating out of Woodstock, Vermont. Sargent went on to say that in Connecticut only the Meridian eyrie remained active and that it had eggs collected in each of the last seven years with no young allowed to fledge. Walter Spofford marked the eggs in 1941 so they would not be collected, but they were subsequently thrown over the cliff. In Massachusetts, rigid enforcement of stringent laws had stamped out egg-collecting. It remained a greater menace in the population centers of New York and New Jersey but was no longer actively pursued in Pennsylvania or upstate New York.

One of Rice's eyries had eggs collected in 1950, so some egg-collectors were active nearly to the end of the Duck Hawk's existence. As a general rule, the rarer the bird the keener the collector is to acquire its eggs (Peterson 1988). Hickey's records confirmed that 75 of the 209 eastern Duck Hawk eyries were probably collected at least once between 1864 and 1931. Lloyd Kiff (unpubl. data) identified 577 sets of Peregrine eggs collected in North America. Of these, 109 sets (usually a four-egg clutch) were collected between 1892 and 1943 in Pennsylvania alone but averaged only two sets per year from a minimum population of 39 recorded territories (Rice 1969). However, 59 of the sets were collected in the 1920s and 25 sets in the 1930s, still a modest percentage of the occupied eyries. Egg-collecting was declining in the 1930s, at the same time the number of birds har-

◀ **Figure 3.20** Richard Herbert (foreground) and Roger Tory Peterson investigate the South Park eyrie in the Hudson River valley, circa 1948.

▲ **Figure 3.21** A Duck Hawk chick rests on remaining eggs in the nest. Note the markings on the eggs, made to discourage egg-collectors.

Figure 3.22 Released Peregrine (1977) at Dauphin Narrows on exact location where Bob Berry observed the last Appalachian Duck Hawk to fledge in 1955.

Bob Berry

Whether or not egg-collectors and falconers had a measurable, sustained impact on the population has been the subject of considerable conjecture and debate.

vested by falconers was increasing. The two user groups were mutually exclusive of one another, and increasing numbers of falconers are thought to have discouraged egg-collecting.

Records of harvest for falconry abound in the early falconry journals and especially in the Archives of American Falconry Interview Series featuring prominent early falconers. A few isolated individuals practiced the sport in the 1920s and early 1930s before the Peregrine Club of Philadelphia was founded in 1933, chiefly comprising college men from the University of Pennsylvania, under the capable leadership of Robert Stabler (Nye 1942). The epicenter of the sport at the time (1930s and 1940s) was in suburban Washington, D.C., the eastern shore of Maryland, and Philadelphia (35 falconers), along with a small group in New York State (12 falconers). Brian McDonald (1990) recounted in his Archives Series interview that he was unaware of early falconers in the south and only a few in New England. Novices generally started with common birds of prey such as the American Kestrel, Red-tailed Hawk, or Cooper's Hawk, but the Duck Hawk was the ultimate goal. Nye (1990) spoke at length of the extremely competitive nature of the sport and especially the feeling about Duck Hawk eyries: "You could measure a falconer's wealth in the early days by two things: one, how many pigeons he had, and second, by how many Peregrine eyries he knew of." The first recorded Duck Hawk harvest by suburban Washington falconers occurred in 1933 at Great Falls, Maryland, on the Potomac River (Nye 1990). According to Nye, fewer than a dozen eyries were most often molested, all close to core centers of falconry, initially in Maryland and expanding to nearby Virginia and West Virginia and north to the Delaware and Susquehanna River systems in New Jersey and Pennsylvania. A few isolated individuals practiced the sport in New York State in the late 1930s, but it was not until 1942 that the Westchester Hawking Club was formed, the first club in New York devoted to falconry (Donahue 1985). I have identified at least 22 falconers as having harvested

one or more Appalachian Duck Hawks in the 1930s and 1940s (Archives of American Falconry Interview Series).

Rice (1969) and Herbert and Herbert (1969) identified 65 eyasses (34%) of 189 fledglings reared that were harvested by falconers from their combined study areas during select periods between 1937 and 1951. Therefore the attrition by falconers may have been significant for certain years in those limited populations of fewer than 31 pairs. However, the harvest from Rice's population declined sharply after 1941, along with the number of Maryland and Pennsylvania falconers, which according to Rice had peaked at only 15 persons (Rice 1969). Attrition on Hudson River eyries was increasing in the 1943–1951 period, with over half of the Herberts' Hudson River productivity (19 of 34) being harvested by falconers (Herbert and Herbert 1969). Nonetheless, an average harvest of between four and five young per year over a 15-year period pales to insignificance with the normal productivity associated with Hickey's 275 recorded eastern eyries. And based on the amount of remote and unexplored country and the rate new eyries were being discovered before 1940, Hickey had estimated the eastern states' population at 350 pairs. Even if the recorded population had declined by Hickey's high-end estimate of 18% by 1940, well over 200 pairs could be expected to produce over 200 young annually, dwarfing the harvest by both falconers and egg-collectors combined.

Whether or not egg-collectors and falconers had a measurable, sustained impact on the population has been the subject of considerable conjecture and debate. That they reduced the numbers of successful nests and fledged young is undeniable, but they argued that a majority of the immature birds might have died anyway from shooting or other natural causes. Furthermore, based on many of the mortality studies conducted on the Peregrine, a decrease in productivity is far less significant to population maintenance than a comparable decrease in adult survival (Young 1969, Hunt 1998).

Summary and Conclusions

The eastern Duck Hawk's nesting population appeared to decline slowly but steadily throughout its range in the first half of the 20th Century, until entering a terminal syndrome in 1947, with elimination of the entire population in another decade (Hickey and Anderson 1969). In a scant 50 years, the most efficient flying machine, the best designed bird, the fiercest and fastest bird had virtually vanished (Peterson 1988). Peregrine researchers have proved conclusively that the unprecedented decline in the numbers of Peregrines on two continents, including the total extirpation of the eastern Duck Hawk, is attributable to reproductive impairment and increased adult mortality induced by organochlorine pesticides. Questions persist regarding the timing and magnitude of the downward spiral. Hickey's terminal syndrome was preceded by the gradual decline of what must have been a sizable nonbreeding population, long capable of quickly filling breeding vacancies and buffering turnover (Hunt 1998). The causes are many and varied but include the combined assaults of increased natural and human predation, physical destruction or marginalization of habitat, indiscriminate shooting, and chemical pollution, all of which compose the residue of human progress. From prehistory to the present, the mindless horsemen of the environmental apocalypse have been habitat destruction, overkill, invasion of alien species, and the diseases carried by these exotics (E.O. Wilson *in* Wilcove 1999). Like the Carolina Parakeet, Passenger Pigeon, Heath Hen, and Ivory-billed Woodpecker, the eastern Appalachian Duck Hawk was victim of man's dominion over nature, plus another 20th Century mindless horseman, chemical pollution.

Could the population have survived if pesticides had not been used so extensively from the mid-1940s to the 1960s? Probably yes, given the experiences in Great Britain. During World War II, the military systematically eliminated a large portion of the continent's Peregrine population to protect homing pigeons. Once protection was reinstated, the population rebounded to 80% of its former numbers in only a decade. And following a second decline during the organochlorine pesticides era of the 1950s and early 1960s, the species is now more abundant in Britain than at any time in the 20th Century (see Chapter 2). Considering today's conservation values and environmental ethics, our laws and avicultural successes, there would be no final chapter for the Appalachian Peregrine.

courtesy Bob Berry

Bob Berry *vividly recalls his childhood, roaming the fields and forest of his southeastern Pennsylvania home near the town of King of Prussia. At the age of 10 he captured a fledgling kestrel which kindled his lifelong passion for the natural world and especially the art of falconry. His close friend and mentor, Jim Rice, became his teacher, and it was through Jim that Bob was a witness to the Appalachian Peregrine's struggle for survival.*

Following in Rice's footsteps, Bob received a B.S. in Business Administration from the Pennsylvania State University and an M.B.A. from the Wharton School of the University of Pennsylvania with a major in insurance. He is now retired as the past President, CEO, and Chairman of the United States Liability Insurance Companies and currently serves as Trustee of the Wolf Creek Charitable Foundation, a nonprofit trust dedicated to a variety of conservation initiatives.

Bob helped found The Peregrine Fund in 1970 and has served continuously as a director and research associate since then. He pioneered important strategies in the artificial insemination of behaviorally imprinted raptors that are currently employed throughout the world in the propagation of endangered cranes as well as birds of prey. He has propagated several hawk and falcon species and currently focuses his attention on the Gyrfalcon and tropical raptors. He is the Founding President of the North American Raptor Breeders' Association, a trustee of the Wyoming Chapter of The Nature Conservancy, and serves on the Advisory Committee of Trout Unlimited's Western Water Project in Wyoming.

Bob lives year around in Wolf, Wyoming, where he and his wife, Carol, operate a working cattle ranch. The Berrys have two daughters, one son, and five grandchildren.

ENDERSON 1982

Chapter 4

Early Peregrine Experiences and Management: Rocky Mountain West

James H. Enderson

W*e are still pondering the rapid increase in numbers and expansion of Peregrines in the vast Rocky Mountain cordillera* and adjacent Colorado Plateau in the last two decades. First, how does the present explosion compare with the poorly known pre-pesticide population? Second, what was the real effect of the great re-introduction efforts by so many dedicated workers on the recovery of this wonderful bird? In the end, answers to these questions, and our growing appreciation of the bird, depend on future work in the field. This chapter describes early attempts to understand the plight of Peregrines, the work of many who were involved, and the ways they made possible the restoration of this phenomenal bird. Now, more than four years since the Victory Celebration in Boise in 1999, the recovery story is far from over.

Early Years

My first amateur raptor experiences were with American Kestrels in the early 1950s. Eventually I studied a dense breeding population near the University of Illinois in 1958. Ominously, in the early 1960s my mentor Richard Graber of the Nat-

ural History Survey, would report to me the population had mysteriously disappeared.

Of course, Peregrines were also stricken at the time. Not yet knowing that, however, I searched the university library for literature revealing eyrie locations. In 1957, I drove to Reelfoot Lake in western Tennessee, where Walter Spofford had found tree-nesting falcons in the early 1940s. I saw no Peregrine. In 1958, Richard Brewer, a fellow student, sent me to Union County, Illinois, where he had seen Peregrines on the bluffs over the Mississippi River. I found no bird. The next April he suggested Lansing, Iowa. When I arrived the game warden said the local pair was inexplicably absent. Unknown to me, Dan Berger had already documented the demise of the upper Midwest Peregrine population.

I began planning a trip to the Appalachians, where the literature suggested there were numerous pairs (also absent at the time). Fortunately, I was diverted to Wyoming to study Prairie Falcons. Graber had introduced me to Bud Tordoff at a seminar. Bud was familiar with Prairie Falcons in western Kansas and reckoned they could be studied on the Plains. A trip east to find Peregrines would have been useless anyway; Jim Rice, Richard Herbert, and others had already seen those eyries become vacant.

◀ Figure 4.1 Drawing by James Enderson. Reproduction rights courtesy of Bill Heinrich.

Jean Finzel

▲ **Figure 4.2** Jim Enderson with a Prairie Falcon banded in a study of wintering birds in Wyoming in 1960. Bud Tordoff first suggested such work was feasible based on his observations in western Kansas.

I finally saw nesting Peregrines in 1962! The late Don Hunter, later a cofounder of The Raptor Research Foundation, invited me to join him and Frank Beebe in the Queen Charlotte Islands, British Columbia. Don and I visited Morley Nelson in Boise, Idaho, on route to Beebe's home on Vancouver Island. Both Frank and Morley were thinking of captive breeding at that time, and both would soon have birds in lofts. The impact of the Queen Charlotte trip on me was permanent. In the wilderness there, Peregrines were spectacular—and abundant. Could it be the bird was somehow especially fragile, sensitive to humans in some obscure and ominous way, in more settled parts of the continent?

In 1962, by a stroke of luck, I joined the faculty at The Colorado College in Colorado Springs. My chairman was Bob Stabler, a falconer and colleague of Richard Bond, Walter Spofford, and Luff Meredith. Stabler urged me to pursue field research and falconry. Further, his sister-in-law, Mary Alice Hamilton, a professor at the college, put me in contact with her old friend Joe Hickey.

First Survey

Hickey had thoroughly searched the literature for Peregrine breeding locations east of the Continental Divide from northern Canada to Mexico in preparation for his 1942 publication in *The Auk* on the eastern population of the Duck Hawk. To my surprise, in response to my inquiry in 1963, he sent his original notes and maps for the enormous Rocky Mountain region. It was a subtle way of encouraging my investigation. An interesting aspect of these notes, written in his tight, graceful

cursive, was that the bulk of the records were from the 1800s and early 1900s. Early ornithologists, including the likes of Arthur Bent, Robert Ridgway, Joseph Allen, and Charles Bendire, reported and collected Duck Hawks from riverbanks on the Plains and from high mountain cliffs. A few observers considered the bird common, which raised the possibility of confusion with the Prairie Falcon. Some of the records were vague regarding location. Not so Charles Aiken's collection of an adult female and a juvenile at Garden of the Gods, Colorado, in 1884. Peregrines nested there at least through 1905. Worrisome as well were sightings of Peregrines in spring from localities where no nest sites were available. These sightings raised the issue of northern migrants. Hickey had only one record from Mexico (in 1939), and one from New Mexico by Alexander Wetmore (in 1918) at Burford Lake. Both cases wholly underestimated the actual distributions.

In 1940, Robert Niedrach, a splendid ornithologist at the Denver Museum of Natural History, reported he had yet to find his first eyrie in Colorado, even after visiting all locations reported up to then. He finally succeeded, discovering a pair with Alfred Bailey near Pagosa Springs in 1943. Hickey had about a dozen records each from Montana and Alberta.

Despite the serendipitous nature of the records, and that no nesting report was less than 20 years old, I thought a survey of the region was feasible in 1964. A survey including so much territory would require specific locations and recent experience to be efficient. William Fischer, a geologist at my college, told of a pair of Peregrines at Osprey Falls in Yellowstone in 1960. Some of the people I contacted were reluctant to disclose locations, but others, like Fischer, were eager to help. These included Tom Smylie in New Mexico, Bob Elgas in Montana, and Kerry Wood and Frank Beebe for Alberta. Luff Meredith had been stationed at the Air Force base at Great Falls, Montana, and wrote of the pairs near there on the Missouri River, corresponding with those seen by Bendire in 1885.

My inquiry continued right up to the spring of 1964. Aretas Saunders, then in his 80s, scratched out the location of a pair he saw on Gallatin River in Montana in 1911. He remembered well shooting at a cliff and the falcon calling high overhead after the smoke cleared from his .45-90 Winchester. Walter Nickell told me of an adult feeding young on the Tabernacle in Salt Lake City in 1951. Russell Grater reported a pair of Peregrines in Black Canyon, Colorado, in 1937 in an obscure paper on bighorn sheep. No record was more impressively established than when, in 1963, Jack Stoddart delivered to my door a magnificent juvenile female a schoolmate had shot at a cliff near Golden, Colorado.

In 1964, no one was aware of the crash of the Peregrine in North America. I fully expected to find many falcons once the search began, but I somehow completely missed the significance of three papers I found then and which still remain in my files. One was by Derek Ratcliffe from 1962 reporting a widespread decline in England by 1957; another was by James Ferguson-Lees from 1963, reporting declines in several birds of prey in Britain; and the third by Stanley Cramp in the same year, published in *British Birds*, outlining the potential problem of toxic chemicals.

My survey took place in spring 1964 and the results were discouraging. I found only 13 pairs at 47 historical eyries. Alberta was especially interesting. Peregrine eyries were once common on high dirt banks along several of the beautiful rivers I floated, where potential prey was abundant. I found a few Peregrine pairs, but Prairie Falcons were frequent, probably as a result of forest clearing. By 1970 Peregrines would be gone from that region and in Wyoming and Montana as well.

Luff Meredith's letter regarding the Great Falls eyries mentioned the fall migration of Peregrines at Padre Island, Texas. The fall flight was similar to that known since the late 1930s on the Maryland/Virginia coast. In fact, Meredith had banded migrant Peregrines on Assateague Island, Maryland, in 1939 and as early as 1952 on Padre Island. I obtained all the band records for Peregrines in the United States (from band recovery reports) and verified the major trapping stations and also a substantial population of migrant northern falcons wintering on the Gulf Coast. Clay White, whom I had written

because of his experience with birds in Dinosaur National Monument, Colorado, went with me to the Texas coast in October 1964. North Padre Island was not yet a national seashore, but it was busy with campers and auto traffic. We only saw nine Peregrines in about 700 miles of beach travel. Matagorda Island, to the north, was an Air Force bombing range. The commanding officer sent a disgruntled sergeant to drive "the bird people" on the deserted beach. This duty was meant to be grave punishment for careless boat driving. The sergeant's attitude changed abruptly when he found out what great sport falcon trapping is!

What had the breeding bird and migrant surveys accomplished? Eyrie occupancy seemed about half of normal or less. How many Peregrines did I miss on the cliffs and banks? No doubt I overlooked some. Joe Hickey once told me the hardest task is to prove vacancy. So I took my results as worst case, but clearly the species was not doing well. Concerning the migrants, our observations on the Gulf Coast were without comparison. I returned to Padre Island many times in the next 30 years. Migrant Peregrines counted there each fall eventually increased as much as three-fold by the 1990s when Tom Maechtle and his co-workers plied the beaches and wash flats with ATVs. Weather, and other variables such as flooding of the flats inland of the beaches, always confounded truly systematic estimates.

Thirty years after Clay White and I converted a sulking sergeant into a falcon trapper, my students Jon Larrabee, Zach Jones, Chris Peper, and Chris Lepisto, with the help of Brian Mutch and Bill Heinrich, tracked Padre Island falcons with radios. They were able to show that Padre Island, and probably the entire Gulf Coast, is held each winter by intensely territorial Peregrines waiting for spring and the return to the Arctic.

R. M. Stabler, courtesy Archives of American Falconry

▲ **Figure 4.3** Colonel R. Luff Meredith (1892–1965), known as "The father of American falconry."

Could it be the bird was somehow especially fragile, sensitive to humans in some obscure and ominous way, in more settled parts of the continent?

Peregrine Memories

Ritt Enderson

I've been told that my first uttered word as a child was *bird*. Not too surprising since I was born into a household shared with a large assemblage of Peregrine and Prairie Falcons. Some of these birds helped form the nucleus of breeding projects mentioned later in this book.

Other words that come to mind that I did not fully understand at the time were *biopsy* and *semen*. Dad was involved in obtaining samples of fatty tissue from wild raptors for pesticide residue analysis. I remember watching him collecting semen samples from male falcons at the outset of work in artificial insemination. At about this time, probably 1969 or 1970, Dan Berger paid our home a visit, bearing a large stack of bumper stickers with bold magenta letters—"Ban DDT." They seemed to evoke a lot of excitement and approval.

Our family spent the 1969–1970 academic year in New York while Dad was on sabbatical at Cornell University with Tom Cade. One particular memory was of Dad's work on radio telemetry systems. He and a collaborator, usually John Snelling or Jim Grier, would hang the transmitters on a tree in the front yard and transport the then bulky receivers about the countryside. This allowed transmitter range and receiver performance evaluation. When Mom's patience waned, she would go outside and disable the transmitter.

After returning from New York, we built a house north of Colorado Springs, Colorado. Here my parents constructed a large barn containing lofts and flight pens that permitted Peregrine courtship and captive breeding. All of this was closely observed and recorded by Dad, concealed behind a plywood partition and viewing through one-way glass. Eggs laid by the Peregrines were removed for artificial incubation, and plaster dummy eggs were left in their place. Once, when Dad was out of town, we suffered a power outage at the house. Mom quickly gathered up the eggs in a styrofoam chest, and with the chest riding on my lap, we transported them to an incubator at The Colorado College.

But the most poignant memory of those years is of the many field trips with Dad to historical eyrie sites around Colorado and northern New Mexico: Wolf Creek, Mesa Verde, Chimney Rock, Burford Lake, and others. At each the situation was the same— no birds, only empty cliffs and hours spent scrutinizing them.

Certainly the most vivid memories are of my participation in Peregrine Falcon survey work on the Colorado Plateau. The remote, rugged, and roadless nature of large expanses of southern and eastern Utah resulted in an incomplete understanding of regional falcon population status. I guess you could say it was the last big "blank spot" on the map in the Lower 48 states. That it should have remained so into the late 1980s was a bit of a surprise.

So on the morning of 23 May 1984, four groups of excited Peregrine surveyors waited in the main canyon at Zion National Park to be airlifted via helicopter to predetermined observation points. Long-time backcountry helicopter pilot Burt Metcalf possessed the patience, skill, and humor to make that survey a success. The survey teams were scheduled to spend two or three observation periods (dawn and dusk) at each observation point and then be shuttled to the next site. This routine would continue for several days at a time before regrouping and moving to the next survey area. We had no idea what to expect, and the first several days the results were not encouraging. Then a trickle of new eyries and territories turned to a torrent, and by the end of the 1984 survey it was plain that we had uncovered one of the largest concentrations of Peregrine Falcons outside the Arctic.

The 1985 survey was of similar but refined strategy, and with the talents of people such as Brian Mutch, Tim Tibbitts, and Gianfranco Basilli, we concentrated on localities that had shown promise in 1984. Federal lands, including Canyonlands and Zion National Parks and Glen Canyon National Recreation Area, became familiar ground, and we filled in blank spots with new nesting territories. An added facet of the 1985 survey was the opportunity to return to several of these Colorado Plateau territories to collect eggshell fragments and prey remains from the eyries. Our crew consisted of Chris Schultz and climbers Rob Ramey,

Cliff Neighbors, and myself. That year, Richard Dick of Thunderbird Helicopters made it all possible, as he had with the survey crews, moving us quickly from site to remote site.

It was apparent from the 1984–1985 fieldwork that Peregrine Falcon territory occupancy and productivity on the Colorado Plateau were robust. Other regions throughout the West were long without their black-helmeted, blue-backed aerialists. Captive propagation with reintroduction via hacking, as well as augmentation, was at its zenith.

I had staffed a hack site near Durango, Colorado, under the supervision of Ed Freienmuth in 1984. My co-attendant, Patsy Hart, and I were responsible for observing and caring for three eyass Peregrines. These young, fresh from The Peregrine Fund "factory," became the latest contribution to what we hoped would become a viable falcon population. Ed's energy, enthusiasm, and dedication to raptor conservation inspired Patsy and me to contend with the daily duties of hack site life: the isolation, hauling of all equipment and supplies several miles and approximately 1,000 vertical feet, dealing with threats to our feathered charges, and the anxiety of a fledgling briefly absent. I gained a beard and lost 20 pounds that summer, and significantly, the reintroduction of the Peregrine Falcons in the Rockies became a part of me. Feelings fostered while watching our birds develop flying skills, tail-

Ritt Enderson, age 6, examines a kestrel.

chase swallows, land, and ultimately disperse will never be forgotten by those of us privileged to operate a hack site.

The summers of 1986 and 1987 saw me, under the guidance of Bill Heinrich and Dan O'Brien, managing several hack sites and scattering eyass Peregrines to sites in Wyoming, Montana, and Colorado. At every turn there were cooperative, if skeptical, landowners, supportive agency personnel, and quail freezer plug-ins. Bright-eyed hack site attendants eagerly awaited the three or four down-covered items of precious cargo, which would be the center of their universe and the objects of their scrutiny for the next six weeks.

The young were raised at The Peregrine Fund in Boise, Idaho, under the constant care of Cal Sandfort and Willard Heck, and many others who watched with trepidation as responsibility was relinquished to us reintroduction assistants. Loaded into

boxes, the young falcons dispersed via airplane or in Peregrine Fund vehicles, affectionately known as the Skunk, the Camel, or simply the Silver Truck. I well remember boxes of eyasses carried mountain-goat-style to remote hack boxes and slung over our shoulders as we rapelled to the hacking ledge below. There was excitement the day the box was opened, and the anxiety of bad weather, aerial predators, or wayward hikers. Always among us was the unspoken sense that what we were doing was going to work.

Nowadays I see Peregrines pretty regularly, whether a wintertime loiterer stalking Brewer's Blackbirds over a suburban Phoenix golf course or an adult female on territory in downtown San Diego. When I do, I don't see them as simply birds but as living memories—of Heinrich's grin, Oakleaf's pipe, the dull thud of chopper blades, or my Dad, peering undistracted through a telescope.

Ritt Enderson is a Doctor of Veterinary Medicine and owns a clinic in Arizona, where he lives with his wife, Angie, and their two children, Emma and Alec.

Pesticide Studies

Contemporary with my search in the Rocky Mountains in 1964 was another quest with a more disastrous result. Dan Berger and Chuck Sindelar were commissioned by Joe Hickey to search for Duck Hawks in the eastern United States. They visited more than 130 historical sites and saw not a falcon (see sidebar, The 1964 Survey of Peregrine Eyries in the Eastern United States, Chapter 3).

Hickey responded by organizing the first Peregrine conference in 1965. The predicament of the Peregrine in North America and Europe was laid bare. Especially disturbing to me was a statement by Ben Glading that fewer than half of California's eyries were in use; fewer than 32 pairs were verified in 1965. Would Peregrines in the western United States go the way of those in the East?

The 1965 conference focused on chlorinated pesticides as a potential cause of the losses. The British suspected dieldrin because of its great toxicity. Ian Prestt, and Lucille and Bill Stickel of the U.S. Fish and Wildlife Service (FWS), urged an inquiry as to its potential role.

Dan Berger and I set out to test the effects of dieldrin at a substantial number of local Prairie Falcon eyries. We focused on eggshell thinning by feeding deliberately contaminated European Starlings to wild Prairie Falcons. We also planned to find out whether dieldrin was present in Peregrines in northern Canada. As it turned out, the dieldrin test with Prairie Falcons was confounded by the presence of DDE (from DDT) in the prey of both test birds and controls. Shell-thinning in the falcons was correlated with higher residues, but the effect of either pesticide was masked by the other.

We did show shell-thinning and poor reproduction were strongly related, but not until 1974 did Dave Peakall prove beyond doubt that DDE and shell-thinning were cause and effect in Peregrines (see sidebar, Settling the Matter Beyond Doubt, Chapter 2). Interestingly, shell-thinning was not mentioned at the 1965 conference in Madison. Not until 1967 did Derek Ratcliffe alert the world to that pervasive disaster.

The reconnaissance to find pesticides in northern Peregrines was indeed a saga for Dan Berger, Skip Walker, and me. In May 1966, the Commissioner of the Northwest Territories issued us a "Scientists and Explorers Permit" to collect Peregrine eggs and prey for pesticide tests. The plan was to travel the Peace, Slave, and Mackenzie Rivers to the Arctic. On the way, we checked three eyries in Alberta that I had seen active in 1964. Two were in use. We obtained a single spoiled egg that proved to be loaded with DDE.

On 3 June we sailed in a 22-ft freight canoe from the town of Peace River, Alberta, and reached

Figure 4.4 Female Peregrine ▶ caught for fat biopsy at Arctic Red River on the lower Mackenzie, 1966. The fat showed significant DDT/DDE, no doubt accumulated from migrant prey in the Arctic, or on the wintering grounds.

Jim Enderson

Courtesy Jim Enderson

▲ Figure 4.5 Dan Berger, Skip Walker, and Jim Enderson leave Peace River, Alberta, in June 1966 bound for the Mackenzie River. Only 13 pairs of Peregrines were found along the 1,900 mi route to the Arctic ocean. A stuffed owl sits on a box of starlings and pigeons, all used for trapping falcons.

the Mackenzie Delta in the first week of July. In 1,900 mi we found 13 pairs of Peregrines, but we surely missed some because the river is nearly two miles wide in many places. Our results showed plenty of DDE in prey and egg contents. In retrospect, these amounts were consistent with serious shell-thinning and population decline. We also caught adult Peregrines and biopsied fat for lab tests, which confirmed great contamination.

The starlings and pigeons we had aboard were a major attraction to the children of the villages along the way. Fortunately, we were warned that the Peace drops 3 m in falls above Wood Buffalo Park and requires a portage. We hired a Cree Indian and his horse-drawn wagon to carry us around the falls. We survived the hordes of mosquitoes on the Slave and the treacherous waves created by strong wind against the current. By hurried exodus, we avoided the aggressive prostitutes at Fort Resolution on Great Slave Lake. Peregrines were absent from several places they had nested, especially at Campbell Lake near the ocean.

As an epilogue, in 1994 we learned that pairs have more than tripled along the Mackenzie since

that trip in 1966. My only regret is that the eggshells were discarded by the lab that did the pesticide tests; we missed the chance to show shell-thinning early on.

In February 1967, Joe Hickey wrote an interesting letter after reviewing our draft manuscript on the high DDE levels found in biopsied fat samples and eggs from the Mackenzie Peregrines. These levels, from a population thought by most to be healthy, exceeded those in the obviously stricken British population. "At the moment I don't know the answer," Joe wrote. "The physiological mechanism (of embryonic mortality, egg breakage, and egg eating by adults) is much more subtle (than toxic effect on embryos)." He mentioned the possibility of toxic effects on adult behavior but concluded, in his precise longhand, "that's straining things, isn't it?" Joe Hickey was baffled, but the answer came soon.

Early in April 1967, Joe sent a mimeograph report to "raptor field investigators" after Ratcliffe had written to him that the weights of eggshells before 1945 were "statistically and startlingly" higher than afterward. The phenomenon appeared in both Peregrines and Sparrowhawks. We needed to determine the scope of such shell weight (and thus thickness) changes in North America, and to correlate these changes with insecticide levels in the field. Hickey suggested that laboratory work might produce shell changes by controlling some variable, such as an insecticide. Within the next six years an overwhelming case would be made against the chlorinated insecticides, and in 1972 DDT, along with the others, would be banned for most uses by the Environmental Protection Agency (EPA). Joe Hickey was a principal witness in the hard-fought pre-ban hearings.

Most who have been to the Far North become transformed and soon plot to return. In 1967, John Campbell, Bob Berry, and I floated the Yukon River from Dawson City in the Yukon Territory into Alaska. Again, we found high DDE levels in biopsied fat samples. During that trip we talked a good deal about captive breeding. A side trip up the Porcupine River to the village of Old Crow revealed several pairs of Peregrines and spectacular scenery. Jerry Swartz and Dave Roseneau also worked the Yukon that same season, so we combined our results and published a joint report.

In 1968 Tom Cade asked me to help survey on the Yukon and Colville Rivers, the latter with Clay White. Production of young that year at both localities was only about one young per pair. At this time the decline in occupancy on the Colville had not yet begun, but the Yukon birds were declining sharply. Peregrines reached their lowest ebb on the Yukon in 1973, and on the Colville between 1975 and 1978 (Ambrose et al. 1988).

In 1968 I took a nestling from southwestern Colorado specifically for captive breeding. In 1969 I took two more Rocky Mountain nestlings for breeding trials and repeated the nesting surveys. I found pairs at only eight of 25 eyries in the entire mountain region.

During the academic year 1969–1970, I was at Cornell University with Tom Cade and his graduate students. Dave Peakall and Clay White were there as well. Students included Jim Grier, Stan Temple, John Snelling, John Haugh, and Jeff Lincer. Jeff was working on the effects of DDE on wild Kestrels and was eventually able to correlate the compound with shell-thinning. It was a wonderful time for discussion. We worked on rudimentary telemetry transmitters and receivers. Modern units had yet to become available. I explored the usefulness of a device that could measure the thickness of an eggshell by counting the rate at which beta particles were back-scattered from the shell; the thicker the shell, the greater the reflection of particles back to the counter.

Stan Temple had developed a reliable time-lapse movie camera for recording behavior in the nest. Roland Clement of the National Audubon Society provided a grant to look for abnormal behavior in Yukon River Peregrines in 1970. With the help of Jerry Swartz of the University of Alaska, we obtained more than 75,000 time-lapse photographs. We recorded egg breakage and nestling mortality but no problem with adult behavior. The Yukon was sometimes exciting. One night a black bear jumped on our tent, landing on Stan. The bear came right up to me and I had to shoot it. We immediately finished the rest of the port wine.

I had taken my two pairs of Peregrines and one pair of Prairie Falcons to Cornell. I lent the oldest female Peregrine, whose mate was too young to breed, to Heinz Meng for the year. The Prairie Falcons were put in a makeshift loft in an old barn and produced fertile eggs; the female, UFO, dated back to 1960 and my days in Wyoming. Her three eggs hatched in a portable incubator while we drove from Ithaca to Colorado in May 1970. The only other success with captive breeding of Prairie Falcons at that time was by Henry Kendall in 1968.

Perhaps the highlight of my Cornell year was a trip with Walter Spofford to investigate a report of a Peregrine on territory at Lake Willoughby, Vermont. No falcon had been seen on a cliff in the eastern United States for several years, and all were presumed extirpated. We found an adult male. I climbed the brush-covered mountain, but no eyrie was evident. When I came down the road, totally exhausted and overheated, Spoff walked up and pulled a cold can of Coors beer from the pocket of his ever-present bush coat! At the time, Coors could be bought only in Colorado.

continued on page 66

▲ **Figure 4.6** John Campbell (right) holds a downy Peregrine while Jim Enderson bands a second.

The bear came right up to me and I had to shoot it. We immediately finished the rest of the port wine.

63

A Pile of Prey Remains

Grainger Hunt

A great mesa standing at the border of Texas and Mexico overlooks the Rio Grande and Big Bend National Park. A tiercel Peregrine owns a certain fine big portion of that mesa, and from its rim, he looks 1,500 ft almost straight down to the river and over a vast desert grassland full of White-winged and Mourning Doves. His command of the area is especially strategic in that these favorite prey must go to water once or twice a day, and the only water is the river. Not only that, but when this bird's young are half grown or so, a healthy chunk of songbirds passes through the area on its way back from Latin America.

My experience with this eyrie began in the early 1970s when you could hardly find a pair of Peregrines. Morley Nelson told me he had seen a pair there during the 1940s, but with all the DDT use in the cotton-growing regions of West Texas and adjacent Mexico, it was a surprise to find them still there producing young. Because the question of whether Peregrines were going extinct in North America still hung thick in the air, it seemed appropriate to find out what the falcons were catching and whether their eggshells were thin. The idea was to wait a few weeks after the young fledged and then climb into the eyrie to see what could be found in the way of prey remains and eggshell fragments.

In observing the eyrie, my friends and I had been amazed to see three young

fledge from a pothole about 30 ft to the right of the one where incubation had taken place, a mystery that would eventually explain itself. The eyrie cliff towered 600 ft above a steep talus slope. Below was another 600 ft cliff that fell to the river. There was a way to hike up the lower tier of cliffs by a ramp-like ledge, but the upper cliff was sheer in both directions for miles and miles. The eyrie itself was badly overhung. Just looking up at that cliff from the bottom made me dizzy, so I did what any manly biologist would have done under the circumstances: I talked my friend David Sleeper into doing the climb. At the time, David was a desert survival instructor and accomplished climber, familiar with the mesa. He had a big dog named Wino who was also comfortable in steep terrain (!) and who went along and performed an important, though unlikely function, as you will see.

It took David two days to reach the top of the cliff, walking from the town of Lajitas with his friend Antonio whose two donkeys each carried a 600 ft length of climbing rope. At the appointed time, I was at the bottom, across the river with my son Philo in my truck looking at David (a dot) through my telescope as he stood on top of the mesa with a hand-held CB radio.

After getting into position above the eyrie, David lowered Wino off the cliff in a harness sling. Wino's job was to guide the rope to the bot-

Peregrines still nested in the canyons of the Rio Grande in Texas' Big Bend National Park in the early 1970s.

tom and, among other things, prove the rope was long enough. Each time the dog got to a ledge, he would, after a little hesitation and verbal coaxing from the top, bail off into space as he had learned to do during his many previous adventures with David. The method used in Wino's training was never revealed to me. As it turned out, Wino made it to the bottom with no extra rope to spare. Steve Belardo and Frid Fridrikkson were there to untie the dog, and with the rope in place, David started his descent.

A while later he was dangling out in front of the eyrie, unable to reach it because of the immense overhang. Steve

and Frid, several hundred feet below, stopped David from spinning by holding the end of the rope, then began swinging him back and forth trying to get him into the eyrie. How those guys survived the falling globs of rotten limestone that David pulled off the cliff each time he attempted to grab onto the eyrie is an interesting and disturbing question. Each time when shouts reached them from above, they bolted for the cliff like quail.

After a dozen more tries, David was exhausted and told me so on the CB, but he vowed to try once more before giving up. The guys at the bottom, appraised of all this by my radio, said that

64

this time would be the one. Sure enough, David stuck, despite the considerable weight of the rope pulling him backward. Tough guy! And by the way, don't try this.

"There's nothing here," David said on the radio. "No feathers, no eggshells. Just a lot of tracks."

Silence.

"Hey, check this out! There's a cave over here to the left. Looks like it swings around back there and comes out again."

This was to be expected since the young had fledged from the wrong ledge. In negotiating the narrow crawlway, David had to move a big rock from its center, remove himself from the rope (which he tied around the rock) and even his hardhat, and squeeze through to the other side. After five minutes of anxious silence, he emerged in the pothole where the pair had incubated. "Nothing here either," he reported.

Soon, however, David began sifting around in the dirt and found a fairly generous collection of eggshell fragments which he placed in a container. But aside from traces of down from the eyasses, David could find not a single bone or feather. You could hear the disappointment in his voice.

Silence.

"Hey," he remarked, "there's a bunch of sticks crammed in back here. What are all these sticks doing in here? Holy smokes, it's a pack rat's nest! I wonder if....Wait a minute." And sure enough, David spent an hour taking the nest apart, making three big Ziploc bags fat with feathers and bones. Before departing the pothole, he did the best he could to put the nest back together (but it was a real "rat's nest"...), and I like to think he left a cookie inside, the fine gentleman.

We visited the Smithsonian Institution in Washington, D.C., a month later and went through all those remains with Roxy Laybourne, the undisputed World's Champion Identifier of Bird Feathers. "Grain-jah," she might announce in her wonderful Southern accent, while holding up a tiny breast feather in one hand and a study specimen in the other, "What you have is a Westun Tanajah." And here's what Roxy identified: Mourning Dove, White-winged Dove, Rock Dove, Lesser Nighthawk, White-throated Swift, Ladder-backed Woodpecker, Horned Lark, Barn Swallow, Cliff Swallow, Cactus Wren, Canyon Wren, Rock Wren, thrush species, Northern Mockingbird, Loggerhead Shrike, thrasher species, Black-headed Grosbeak, Pyrrhuloxia, Green-tailed Towee, junco species, Lark Bunting, meadowlark,

Each time the dog got to a ledge, he would, after a little hesitation and verbal coaxing from the top, bail off into space . . .

Brewer's Blackbird, Brown-headed Cowbird, Western Tanager, Lesser Goldfinch, Pine Siskin, House Finch, duck, Sora, Killdeer, dowitcher, Great Blue Heron, Mexican free-tailed bat, and antelope ground squirrel.

It is thrilling to see falcons chase their quarry and even to hear stories of falcons chasing. To experience that momentary vicarious joy of being the falcon—accelerating from the airy dimension of that great cliff to flash over the treetops by the river as if the vast distance were nothing. To burst into existence, close with prey, strike it dead in passing, then shoot vertically upward, dissipating energy. To fold a wing, drop, and catch the falling prize. To ascend easily on up-slope winds, so far, far upward. To course back and forth among the updrafts of the towering cliff face, ever rising. To call. To be borne home to the waiting family.

A pile of prey remains from a Peregrine's nest or plucking perch is a pile of such stories told by the falcons themselves about wild adventure in three enormous dimensions. Prey items are records of such adventure and reflections of the landscape and the richness of life it generates. What speedy, breath-taking moment do we imagine when we pick out the primaries of a White-throated Swift in a pile of feathers? And what was that Great Blue Heron bone doing there?

Grainger Hunt *studied Peregrine migration and foraging behavior in coastal Texas for his 1966 Master's thesis and has since researched the ecology of nesting Peregrines in Texas, Mexico, and the California Channel Islands. As a pilot, he tracked radio-tagged Peregrines on long-distance migrations and studied Peregrine ranging and habitat selection. He was a member of the recovery team for the western United States. Grainger is research director for The Peregrine Fund's California Condor and Aplomado Falcon projects.*

Captive Breeding

In 1971 I took my last nestling, named BC, for captive breeding from an eyrie west of Denver. He was fully imprinted on people and would not accept a potential mate. This disaster turned into great fortune after Les Boyd showed the world how to induce imprinted males to copulate with a hat worn by its handler. BC would father scores of offspring in later years at The Peregrine Fund facilities (see Chapter 19).

In 1971 my old female Lil from Wyoming laid many infertile eggs, including 13 in one string. In all, my two females laid 25 infertile eggs that year. This was very discouraging. Late that summer we built a new loft with five chambers. My students Reid Kelly and Dan Hartman made the work tolerable.

In 1972 the New York Zoological Society provided a grant of $1,100 to support the project. This grant was crucial because by then I had three pairs of Peregrines and four of Prairie Falcons. Morgan Berthrong and Tom Ray had loaned me their male and female Peregrines, respectively. That year Peregrines held by Tom Smylie in New Mexico produced a fertile egg which failed to hatch.

Jim Enderson

▲ **Figure 4.7** Alpha, in 1973, was the first Peregrine from *anatum* stock in temperate North America to be produced in captivity. One of her several offspring produced the first F$_2$ captive-produced Peregrines at The Peregrine Fund in Fort Collins.

We knew we were getting close to producing captive birds.

In the spring of 1972, Stan Temple came to Colorado to help with artificial insemination (AI). We trapped a wild male Prairie Falcon and learned how to manipulate the bird to get semen. By the end of the 1972 season AI was clearly practical.

At this time Colorado became the first Western state to hire a raptor biologist. Jerry Craig had grown up in the Colorado Springs area and would help establish a branch of The Peregrine Fund in Fort Collins in 1975.

The real breakthrough in captive breeding came in 1973. John Campbell in Alberta produced three young from northern birds, and the Cornell project produced 20 young from three naturally

breeding pairs. I produced one young by AI from the 1968 female and three naturally from the old Wyoming female. One of these latter young soon died of herpes virus infection. The Prairie Falcons also produced young for a fourth year, and I used these to test the rearing skills of the adult Peregrines. The Colorado Division of Wildlife provided $3,000 in 1974-1975. In late 1975 I disbanded the project after producing 13 *anatum* Peregrines at a total cost of about $10,000. Two of the young were loaned to the late Ed Freienmuth, but eventually all five adults and 13 offspring ended up in Fort Collins. There they joined Tom Smylie's pair and two pairs of Colorado birds from Bill Burnham. These birds were essentially the parent stock that Dan Konkel, and later Cal Sandfort, would cultivate so effectively.

Early Peregrine Management

In 1973 Jerry Craig and I published a status report on Peregrines in the Rocky Mountains. About a third of the historical eyries were still in use by pairs, and addled eggs from four eyries averaged 20% thinner than normal, a degree now known to be typical of declining populations. Indeed, in the next several years the population would reach its lowest number. Peregrines east of the Continental Divide in Colorado would virtually disappear, as would birds in Wyoming and Montana. We knew of about 15 pairs still present in western Colorado and New Mexico, but in 1975 only four pairs were known in all of Utah and Arizona.

In 1974, Craig and I put two Prairie Falcon eggs in a Peregrine site in the Royal Gorge where we had found broken eggs. At our request, Jim Weaver flew in from Cornell with two Arctic Peregrine chicks. They fledged, and I last saw them soaring high above the canyon. This was the first successful release in the western United States.

In 1975 the Rocky Mountain/Southwestern Peregrine Falcon Recovery Team was formed with Jerry Craig as its leader. DDT had been banned in 1972, and generally we were optimistic about the prospects of fostering wild young hatched in captivity and of releasing captive-bred young. The team had nine members, and of these, Frank Bond, Morley Nelson, and I were falconers. The team members were enthusiastic and worked well together. An early meeting in Cheyenne caught the game officials there off-guard—what was this recovery team thing anyway? The team immediately embraced the idea of restocking Peregrines because of the recent captive-breeding successes.

In the recovery plan, we boldly predicted up to 100 young could be produced annually for release; by 1985 actual production was well above that estimate.

In the years 1974–1976, World Wildlife Fund provided me about $1,000 a year to keep track of the small Rocky Mountain population of Peregrines. The funds actually originated from FWS. The few remaining sites were scattered from Yellowstone to northern New Mexico. In 1976, Dan Berger came from Wisconsin to help with the survey, the first year of the long and crucial role he played in managing Colorado Peregrines. That year only four pairs were known to produce eggs in the state, and we interceded at half of those eyries. We felt our way carefully, first replacing the natural eggs with dummy eggs, then the dummy eggs with downy Prairie Falcons, then substituting those with Peregrine chicks. That work was very important to me; three of the five young were from my old Wyoming female at Fort Collins. Also in 1976, the first second-generation captive-bred Peregrine was produced from my first 1973 youngster.

Marcy Cottrell Houle, one of my students, was early in a long line of students to work on Peregrines in the field in Colorado in 1976. She watched falcons in southwest Colorado and eventually wrote of her experiences in a popular book, *Wings for My Flight*. That year I went to Scotland for a few weeks to help Ian Newton and Richard Mearns trap and mark adults in a longevity study. Richard's father had told him he had better get a "proper job" and give up these bird antics. Richard became a well-known field biologist.

In 1977 we took eggs from six sites in Colorado and two in New Mexico. Eggs with cracked shells were found in at least three eyries. We were convinced fostering was worthwhile. That year, fostered pairs produced about 2.5 young per pair on average compared with roughly 1.5 young per pair for unfostered pairs. But the effort and costs were high, and some questioned its usefulness.

In about 1978, John Hubbard of the New Mexico Game and Fish Department circulated an undated five-page memorandum on Peregrine management in New Mexico. He stated that a decline had not been documented in New Mexico even though eggshells recovered from one eyrie over a 10-year period were 20% thinner than those collected elsewhere prior to DDT. No base sample from that region was available. Hubbard wrote that the species should fend for itself if passive management such as nest surveys was "not sufficient to achieve survival." He argued

Figure 4.8 This was the first attempt to foster captive-bred Peregrines to wild parents (Royal Gorge, Colorado, 1974). Two Prairie Falcons (background), placed earlier to occupy the adult Peregrines, are here replaced by two Peregrines from The Peregrine Fund at Cornell University. The Prairie Falcons were taken back to their wild parents, and the Peregrines fledged successfully.

Figure 4.9 Royal Gorge, Colorado.

that "threats to survival" must be documented (by the state) and that only then should active management be considered.

Hubbard's statements followed our three years of searches in the state, and only five of the 20 or so historical sites were known to be in use. Subsequent surveys by the state were done beginning in 1979, and about 10 previously unknown pairs were found. The last two fosterings in New Mexico in

Jim Enderson

▲ **Figure 4.10** A male adult above an eyrie in Colorado, 1980, the first released captive-bred Peregrine known to have bred in the wild in western North America.

File photo

Figure 4.11 Jim Enderson ▶ watches from the cockpit as Cal Sandfort unloads a box of chicks in Boise.

Jim Enderson

▲ **Figure 4.12** Jim Enderson's survey team found scores of previously unknown Peregrine territories in the national parks on the Colorado Plateau in 1985. Left to right: Cliff Neighbors, Rob Ramey, Ritt Enderson, Chris Schultz, and pilot Richard Dick.

1979 failed. Curiously, in the 1990s officials there attempted to show reproduction was seriously declining, but I felt the notion was based on inadequate samples from the 1970s and early 1980s. In most later years, production was not below a "normal" 1.5 young per territorial pair. In retrospect, Peregrines in New Mexico may not have declined as seriously as they clearly did northward. In the last two decades, workers there became aware of many more pairs; the contribution by dispersal of hundreds of released Peregrines in adjacent Colorado to that result is unclear.

Population Expansion

The hacking of Peregrines began with one site in Colorado in 1978, and up to seven per year were operated in the mid-1980s. The numbers of Peregrines released by hacking and fostering were roughly equal and approached about 500 by 1990 when releases ceased. Hacking was also important in many other Rocky Mountain/Southwestern states except Arizona. Released falcons became numerous in the Colorado population.

Like New Mexico, Arizona may not have been as deeply involved in the decline as northern states were. Dave Ellis wrote a letter to the recovery team in 1983, sharply critical of the draft revision of the regional recovery plan which emphasized captive breeding and release. He urged patience. In his view, the falcons of the West would return without releases because of the banning of DDT. He cited the recovery of the British population as evidence. His surveys in Arizona from 1978 onward had resulted in discovery of "new" pairs and a total count of about 24 pairs in 1982. He argued that not all pairs had been discovered (of course he was right), and that given time the existing pairs would expand without management. Credence is given to his argument by great increases of other bird- and fish-eating raptors since 1985, and the three-fold expansion of the Arctic Peregrine, which was never augmented.

In fact, the known population of breeding pairs in the Rocky Mountain/Southwestern region grew markedly in the 1980s. At least in Colorado, and northward, where early repeated searches had shown few pairs, reestablishment depended mainly on actual population growth. The unheard of numbers in Arizona and the Colorado Plateau were probably due in part to just plain searching in areas that had never been sufficiently surveyed for Peregrines.

By 1983 The Peregrine Fund in Fort Collins was operating hack sites in Idaho, Utah, Montana, and Wyoming, as well as Colorado. That year 99 young Peregrines went out of the facility. In the late 1970s I had ferried young to release sites in New Mexico in my plane. Later, my role included taking eggs to Fort Collins from sites to be fostered, and delivering young. Up to 21 young at a time were flown to release sites, greatly reducing stress on the birds compared to surface travel. When the Fund moved to Boise, use of the plane grew; I took eggs from Colorado to the new facility, and young from there went to foster and hack sites in several states. In all, hundreds of 35- to 38-day-old young were delivered, and there are those who to this day claim the odor of Peregrine chicks still lingers in the aircraft.

The National Park Service contracted The Peregrine Fund to survey several western parks in 1984–1985, especially Zion, Canyonlands, Dinosaur (where Steve Petersburg had located several eyries), and Big Bend in Texas. I was in charge of the work involving pairs of observers placed by helicopter at vantage points to observe the best habitat. In brief, we found many Peregrines, thanks to the hard work of observers Jim Sailer, Sherry Theresa, Ritt Enderson, Anne Van Sweringen, Chris Schultz, Beth Braker, Kurt Stolzenburg, Charlie Roe, Rob Ramey, Lynn Woodward, Patty Harte, Tim Tibbitts, and Dale Kohlmoos. Park personnel who were especially helpful included Jeff Connor, Larry Belli, and Larry Hayes. The last had enormous enthusiasm for these birds and eventually showed that Zion was packed tight with Peregrine territories. In fact, we were able to find about 40 pairs in southern Utah and verified good reproduction. In 1988, a survey in northern Utah directed by Clay White and me, using a helicopter and competent observers, including Ken Keller, Gian Basilli, Anne Enderson, Joe DiDonato, Chuck Kilpatrick, and Anne Van Sweringen, found only one pair. The Wasatch Front had yet to be recolonized.

These surveys in the mid-1980s verified the existence of a large population of birds on the Colorado Plateau continuous with that found by Rich Glinsky and Byran Brown in Arizona. Eastward and northward the species was much rarer; only a few pairs were known in all of Wyoming, Montana, and Alberta south of the taiga. In fact, only 12 pairs produced eggs in Colorado in 1985, only twice the number a decade earlier. This slow increase occurred despite the release of 184 young in the state through 1983.

In the 1970s and early 1980s Jerry Craig and I relied importantly on students at The Colorado College. Some have already been mentioned; others were Mike Berman, Brad Branski, Jon Patz,

Brian Pendleton, Peter Schoonmaker, Rachel Wood, Mike Stiehl, Peter Wrege, Tom Bohannon, Elizabeth Bauer, Tom Sisk, and Elizabeth Bowden. Later, students would help with surveys, fostering, hacking, and related studies; these included Mark Robert, Gary Beauvais, Lou Berner, Dan Durland, Jane Hines, Dan Kim, Niels Maumenee, Emil McCain, and Ryan Pleune. Most of these people were involved in more than one season.

▲ **Figure 4.13** Gates of Lodore at Dinosaur National Monument, one of several western regions where healthy populations of Peregrines were found in the mid-1980s.

Conclusions

So what had really happened to the Peregrine in the region after the introduction of DDT? What have we all actually brought about, viewed from our perspective of the fourth anniversary of the delisting and the celebration? Peregrines throughout the Rockies were surely laden with DDT, and I believe the contamination and resulting shell-thinning were more pronounced northward, than in the southwestern United States. Big Bend, Texas, was perhaps an exception.

Lowered reproduction may have occurred throughout the region, but that effect was surely more severe to the north, resulting in recruitment inadequate to replace adult loss. Dave Ellis felt that a clear increase in eyrie occupancy took place in Arizona in 1975–1985. If so, then it is consistent with my view that the bird was depleted from 1947 to 1975, even in the Southwest and Mexico.

In the mid-1980s, a major population expansion was underway at least in Arizona and southern Utah. By the early 1990s, this expansion, powered by good reproduction, collided with growing pools of released birds and their progeny in Colorado and the northern tier of western states. By the mid-1990s, the increase was clearly in full momentum, and remarkable recent growth

Searching the Mountains of Mexico

Grainger Hunt

Roland Wauer and simple logic sent us to the Mexican highlands in April 1975. Roland, the naturalist at Big Bend National Park in West Texas, had found several pairs of Peregrines breeding there and, on impulse, gave me $500 to find some more. In deciding how best to spend the money, my volunteer friends and I at the Chihuahuan Desert Research Institute thought of those cliffy mountains we could see to the south of the Big Bend on a clear day. We soon had aviation charts of Mexico (ideal for showing terrain features) spread all over the floor, and there were the Sierra Madres! If there were Peregrines in Big Bend, there had to be many more in Mexico.

Five of us (Curt Griffin, Frank Earhart, Mariel Brockway, Mark Hitchcock, and I) took my VW van 400 miles to the foot of a great mountain in the Sierra Madre Oriental where an adult Peregrine had been reported in the 1950s. We hiked up through pines and agaves, making bets on what we would find. I bet on the Peregrines but was disappointed when a pair of Prairie Falcons flew from the best-looking cliff halfway up. We puffed on until dusk, and just as we were about to turn back, we rounded a blind corner and flushed an adult male Peregrine from a small cliff. Wow!

Next day, we drove across the valley through prickly pear farms and orchards lined with rock fences to an Italian-looking village under a towering cliff. The town's mayor took us to the home of Jesús

Espinosa, a tall hunter in his early forties with steady eyes. As we stood with him in the street in front of his house, we brought out our field guide to Mexican birds and opened up to the page with the falcons. "Do you ever see these birds around here?" we asked in our version of Spanish.

He squinted at the page, studying the drawings. It was clear that he had never seen a book of bird identification, and certainly he could not have anticipated such a question. After a while he softly said, "Sí," nodding his head. Then we pointed to the picture of the Peregrine, the bird we were calling "Halcón Azúl." Again, he seemed to examine the tiniest details of the illustration, then paused for reflection. "...Sí." We held our breath when we asked whether he happened to know the whereabouts of a nest. You could tell he was really searching his memory "...Sí."

Jesús was waiting for us at 6:00 a.m. in pressed slacks and spit-polished cowboy boots. On the way out of town, we dropped Mark off to check out the promising cliff above town, then proceeded down the road with our guide. After a while, though, it became apparent we were heading away from what we regarded as Peregrine country and into lower, dryer, somewhat boring terrain. Twenty-five miles later, when we were all convinced the day was being wasted, we were directed into a dry creek bed. We parked and began hiking up its narrow, rocky floor, not at all hopeful of finding a

Peregrine. We were soon seeing pools of running water and an increasing diversity of shrubs, however, and as we continued, we saw a flock of Band-tailed Pigeons and the top of a nice cliff beginning to show above us. As more of the cliff emerged, we were looking up at a pair of Peregrines soaring along its face.

I climbed out of the canyon bottom, found what I thought was the eyrie, and after an hour, returned to the creek. There were my friends standing next to Jesús, who was again intently examining a page in the bird book. As I approached, Mariel called me over in wonder and astonishment to tell me that Jesús was identifying songbirds in the surrounding vegetation, not by seeing them but by hearing their vocalizations. He seemed to know them all! Needless to say, that was a satisfying day, and we were all deeply moved by our meeting with that patient observer with such deep curiosity and character and knowledge, and with never the prospect of sharing it with anybody. This naturalist, who had never seen a guide book, increased our understanding of integrity and gave us a glimpse of how mankind came to plumb the secrets of the world.

We found Mark back in town with news of yet another pair of Peregrines chasing away flocks of Maroon-fronted Parrots passing the eyrie cliff, and over

the next three days, before returning to Texas, we found two more pairs. Our success prompted the U.S. Fish and Wildlife Service and World Wildlife Fund to fund more surveys over the next several years, and we continued to find Peregrines at a time when they were very hard to find. Dirk Lanning, Peter Lawson, David Whitacre, and Gary Falxa concentrated in the eastern Sierra Madre, and Mark Hitchcock, Steve Belardo, Joan Fryxell, and Carl Vance surveyed the western range. All these guys were tough as nails and motivated beyond the normal concept of that word.

The country was grand, and it was wonderful to find Peregrines there! There were places where we could travel from hard desert to a near tropical rainforest in a half-day's drive on a dirt road and see plants and animals new to us. There were many, many likely looking cliffs just too far away or too immense to survey. We tried lots of things, and Peter and Dirk even made a radio-controlled model Golden Eagle airplane to draw Peregrines out. Among the other hardworking people on these adventures in Mexico were John Bean, Tom Connor, Frid Fridrikkson, David Gaddis, Burnell Hill, Laurie Hill, Philo Hunt, Brenda Johnson, Howard Postivit, Roger Skaggs, Vic Wade, and Scott Williams.

Biographical information for Grainger Hunt can be found with the earlier sidebar by him in this chapter.

discovered in 2001 suggests the phenomenon continues unabated.

So our role, beside the elementary task of documenting this vast Peregrine population, was to speed the increases in number and distribution markedly. This result was so swift as to justify delisting several years before 1999. Had there been no active management, delisting would not have happened, and I think it would have become even more difficult to obtain politically in the future than it was in 1999.

Was the Peregrine as abundant before DDT as it seems destined to be in the coming decades? The paucity of historical records was due to the massive settings of nesting habitat, so that only the alert and lucky observer discovered an eyrie. No Peregrine habitat requirement has really changed since the 1800s; the cliffs are still there, and the food is still there and probably as abundant and available as ever. I believe we are now seeing a return to the abundance the species enjoyed down through history.

Where will the expansion end? Ian Newton once told me our falcons will increase until almost all useful breeding sites are held by territorial pairs that resist further crowding. Thanks to all who worked so hard to see this bird recover, there are signs locally throughout the West that local saturation of nesting habitat is already happening.

Best of all, the management and husbandry developed then have made the Peregrine failsafe as a species in the future. I am grateful to have been a part of it, and to have had so many dedicated co-workers.

Had there been no active management, delisting would not have happened, and I think it would have become even more difficult to obtain politically in the future than it was in 1999.

Jim Enderson *is Professor Emeritus of biology at The Colorado College in Colorado Springs. Since the delisting of the Peregrine, he has helped draft monitoring and falconry harvest protocols. He was a member of a group of advisors to the US Fish and Wildlife Service that urged delisting of the Hawaiian Hawk. Jim continues annual surveys of nesting Peregrines and remains dedicated to the practice of falconry. He is a long-term member of The Peregrine Fund Board of Directors.*

Chapter 5

Starting The Peregrine Fund at Cornell University and Eastern Reintroduction

Tom J. Cade

What does an ivory tower professor do to start a major falcon propagating facility and reintroduction program for the Peregrine Falcon?

That was the dilemma I faced in 1967 when I joined the faculty at Cornell University, a campus that proved most congenial to the development of unusual projects. I needed facilities, staff, birds, and money. In the past all my experience in acquiring such things was by the usual academic procedure of applying for research grants from outfits such as the Office of Naval Research, National Science Foundation (NSF), and National Institutes of Health.

The Peregrine Fund at Cornell

Fortunately I was able to convince the university to build the facility as a condition of my hiring. It took the administration three years to find the money, but thanks to the efforts of Vice President for Research Frank Long, and especially Bob Morison, first Director of the Division of Biologi-

cal Sciences, in 1970, with $125,000 from the IBM Corporation, we built a 40-chamber pole barn near Cornell's Laboratory of Ornithology on Sapsucker Woods Road. Officially designated the Behavioral Ecology Building, it was better known to locals as the Peregrine Palace, and by staff and close associates simply as the Hawk Barn. In retrospect, I believe it was a kind of Camelot—a special place, at a special time, with very special people who were totally committed to restoring the Peregrine in nature. It no longer exists as a physical structure, but it is still very substantial in the memories of those who worked there so stout heartedly for nearly 20 years to make the return of the Peregrine a dream come true.

At first I tried to operate the program with interested graduate and undergraduate students. I was privileged to have several talented raptor enthusiasts working on degrees with me—people such as Ludlow Clark, Jim Grier, John Haugh, Jeff Lincer, Joe Platt, Steve Sherrod, John Snelling, Paul Spitzer, Stan Temple, and Peter Wrege. I put Jim Grier in charge of routine management of the facility and birds, but graduate students have their own agendas, and Jim soon felt torn between his need to finish his graduate research and his responsibilities to manage the fledgling falcon

◀ Figure 5.1 Painting by Hans Peeters used as the logo of The Peregrine Fund. Reproduction rights courtesy of The Peregrine Fund.

Figure 5.2 Jim Grier with imprinted Golden Eagle, Furious, one of the first raptors employed in cooperative artificial insemination.

► Figure 5.3 Phyllis Dague and poster developed to enhance reports of Peregrine sightings.

Jim Weaver

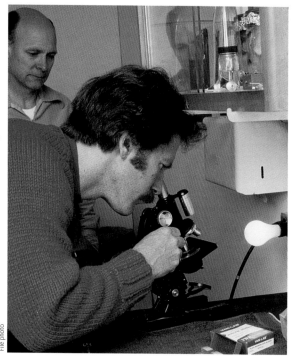

Figure 5.4 Jim Weaver ► examines falcon semen with Tom Cade looking over his shoulder.

File photo

program. He solved his problem by introducing me to two friends he had known before coming to Cornell and convincing me to hire them. Those two became the cornerstones of the highly successful breeding and release program at Cornell from 1972 to 1988.

One was Phyllis Dague, the other, Jim Weaver. Phyllis did everything. She was sometimes a secretary, accountant, fund-raiser, baby-bird feeder, field assistant—she did whatever others could not or would not do! Jim, of course, was a great manager and leader. I had known about his travels in arctic Alaska and Canada in search of falcons before he came to Cornell, and he greatly impressed me by curing one of my Peregrines with an advanced case of bumblefoot. Named Cadey from arctic Alaska, she later became one of our most prolific breeders. A first-rate falconer, Jim had an uncanny ability to handle and keep birds fit in captivity. He was also a good judge of other people's abilities and attracted loyal and devoted co-workers to the program, including Bill Burnham, whom he found and recruited on a trip to West Greenland in 1974. Others who came to work with Jim included Willard Heck, the third member of the triumvirate that kept the Cornell program going, Vic Hardaswick, Peter Harrity, Tom Maechtle, Steve Sherrod, Jack Barclay, and Marty Gilroy.

Our falcons for the program came from the wild and from falconers. After the Madison conference in 1965, several of my associates and I were able to obtain a few nestling Peregrines from the wild in Alaska; Clayton White and John Haugh were importantly involved. Later we also got wild nestlings from Ungava, Mexico, Spain, and Scotland. Many of our birds came from falconers, who either donated or loaned their birds to our program. One of the first to do so was former Cornellian Heinz Meng, who had successfully bred a pair of Peale's Falcons in 1971 and 1972. In 1972 he generously loaned his breeding pair and some of their progeny to the Cornell program. Among the latter was a tiercel named Prince Philip. An imprinted bird used in artificial insemination (AI), the Prince fathered many Peregrines released into the eastern United States. Other birds I especially remember were Grainger Hunt's Sergeant Pepper, a California tiercel which, after rejecting eight females in a row, fell in love with a little Latin lady from Chile and produced numerous progeny with her; Jack Oar's Heyoka from the Tanana River, Alaska; and Don Hunter's pair of Peale's Falcons, which tried to mate with the male facing in the wrong direction for two years before finally getting it right.

File photo

Figure 5.5 Heinz Meng and Tom Cade in the hack box on the Faculty College Tower, State University College at New Paltz, 1974.

The Lab of Ornithology set up a special account to receive these funds, and we began refer- ring to it informally as The Peregrine Fund account.

Money was hard to come by. At first I tried the usual scientific avenues for securing research funds and succeeded in obtaining modest support from the NSF for the first six years. Our work, however, was too applied and nontheoretical to sustain long-term support from the science-fund- ing agencies, and I often wondered how Fran James, my NSF program director, managed to keep the funds flowing as long as they did. Con- servation organizations seemed a likely source of help, but we were somewhat suspect among con- servationists because of our interests in falconry. That changed, however, when men such as Roland Clement, then Vice President for Science at the National Audubon Society (NAS), and the President, Elvis J. Stahr, began speaking out in favor of what we were doing. Then the Massachu- setts Audubon Society (MAS) became the first conservation organization to provide financial support—thanks to then-President Allen Morgan, staff biologists Bill Drury, Jr., and Ian Nisbet, and later, Jim Baird, who served on the Eastern Pere- grine Falcon Recovery Team. The World Wildlife Fund, thanks to Tom Lovejoy, soon followed suit with several years of financial aid. By helping us gain acceptance in the conservation community, these organizations provided moral support to our program that was in many ways more impor- tant than their monetary help.

The public rather quickly became aware of the falcon program at Cornell, thanks to timely reporting in various newspapers and magazines and on television (see, for example, articles by David R. Zimmerman and his book *To Save a Bird in Peril* [1975]), and the Lab of Ornithology began receiving unsolicited contributions to support the work. These unsolicited funds suggested there might be more money in the private sector if we started asking for it. The Lab of Ornithology set up a special account to receive these funds, and we began referring to it informally as The Pere- grine Fund account. Later we decided it would be best to incorporate the fund as a nonprofit organ- ization separate from the university. The founders and first directors of The Peregrine Fund, Inc., were Bob Berry, Frank Bond, Jim Weaver, and Tom Cade. Other early directors included Jim Ender- son, Kent Carnie, Dan Brimm, and Bill Burnham. Later, Bill became the fifth founder.

The Peregrine Fund began to flourish with annual contributions from hundreds of individuals from all walks of life, conservation organizations (many local Audubon Society chapters), founda- tions (notably the Arcadia Foundation [Mrs. Lyman K. Stuart], Hanes Foundation [John Hanes, Jr.], Lau- rel Foundation [Cordelia Scaife May], and Richard King Mellon Foundation [Prosser Mellon]), and corporations, falconry clubs, and some unlikely sources such as the Edison Electric Institute (through Richard Thorsell's influence), and—my favorite of all—Cheeselovers International, Ltd.

The federal and state agencies came into play when the reintroduction work began in earnest in 1975. With passage of the Endangered Species Act (ESA) of 1973, we naturally looked to the U.S. Fish and Wildlife Service (FWS) for major sup- port, but officials in the Office of Endangered Species explained to me that although they liked what we were doing, they had only a small budget and the Peregrine Falcon was not high on their

Hawk Barn Days

Phyllis R. Dague

My first days at the Hawk Barn in 1971 were as an enthusiastic volunteer when I was working at the Lab of Ornithology editing bird-nesting data for the Nest Record Card Program. I watched as the area was cleared, tons of dirt fill brought in, and the construction done of the long narrow building, the Behavioral Ecology Building, that came to be known as the Hawk Barn. In those early days the barn housed four Peregrines, kestrels, Harris's Hawks, Turkey Vultures, Lanner Falcons, Loggerhead Shrikes, Red-tailed Hawks, and Dave Peakall's Ring-necked Doves. Then there were more Peregrines, more people, more publicity, more money, and more meetings. The Peregrine Fund started to grow. My volunteering evolved into a paid assistant to Tom Cade.

The Barn was my home for many years, even though the Cornell fire inspectors would send us a notice every year to discontinue living in the upstairs "office." Jim Weaver believed we should have somebody in the building with the falcons at all times for security, so we ignored those notices every year!

Living in the Barn was not your typical "housekeeping" situation. For years I cooked on a two-burner hot plate and a toaster oven in the "kitchen" on the first floor, then carried dinner on a tray upstairs to the "office." The shower arrangement left a lot to be desired. There wasn't a shower or bathtub! I was happy to have hot and cold running water, even though we used a garden hose for our showers. The cooking and shower situations did eventually change. Living in the upstairs of the Barn was like entering the inner sanctum of a cave; there was no outside light, until I received a window for a birthday present. My children still have fond memories of the Barn and remember when they would push each other up and down the long hallway on specially made chairs with wheels and play hide-and-seek in the dark hall upstairs.

Living in the Barn was not your typical "housekeeping" situation.

The worst thing about the Hawk Barn was chamber cleaning. The halls were nasty and smelly for days and were always cleaned during the hottest part of the summer. It was also a spooky place at times if you were the only one in it on a dark windy night.

A lot of wonderful people passed through the front door of the Barn, and I always enjoyed giving them tours and showing off the falcons during the nonbreeding season. I still meet people today who remember those tours from years ago.

The other day as I took my noontime walk through Sapsucker Woods, the spring peepers were deafening, but I could still almost hear the courtship "e-chip" sounds coming from the Barn. The Hawk Barn was dismantled in 2001 to make way for the rerouting of Sapsucker Woods Road. The change in the road will accommodate the new 80,000-sq-ft facility for the Lab of Ornithology. I was there to watch as workers dismantled an important part of Peregrine history.

Phyllis Dague *is Assistant to the Director at the Cornell Laboratory of Ornithology. Phyllis worked with The Peregrine Fund from 1970 to 1988 when it left Cornell. She worked at the Cornell Veterinary College and as Assistant to the Dean at the College of Human Ecology until her return to the Lab of Ornithology in 1996 when John Fitzpatrick took over as Director.*

list of priorities—they were more interested in species such as the red wolf, Whooping Crane, Bald Eagle, snail darter, and American alligator.

What to do next? I went back to Cornell and reread the Endangered Species Act. Right up front in the section "Findings, Purposes, and Policy," it states: "It is further declared to be the Policy of Congress that all Federal departments and agencies shall utilize their authorities in furtherance of the purposes of this Act." That struck a promising note. I went to see Scott Ward who not only trapped and banded migrant Peregrines on Assateague Island but who also headed up an environmental program for the U.S. Army at the Edgewood Arsenal and Aberdeen Proving Grounds in Maryland where, among other things, he conducted work on local Bald Eagles. I asked Scott whether he thought he could convince his commanding officers to use their authority to fund the release of Peregrines on their properties in Maryland. It turned out he was able to make an arrangement. In short, the Army offered $15,000 if FWS would match it. I went back to the Office of Endangered Species with an offer they could not refuse, and that is how the federal government first became involved in funding the release of captive-bred Peregrines.

Because FWS was uncertain about contracting with our newly incorporated organization, and in order to avoid university overhead charges, we arranged through the good offices of Dick Plunkett, on the science staff for the National Audubon Society, to serve as the prime contractor for these funds at no cost for their administrative services, and it in turn subcontracted the work to The Peregrine Fund, Inc. This two-year arrangement worked extremely well and generated enthusiasm within the National Audubon hierarchy to provide some of its own funds from the Estate of Captain George Whittell for subsequent projects in Colorado.

Other federal agencies soon began to help with Peregrine restoration too—notably the National Park Service, U.S. Forest Service (USFS), and Bureau of Land Management. At first, Nat Reed, Assistant Secretary of the Interior for Fish, Wildlife, and Parks, coaxed some of his agency heads to offer small contracts to The Peregrine Fund. Later, with the development of recovery plans for the Peregrine and implementation of the Section 6 federal/state cooperative funding provision of the ESA, about 14 state wildlife agencies became involved in the East. The State of New Jersey was the first, and I would be remiss not to mention Pete McLain, the man in charge of the state's endangered species program, who showed us how to build hack towers that would

not sink in the coastal salt marshes and whose enthusiasm for the project carried us through many difficulties, the solutions to some of which are just as well not recounted in print.

Important state cooperators also included Charlie Todd in Maine, John Lanier with the White Mountain National Forest and Chris Martin in New Hampshire, also Tom Sears and Diane Pence in Vermont and various staff of the Vermont Institute of Natural Sciences, especially Chris Rimmer and Jeffrey Corser, Tom French in Massachusetts, Barbara Loucks and Pete Nye in New York State, Chris Nadareski in New York City, Dan Brunning in Pennsylvania, Kathy Clark in New Jersey, Gary Taylor in Maryland, Mitchell Byrd in Virginia, Allen Boynton in North Carolina, Jim Sorrow in South Carolina, and Bob Hatcher in Tennessee.

The idea of producing "recovery plans" for endangered species originated, I believe, with Earl

▲ **Figure** 5.6 Aerial view of the Hawk Barn at Cornell, circa 1975.

▲ **Figure** 5.7 Hungry Peregrines beg to be fed. Their brooder is lined with a newspaper showing a 1976 date.

Baysinger in the early 1970s when he was for a time in charge of the Office of Endangered Species and International Affairs for FWS. I submitted a three-page outline of Peregrine recovery to him and asked if that was what he had in mind. He thought it looked just right, but recovery plans did not become official policy until later. By that time they had evolved into a much more complicated, bureaucratic process requiring years to complete.

In 1974 FWS established four recovery teams for the Peregrine Falcon, each responsible for developing a regional recovery plan. The eastern team originally consisted of Rene Bollengier, Jr., FWS, as team leader; Jim Baird, Massachusetts Audubon Society; Lawrence P. Brown (later replaced by Eugene McCaffrey), New York Department of Environmental Conservation; Tom Cade, Cornell University; Malcolm M. Edwards, U.S. Forest Service; Donald C. Hagar, U.S. Forest Service; and Bernard Halla, Maryland Fish and Wildlife Administration—a good mix of federal, state, and non-governmental organization interests. Lynn A. Greenwalt, Director of FWS, approved a 147-page recovery plan in May 1979, five years after the team had been established.

Although the original idea was that recovery teams would draft plans and then retire after their official adoption, the eastern team continued to function in an advisory capacity to FWS and met annually through 1992 to fine-tune management and funding strategies for eastern Peregrine recovery. The team's functions in that regard were greatly facilitated by Paul Nickerson, the endangered species coordinator for Region 5 of FWS, who had learned how to work effectively within the Byzantine bureaucracy of the federal government and also to interface with state agencies (see Chapter 18). He genuinely strove to make actions happen on the ground. Gene McCaffrey took over as team leader from Rene Bollengier on the latter's transfer to the U.S. Department of Agriculture, and Pete McLain and Mitchell Byrd, College of William and Mary, Virginia, replaced Malcolm Edwards and Bud Halla. Later, Pat Redig also joined the team to represent the flourishing Midwestern program.

As more and more state wildlife agencies became involved in Peregrine recovery through the cooperative funding provisions of Section 6 of the ESA, the states began to seek more direct dialogue with the recovery team, as some conflicts developed over when states were scheduled to receive Peregrines for release and how many. This need was met by holding open team meetings, which state coordinators and other interested parties attended, followed by a state coordinators' meeting. This arrangement worked well, with the

Dream Job of a Lifetime

James D. Weaver

Many years ago, as an avid young bird watcher, I was fascinated by the books, articles, and photographs of Arthur Allen of Cornell University's Laboratory of Ornithology. I dreamed that one day I would go there and maybe even do something important. Well, eventually I was able to go there and, owing to the vision of one man, Tom Cade, I did manage to get involved in something important. My friends Jim Grier and Phyllis Dague were responsible for my being in that right place at that right time. The Peregrine project was underway, with Tom's graduate students Jim Grier, Stan Temple, John Snelling, Jeff Lincer, Ludlow Clark, and Peter Wrege all helping with the work. We shared an understanding of what the problem was, and we all felt we could do something about it. Failure was not an option, and I do not recall ever discussing that possibility. We were generally a very close, upbeat group.

As Tom's students moved on, Willard Heck, Peter Harrity, and Vic Hardaswick came on to keep things rolling. And roll they did. The first fertile Peregrine egg appeared in 1972. In 1973, 20 young were raised. In 1974 some token releases were made at the Royal Gorge in Colorado and at the Faculty Tower in New Paltz, New York, where Heinz Meng was a professor. Production and numbers of young for release increased rapidly. Under the guidance of our release and monitoring team of Steve Sherrod, Jack Barclay, Marty Gilroy, and hundreds of hack site attendants, we released Peregrines on buildings, towers, bridges, and cliffs.

By 1977 returning falcons were being seen, and in 1978 there was a pair at a tower in the New Jersey salt marshes. That same year Scarlett showed up in Baltimore, and we began to study the potential of enhancing eyrie sites on naturally attractive, man-made structures. The first known nesting of our birds occurred at Manahawkin, New Jersey, in 1979, but no young were raised. In the spring of 1980 two pairs raised young on the marsh towers, and David Bird of McGill University found a Cornell-banded female mated with an unbanded male at Lister Lake in southern Quebec.

All this was thrilling, but perhaps the biggest thrill for me occurred in 1981 when I found myself sitting in an eyrie at an historical site in New Hampshire. This would be the first such site to produce young in the eastern United States since the 1950s. What a feeling! I did not want to come down, and in

File photo

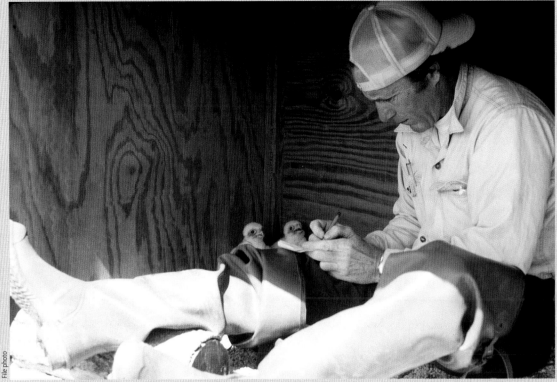

Jim Weaver is a Founding Board Member of The Peregrine Fund and directed the Cornell University captive-breeding facility and contributed to the organization and Peregrine Falcon restoration program in many ways. Jim continues to be involved with wildlife and conservation through his activities on his ranch in New Mexico, his foundation, as a former commissioner of the New Mexico Department of Game and Fish, and as a Peregrine Fund board member.

some ways I guess I never have. It was a big deal. The numbers of successful nestings continued to increase, and by 1983 Peregrines were nesting on bridges all over the Eastern Seaboard as well as on casinos and churches and mothballed ships. They were coming back!

In 1987 The Peregrine Fund released its 2,000th Peregrine. In 1988, with our eastern work nearly completed, the Hawk Barn at Cornell closed down. (The physical structure was demolished in the summer of 2001 to make room for a parking lot for the new Laboratory of Ornithology.) Our eastern releases continued through 1991 and actually continued for several more years in a limited way through the hard work and generosity of falconers and breeders around the country.

A word here about the willingness of all kinds of people to help with what we were doing. It has never been a secret, but we could not have done what we did without the help of dedicated volunteers. There are thousands of you out there. You have given money, time, effort, and knowledge. You have provided trucks, boats, airplanes, helicopters, bear traps, telephone poles, freezers, showers, tents, houses, food, cold beer, and first aid. You have fed, carried, and saved birds. You have hauled the supplies, held our ropes, and found nests. I can only hope you all realize how important you have been to this program. Together we have accomplished something quite remarkable, and in so doing we have set an example. Most of the people who will see this bird in the future and marvel at its presence will never know of your work. But those of us who were there know, and now this book will be a permanent record for others who care to find out.

While we have been working, 30 years have passed. A human generation has come full circle. Phyllis's children, Bryan and Penny, grew up in and around the Hawk Barn at Cornell. Bryan graduated from Cornell with an engineering degree and moved to Boston. Penny lives in New Hampshire, and both are now adults with growing families of their own. Three generations of Hawk Barn dogs have all gone on to the big field trial in the sky. But the falcons are out there for all to see, and they will be around for as long as somebody cares about them and what they stand for. And do we not all wish that the solutions to the rest of the world's problems were so easy to define and to solve? Thank you, Tom, for trusting me with the dream job of a lifetime. Thank you, Phyllis, and thank you, Willard. I thank all who were involved very much for making it work.

It has never been a secret, but we could not have done what we did without the help of dedicated volunteers.

recovery team setting out the overall strategy for recovery and the state coordinators and other collaborators developing the tactics for accomplishing objectives. The work got done with a minimum of conflict and delay. All things considered, the Eastern Peregrine Falcon Recovery Team was a remarkably effective group because each member remained highly focused on the goal.

Still, by the late 1970s overall funding of our programs continued to fall short of what we knew would be required in the 1980s to complete the job of recovery in the East and in the Rocky Mountains. The officially approved recovery plans each projected detailed budgets in the hundreds of thousands of dollars per year, to be shared among various federal and state agencies; but no one ever paid any serious attention to these budgets after the plans were approved. They were just "pie in the sky."

It seemed to those of us in The Peregrine Fund that as the lead agency responsible for carrying out the provisions of the 1973 ESA, the FWS should play the major role in funding Peregrine recovery. The original authorizations for expenditures under the ESA were, in fact, rather generous for the times, but FWS's annual budgetary requests always fell well short of the authorized limits, except for the Division of Law Enforcement, even though members of the House and Senate Interior Appropriations Subcommittees often indicated a willingness to provide more, if the FWS would only ask for it. Unfortunately, ESA funding for FWS had to compete with other programmatic priorities within Interior's established limit for its overall annual budget request.

In discussing this problem with some of our politically savvy friends in other conservation organizations, we learned there is a process by which citizens can influence these budgetary decisions through direct testimony before appropriations subcommittees. In particular, Gene Knoder, at that time a biologist for the National Audubon Society but formerly with the FWS, encouraged us on several occasions to seek an "add-on" to the FWS budget specifically for propagation and reintroduction of Peregrine Falcons. Needless to say, when we broached this subject with FWS officials

we received negative comments and indications that there would be no support for such an approach; but significantly, as it turned out, they did not say they would oppose it.

When officials of the International Association of Fish and Wildlife Agencies (IAFWA) informed us they would support such an add-on, I prepared testimony to present before the House Interior Subcommittee on Appropriations, chaired by Sid Yates from Illinois, for the fiscal year 81 budget. We had supporting testimony from John Gottschalk (a former FWS director) representing the IAFWA, from Wayne Sandfort of the Colorado Division of Wildlife, and from Amos Eno of the National Audubon Society.

As my turn to speak approached, Gottschalk leaned over and whispered in my ear, "Tom, you've got five minutes. Don't try to read your written statement—it'll be published in the Congressional Record. Just look Sid Yates straight in the eyes and tell him in your own words why you think the project is important and should be supported with federal dollars." It worked. Yates asked several leading, and friendly, questions; but his last question—the one he kept asking each time I returned for the next three budgetary cycles—was, "How long will it take?" I gulped and said, "About five to 10 years." His eyes narrowed a bit; I think he smiled. But we got our request for $300,000 with the help of staffer Neal Sigmon.

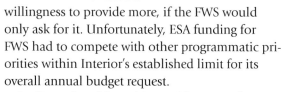

▲ **Figure 5.8** Senator Jim McClure (left) and Jeff Cilek.

File photo

This increase in the FWS endangered species budget continues to the present and now helps support work on the restoration of California Condors in Arizona. After the fourth year, when we were starting to move our operations to Idaho, Sid Yates turned us over to his counterpart on the Senate subcommittee, chaired by Senator Jim McClure of Idaho, and said to him, "Now it's your turn to take care of these falcons." McClure and his staff, Frank Cushing, Don Knowles, and Jeff Cilek, did a great job. In fact, Jeff did such a good job that The Peregrine Fund ended up hiring him as a vice president in charge of raising money. After Jim McClure, Senators Mark Hatfield and Pete Domenici looked after the Peregrine money when Hatfield assumed leadership for the subcommittee.

Learning How to Breed Falcons in Captivity

Our first breeding season in the new facility was in the spring of 1971. We had three potential breeding pairs of Peregrines, three pairs of Prairie Falcons, a pair of John Snelling's Lanners from South Africa, and several pairs of Harris's Hawks and American Kestrels, as well as human-imprinted Golden Eagles, a pair of Loggerhead Shrikes, and a homosexual pair of female Red-shouldered Hawks that brooded their infertile eggs side by side in the same nest. All of these birds provided us with experience and information about how—and how not—to handle raptors for propagation in captivity.

Only a few birds of prey had been bred successfully in captivity at that time (Cade 1986), and useful information on how to succeed was limited. In Europe, the German falconer and wildlife artist Renz Waller raised young in two consecutive years from an old pair of Peregrines housed in rather unusual and difficult circumstances during World War II, when Allied bombs were dropping all around his place in Dusseldorf; often he had only stray cats to feed to his birds (Spuhler 1968, Awender 1979-1980). In 1970 other German workers produced the first Peregrine using the technique of AI (Maatsch and Beyerbach 1971). Canadian falconer Frank Beebe (1967) had an old pair of Peale's Falcons incubate and hatch their eggs in 1967, but the chicks unfortunately died soon afterward. Larry Schramm in Oregon produced the first fully fledged young in North America from his pair of Peale's Falcons in 1968 (Petersen 1968) (also see Chapter 16).

These and a few other early cases proved that breeding Peregrines in captivity was possible but not necessarily that it could be done routinely and on a scale that would be sufficient for a major reintroduction effort. The prevailing attitude among most conservationists at the time was perhaps best summed up by Faith McNulty (1972) in her widely read *New Yorker* article about the robbing of eyasses from the eyrie at Morro Rock on the California coast: "Within the last two years, several peregrines have been reared . . . , but the feat is so difficult that it cannot repopulate the wild or provide birds for fanciers. Thus, stolen nestlings are the only source of birds for fanciers." More than 10,000 captive-produced Peregrines later, her evaluation now seems quaintly remote from reality, but it revealed the magnitude of the challenge falcon breeders faced at the time. Also, for the record, there are now two pairs of Peregrines nesting on Morro Rock!

Roy Morsch

▲ **Figure 5.9** Captive Peregrine Falcon in breeding chamber.

Figures 5.10–5.13 Photos at right document courtship through raising of young Peregrines at the Cornell Hawk Barn. Though these are now common events in the captive breeding of raptors, they were major breakthroughs in the 1970s.

Courtship display includes bowing at the nest scrape (top) prior to copulation (second). The female incubates the resulting eggs (third). Imprinted adults often cared for fostered chicks (below).

The mass production of large numbers of falcons in captivity was first demonstrated with the American Kestrel. While working on my graduate degrees at UCLA in the early 1950s, I kept a pair of wild-caught kestrels in a small cage (3 x 3 x 3 ft) provided with a wooden nest box. These birds courted, copulated, and incubated fertile eggs that died before hatching. Later, at Syracuse University, my graduate student Ernie Willoughby and I maintained several breeding pairs of kestrels in plywood cubicles in a large space underneath the belfry of Lyman Hall, for the purpose of behavioral studies related to reversed sexual size dimorphism (Willoughby and Cade 1964). We had to pass through the zoology library to gain access to these birds, and our daily food deliveries of dead mice and chunks of beef heart caused no little distress to the matronly librarian, particularly the day I dropped a pan full of victuals on the floor among the reference books, including a large, opened Webster's unabridged dictionary, which received a splatter of blood.

Following our successful breeding of kestrels at Syracuse, Lucille and Bill Stickel, researchers at the FWS Patuxent Wildlife Research Center in Maryland, asked me to consult with them on the feasibility of establishing a captive colony of breeding kestrels for use in studying the toxicological effects of pesticides on a species of falcon. Eventually, under the scientific management of Richard D. Porter and Stanley A. Wiemeyer, Patuxent developed a large colony of several dozen breeding pairs of kestrels, which provided birds for research on the effects of DDT and other organochlorine pesticides on eggshell thinning and related behavioral and physiological problems (Porter and Wiemeyer 1969, Wiemeyer and Porter 1970).

Porter and Wiemeyer (1970) also showed that it is possible to manage a large captive population of falcons and achieve large-scale production of young from them, including reproduction by F1 progeny. Their demonstration was a big encouragement to those trying to do the same thing with Peregrine Falcons.

At Cornell our main concern was to determine as quickly as possible what combination of factors is most conducive to producing a Peregrine that will breed in confinement. Answers could only be obtained after a lot of trial-and-error experimentation. After several years, Cade and Fyfe (1978) still found it difficult to come up with a clear set of guidelines that would guarantee success; 30 years later it is still not possible, as it turns out there is more than one way to skin the proverbial cat. External factors such as cage design

Adapt, Adjust, and Improvise

Willard Heck

Adapt, adjust, and improvise! A friend rattled off this motto one day not long ago when we were trying to fashion a machinery repair without the proper parts. He learned it from his father, a career military officer. I did not think much of it at the time, but a few days later it occurred to me that those three words accurately and succinctly describe the successful efforts of The Peregrine Fund to return Peregrine Falcons to their native habitats.

When Tom Cade first started The Peregrine Fund, the only things he and his small staff knew for sure were that they possessed ample enthusiasm for the project and a good general knowledge of Peregrines through falconry and biological study. They also knew that a few falconers had succeeded in breeding individual pairs of Peregrines in captivity and that falconers for centuries have been training young raptors to hunt without the benefit of tutoring parents through the age-old process of hacking. Could these past small successes and knowledge of the centuries be adapted and joined into a project that would work for Peregrines on a scale large enough to restart a population?

The only way to know was to try. No one had ever housed 40 pairs of Peregrines for breeding before, so when Jim Weaver set about designing and constructing the breeding chambers in our first Hawk Barn, he adapted mews designs he had already used successfully to house raptors. Most of the knowledge on egg incubation dealt with large lots of chicken eggs in closet-sized incubators. We adapted that knowledge to a smaller scale and adjusted parameters such as temperature and humidity to optimize the potential of each egg. When incubators or other equipment did not meet our needs, we improvised and created new designs that worked better. When those efforts succeeded and young Peregrines were available for release, we set about hacking them back to the wild, adjusting and adapting the ancient falconer's process to condition the fledglings for a life of independence rather than returning them to the falconer's hand. Through it

... we individually and as an organization packed this lesson along and found it invaluable...

Willard Heck feeds Mauritius Kestrel chicks, once the world's most endangered falcon, island of Mauritius, Indian Ocean.

Willard Heck *joined The Peregrine Fund in 1975 following graduation from Cornell University, to assist Jim Weaver with the captive propagation of Peregrines at the Cornell facility. He later assumed the leadership role for the propagation of Peregrines, both at Cornell and later at the World Center for Birds of Prey, for release in the eastern United States. Beyond his work with the Peregrine, possibly his most significant contribution to raptor conservation has been toward restoration of the Mauritius Kestrel, once the world's rarest raptor when it was reduced to two known pairs. Willard has raised more than 300 Mauritius Kestrels and about 1,000 Peregrines!*

all was the need for innovative thinking when dealing with fund-raising and the cooperative agreements necessary to work with federal and state governments and private entities.

Adapt, adjust, and improvise! It was our way of life, although we did not have a motto to describe or call attention to it. It was not at the front of our consciousness. We did not knowingly learn to operate that way. It was just what we did and what we had to do to make things work. It is what made The Peregrine Fund a hands-on, results-oriented organization able to respond quickly to new problems.

When the opportunities arose to reach out and aid other species, we individually and as an organization packed this lesson along and found it invaluable in dealing with the problems faced by the Mauritius Kestrel, Aplomado Falcon, and California Condor. It helped us facilitate the formation of a national park in Madagascar and the development of local conservationists in Guatemala. And without doubt, the lesson is guiding staff today in new areas of concern such as Honduras, Mongolia, Greenland, and New Guinea.

Adapt, adjust, and improvise! It's a lesson for life. And as a lesson for life learned, it is one of the things I value most about my 18 years at The Peregrine Fund.

Figure 5.14 Incubator at Cornell breeding facility with four falcon eggs to left and device for candling eggs behind. The bottom of the hatcher can be seen to the right.

Figure 5.15 (Below) After an embryo pips (breaks its shell), it is moved into a hatcher.

and size, photoperiod (so frequently discussed in the early years), food (live vs. dead, mammal vs. bird), and other such factors can vary greatly among successfully breeding pairs.

The two factors that turned out to be most important are the age at which wild Peregrines are taken into captivity for breeding and the manner in which they are handled and treated in captivity before reaching breeding age. Unlike kestrels, which breed readily in captivity when taken as adults, very few Peregrines taken after they have left the nest, either as fall migrants or as full adults, will breed in captivity regardless of how they are kept and treated. There have been a few exceptions, usually very old or injured birds long held and very tame in confinement (Cade 1988a).

This lesson was hard won and expensive. Several falconers, notably Heinz Meng, trapped several passage *tundrius* Peregrines in the late 1960s (up to 1970 when the Peregrine was put on the endangered species list) in the hope they could be induced to breed in captivity. Some of these pairs were held up to 10 years or more but never produced an egg. The endangered species unit at the Patuxent Wildlife Research Center tried the same thing with a dozen or more pairs of *tundrius* with the same negative result.

Fortunately, at Cornell we started out mostly with falcons taken as nestlings, as did other programs in Canada and California, as well as many of the private breeders. Again, generalizations about these birds are hard to make. Chicks taken from the first day of hatch all the way to the fledgling and immediate postfledgling, independent stage have grown up to become breeders in captivity, but by no means all of them do. Best results (highest percentage of later breeders) usually come from rearing the young in groups separated

from their parents after the second or third week of age, keeping them tame toward humans by handling and feeding them, then continuing to man them for several months or to train them for falconry. The older they are when taken from their parents (wild or captive), the longer this manning and training period needs to be. Reared in groups this way, the young birds do not become socially imprinted on humans but remain tame enough that the conditions of captivity do not impose a physiological stress that interferes with reproduction; but there are exceptions to this generalization (Cade and Fyfe 1978).

We made a serious mistake with the first 20 young reared at Cornell in 1973 by leaving them with their parents until nearly fledged and not handling them enough to keep them tame. We thought growing up in confinement would be sufficient conditioning to circumvent captivity-induced stress, but the birds turned out to be as wild and nervous in confinement as wild, passage falcons. Few of them became productive breeders. Such treatment, however, is best for young birds that are to be released, as they should be as wild as possible.

Only about half of all Peregrines paired for breeding end up producing fertile eggs and young on their own, but many of the other paired females do lay eggs that are not fertilized, either because the male refuses to copulate or the female refuses to allow him to mount. AI therefore became an important technique for maximizing the production of young. At first we tried the standard poultry method of massaging the male to ejaculate, but this technique does not work as well with falcons as it does with roosters or tom turkeys. More often than not, we ended up applying enough pressure to the cloaca to squeeze a few drops of ejaculate from the seminal sacs rather than inducing actual ejaculation.

The solution to this problem came with the realization that male falcons sexually imprinted on their human handlers could be stimulated into actually mounting and ejaculating on some part of their human partners—sometimes the gloved fist or cupped hand, a shoe, a shoulder, and frequently on top of the head. Bob Berry (1972) first tried this technique successfully with a male and female Goshawk, and at about the same time Stan Temple (1972) and Jim Grier (1973) accomplished the same feat with Red-tailed Hawks and Golden Eagles at Cornell. Les Boyd (1978) designed the infamous "copulation hat" on which imprinted males are trained to ejaculate their semen, which is then taken up into a capillary tube or pipette for injection into the everted oviduct of an egg-laying female.

The great advantage of these imprinted semen donors is that they produce larger quantities of higher quality semen over a much longer period of time than do males that are forcibly "stripped" for semen. The imprinted males typically produce semen over a period of six weeks, some as long as three months. The main disadvantage is that managing and handling these birds are highly labor intensive, requiring daily social interaction (courtship) and contact with a human handler during the breeding season. They are, however, extremely delightful creatures and form strong bonds of attachment to their human companions, bordering on true affection.

Imprinted females have also been used in captive propagation. They can be trained to accept AI cooperatively, assuming the copulatory stance for the handler and everting their cloacal lips to receive semen from a modified syringe. Their overall productivity, however, is no better than that of artificially inseminated nonimprinted females, and the cost of maintaining them is greater than for other females.

Courtesy Lester Boyd

Both male and female imprinted falcons make excellent parents for rearing young birds hatched by artificial incubation. They are usually given young that have first been hand-reared for several days, and they will continue to feed older nestlings throughout the summer months, sometimes caring for as many as three separate broods or young of different ages added and removed as they reach the age for hacking at five weeks. Thus, we could maximize the annual production of young by employing different techniques and protocols to take advantage of the many idiosyncratic characteristics of individual falcons.

Incubation was another problem we attacked early on at Cornell, and again we learned that best results came from treating each egg as an individual. Even basic facts about the incubation

▲ Figure 5.16 An imprinted male falcon mating on a specially designed hat on Les Boyd's head.

Breeding Peregrines and Releasing Their Young to the Wild

Heinz Meng

Courtesy Heinz Meng

Since the "secret" of producing Peregrines was out, the next step was to release captive-bred birds to the wild.

It all began on 12 October 1941, when I unexpectedly caught a passage female Peregrine along the south shore of Long Island, New York. I had been surf casting with my father but the fishing was poor, so I decided to wander around in the sand dunes. It was a beautiful breezy day with many migrating birds and insects. Among the hundreds of monarch butterflies fluttering around the beach goldenrods was a buckeye butterfly. I tried to catch it for my collection, but it flew off. I chased it over many dunes until it landed, and I was able to catch it. Several yards behind the dunes, among a large stand of reed grass, I noticed feathers being blown by the wind. Investigating led me to a Peregrine on her kill. She was beautiful, and I wanted her; but how could she be caught? I took off my leather jacket and held it in front of me as I slowly crept toward her. When I got close enough I jumped and flung the jacket over her. Her prey turned out to be an immature Northern Harrier.

After returning home I contacted the American Museum of Natural History in New York City and was told to phone George Goodwin, curator of mammals, who was also a falconer. He graciously invited me to his home and introduced me to falconry. A hood and jesses were put on the falcon, and then he told me how to care for and start manning the falcon. At the time I was a junior in Great Neck High School and had applied to Cornell University to study under the famous ornithologists Arthur

A. Allen and Peter Paul Kellogg. Years before, when I was in grade school, I had found *The Book of Bird Life* in the library. The frontispiece was a color photograph of a Peregrine sitting on a dead branch, silhouetted against Taughannock Falls near Ithaca, New York, the home of Cornell. The photographer was Arthur A. Allen, and back on that day I decided I would go to Cornell to study ornithology.

At Cornell I was able to study the half-finished paintings of Louis Agassiz Fuertes and meet and study with George M. Sutton, his star pupil. After getting my B.S. and Ph.D., with a treatise on the Cooper's Hawk, I accepted a teaching position at the State University of New York at New Paltz in 1951. A few miles west of New Paltz, in the Shawangunk Mountains overlooking the Hudson River Valley, were two historical Peregrine eyries that had been occupied for many years. What a great opportunity to study and photograph Peregrines, I thought.

By 1957 only one of the eyries was productive, and by 1958 both were empty. The decline of the Peregrine was well underway, and I began thinking about the possibilities of breeding these falcons in captivity. Renz Waller, the German artist and falconer, had put his two Peregrines together for molting, and to his surprise they produced young in 1942 and 1943.

As a result, in 1964 I finally decided to try breeding Peregrines. That summer I added a large extension to my hawk house and furnished it with

various perches and nest ledges. In early October of that year I trapped a pair of passage Tundra Peregrines on Assateague Island, Maryland, and placed them in my new experimental breeding chamber. In 1967 Frank Beebe and David Hancock offered me a pair of five-week-old Peale's Peregrines from the Queen Charlotte Islands in British Columbia. To make room for this new pair I divided the breeding chamber into two sections.

Four years later, in 1971, this pair of Peale's Peregrines laid eggs and hatched four young. In 1972, by double-clutching and using incubators I was able to produce seven young. In all this time the first pair of Tundra Peregrines had never shown any signs of courtship, and I released them. Apparently passage Peregrines were poor candidates for breeding, but five-week-old young raised by their parents were the correct ones to use.

The Laboratory of Ornithology at Cornell University, under the leadership of Tom Cade, had built a large breeding facility and in 1970 began acquiring young Peregrines to be raised for possible breeders. When the news spread of my successes, Tom and Jim Weaver came to New Paltz to examine my facilities and ask about my experience and methods. Taking care of breeding Peregrines and raising their young by myself, in addition to my teaching responsibilities, was overwhelming, so I gave Cornell my breeding pair and several of the young. In 1973 my pair, then housed at the

Heinz Meng, Ph.D., *is Professor Emeritus of biology at the State University of New York at New Paltz and Founder and Chairman of the Board of the New Paltz Peregrine Falcon Foundation, Inc.*

▲ **Figure 5.17** An embryo emerges from its egg, 1976.

Cornell "Peregrine Palace" in Ithaca, produced more young and continued to do so for several years.

Since the "secret" of producing Peregrines was out, the next step was to release captive-bred birds to the wild. In July 1974 two Cornell-produced young, which had been raised by adult falcons, were brought to New Paltz and placed in a hacking facility I had built on top of the 10-story college Faculty Tower. The traditional hacking procedure was used and proved to be successful. In 1975 and 1976 the next hacking site was on a cliff ledge in the Shawangunks below the Mohonk Mountain House Memorial Tower. In 1975 two males and one female were hacked, and in 1976 one female and one male, all with complete success.

With the help of thousands of people all over the United States and Canada, the Peregrine now has made a complete recovery. Today almost every Hudson River bridge has breeding Peregrines, and many pairs are breeding in New York City. To me, the most gratifying event was the 1998 return of Peregrines to the Shawangunk Mountains, 41 years after the last eyrie appeared to sound their death knell.

A released falcon tries her wings.

of falcon eggs were poorly understood when we began. For example, the normal incubation period was variously given as 28, 30, 32, or 36 days depending on which "authority" one read, not to mention more abstruse variables such as optimum temperature and humidity conditions, about which nothing was known.

Leaving the eggs with the falcons for natural incubation was one option, on the assumption that "mother knows best"; but not all laying females incubate normally in confinement, and some falcons are prone to eating their eggs or chicks at the time of hatching. Also, the procedure of removing the first clutch of eggs to stimulate further production requires an alternative way to incubate the eggs first removed. The great advantage of artificial incubation soon emerged.

In 1972, Heinz Meng demonstrated the value of using a small, countertop incubator designed for game-bird eggs—the now famous Roll-X Incubator manufactured by Marsh Farms—for hatching falcon eggs. He placed a first clutch of four eggs in this incubator and hatched three of them (one had been damaged by opening a hole in the shell for visual examination); meanwhile his pair of Peale's Falcons recycled, and the female laid a second set of five eggs, which the parents incubated until near the time of hatching. Meng then put those eggs in the incubator and hatched all five. From these eggs he reared seven birds to adult age, effectively doubling the normal annual production of a pair of Peregrines (Kaufman and Meng 1992). The economic and practical advantages of such increased production are enormous for a large-scale breeding operation.

At Cornell we began our experiments with artificial incubation by following standard poultry science procedures (Romanoff and Romanoff 1949), as the common view then was that all birds' eggs required about the same conditions for incubation. In 1972 we obtained one clutch of fertile eggs out of four clutches laid by two pairs of arctic Peregrines. We put these eggs into a large, commercial incubator located in Cornell's Rice Hall amongst hundreds of chicken eggs. They developed to the hatching stage, but after pipping the shell, the chicks were unable to break out on their own, and even though we tried to help them out, they all died with large, unretracted yolk-sacs. Humidity in the poultry incubator was apparently too high for falcon eggs.

▼ **Figure 5.18** Hungry mouths waiting to be fed.

Roy Morsch

We then searched for information on incubation outside the standard poultry science literature and gained some insights from studies on the incubation of wild birds' eggs. Work by the Dutch ornithologist Rudolf Drent (1970, 1973, 1975) on natural incubation of Herring Gull eggs and on the natural history of incubation in wild birds proved helpful, especially in the 1973 and 1974 breeding seasons; but the two collaborative studies carried out by Herman Rahn, A. Ar, and C. V. Paganelli and associates (Rahn and Ar 1974, Ar et al. 1974) were most useful. These researchers showed the precise relationships existing between egg size and incubation time, incubation time and water loss from the egg, influence of atmospheric pressure and humidity on water loss, and how eggshell thickness and functional pore area of the shell influence the rate of water conductance from the egg to the environment.

Differences in variables such as egg size, shell thickness, and shell porosity are related not only to differences among species but also, often, to differences among individual eggs of the same species. Hence the desirability of monitoring each egg during the course of incubation, especially an egg that might have some degree of abnormal shell thinning or change in porosity resulting from the effects of DDE.

Armed with the empirical equations for normal rate of water loss and other variables associated with an incubating egg, and our trial-and-error finding that eggs receiving 5 to 10 days of natural incubation under a falcon or setting hen have a much higher rate of hatching in incubators than eggs artificially incubated from the first day, we set up a series of Roll-X incubators that allowed us to regulate temperature and humidity to fit the requirements of individual eggs to hatch with the proper weight loss of about 18% of initial mass (Burnham 1983).

We made all these details, and many more having to do with the care and husbandry of eggs and young falcons, available to other raptor breeders as soon as possible through the Breeding Project Information Exchange of The Raptor Research Foundation in 1974 and in a series of publications that culminated in a booklet entitled *Falcon Propagation, A Manual on Captive Breeding*, edited by J. D. Weaver and T. J. Cade and first published by The Peregrine Fund, Inc. in 1983. It is hard to estimate the total influence this manual has had on the propagation of raptors in captivity, but it has gone through two revisions, been circulated around the world, and been translated into at least five foreign languages. Several refinements and new techniques have been added by others in recent years (e.g., N. Fox 1995 and M. Heidenrich 1997), but the fundamentals of this art, forged by the cooperation of a small, dedicated group of breeders in the late 1960s and early 1970s in order to save the Peregrine Falcon, have not changed. It was a unique time of rapid and free exchange of information, unparalleled in the annals of aviculture and wildlife management, and led to large-scale production of Peregrines and other raptors in a period of 10 years.

Our big breakthrough came in 1973, when three naturally mating females produced 20 young that survived to the fully fledged, juvenile stage. By using the Roll-X incubators Heinz Meng had introduced to us, better understanding of optimum temperature and humidity conditions for falcon eggs, and taking clutches away from females after 7 to 10 days of natural incubation (causing them to lay second and third clutches), we obtained 26 fertile eggs, of which 22 hatched and from which 20 young were raised. We knew then that large-scale production of Peregrines was feasible in captivity. Over the next 17 years we raised between 50 and 100 young falcons per year at Cornell and released nearly 1,300 of them to the wild.

Defending the Eyrie in Massachusetts

Tom French

Bill Byrne, Massachusetts Division of Fisheries & Wildlife

Archie Hagar, the Massachusetts State Ornithologist, built a small blind in 1947 by the cliff on Rattlesnake Mountain overlooking Quabbin Reservoir, which had just completed filling the year before. Here he spent hours quietly observing family life on a Peregrine Falcon nest ledge. This was the first year he noticed broken eggs that marked the beginning of the population decline of the DDT era. Ten years later the last native Massachusetts Peregrine chick would fledge from Monument Mountain in the Berkshires.

After a 30-year absence and considerable recovery efforts, Peregrines returned to nest again in Massachusetts beginning in 1987. This time, the pioneering birds moved into the cities to nest on skyscrapers in Boston and Springfield. Now the intimate details of their family lives could be observed at leisure through windows just a foot or two from the nest scrapes.

It was not unusual to watch an egg being laid or a chick struggling to hatch, events that Archie Hagar may never have seen despite his many hours of effort. With most of the population banded, it is also possible to follow individuals throughout their lives. In the 1930s and early 1940s, when the population was still healthy, Hagar observed females visiting occupied nest cliffs and noted that vacancies were rapidly filled. Today, some of the same observations are being made but with greater detail. These observations have shown that for female Peregrine Falcons, defending territory can be time-consuming, disruptive, and even deadly.

The first returning pair nested in Boston in 1987. It was made up of a male, hacked in downtown Boston in 1984, that returned to stake out a territory in 1985 and that attracted a mate in 1986. The female was the same age and had been hacked in downtown Toronto. As they began nesting in 1987, a two-year-old female, also hacked in Toronto a year after the first, was staking out territory in downtown Springfield, 80 miles west of Boston. During that first nesting year in Boston, the resident female was frequently seen in the air doing battle with an intruding female over her nest site and at nearby Logan Airport. Since the intruder could never be identified during a battle, it was not clear whether there was only one

... observers saw aerial combat with intruding females in both Boston and Springfield nearly every spring.

challenger or more. On one occasion, however, the unmated female from Springfield was captured by a raptor bander, Norman Smith, at the airport, where the resident pair spent much of their time hunting. A few days later the resident female engaged in a visibly bloody battle in the air at the airport, which lasted for two hours. During this conflict the resident pair fought another adult pair that appeared to include the Springfield female. Between bouts of battle the females would perch and the males would gain enough courage to swoop on the opposing resting female. Although the identity of the challenging female was only confirmed once, her plumage and band pattern suggested she was the Springfield bird on at least several occasions. If so, she was apparently making regular excursions from Springfield, where her identity was frequently confirmed, to Boston to challenge the resident female. The following year, 1988, the Springfield female settled down with her own mate, a one-year-old hacked in Albany, New York, and was never again seen far from her nest site.

From then on, observers saw aerial combat with intruding females in both Boston and Springfield nearly every spring. One of the most intense battles occurred on 30 March 1993 when the Boston female was bound to another banded but unidentified adult-plumaged female on a 19th-floor skyscraper balcony. Each bird was resting on its rump with both feet locked onto its opponent's chest. They would occasionally bite at each other's face, and both birds had bloody ceres. Periodically, one bird would release and make a fresh grab,

... the birds had become local celebrities in the city, and a sign of their popularity was the naming of the city's new professional hockey team, the Falcons.

causing an active period of jousting, but much of the time both birds just sat in a heap staring at each other with their head feathers puffed out. Several times the resident male came and landed on the 3-ft retaining wall around the balcony and looked on. On one occasion he brought a small plucked bird and left it on the wall, but it soon blew off the building. This fight was first discovered at 7:00 a.m., and finally, after three and a half hours, the resident bird broke it off and flew away with her mate. The next morning a check of the nest revealed a single rain-soaked egg that was probably laid before the battle began. Since the egg was never tended and not followed by any other eggs, it could well have been laid by the intruder. The resident pair were actively courting for the next several days and ignored the egg. After being pushed out of the nest scrape and partially buried, the egg was taken and artificially incubated. Although it did not hatch, it was fertile. The resident pair did not initiate another clutch, which could have been a renesting, until 20 April and eventually fledged four chicks.

The next year, 1994, this tough old female was not so lucky. During a nest check on 4 April, the 10-year-old resident female was found dead on a balcony directly below the nest site. She had apparently been killed in a battle about a week before. Her chest had several talon punctures, but she died after her opponent tore the skin and muscle from the back of her neck at the base of her skull. A check of the nest revealed that the intruder's victory had rewarded her with the nest site and the resident mate. She

was already tending two eggs of her own and eventually fledged four chicks. This new bird was a three-year-old that had been hacked on Borestone Mountain in Monson, Maine.

In Springfield in 1993, the resident female disappeared in midmorning on 12 April with one egg in the nest. She remained away for three days, during which the second egg should have been laid. When she returned at 10:00 a.m. on 15 April, she crash-landed onto the nest tray and sat in the corner with her feathers fluffed up and her eyes half-closed. One wing drooped and her chest was bloody underneath. By the next day she was better but still showing the effects of her injuries. That day she laid a second egg in the nest, which should have been her third. Although no conflicts were seen for the next several days, her fourth egg, which should have been laid on 18 April, never appeared. Everything seemed fairly calm until 21 April when a subadult-plumaged female was seen as she flew onto the nest tray, which held two eggs and the male. The male opened his wings and vocalized in protest. The resident female flew in to attack, and the fight went to the air. The two females were seen locking talons and falling nearly to the ground before separating and flying back up to fight. The male flew nearby but did not join in. When the two females disappeared after an hour of battle, the male returned to the eggs. The resident female remained away until the next morning and by afternoon was gone again for four days. After she returned it was noticed that her beak was badly split and part of the hook was broken off. That season only two eggs were

laid in the nest, and one of them was infertile. The remaining egg hatched and was raised to fledging.

This pair had a relatively calm season in 1994 and fledged four chicks. The next year, however, the nearly 10-year-old female was killed on 15 February when she struck a glassed-in stairway on top of a five-story parking garage as she tried to capture a pigeon on the opposite side. She had been featured for six consecutive breeding seasons on a dedicated public access cable television channel, known as The Falcon Channel, and there was great concern that the death of this founding bird, Amelia, would be the end of Peregrine Falcon nesting in Springfield. During those years the birds had become local celebrities in the city, and a sign of their popularity was the naming of the city's new professional hockey team, the Falcons. For three consecutive days after Amelia's death I was busy with interviews for the local newspaper, television, and radio stations. This led to a frequently quoted assurance that "Peregrines mate for life, but they don't mourn for a moment." True to form, the male, Andy, was seen in the nest tray six days later with a new female. The new bird was a three-year-old hatched on the Throgs Neck Bridge in New York City. The new pair went on to lay three eggs and fledge three chicks in their first season.

Not all Peregrine pairs are hostile toward other falcons. The second pair to set up a territory in Boston has nested on the Christian Science Church Administration Building since 1996. This pair was formed by a two-year-old female from the Precipice on Champlain Mountain in Acadia National Park, Maine, and an unbanded male in full juvenile plumage. In their first year they raised four chicks, but not without help. Throughout the nesting period a second unbanded subadult female helped with the nest duties. Although the nest is not in direct view, it appeared that she shared incubation, and she certainly shared in hunting and feeding duties and seemed to be completely tolerated by the pair. On the day the chicks were banded, all three birds were there to defend the nest. The second year an unbanded adult male helped the pair throughout the season and was an active food provider for the chicks. Every year since then the pair has appeared to be on its own, but on the day the chicks are banded a third adult has shown up for a short time but has not participated in defending the nest. In 2002 two extra adults, a possible pair, made a brief appearance. The identity of these extra birds is still a mystery, but it shows that this particular resident pair is extremely tolerant of other Peregrine Falcons of both sexes.

As the number of territorial pairs continues to grow in Massachusetts, 10 pairs in 2003 including the first cliff nesters, it will be increasingly difficult to piece together the relationships and interactions between the individuals. These new pairs are succeeding in their efforts to find mates and locate new unoccupied nest sites. For some females, however, finding an established pair and taking over by force may continue to be the strategy of choice.

Thomas W. French *was born and grew up in Atlanta, Georgia. His educational background includes a B.S. in biology from Georgia State University, an M.S. in zoology from Auburn University, a Ph.D. in ecology and systematics from Indiana State University, and a postdoctoral position at Cornell University. He was formerly a zoologist with The Nature Conservancy and an instructor-naturalist and researcher with the National Audubon Society. He is now Assistant Director of the Massachusetts Division of Fisheries and Wildlife, where he serves as Director of the Natural Heritage and Endangered Species Program. Tom is a past president of the Nuttall Ornithological Club, a life member of the American Society of Mammalogists, and Chair of the Northeast Implementation Team which was established to advise the National Marine Fisheries Service on the implementation of the northern right whale and humpback whale recovery plans. He has written more than 40 papers on small mammals, birds, and herptiles and has served on numerous graduate student committees. He currently lives in central Massachusetts with his wife, Diane, daughter, Alexandra, and son, Peter.*

▲ **Figure 5.19** Wild adults in Colorado's Royal Gorge received the first fostered Peregrine chicks, 1974. The coloring on their heads is used in the laboratory to identify individuals before banding.

Eastern Reintroduction

Because some critics of the program had stated publicly that "The Peregrine Fund will never release a single Peregrine" (they were among those who earlier had said we would never be able to breed falcons in captivity), we felt it was important to begin releasing some falcons as soon as possible, even though we needed to keep most of the captive-produced progeny for breeding stock during the first two years of successful breeding. Also, we needed a little lead time to develop the best methods for releasing young falcons on a large scale. Hacking, fostering, crossfostering, and releasing adult mated pairs were all methods we wanted to try (Cade 1974).

Consequently, we sent four of the 23 Peregrines produced in 1974 back to the wild. Two were fostered to a pair of Peregrines in the Royal Gorge of Colorado. This pair had lost two clutches of eggs to shell breakage earlier in the season and was caring for a fostered Prairie Falcon chick when Jim Weaver exchanged two of our Cornell Peregrine chicks for the baby Prairie Falcon. Both young Peregrines fledged successfully, and Jim Enderson had fun watching them fly up and down the gorge later in summer, perfecting their hunting skills.

We hacked the other two, young Peale's Falcons, in cooperation with Heinz Meng, from the roof of the Faculty Tower on the campus of the State University of New York at New Paltz, where Meng was a professor. These two falcons also fledged successfully and were at the point of becoming independent juveniles when some vandal apparently did them in: Meng found the severed wings of a young Peregrine in a trash bin in the New Paltz city park. We never learned anything further about this incident; but the effort did convince us that hacking would be a good method for establishing domestically raised Peregrines back into nature. This conclusion was strengthened by the successful results of hacking a number of our captive-produced Prairie Falcons at a site in New Mexico with the capable assistance of Tom Smylie.

In 1975 we were able to test the hacking procedure at five different locations in the East, with a total of 16 young Peregrines. Just back from a stint working with the Mauritius Kestrel and Seychelles Kestrel on islands in the Indian Ocean, Stan Temple was in charge of the release effort that year. Two of the sites were historical Peregrine eyries: Taughannock Falls on Cayuga Lake near Cornell and the Mohonk cliff in the Shawangunk Mountains near New Paltz, New York. Three were artificial sites: a 75-ft steel gunnery tower on Carroll Island at the Edgewood Arsenal, Maryland, made available through Scott Ward and his army associates (see sidebar, Beating the Bureaucracy, Chapter 1); and two specially built "hack towers" on Sedge Island, New Jersey, constructed with help from Pete McLain and his liberated assistant, Teddy Moritz, who could wield a mean hammer despite her small size, and at the Massachusetts Audubon Society's Drumlin Farm Sanctuary near Lincoln with the help of Jim Baird.

The variety of these locations gave us an indication of the problems we would face in mounting a major reintroduction effort. The released Peregrines were wiped out by Great Horned Owls at Taughannock Falls, now a heavily forested ravine, and one of three birds at Drumlin Farm was electrocuted when it perched on a power-line transformer. But 12 of the 16 hacked falcons made it to the stage of independent existence and dispersed naturally from their hack sites. For example, we later had reports of the birds from Carroll Island on the Chesapeake Bay Bridge, two in the inner harbor of Baltimore, and one roosting regularly on the 32nd-floor ledge of the U.S. Fidelity and Guaranty (USF&G) building in downtown Baltimore (not Scarlett; she came later). Other birds were seen in New Jersey and in New York City. The following spring at least five, probably six, of these birds were sighted at three of the hack sites and at other nearby locales. A first-year return rate of 50% was most encouraging and gave us renewed enthusiasm to expand the hacking program.

Figure 5.20 Peregrine Falcon at Taughannock Falls. Circa 1940.   ▶

Tom Cade

▲ **Figure 5.21** Jim Weaver (left) and Steve Sherrod at the Taughannock Falls hack site, the location of the famous Peregrine eyrie photographed by Arthur Allen (opposite page). The hack box was built into the cliff. Young falcons are being lowered over the cliff in a box, 1975.

File photo

File photo

File photo

▲ **Figure 5.22** Stan Temple (left) and Jack Barclay band a young Peregrine. Circa 1976.

▲ **Figure 5.23** Marty Gilroy removes a Peregrine from a transport kennel to place it in a hack box.

◀ **Figure 5.24** Tom Maechtle holds a young Peregrine while Steve Sherrod attaches a radio transmitter. Circa 1975–1976.

Figure 5.25 First seven years of Peregrine population growth in the eastern United States.

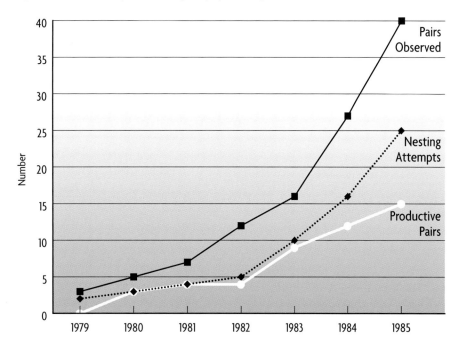

Figure 5.26 Two eggs laid in ▶ a hack box in the Manahawkin, New Jersey, wetlands in May 1979. This marks the first time in more than 20 years that Peregrines mated and laid eggs in an eyrie in the eastern United States.

Figure 5.27 Three of the ▶ first young to be hatched and raised by wild Peregrines east of the Mississippi River since the 1950s (Manahawkin, New Jersey, 3 May 1980).

Under Steve Sherrod's supervision, the release program became fully operational in 1976, and by 1978, when Jack Barclay took over, we had released more than 100 young falcons in the East. Both single and paired Peregrines had set up territories at several hack sites and other locations from New Hampshire to Maryland. At least 10 adult or year-old birds were present at eight of our hack sites, and another immature bird, Scarlett, had taken up residence on the USF&G building in Baltimore. In 1979 Scarlett, still unmated, laid a clutch of eggs on the 33rd-floor ledge and later successfully fledged four fostered young; another immature female at a hack tower in New Jersey laid two or three eggs that appeared to be fertile when candled, but marauding crows disrupted her nesting before the eggs hatched (see Chapter 19).

The year 1980 saw the first successful breeding of Peregrines in eastern North America in more than 20 years. Two pairs nesting on hack towers in the New Jersey salt marshes fledged their young, and one of our released females was discovered with a wild tiercel at an historical eyrie in southern Quebec, where she also fledged two young despite having a broken leg that dangled when she flew. Scarlett also acquired a mate, and they successfully fledged more fostered young. From that point on, the number of nesting pairs increased exponentially until 1990 and then continued at a slower rate, as Marty Gilroy brought the release program to a successful conclusion in 1992 (Figure 5.25).

One of the most interesting and unexpected results of hacking Peregrines in North America has been the number of pairs that have become established on manmade structures in urban and industrial environments. Although historically the use by Peregrines of manmade nesting structures in Europe was a widespread, if uncommon, habit, few pairs were ever known to do so in North America. The most notable cases were on the St. Regis Hotel in Manhattan in the 1940s, on the old City Hall of Philadelphia in 1946 and 1949, once on a church steeple in Harrisburg, Pennsylvania, on an abandoned bridge pier in the Susquehanna River, and most successfully from 1940 to 1952 on the Sun Life Assurance building in Montreal (Cade and Bird 1990). From the very beginning of the hacking projects in Canada and the United States, some of the released Peregrines began showing attachments to buildings and bridges in and around urban areas, and by the early 1980s pairs had become established in places such as Edmonton, Montreal, Baltimore, New York City, Boston, Philadelphia, Salt Lake City, San Francisco, and Los Angeles.

Lightning at Carroll Island

Stanley A. Temple

Tom Cade

Stan Temple

Stan Temple

By 1975 The Peregrine Fund's success at captive breeding, and the lessons learned from trial hacking experiments in 1974, had made the dream of releasing large numbers of young Peregrines a reality. The initial releases in 1975 attracted much media interest, and to accommodate often disruptive publicity demands, we decided to focus much of the media attention on a few key hack sites. The first of these was the Carroll Island site on the Aberdeen Proving Grounds near Edgewood, Maryland. Scott Ward, who worked on the site, had arranged an extravaganza with reporters, top brass from the military, U.S. Fish and Wildlife Service officials, and other cooperators being helicoptered in to the remote island site on the day that four young Peregrines were placed in the hack box.

This particular hack site was unusual in several ways. It was the first of many subsequent releases that had no natural nesting site nearby. We placed the hack box atop an old steel tower that had once been fitted with a cannon used to shoot chemical warfare munitions into a test area on the island. From the top of the tower the young Peregrines had a sweeping view of the island and the surrounding Chesapeake Bay.

All went well during the media session, and by early evening everyone had departed, leaving me alone on the island with the four young Peregrines, now safely (or so I thought) in the hack box atop the tower. Shortly after dark,

just as I was settling in for the night in a nearby building, a severe thunderstorm built up in the distance. Looking out the window, I noticed that the intense lightning was backlighting the tower, so I snapped a photo of the spectacular scene. Only then did it sink in that the storm was coming straight at the island, and the hack box full of Peregrines was on top of the tallest metal structure for miles around. It was a lightning strike waiting to happen!

I quickly pulled on my boots and raincoat and ran out to the tower. As I climbed the ladder, it started raining, and bolts of lightning were hitting only a mile or so away. I quickly grabbed the four birds, stuffed them into a box, and descended the tower in record time. As I made it back to the building, the storm hit the island. I looked out the window just in time to see the hack box get hit by successive bolts of lightning.

My knees buckled as I realized that if I had delayed even a few minutes there might have been five dead bodies on the tower! I didn't sleep well that night, but the Peregrines seemed none the worse for the experience.

At first light I climbed the tower to inspect the damage. It was as bad as I had imagined. The plywood box had been ripped apart, the screws that held it together had melted in their holes, the gravel on the floor of the box had exploded outward like shrapnel, and the galvanizing on the metal subfloor had boiled off! Having no telephone on the island, I drove to Scott's home to tell him what had happened. The dramatic story attracted almost as much media coverage as the event the previous day, and that night the story of the Peregrines' rescue was on all the network news shows. The Army promptly installed an impressive array of lightning

rods on the tower and proclaimed it safe to return the young to the repaired hack box. Despite this dramatic beginning, the rest of the release work at the site was uneventful, and all four Peregrines fledged successfully. Needless to say, all subsequent hack towers were fitted with lightning rods.

Stanley A. Temple *is the Beers-Bascom Professor in Conservation in the Department of Wildlife Ecology and Chairman of the Conservation Biology and Sustainable Development Program in the Institute for Environmental Studies at the University of Wisconsin-Madison. He has worked on conservation problems in 20 countries and has helped save some of the world's rarest and most endangered bird species. He teaches courses in ecology and conservation that were once taught by Aldo Leopold. Professor Temple's service to the conservation community at large is extensive, including serving as President of The Society for Conservation Biology.*

Tom Cade

Thruway Authority

▲ **Figure 5.28** Peregrine on Tappan Zee Bridge, New York.

Figure 5.29 Jim Weaver ▶ climbs to a nest box on an abandoned water tank tower, Tuckerton Fish Factory, New Jersey.

Figure 5.30 City hack sites ▶ like this one in New York on the former Manhattan Life Insurance Building provide an environment free of many predators that threaten young Peregrines in the wild.

Tom Cade

In part this movement into cities was abetted by hacking young falcons at urban release sites. We began using release sites in cities as a way to avoid the problem of predation by Great Horned Owls and other predators encountered in the country. As with our use of hack towers in the coastal salt marshes, we thought city-released falcons would disperse to areas where suitable nesting cliffs occur and settle on them to breed. Only later did it become evident that Peregrines show a strong proclivity to nest on the same kind of structure as their natal nesting site (Cade and Bird 1990, Cade et al. 1996, Tordoff et al. 1998a). Some individuals do shift from one type of site to another, but more released Peregrines have moved from the country into cities than vice versa.

By 1988 a survey revealed 30 to 32 pairs of Peregrines on territories in at least 24 cities and towns in North America, and they produced 42 to 45 fledglings, a rate of productivity statistically indistinguishable from that of falcons nesting in natural circumstances (Cade and Bird 1990), although

bridge-nesting pairs were less successful than others (Frank 1994, Bell et al. 1996). The last continent-wide survey, in 1993, tallied 88 territorial pairs in 60 urban settings (Cade et al. 1996). Most nests have been located on tall buildings and bridges, but other sites include power-plant smokestacks (Septon et al. 1996)(see sidebar, Peregrine Recovery and the Role of Power Plants in the Midwest: A Brief History and Current Status, Chapter 10), a loading crane, decommissioned ships in harbor, quarries, water towers, and silos.

These urban-dwelling Peregrines have continued to increase and certainly numbered well over 150 pairs by 2000, with 15 or so pairs in New York City (C. Nadareski pers. comm., see sidebar, Peregrine Falcons and How They Have Changed the Skies of New York, this chapter), six pairs in the St. Paul-Minneapolis area, five to six pairs in the greater Philadelphia area and associated bridges over the Skuylkill and Delaware Rivers, and seven pairs in a 25-sq-km area of the Long Beach city and harbor area (B. Walton pers. comm.). In the Midwest in 2001, from a total of 133 reported pairs, 57 were on buildings, 24 on smokestacks, and 12 on bridges, or 70% of the total population (Tordoff et al. 2000). Obviously urban Peregrines have become an important part of the falcon

continued on page 102

Peregrine Falcons and How They Have Changed the Skies of New York

Christopher A. Nadareski

Awakening in the middle of the night at 2:30 a.m. and staying awake into the early evening is part of a work routine each spring that I have accustomed myself to as a New York City wildlife biologist. From my bedroom window each morning, the lighted tower on Skytop, referred to as Pinnacle Rock by the late, great naturalist of Mohonk, Daniel Smiley, shines over the immense cliff face of the Shawangunk Mountains, a former stronghold of the Peregrine. After nearly four decades without Peregrines in the area, a second pair of reintroduced Peregrine Falcons has conquered the "cliff sky" with incredible stoops and gentle "ee-chupping," which I saw and heard on a recent visit with the Mohonk Preserve Research Team.

© Ralph Ginzburg 2001

The daily drive from my home in New Paltz, New York, to New York City in the middle of the night, a reprieve from daytime commuter congestion, takes me past the tallest building in the village on the campus of the State University of New York (SUNY) at New Paltz. It is a mere pedestal compared with those concrete peaks at my destination in the City. Faculty Tower on the SUNY campus is remembered as the location of the first Peregrine Falcon release effort where Tom Cade and Heinz Meng conducted hacking experiments in the early 1970s. This team approach, not unlike today's active management of the Peregrine, has allowed me to be part of one of the world's most successful endangered species restoration efforts.

A two-hour drive south takes me over one of New York's busiest bridges and home to a Peregrine Falcon nest since 1988, the Tappan Zee Bridge (TZB) with its sparkling necklace of night lights. With a keen eye one can see two falcon nest boxes that blend with the color of the steel where they have been carefully placed on each tower to offer the falcons a choice of nesting opportunity. Annual construction projects could spoil a successful nest if the two-box option were not available. South and north of the TZB, mostly along the west shore of the Hudson River, including the Palisades and Hudson Highlands, several historical eyries remain with-out falcons. This new breed of falcon seems to prefer human-built structures to the Hudson's naturally sculpted cliffs where the Peregrine once ruled but where Great Horned Owls have taken over.

My scheduled visit to the TZB nest later today will involve a climb up the steel approximately 120 ft above the roadway, dodging aerial assaults to see whether the falcon has laid her eggs yet. Previous site visits in other years provoked suicidal-like flights through ladder rungs to protect their offspring. Right now, though, my thoughts remain focused on which highway route to take to reach the City's boundaries before rush hour.

Eight nest-site visits are scheduled for today, includ-ing three bridges, three towers, and two building eyries. Upon arrival at New York's Central Park I head on foot to an underground rail system, the 4-5-6 subway, which arrives at Wall Street in lower Manhattan 20 minutes later; the site of New York's most famous Peregrine nest. The original Wall Street pair moved to 55 Water Street, a few blocks to the east, in the late 1990s after the 10-year-old resident female was found with a fractured wing on the sidewalk near the New York State Stock Exchange. Wildlife rehabilitators at The Raptor Trust in New Jersey nursed the falcon back to flight, and I subsequently released her at Gateway National Park in the fall of 1998. Flying unbalanced and holding a crooked wing, she ended her first post rehabilitation flight in what appeared to be a disaster. By late February of the next year, however, the same female appeared with her original mate, hatched at the Verrazano Narrows Bridge in 1990, and they reared two young at the Water Street site.

After another underground ride back uptown to the Met Life Building, 57 floors above Grand Central Terminal, I see soaring falcons providing lunchtime entertainment to casual observers from the steps of the New York Public Library along 42nd Street. The Met Life Building, formerly named Pan Am, opened its doors to its first falcon tenants in 1989, when I observed eggs deposited on two ledges separated by a concrete column. Each egg was incubated simultaneously, one by the female and one by the tiercel. Needless to say, the nest(s) failed that year, but the falcons have nested successfully most years since then.

Parking courtesies are often extended to me, "New York's falcon guy" as I am often called, at the New York Presbyterian Hospital nest site for a simple exchange of information about the hospital nest. The parking attendants are familiar with the "chief residents" and often report stories of pigeon-muggings and skeletal finds. The nest overlooks the East River and has occasionally produced five young. Although shorebirds still have a tendency to have elevated organochlorines (DDT) in their systems, woodcock tends to be a favorite menu item for this window-ledge pair. Annual eyass bandings were generally hosted with a formal reception by John Aronian, wheeling in a hospital gurney and

closely followed by the New York Press corps, until his retirement a few years ago. Along with my banding gear (pliers, bands, lice spray, etc.) I require a stepladder, motorcycle helmet, climbing harness, and an electrifying statement on the status of the NYC Peregrines for the TV camera. John, aside from assisting with the bandings, once rescued a fledgling overcome by smoke while perched on a stack. The young survived, without injury, a 200-ft free-fall down inside the smokestack and was brought back to the nest ledge safely.

Back in 1989 the hospital nest produced siblings that mated successfully on a bridge eyrie the following year just east of Coney Island in Jamaica Bay. Unfortunately, the female was the victim of a hit-and-run during the nesting period, leaving the tiercel, named Little John, to provide for the two young. An obituary on Little John's mate appeared in the *New York Observer* that year.

Going from the upper east side to the upper west side, I reach the Riverside Church eyrie, my favorite, which overlooks the Hudson River and Riverside Park about 300 ft above the sidewalk. Over 80 species of prey have been recorded at this Manhattan nest site, including a Northern Phalarope. It was back in the early 1940s that the former Peregrine congregants, part of the wintering population in NYC, were looked upon unfavorably by the rector of the church as they killed pigeons in view from the front of the church, according to the late Roger Tory Peterson. The step-like roof of President Grant's Tomb across Riverside Drive is available to the fledglings

A Peregrine attacks as the author attempts to band its young.

Interior Secretary Bruce Babbitt, Tom Cade, and officials from the New York City Department of Environmental Protection and the New York State Department of Environmental Conservation gathered with the press to announce notice of intent to delist the American Peregrine Falcon, June 1995.

from this nest for safe landings. Occasionally young falcons get into trouble on their maiden flights, as was the case in 1995 when a Riverside young landed on the top of a parked ambulance below the church ledges. Children playing in a nearby park heroically flagged the ambulance driver before the illegal hitchhiker got away. Good work!

New York City was the first site in the state to have falcons return to nest in 1983 after extirpation two decades earlier. Attractive to the public like no other bird in New York City, this state endangered species continues to magnetize flocks of birders and falcon enthusiasts, who seek a glimpse or want to hear the jet-like sounds of a stoop at unsuspecting prey. The Peregrine has a somewhat controversial image in New York, on the one hand having

achieved one of the world's highest breeding densities amongst the canyons of steel, concrete, and glass, and on the other hand wreaking havoc on routine management and construction projects on the city's bridges and buildings. Despite its glamour, the Peregrine requires a personalized public relations campaign manager. This is where I come in—as an Urban Wildlife Biologist with a lot of public relations duties. I have had the pleasure of introducing this endangered species program to hundreds of both enthusiastic and not-so-enthusiastic people. Without such a public relations campaign, the program would be in a constant bureaucratic flux between the fulfillment of the state Endangered Species Act and the public safety requirements in maintaining bridges and buildings. Fortunately, with a little talk, these conflicts are usually resolved with outcomes favorable to both the falcon's survival and the structural integrity of the facilities on which the birds nest.

Of the 15 nesting territories used in NYC, 12 were occupied by pairs in 2002. Each nest becomes loosely adopted by an individual or group of individuals who maintain constant vigil on the whereabouts of both young and adults. Routine site visits often include one of a variety of activities such as nest-box construction, determining nesting status, collecting prey remains, or banding young, and usually a volunteer or cooperating government official accompanies me. From the George Washington Bridge approximately 500 ft above the Hudson River to a 14th-floor setback on a building on Water Street, a few blocks from the former World Trade Center complex, the falcons now occupy nesting sites that the former Peregrine population could only have dreamed of maintaining. Peregrines were often persecuted in the past because they are predators, and in New York their historical nests were usually destroyed or raided for falconry prior to the 1960s.

New York City is truly a place of celebrity sightings: Jack and Jill of the 55 Water Street family are often observed ledge-hopping near the Wall Street market; Henry and Henrietta from the multi congregational Riverside Church hang out along Manhattan's upper west side; Lois and Clarke live the fast-paced lifestyle of the Met Life Building in midtown; Red-Red and P.J. are a health-conscious couple who formerly resided at New York Presby-

terian/Cornell Medical Center; and Rio and Queen, who held sway on the Throgs Neck Bridge in Queens for many years, now have family scattered from New England to Virginia. Of New York's high-flying celebrities, most have neglected their winter getaways and usually show up at the city galas and in the press year-round. Only a select, privileged cast of biologists and maintenance workers get the opportunity to have their scalps autographed by the falcons' talons, and I have personally had the honor of multiple body parts autographed.

Over the years, I have been inspired by the level of effort exerted by the variety of people involved in caring for the New York Peregrines— from government officials to facility managers, volunteers, construction contractors, rehabilitators, veterinarians, students, the press, and most importantly mem-

bers of The Peregrine Fund (Marty Gilroy and Jack Barclay) and New York State Department of Environmental Conservation (Barbara Allen Loucks), who helped shape my career. As most Peregrine biologists know, working with a species of such superlative adaptive skills is truly a life commitment. Telephone calls received from the Metropolitan Transit Authority or the Port Authority of New York and New Jersey in the middle of the night about a fledgling retrieved from traffic on one of its bridges often carries a similar tone of satisfaction that every individual falcon is cared for.

With the advent of the nest box video cameras, New York City, along with many other urban settings, has the world's eyes focused on every aspect of falcon behavior from courtship through first flight. There may

come a time when the urban biologist will move his or her computer mouse more frequently than clip carabineers along a safety line while climbing to a falcon's nest.

During my nearly two decades of involvement in Peregrine work, no experience has imprinted itself more deeply in my memory than my visit to the World Trade Center on a nightshift bucket brigade a few days following September 11. Although my intentions were inspired by that innate New Yorker spirit observed during recovery efforts, I was not able to provide much assistance because of the large machinery operating around me. It was during my shift, while feeling overwhelmed and awed by the devastation, that my attention turned to the sky above the 40 to 50 stories of swirling brown smoke where I spotted a sign of survival. A pair of Peregrine Falcons circled this newly created void and landed on the observation deck of the Woolworth Building, once New York's tallest structure and now a familiar roost for the pair of falcons that nest on the Brooklyn Bridge. Somehow my depression in this ravaged gravesite was temporarily overcome by the falcons displaying their solidarity with fellow New Yorkers.

> *Somehow my depression in this ravaged gravesite was temporarily overcome by the falcons displaying their solidarity with fellow New Yorkers.*

© Ralph Ginzburg 2002

Christopher A. Nadareski *is a research scientist for the New York City Department of Environmental Protection (DEP). He received a Master of Science degree from the State University of New York at New Paltz with a thesis on prey selection and contaminants in the prey of urban nesting Peregrine Falcons in New York City. As supervisor of the Wildlife Studies Group in DEP, he is responsible for developing and implementing a wildlife management program investigating links between wildlife and their impacts on New York City's drinking-water supply. Christopher has been actively involved with New York State's Peregrine Falcon restoration and management efforts since the mid-1980s. Having worked as a Peregrine hack site attendant in Albany, New York, and Lake Jocassee, South Carolina, he subsequently established a Peregrine nest site management program between the New York State Department of Environmental Conservation and New York City government. At present, he is responsible for managing the world's largest urban concentration of nesting Peregrines, in New York City. Since the early 1990s he has banded more than 400 Peregrines and currently manages more than 20 nesting pairs in New York State. He lives with his wife and two children in New Paltz, New York, where the first Peregrine hack releases in the Eastern United States took place.*

A Pair of Green Falcons

Pete McLain

When a 41-ft long U.S. Coast Guard boat pulled up alongside my 12-ft aluminum outboard on Barnegat Bay, New Jersey, and the commanding officer advised me to "heave to" and asked for permission to come aboard, I felt like the flea crawling up an elephant's leg with rape in mind.

As three of us steadied my boat, a brute of a man, who hadn't seen his shoes over his belly in 10 years, introduced himself as the Chief Petty Officer. He asked if I was involved in that "boyd" house on Sedge Island. I replied in the affirmative and questioned his interest.

He announced, "Those 'boyds' that live in that house on Sedge Island come down to the U.S. Coast Guard Station at Barnegat Inlet almost every day and chase the pigeons." At first blush I thought the Peregrines might be chasing some special U.S. Coast Guard messenger pigeons.

Before I could respond, he said, "What are those boyds anyway?" I explained they were Peregrine Falcons, an endangered species that The Peregrine Fund at Cornell University was trying to reintroduce into their former range.

"You know," he said, "them boyds are the best thing that ever happened to the Barnegat Light Coast Guard Station." He related that he was the person in charge of all eight of the lifesaving boats. He said there was an old wooden early-century surf boat, which served faithfully for 30 years before it was retired, and he kept in mint condition for special occasions. You could tell by his voice that it was his favorite craft and woe be unto anyone who climbed aboard her with a little sand on his shoes, which might scratch the high gloss varnish.

The boats were housed and maintained inside a great barnlike building about 75 ft long and 40 ft high. This super structure served as a roosting area for a few dozen pigeons, which demonstrated perfect aim in hitting the Chief's pride and joy with their droppings. They also violated several other boats, and anything else below their roosting area.

> "You know," he said, "them boyds are the best thing that ever happened to the Barnegat Light Coast Guard Station."

"I'll tell you one thing, when I see just a suggestion that a pigeon hit on one of my boats, I have all hands on deck scrubbing, sanding, and generally cleaning up after those pigeons."

He went on to tell about how those boyds would perch on the Coast Guard radio antenna and watch for pigeons in the area, and especially those going in and out of the building, which was open at both ends.

He said it took those boyds about a week of almost constant pigeon harassment and a number of kills for the pigeons to learn they were not welcome in the boat shed or the Barnegat Light Coast Guard Station. He reported the U.S. Coast Guard had professional exterminators trying to figure how to keep the pigeons out, but those hawks, or whatever they are, did the job.

"What did you call those boyds?" he asked. I replied, "Peregrine Falcons." His face lit up and he said, "Where can I get a pair of them green falcons?" I explained these were experimental birds, under a well-controlled situation and not available to the government or the public at any cost. However, The Peregrine Fund would be happy to know that the Peregrine Falcon is cooperating closely with the U.S. Coast Guard.

The Chief Petty Officer returned to his own boat. As he eased forward on the throttle, I heard him say to one of the crew, "I am going to get me a pair of them green falcons."

Pete McLain holds a mounted Peregrine. Although it was wearing a Cornell color band and radio transmitter, the bird was shot by a New Jersey pigeon hunter, kept in a freezer for a year, then mounted by a local taxidermist. The shooter was fined $2,000, the estimated cost to rear and release the falcon.

Peter McLain *was Deputy Director of the Division of Fish, Game and Wildlife for New Jersey, which was the first state to participate in Peregrine Falcon restoration.*

Hacking at Cobb Island, Virginia

Renetta Cade

Tom Cade

Tom Cade

In late June and early July of 1978 Tom and I had a wonderful experience hacking young Peregrines on Cobb Island off the coast of Virginia, accompanied by Doug Davis. For some time Tom had been itching to do a hack site to gain personal familiarity with what it is like to watch over a group of young falcons as they learn to fly, hone their skills as hunters, and eventually fly off as wild, independent Peregrines. He had heard about the bird life on Cobb Island from a colleague at the Laboratory of Ornithology, Olin Sewall Pettingill, who had spent his honeymoon with his bride, Eleanor, studying and photographing the mixed nesting colony of terns, gulls, and skimmers on Little Cobb Island, a stone's throw across a tidal channel from the main island at its southern end.

Cobb Island became a part of the Virginia Coast Reserve of The Nature Conservancy, and when an opportunity arose to participate in a cooperative effort to release Peregrines on Virginia's barrier islands with the Virginia Commission of Game and Inland Fisheries, Mitchell Byrd of the College of William and Mary, and The Nature Conservancy, Tom jumped at the chance. He and Mitchell Byrd examined several of the barrier islands as potential hack sites and agreed that the south end of Cobb would be the best place to start. Not only was the habitat superior for Peregrines with wide open marshes, broad, low sand dunes, and extensive tidal

flats, all with an abundance of bird life, but there was also an old, abandoned Coast Guard Station that could serve as living quarters for attendants, with a fourth floor observation cupola that looked suitable as a place to hack the young falcons. It sounded like a cozy arrangement when Tom described it to me.

Mitchell Byrd took us out to the island in his comfortable boat, along with supplies, five baby falcons, and about 200 live Coturnix Quail, and Doug followed in his smaller skiff and outboard motor. In calm weather it was an easy 7.5 mi ride across the shallow waters from Oyster to the island. In a storm it could be something else, and Cobb Island has a long history of involvement with shipwrecks and salvage operations.

We set up housekeeping with Doug quartered in a room on the first floor, Tom and I took over a dormitory at the south end of the second floor, the quail were caged on the third floor, and the five young falcons were let loose in the cupola, where they could be fed through a trap door in the floor and would have access to the outside through open windows facing toward Little Cobb Island, as soon as they could fly.

Although suitable for a temporary stay, the station soon revealed its inadequacies. We knew ahead of time, of course, that there would be no running water, plumbing facilities, or electricity and that we would essentially be "camping out" inside a large building. The station had been vacant for

many years, and unfortunately vandals had stripped it of anything valuable, especially the copper wiring and roofing. When it rained there were leaks everywhere, and it took us time to discover the one spot in the dormitory where we could place our sleeping bag and remain dry during a storm. We rigged up an outside privy about 50 yards east of the station with a back and sidewalls but fully exposed in front to a magnificent view of the ocean and the many passing ships; I often wondered what the view from the opposite direction might be like. Fresh water was at a premium, and so we waited for rain squalls and took our showers under broken off downspouts draining the building's gutters.

It sounded like a cozy arrangement when Tom described it to me.

The veranda on the south end of the station was a pleasant place to eat meals and to watch seabirds, ships, and, of course, Peregrines. We lived off the land to some extent. Clams and oysters were readily available in the tidal channel between the two islands—Tom and Doug liked to eat them raw—but I abstained. There was also a lovely, pan-sized flounder that could be seined in knee-deep water at high tide, and when steamed with a little butter, lemon pepper spice, and ginger, it made a tasty dish. For breakfast we often ate scrambled quail eggs. It takes many quail eggs to make a meal for three people, but a hundred or more female quail lay a lot of eggs.

One day Doug and I made a food and water run to the

Tom Cade

mainland in his small boat, leaving Tom to watch after the falcons. On our return trip the water became very rough as a storm approached, and we noticed that all the other boats were passing us as they headed back to harbor, not a comforting sign. We eventually had to give up after getting thoroughly soaked. We spent the night onshore and went to Sears the next morning to buy life jackets. I guess Doug figured it would not be prudent to lose Tom's wife. My husband was a little frantic as it was, because our radio communication system had broken down and he had no way to know what had happened to us.

The five fledged falcons loved to jump about on the roof and dormers of the Coast Guard Station, or perch quietly on the railing around the cupola, until something like a fiddler crab caught their attention, and then they would sally out to do mock attacks on the odd creature or tail chase Willets and other birds. Unfortunately, there were no really well-protected roosting places on the building, and both of the less fully developed females were

blown away at night in separate storms and probably downed over water. The three feisty tiercels all made it to independence; one was later trapped as a breeding bird at the hack tower on Chincoteague National Wildlife Refuge in 1986, and another was found dead near the eyrie on the James River bridge in April of 1995 when he was nearly 17 years old, the longest lived bird known at that date among all those released in the East.

After this first release, Mitchell Byrd had a regular hack tower constructed farther out in the marsh away from the station. An additional 35 falcons were hacked on Cobb until 1985, when the tower was taken over by a territorial pair of released falcons. It has remained occupied ever since.

It was such a privilege to learn to know a locale in nature really well and to have had a part in the process of establishing a completely new tradition of use of a site by nesting Peregrines. Just so, one eyrie at a time, the Eastern falcon population was rebuilt with care and dedication.

Renetta Cade *was born in Illinois and moved to southern California at the age of nine. She attended schools in California, except for one college year in Washington. She and Tom were married in 1952, and she received her B.A. degree in education from Los Angeles State College the same year. After learning to put up with hibernating chipmunks and dead birds in her refrigerator, she followed Tom from UCLA to Berkeley, Syracuse, Africa, Cornell, and now Boise, Idaho, but she refuses to consider moving to Pep, New Mexico. She and Tom have five children and nine grandchildren scattered around the country.*

population in temperate North America, and the public's continuing fascination with these readily observed falcons is indicated by the growing number of websites devoted to the daily recording of activities at their eyries, including some eye-opening encounters between adult females fighting over possession of a nest site.

By 1999, when the *anatum* Peregrine was in the final stage of being considered for removal from the federal list of endangered species, the eastern breeding population numbered about 156 pairs distributed in 16 states from Maine to Georgia. These pairs occupied 56 cliffs in the northeastern states and 13 cliffs in the southern Appalachian Mountains. Approximately 28 pairs nested on former hack towers in the salt marshes of New Jersey, Maryland, and Virginia, and the remaining 59 pairs were in urban areas, nesting mostly on buildings and bridges.

Once a pair has become established, most eyries have remained continually occupied, the exceptions being owl-infested cliffs of West Virginia, Virginia, and North Carolina and towers along the shoreline of Delaware Bay, or in cases where nest sites have been physically removed, such as the old water tower at Tuckerton, New Jersey. Several pairs also have alternate nest sites within the same breeding territory.

The official recovery goal for the "eastern region" (including the Midwest) was 175 to 200 nesting pairs with a minimum of 20 to 25 pairs in each of five recovery areas, demonstrating successful, sustained reproduction for a minimum of three years. In 1999 there were 248 known pairs east of 90°W longitude in the United States, although one recovery area (southern New England and northern Appalachians) was still below 20 pairs. The FWS determined that the latter was inconsequential in view of the substantial recovery that had occurred in the other areas.

Conclusion

As stated by Cade, Tordoff, and Barclay (2000): "Although these reestablished Peregrines come from parents with diverse genetic and geographic origins external to the eastern United States, they have converged rather closely to the former, indigenous Duck Hawks in their habits and ecology, except that some birds of northern, migratory stock winter farther south than the Duck Hawks did. Survival, productivity, natal dispersal, exchange of individuals among remote populations, and persistence of nesting territories over many years are all characteristic of a viable, regional Peregrine population (Tordoff and Redig 1997, Corser et al. 1999).

"This newly established falcon population shows all the signs of viability required for continued existence into the indefinite future. Its size has now exceeded the stated recovery goal and approaches that of the original duck hawks; it continues to increase at a rate of about 10% per year with little or no further augmentation. The eastern and midwestern populations exchange individuals (and genes) between themselves, as well as with Canadian populations to the north.

"The main shortcomings of the program relate to distribution rather than to population size and demographic viability. So far the reestablished falcons have been able to occupy only a few of the former breeding locations along the lowland river systems and in the central Appalachians owing to predation by abundant Great Horned Owls. This same sort of exclusion has been noted in Europe where Eagle Owls occupy habitats suitable for nesting Peregrines. Also, our tactical assumption that falcons released from towers in the coastal salt marshes, and the progeny of established pairs there, would disperse to settle on inland cliffs has proved to be incorrect, as these birds have shown little inclination to move away from the coast, or else those that do disperse inland succumb to owls.

"Species restoration, like habitat restoration, is usually a compromise between the ideal of return to the original, pristine condition and the practical limitations of what is possible in a drastically altered, human-dominated landscape. The habitats available to Peregrines in the eastern United States today are not entirely the same as the habitats in which the original duck hawks settled and evolved. While the natural cliffs that served as eyries before World War II have not been reoccupied in parts of the range, the reestablished falcons have found other areas in coastal salt marshes, in cities, and in industrial zones where they can survive and reproduce. The overall eastern population is certainly capable of existing into the indefinite future, and as natural selection continues its work, eventually a Peregrine that can coexist with owls may yet emerge to regain more of the cliffs along the lowland rivers and in the Appalachian Mountains. Until then, the Peregrine will be there in the eastern environment to occupy its unique niche in the community of living organisms and to be seen and admired by *Homo sapiens,* the wise species that refused to allow this fellow globetrotter to pass into oblivion."

Note: Recently there has been significant movement of successfully breeding Peregrines back onto cliffs of major eastern rivers, first along the upper Mississippi beginning in 2000 (see Chapter 10), and subsequently in the Atlantic region. In 2003 pairs were nesting on cliffs in Connecticut, two pairs in Massachusetts, including Sugar Loaf on the Connecticut River, two pairs on the Shawangunks against the Hudson River Valley in New York, two on the lower Hudson River palisades in New Jersey, and two in Pennsylvania, on the Susquehanna and at the Delaware Water Gap.

▲ **Figure 5.31** Tom Cade with Peale's tiercel Edac, trained as a semen donor.

Tom J. Cade *(at right with Renetta Cade) was born in 1928 in San Angelo, Texas, and received his Ph.D. from the University of California, Los Angeles in 1958. From 1967 to 1988 he was Professor of Ornithology and Curator of the Bird Collection (1967-1973) at Cornell University and Director of Raptor Research (1974-1988) at the Cornell Laboratory of Ornithology. He became Professor Emeritus at Cornell in 1988. That year Tom joined the Boise State University (BSU) faculty as Professor of Biology and Director of the Raptor Research Center. He also served as Co-Leader of the Raptor Research and Technical Assistance Center, also located at BSU, retiring in 1993, and was awarded Professor Emeritus status. Over his career he has conducted research internationally on birds, mammals, and fish, publishing about 250 articles and scientific papers and three books. He founded The Peregrine Fund in 1970 and serves as Founding Chairman of the Board. He has been honored by several awards, including the Elliot Coues Award by the American Ornithologists' Union for his contribution to knowledge on birds of prey and the Arthur A. Allen Award from the Cornell Laboratory of Ornithology for his work on the Peregrine Falcon.*

14/25   Robert Bateman

The Canadian *anatum* Peregrine Falcon Recovery Program

Richard Fyfe, Ursula Banasch, and Harry Armbruster

The Canadian Wildlife Service's (CWS's) Peregrine Falcon (Falco peregrinus anatum) Recovery Program consisted of two separate though related endeavors.

The first included population surveys and pesticide monitoring; the second focused on the captive breeding and reintroduction of *anatum* Peregrines.

The initial credit for the recovery of the Peregrine in North America and Europe belongs to Joseph Hickey. His foresight and action in calling the International Peregrine Conference at Madison, Wisconsin, in 1965 resulted in an initial awareness of the plight of the species. Data presented by Derek Ratcliffe at this conference were particularly significant because they suggested that the population decline and aberrant behavior, which had been observed in Europe and North America, might be linked to contamination by pesticides. British researchers had documented egg-eating and egg-loss and had also observed adult mortality. Equally important, analyses of some eggs and carcasses indicated organochlorine contamination (Ratcliffe 1969). Soon after the conference Ratcliffe (1967) reported his breakthrough findings on eggshell thinning.

These data were the first indication that the primary factor influencing the decline of this species might be linked to toxic chemical use. The results of the conference prompted population and pesticide monitoring of raptors and their prey species throughout Canada and the United States. Consequently, many researchers returned to their respective jurisdictions with two specific goals in mind: first, to monitor raptor populations and specifically to survey Peregrine Falcon populations, and second, to investigate levels of toxic chemicals in raptors and their prey species.

Population Surveys and Pesticide Monitoring

From 1966 to 1968, CWS coordinated raptor surveys in Canada to determine if Peregrine population declines had occurred in Canada and if other raptor populations were affected. Initial surveys indicated that *anatum* Peregrine populations had declined severely and that Prairie Falcons and Merlins appeared to have declined locally but not as severely.

Pesticide monitoring of raptor eggs and of prey species was increased both in conjunction with and outside the raptor surveys. Some individual samples had high levels of organochlorine

◀ **Figure 6.1** *Peregrine Falcon Drawing* ©Robert Bateman. Reproduction rights courtesy Boshkung Inc. and Mill Pond Press.

residues, although in general the results indicated that residues in raptor tissues and eggs were not alarming (Fyfe et al. 1969, Fimreite et al. 1970, Fyfe 1976). By the end of the 1960s, there was documented evidence of high residues of dichlorodiphenyltrichloroethane (DDT), organic mercury (Hg), and cyclodienes (aldrin, dieldrin, endrin, and heptachlor epoxide) in the eggs of Peregrines and other raptors and in some prey species. Monitoring pesticide levels in Canadian wildlife proved to be a useful indicator of potential environmental problems (Fyfe et al. 1969, Fimreite et al. 1970) and was primarily responsible for the studies that led to restrictions on DDT and Hg use in Canada in 1969 and 1970.

▲ Figures 6.2 and 6.3
Survey crew on Horton River (above) and near Rankin Inlet, Northwest Territories (below).

This monitoring provided evidence that the toxic chemical residues in tundra Peregrines (*F. p. tundrius*) and their prey species were generally lower than those recorded farther south in *anatum* populations. The presence of even low residues in the northern population was unexpected as the chemicals had not been used extensively in arctic North America. One probable explanation was that these Peregrines and their prey species were accumulating residues while on migration or in the wintering range. They then carried these pollutants back to the breeding areas in their tissues. This hypothesis led us to undertake surveys of pesticide residues in Peregrines and their prey on the wintering grounds in South America. In the 1970s and 1980s considerable evidence accumulated implicating DDT as the principal agent responsible for eggshell thinning and consequent population declines (summarized in Cade et al. 1988).

A second Raptor Research planning conference was held from 7 to 9 November 1969 at Cornell University. The most recent Peregrine data were presented and discussed. It was agreed that pesticide monitoring should continue and that Peregrine Falcon surveys should be initiated and repeated at five-year intervals until such time as populations had stabilized throughout their range in North America. Five-year surveys began in 1970 and continued until 1985–1986. From then until 2000, a more limited format prevailed.

In 1970, researchers and volunteers conducted the first North American Peregrine Falcon Survey. An attempt was made to check the occupancy of all previously known Peregrine nest sites. Before the survey's completion, it was evident that in Canada *F. p. anatum* had all but disappeared from its former range south of the boreal forest and east of the Rocky Mountains. By early July, we had nearly completed the survey of all previously known nest sites south of 60°N and had located only one nesting pair of *anatum* Peregrines (Cade and Fyfe 1970). Surveys also included previously known nest sites of *F. p. tundrius* and *F. p. pealei*. In these races the evidence indicated declines in some localities but no overall declines in either race.

CWS began monitoring toxic chemical residues in Canadian wildlife in the early 1960s. By 1966 we had monitored residue levels in birds of prey and their prey species. In 1967 we began specifically using Prairie Falcons and Merlins as indicator species for long-term monitoring of residue trends in western Canadian ecosystems. Following the identification of elevated mercury residues in wildlife in 1969, CWS began working more closely with other agencies monitoring pesticides and researching the potential effects of new chemicals on the environment.

The initial 1970 North American Peregrine Falcon Survey indicated that south of 60°N latitude and east of the Rocky Mountains, the *anatum* Peregrine had been almost extirpated as a breeding bird. Available data suggested the decline was due to the accumulation of chemical residues of DDT and its metabolites as well as other toxic chemicals ingested from prey. It is generally accepted that the source of the residues in the Peregrines was their prey species (Enderson et al. 1982). In turn, the prey species probably picked up the residues in areas where the chemicals were either used extensively or where residues accumulated in organic material, e.g., in some river estuaries. These pollutants were responsible for eggshell thinning and a resulting lack of production in wild populations. Following the 1980 and 1981 monitoring for toxic chemical residues in Peregrine eggs and prey species, it was possible to compare earlier data with the more recent samples. These comparisons indicated some improvement in the current level of DDE residues in Canadian Peregrines. However, it was clear that some of the Peregrines that had been sampled were still accumulating high

Figure 6.4 Richard Fyfe and his wife, Lorraine, dissecting samples in Suriname for pesticide analysis.

enough levels of organochlorines to affect production adversely. In contrast, samples of tundra Peregrines from the eastern and central Arctic had lower residue levels, which should not have adversely affected reproduction.

Although some prey species had elevated levels of DDE in their tissues, it was unknown which prey species accounted for the majority of the contamination in Peregrines or which areas in the wintering range contributed significantly to the contamination. In the same context, it was unknown what percentage of these residues the Peregrines accumulated during migration, on the wintering range, or on the breeding grounds. Research data indicated that whole body residue levels of 1 ppm DDE wet weight in prey species are sufficient to allow predatory birds to accumulate levels that affect reproduction (Enderson et al. 1982). Similarly, research by Peakall et al. (1975) indicated that a level of 15 to 20 ppm DDE in the eggs is associated with 20% eggshell thinning and in turn reproductive failure. In this context, the limited Canadian sampling from 1981 indicated that residue levels in the prey species in all areas but one were sufficient to be of concern.

Regulations regarding use of persistent chemicals such as organochlorines and mercury were modified so that in general they no longer posed a serious threat in the United States and Canada. However, the principal use of organochlorines, DDT in particular, had

shifted to the developing countries where these chemicals had widespread use in tropical and subtropical regions. In response, CWS initiated an experimental monitoring project of prey species in the wintering range through a cooperative project in Suriname in 1979 and 1980 (Fyfe et al. 1990).

In 1981, the Western Raptor Technical Committee recommended that CWS continue monitoring residues in Canadian Peregrine populations and in their principal prey species. These data were necessary prior to initiating new reintroductions and to identify which prey species might contribute significant residue levels to wild Peregrines. Consequently CWS continued monitoring residues in Peregrine populations and the cooperative monitoring program of Peregrine prey species in the wintering range in Peru and Ecuador during 1983 and 1984, and in Panama and Costa Rica during 1984 and 1985. Following Fyfe's retirement in 1987, this program continued in Mexico and Venezuela (Banasch et al. 1992).

Captive Breeding and Reintroduction

As project leader, Richard Fyfe was granted permission to attend the 1970 Federal/Provincial Wildlife Directors annual meeting in Yellowknife to advise the directors of the survey results. He indicated that although a few pairs could be expected in the Mackenzie Valley, the *anatum* Peregrine was near extinction in Canada. He fur-

... the principal use of organochlorines, DDT in particular, had shifted to the developing countries where these chemicals had widespread use in tropical and subtropical regions.

ther indicated that Peregrine researchers were convinced that pesticide contamination was the cause of this decline and that in order to effect recovery of this species, it was necessary to decrease DDT contamination in the environment. However, Fyfe also indicated that with pending restrictions on DDT use, this factor would likely no longer be a threat to Peregrines. Nevertheless, it was clear that unless a small number of the remaining *anatum* birds were taken into captivity, this race could become extinct in the wild before lower pesticide levels permitted recovery.

In a closed meeting, Fyfe then specifically asked the directors for permission to take a small number of young *anatum* Peregrines into captivity from any nests we could locate. CWS was granted permission and was directed to take a small number of young Peregrines into captivity to maintain the *anatum* gene pool. Unlike in the U.S. Eastern Peregrine Falcon Recovery Program, which reintroduced Peregrines of different subspecies, it was made clear that our mandate was to work only with the *anatum* race of Peregrines.

In Canada, CWS, a branch of the federal government, initiated this project. In the United States, however, the captive-breeding program was initiated as a private project associated with Cornell University and later extended to the University of California, Santa Cruz. The Canadian project encountered heavy opposition from the beginning. Many of our peers, naturalists, and members of the public believed it was impossible to breed falcons in captivity. A few were extremely vocal in their condemnation of what we were doing. Others felt we should leave the birds to their fate in the wild. Some even suggested it was cruel to take such free-spirited birds into captivity for the remainder of their lives. Ironically, however, throughout the project the biggest hurdles to overcome were from within CWS itself. As a government agency, we competed annually with other CWS projects for both funding and manpower. Each year we lived in fear of budget cuts because most of the basic project requirements and costs were fixed. This was further complicated by several changes in the administrative staff over the lifetime of the project. Each change tended to bring new ideas and priorities.

This project was always an easy target because it was not one of the traditional areas of responsibility for CWS. Traditionally CWS had been primarily concerned with migratory game species. Consequently many of our peers and managers disagreed with diverting funding and effort into nongame species projects. They definitely did not want to divert funding and effort into research on birds of prey since raptorial birds were a provincial and territorial responsibility. We received constant reminders of this dilemma and were aware that it was a serious concern to our administrators. During Fyfe's tenure, three different directors personally informed him that this project was to be terminated. Fortunately the project outlasted those directors.

How were we able to initiate and maintain this project in such an environment? It was because we were fortunate to have had immediate supervisors who not only supported us but also guided us through the administrative hurdles necessary to initiate and maintain the project. In particular, Tony Keith looked after our interests in the CWS head office, and Ward Stevens guided and encouraged us and fought many administrative battles on our behalf in the regional office.

At the initiation of this project, we were unaware of any *anatum* birds in captivity in Canada. Consequently we were obliged to obtain the majority, if not all, of the birds for the project from the wild. The first 12 young Peregrines originated from nests along the Mackenzie River, the southern Yukon, Labrador, and southern Alberta. These young were taken into captivity specifically to maintain the *anatum* gene pool (which by conventional definition extended through all of Canada south of the tundra zones, excluding the Pacific coast of British Columbia) to find methods of captive breeding; and to determine methods for reintroduction, should captive breeding be successful.

▲ **Figure 6.5** Keith Hodson (below) holds dead young found in nest near Bathurst Inlet, Northwest Territories.

Richard Fyfe

Black Diamond Peregrines

John A. Campbell

Like most raptor biologists and falconers, I knew the Peregrine was in danger of extinction in the 1960s. I decided to try to prevent this possibility from happening.

In the winter of 1966, I researched Peregrine records for Canada. At that time, Peregrines were considered of little value, or worse yet, as pests. Bureaucrats and non-raptor biologists were as yet unaware that Peregrine populations had crashed on two continents.

I discovered that the Yukon and Porcupine Rivers had recorded Peregrine sightings in the past. I decided to survey from Dawson to Fort Yukon on the Yukon River and then up the Porcupine River to Old Crow, a distance of about 700 miles. On this trip we found over 30 nests averaging 2.5 young. I wanted to take some eyasses, and this is how I obtained my breeding stock.

At first the pair I kept did not breed successfully. However, I made another trip to Old Crow in 1969 and obtained another tiercel. By 1971 the falcon had not even laid eggs, and there was no sign of courtship. In 1972 I changed tiercels, and the new tiercel actively courted the falcon. She laid eggs, but unfortunately they were infertile. I left the pair together, and in 1973 they raised three young.

Between 1973 and 1985 I bred 85 young Peregrines at my ranch near Black Diamond, Alberta. They were moved near fledging by the Canadian Wildlife Service (CWS) or Provincial Fish and Wildlife personnel and released all across Canada from the Bay of Fundy in the east to Alberta. Some were added to breeding projects at the CWS project at Wainwright, Alberta, the University of Saskatchewan project, and The Peregrine Fund. In return, I was given some young birds from the CWS project to develop into breeding pairs.

My released birds returned to breed successfully in the wild at Arnprior, Ontario, Calgary, Alberta, and northern Alberta. One year a young falcon paired with an old tiercel of a breeding pair in Edmonton, but the old female returned a week later and drove the young bird off.

In another year a tiercel, which had been released six years earlier, suddenly appeared at a release site on the Red Deer River and jealously guarded the young birds from predators.

In working to develop successful breeding techniques, the thing I enjoyed and appreciated most was that all the breeders worked together to help each other. It helped that nearly all of us already knew each other because we were all falconers. If I had a problem I could phone breeders who had probably already solved it. It helped also that we all knew our birds individually and were totally dedicated. Nobody really cared who was success-

John Campbell *was one of the many falconers who contributed to the Peregrine restoration program.*

ful so long as we as a group were successful.

In spite of the above facts, bureaucrats and non-falconer biologists still thought Peregrines were impossible to breed in captivity and that we were all either selfish to try (breeding was just an excuse to have Peregrines before they became extinct) or foolish.

Falconers, however, knew that Renz Waller in Germany had successfully bred falcons during World War II, and Heinz Meng and other falconers had already succeeded in North America. Failing was not an option to us. We had to succeed before Peregrines became extinct in the wild.

With this cooperation and positive attitude we succeeded in developing techniques in the remarkably short time of 10 to 15 years. Without the help and cooperation of all breeders, successfully breeding Peregrines in captivity would have been much harder and taken much longer to do. I greatly appreciated all of the help given me by other breeders, and I enjoyed working with them all.

> *Failing was not an option to us. We had to succeed before Peregrines became extinct in the wild.*

▲ **Figure 6.6** Adult Peregrine in outdoor pen at Wainwright.

Initially our major concerns were to obtain *anatum* young from the wild and to develop methods for the successful husbandry of these birds in captivity. We had to house the birds, locate someone to care for them, and provide a suitable food supply. To provide temporary housing, we converted farm buildings into holding pens on Fyfe's private acreage. Our manpower problem was solved during the first year when we hired Keith Hodson, a young graduate student from British Columbia with a falconry background. He lived in a converted van in the yard and took over the maintenance of the falcons. Our initial source of food was poultry, which we purchased from packing houses and other sources.

In 1971, the second year of the project, we obtained more young birds and simply converted more of Fyfe's sheds and granaries to house them. Keith went back to university, and Phil Trefry, a young falconer, was hired to care for the birds. To provide a residence for Phil, CWS purchased a trailer that was temporarily placed on

Fyfe's acreage. Another food source was secured with the provision of spent breeding pheasants, thanks to the assistance and cooperation of the Alberta Fish and Wildlife Division. Subsequently, after discussions in 1976 with the Alberta Fish and Wildlife Division, they agreed to raise and provide live Japanese Quail and spent pheasants as a food supply for the project. This arrangement continued until we began raising quail at the facility in 1986.

From the onset, we agreed that we needed to establish a permanent facility for the project. Our choice of a site was limited as it needed to be on government land and had to have access to full facilities, i.e., power, natural gas for heating, water, and sewage disposal. After several months and a considerable amount of time spent investigating possible locations, a suitable site was located on the Department of National Defense Camp Wainwright base in east-central Alberta.

In designing the breeding facility, we decided to construct large outdoor pens to house the breeding birds, plus a single two-story heated

Richard Fyfe

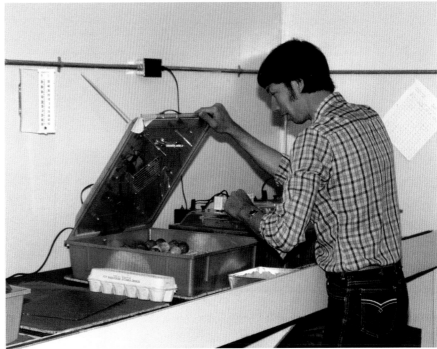

Richard Fyfe

building to house a shop, incubators, and a small number of indoor pens. Construction of the facility began in 1971. By the fall of 1972, the trailer in Fyfe's yard was moved to the facility to provide housing for staff. The project had 40 falcons. With the completion of much of the facility in 1972, Phil Trefry and all of the birds were moved to the new facility.

Once the birds were housed, problems related to overwintering, establishing pair-bonds, egg-laying, copulation, and artificial incubation had to be overcome. Although many of these concerns were solved, problems related to the establishment of pair-bonds and aspects of artificial incubation remain to this day. Throughout the project, the greatest risk was the ever-present concern of disease at the facility.

Over several years, we attempted to increase the gene pool of *anatum* birds by acquiring a small number of young from northern Alberta, the Yukon, and the Northwest Territories. At the same time, through the cooperation of the provincial and territorial wildlife agencies, we also obtained several pairs of Prairie Falcons and Gyrfalcons. These birds were used specifically for experimental pairing, breeding, incubation, and initial releases. The larger falcons also functioned as foster incubators. Falconers donated a few falcons to the project. A small number of Merlins, Cooper's Hawks, and Sharp-shinned Hawks were acquired for breeding and incubation experiments.

Today captive breeding is widely practiced by many private individuals who breed a wide range of falcons and other raptors. It must be almost beyond understanding for those involved in cap-

tive breeding today to appreciate the lack of information available to us when we began. Just to put things in perspective, the following list gives an idea of some of the knowledge we lacked:

- We had little or no knowledge of whether these birds would pair in captivity.
- We did not know if mates could remain in the same pens for any length of time, let alone when to introduce them to one another.
- We soon learned that in some species females killed the males. This seemed to depend on when the mates were introduced to each other.
- We did not know if they would breed in small cages or if they required large flight pens.
- We did not know if the males required escape areas to get away from aggressive females.
- We did not know if they could or would breed within sight or sound of one another.
- We did not know the effects of disturbance.
- We did not know if we could overwinter them outdoors at our latitude or if we would have to house them indoors.

If they did breed,

- We did not know if we could increase production by double-clutching, as occurs when first sets are removed in the wild, or if we could practice sequential egg pulling in order to get a larger number of fertile eggs.
- We did not know if it was possible to collect semen from males and inseminate females artificially.

And

- We certainly did not dream it would be possible to get semen voluntarily from imprinted male falcons.

◀ **Figure 6.7** Aerial photograph of CWS facility showing outdoor pens shortly after construction.

▲ **Figure 6.8** Phil Trefry checks incubating Peregrine eggs, 1983.

Figure 6.9 Richard Fyfe collects wild-laid Peregrine eggs with high DDT/DDE residue and thin shells for incubation and hatching at Wainwright.

Richard Fyfe

. . . releases provided a unique opportunity for excellent public relations, not only for Peregrines but for all endangered species.

The initial breeding success for this project came in 1972 with captive Prairie Falcons. In 1973, just one year after the move to Wainwright, we had four pairs of *anatum* Peregrines of breeding age, and two pairs copulated. Although we obtained 18 eggs, only six were fertile but no young hatched. Successful breeding occurred in 1974 with the production of five *anatum* Peregrine young of which four survived.

In 1975, two years after our initial Peregrine breeding success, 18 young were fledged and initial experimental releases were attempted. Our intent was to explore the feasibility of release and at the same time determine which methods might be used for the successful reintroduction of young back to the wild. We fostered six captive-bred young to the few remaining wild *anatum* pairs in northern Alberta (Fyfe et al. *in* Temple 1977). At the same time, to increase the gene pool of the captive birds, we exchanged captive-bred young from the project with young from some of the remaining wild pairs. In 1976, experimental hacking of 36 young occurred in Edmonton, Hull, Black Diamond, Montreal, and one previously known nest site on the North Saskatchewan River. Subsequently other experimental releases were carried out in both rural and urban areas using methods such as fostering, cross-fostering, hacking, and multiple hack releases. In general, all of these methods were found to be feasible; however, fostering and hacking became the principal methods of release in Canada as elsewhere in North America.

The reintroduction program was well received in Canada. The provincial wildlife agencies and

World Wildlife Fund soon realized these releases provided a unique opportunity for excellent public relations, not only for Peregrines but for all endangered species. One fascinating sideline to the success of the captive breeding and the good public relations was the dramatic change in attitude of the provincial agencies. In Canada, the jurisdiction for birds of prey rests with the provinces and territories. Consequently we had to obtain permission from these jurisdictions to conduct raptor surveys and to collect pesticide samples. Initially these requests were given an instant blessing by the provinces and territories because they were not working in these areas and appeared to have little or no intention of becoming involved.

Following the successful captive breeding and initial releases, we visited all provincial wildlife agencies from Alberta to the Maritimes to ask if they wished to become involved in the release program. We received most encouraging responses. Alberta, Saskatchewan, Manitoba, and Ontario all chose to participate. Quebec and the Maritime provinces were comfortable with the program but decided they would prefer CWS to carry out the releases. In addition, David Bird of McGill University indicated he would like to release birds in Montreal; Parks Canada indicated it would like to release birds in Fundy National Park, New Brunswick. All release sites received information kits, and often we were asked for advice relative to the releases. In particular, Ontario and Parks Canada requested that we visit the release sites and advise the project coordinators on release techniques and potential problems.

In 1976 some detractors of the program rightly pointed out that although captive breeding had been successful and the releases appeared to be working both here and in the United States, no evidence existed to indicate that released birds had returned to nest successfully in the wild. This was also a concern of our supporters and of CWS administration. Although we felt it was still too early to express these concerns, since few Peregrines breed before two to three years of age, we were aware that considerable time, effort, and funding had been directed into the project with no tangible results. In practical terms, the experimental releases were considered unsuccessful until we had evidence of captive-bred birds breeding in the wild. The first successful breeding of a captive-bred bird in the wild was documented in northern Alberta, in 1977 (Fyfe et al. *in* Temple 1977). This information essentially silenced detractors of the Peregrine captive-breeding projects and ensured continuation of the recovery program in Canada.

Project staff shipped young for release at about four weeks of age. They were grouped by age, the sexes were divided equally (unless a specific request was received for young of a particular sex), and to some extent the young were screened to ensure genetic diversity at release sites. All young were banded and detailed records kept on each bird produced and sent from the facility. Our staff maintained close contact with the liaison person at each release site to coordinate the releases. Most shipments occurred by air in specially designed wooden boxes. The liaison person was advised by telephone of the airline and flight times to eliminate problems and potential losses in shipping. Our responsibility ended there, and the respective agencies carried out the releases.

Hack releases occurred at both rural and urban sites. Usually sites were selected using several criteria: location of suitable release locations, availability of prey, availability of suitable nest ledges, preliminary assessment of avian predators, and relative proximity to previously known Peregrine nest sites. Urban releases were carried out beginning in1976. They became popular because of the excellent opportunity for public relations, relative absence of avian predators, and availability of potential observers to report returning birds. It is of interest to note that the urban and rural releases had almost identical fledging success rates of 88 and 89%, respectively. This similarity suggested that perhaps the advantages of urban over wild releases were offset to some extent by the apparent losses to misadventure, such as injuries at fledging, hitting glass windows in office towers, and falling down chimneys.

Following the initial captive-breeding success with the Peregrines, production increased steadily into the 1980s (Table 6.1). The average age of introduction into the hack box varied from 31 to 33 days of age. Average confinement in the box varied from 11 to 16 days, which included the time from the day the birds were introduced until the day the door or bars were removed. The resulting average age of release varied from 43 to 48 days of age. Following release, the young tended to remain in the area for 23 to 28 days with the age of departure usually between 66 and 75 days (CWS unpubl. data).

In the first 17 years of operation, the best productivity was in 1981 with 99 young fledged (Table 6.1). However, by 1981 our main breeders averaged about 11 years of age, and while they still showed high fertility, they laid fewer viable eggs and fewer young fledged. Production then began

◀ **Figure 6.10** Hack box at the Kananaskis site on release day, 6 July 1980.

Julie Bauer

Table 6.1 Productivity of *anatum* Peregrine Falcon pairs at CWS facility from 1973 to 1987 (figures in brackets indicate number of pairs copulating/ laying) (CWS unpubl. data).

Year	No. pairs	No. eggs laid	No. young hatched	No. young died	No. young fledged	No. young released	No. young held
1973	4 (2)	18	0	0	0	0	0
1974	6 (2)	32	5	1	4	0	4
1975	7 (5)	66	18	0	18	6	12
1976	9 (6)	100	42	1	41	36	5
1977	10 (7)	106	40	2	36	31	7
1978	7 (6)	82	46	6	40	33	7
1979	11 (10)	121	45	6	39	33	6
1980	16 (13)	174	100	10	90	88	2
1981	17 (14)	170	104	5	99	92	7
1982	21 (16)	208	93	16	77	62	15
1983	20 (13)	208	54	4	50	46	5
1984	22 (14)	214	90	11	79	78	1
1985	24 (12)	230	81	13	68	61	7
1986	22 (12)	229	76	7	69	64	5
1987	20 (14)	192	80	3	77	74	3
Totals		2150	874	85	787	704	86

to fall, possibly owing principally to the age of our breeding birds. Maintaining production for releases across the country was a serious concern. Therefore, in 1983 we began experimenting with new pairings by mating young inexperienced birds or noncopulating egg-layers with our older, experienced birds. Our purpose was to bring more young birds into full breeding condition with the hope that production would increase. If not, we knew we would have to resort to artificial insemination, which is labor intensive and would therefore present new problems for the project.

▲ **Figure 6.11** Female of the last *anatum* pair known in Alberta, brooding young in the spring of 1970.

We managed to continue the releases but at a somewhat lower level than in 1981 (Table 6.1). In 1987, a review of past production and release data for the facility indicated we had produced 789 Peregrines of which 704 had been released. The majority (532) were hacked in rural and urban releases, 155 were fostered, 13 were cross-fostered, and four were released by falconers. Available information suggested an additional 217 Peregrines had been produced at the three other Canadian facilities involved in the *anatum* Peregrine Falcon Recovery Program (Black Diamond, University of Saskatchewan, and McGill University).

With increased provincial and territorial involvement in the early 1980s, there was a growing recognition of the need for a Canadian *anatum* Peregrine Falcon Recovery Plan. Fyfe was asked to prepare an initial recovery plan document, which was then circulated to the provinces and territories. This document was modified to form the basis for the final recovery plan. A Canadian *anatum* Peregrine Falcon Recovery Team was formed in 1986 and met for the first time in Montreal. This team was responsible for the continuing work and eventual success of the *anatum* Peregrine recovery in Canada.

We think it is fair to say that no one person or agency alone deserves the credit for the success of this recovery project. The goal throughout the program was to return Peregrines to the wild. The excellent cooperation of many persons and agencies made this program successful. The success of the several Peregrine recovery projects is an example of what can be done if all agencies work together for the welfare of the resource.

Operation Falcon

In 1985, the entire project was placed in jeopardy with the disclosure that Richard Fyfe had been listed as a suspect in a falcon smuggling operation (code named Operation Falcon) being investigated by the U.S. Fish and Wildlife Service (FWS). Accusations made against Fyfe, Tom Cade, and several other prominent falcon breeders, in particular by one British culprit who escaped from Canada to Saudi Arabia and was never apprehended, were so vicious and unbelievable that it remains inexplicable to this day how law-enforcement officials could have considered them probative leads for further investigation. But both American and Canadian operatives were all too ready to give credence to slander. The history and social pathology of Operation Falcon and its influence on conservation and biological research have been well documented by Shor (1984, 1988) and McKay (1989).

As a result of allegations made by suspects to an undercover informer, Fyfe's name was included in a document circulated in the United States and internationally (correspondence and documents from J. Ruos 03/04/85). Based on these slanders, CWS and provincial wildlife agencies began investigations of Fyfe and the CWS captive-breeding program. We believe it is reasonable to suggest that had they found any impropriety, the program would have been terminated.

Within CWS, the investigation took the form of an audit wherein every adult bird, egg, and chick was accounted for. These data were gathered and then arranged and rearranged to various formats requested by the enforcement staff. The audit took roughly six months to complete and was an arduous and stressful time for all staff involved.

It should be clear that throughout the investigation Fyfe was the only suspect, and at no time were any members of his support staff under investigation (correspondence from G. Kerr to Hugh Monahan 04/29/86). The internal audit was concluded in 1986, and the Wainwright staff members were cleared of any impropriety; however, CWS then requested that a criminal investigation of Fyfe be carried out by the Royal Canadian Mounted Police (RCMP). To the best of our knowledge there was no evidence to suggest Fyfe was implicated, and the investigation was eventually terminated.

Although the entire investigation was based on hearsay and there was no evidence against Fyfe, Operation Falcon cast a long shadow on the CWS captive-breeding program. The wide dissemination of the document listing Fyfe as a suspect, the concurrent investigations by CWS and provincial enforcement staff, and the subsequent RCMP criminal investigation were devastating to self-esteem, and Fyfe's personal reputation and scientific credibility appeared to be shattered beyond repair.

Fyfe received an official letter of apology from his director for the grief he was put through and was informed he could remain with CWS but that his future was uncertain. Indeed, were he to remain, it was an open question if he or the project would receive essential support from an administration that had just requested his criminal investigation by the RCMP. Following

that investigation it was also questionable if Fyfe would be acceptable to cooperating provincial agencies as project leader of the program, let alone as a member of the proposed Canadian Peregrine Recovery Team. Richard Fyfe retired from CWS in 1987.

Following Fyfe's retirement, Geoff Holroyd moved from administration to head up the Peregrine Program (see Chapter 7).

Editors' Note: Thirteen years after his retirement, Richard Fyfe was fully vindicated. In April 2000 he was awarded The Order of Canada, the nation's highest civilian award, for his primary role in restoration of the *anatum* Peregrine in Canada. His work was also recognized in an interesting history of CWS, which Richard faithfully and honorably served for 25 years, published as a special feature in *The Canadian Field-Naturalist* (Burnett 1999). Richard Fyfe has the further distinction of being the only falcon breeder under suspicion and investigation by Canadian and U.S. authorities to be publicly exonerated by his government.

The success of the several Peregrine recovery projects is an example of what can be done if all agencies work together for the welfare of the resource.

Richard Fyfe, *B.A., C.M., is an environmental consultant and retired research scientist from the Canadian Wildlife Service. While working with the Canadian Wildlife Service (CWS) he was involved in toxic chemical monitoring in Canada and Latin America and coordinated the Canadian portion of the North American Peregrine Surveys. He was the Biologist in Charge of CWS Peregrine Breeding Program from 1970 until he retired in 1987. He was actively involved in international conservation and served as Chairman of the IUCN, ICBP Specialist Group on Birds of Prey from 1975 to 1982.*

Courtesy Richard Fyfe

Ursula Banasch, *B. Sc., has been a biologist with CWS since 1972. She has worked in the western Arctic, Alberta, Saskatchewan, Manitoba, Costa Rica, Panama, Mexico, Venezuela, Ecuador, and Peru. There she studied mainly Peregrine Falcons as well as other raptor species. After Richard Fyfe's retirement she managed the Peregrine Falcon captive-breeding facility.*

Sam Barry

Harry Armbruster *has been a wildlife technician with CWS since 1967 and has conducted fieldwork in western Canada and the Arctic. He has worked with Peregrine and Prairie Falcons, Swainson's and Ferruginous Hawks, Merlins, Piping Plovers, caribou, wolves, coyotes, swift fox, ungulates, and ground squirrels.*

Sam Barry

Chapter 7

The Return of the *anatum* Peregrine to Southern Canada, 1985 to 2000 — A Personal Perspective

Geoffrey L. Holroyd

In 1999, after over 30 years in jeopardy, the anatum Peregrine Falcon was down-listed from endangered to threatened in Canada.

The 1995 national surveys found that falcon populations in the Yukon and Mackenzie Valley appeared to be stabilized at an estimated 400 pairs, and the number of pairs in southern Canada had increased to at least 162 pairs. The recovery of the *anatum* Peregrine Falcon population in Canada is a true conservation success story.

The Committee on the Status of Endangered Wildlife in Canada (COSEWIC) first listed the *anatum* Peregrine as endangered in 1979 at one of its first meetings. In fact, the Peregrine Falcon, along with the Whooping Crane, was an early icon of endangered species conservation in Canada. The story of the Peregrine's recovery in Canada is also the story of the development of the present-day administrative programs that benefit all species at risk in Canada. The return of the Peregrine illustrates what can be achieved when a diverse group of people pull together for the same objectives.

When I saw my first Peregrine Falcon at Long Point, Ontario, in the autumn of 1961, I had little idea how intimately part of my career would be interwoven with this falcon, other endangered species, and the many conservationists who were and are involved in its recovery. When I became directly involved in the Peregrine's recovery program in the mid-1980s, the species' recovery in Canada was well underway, yet just beginning in other ways. Captive breeding was proven and the techniques better understood. Although other initiatives had floundered, the federal captive-breeding facility at Canadian Forces Base Wainwright was successful and efficient, but staff were dispirited after several years of neglect by busy regional managers and unsuccessful experiments by dedicated staff.

After serious staff cuts to the Canadian Wildlife Service (CWS) in 1984–1985, regional managers reorganized the remaining staff, and I became Section Head of the newly formed Endangered

◀ Figure 7.1 *Peregrine in Cornwall* © R. B. Treleaven. Reproduction rights courtesy of Bill Heinrich.

▲ **Figure 7.2** Helen and Phil Trefry, 2003.

By the end of the decade, the improvements at the captive-breeding facility over the previous five years were paying dividends.

Species Section, effective 1 April 1985. The following week, on 9 April 1985, I traveled to the facility with Richard Fyfe and Ursula Banasch and met with the station's full-time staff, Harry Armbruster, Phil Trefry, and Helen Trefry. I remember my eagerness to help this dedicated group, but also some intimidation, since they knew more than I did about falcons, how to breed them, and how to release them. I was simply a newly assigned manager, eager to help.

The problems facing the Wainwright staff were many: an unfinished quail-rearing building, which was a shell with a dirt floor; no septic field, requiring a semimonthly trip with a "honey wagon," a task I never did volunteer for (apologies to Harry and Phil); aging breeding pens; an overcrowded falcon barn; an inadequate audio-visual system used to monitor mating behavior of pairs; regular disruption by interested visitors who arrived for tours; lack of accommodation for summer staff; and an aging, unreliable egg incubator. After several meetings that winter, Regional Director Gordon Kerr approved the capital expenditures to improve the facility and agreed to a minimum five-year mandate for the facility, to remove the anxiety of annual program reviews.

Over the next two years, we fixed all these problems and more. In the quail barn, under the direction of Harry and Phil, an in-floor heating system, quail pens, new incubators, and workshop were installed. Each month 1,000 quail were raised for consumption by the falcons and their young, eliminating the need to travel to the Alberta pheasant-breeding facility and to private breeders, (often half a day's drive away) and reducing the risks of inadvertently introducing disease. State-of-the-art closed circuit TV allowed staff to watch and

listen to the falcons to monitor behavior and determine where to conduct artificial insemination (AI). New, large breeding pens improved breeding success and eliminated crowding in the barn. A septic field was a welcome improvement that saved Phil and Harry from an unpleasant task. A large house trailer provided so much space for summer staff that a ping-pong table was installed.

In cooperation with the Wainwright town council and military base, we started the Wainwright and District Wildlife Society. The society, with Helen as a leader, hired summer staff to operate frequent tours onto the military base, reducing the need for staff to leave regular activities and adding to the community profile of the facility, which was suddenly a significant tourist attraction. Susan Popowich, our draftsperson, helped create an interpretive display in the falcon barn.

The construction of new breeding pens allowed the expansion of the number of falcon pairs and permitted the housing of more imprinted falcons. As staff became more skilled at AI and used falconry techniques to tame potential breeders, the number of unproductive pairs declined. The net effect was greater annual production of young. By the end of the decade, the improvements at the captive-breeding facility over the previous five years were paying dividends. The facility's staff shipped 130 young for release across Canada. In 1989, 1,149 visitors toured the breeding facility at Wainwright through the cooperating association.

The cost recovery funding arrived first in 1984. Before that, the federal government bore the total cost of the Wainwright facility. With the development of the recovery plan, the provincial governments agreed to cost-share the production of young falcons they received for release. By 1986, cost recovery funding and improved operational efficiencies of the Wainwright operation allowed us to review the manpower allocation at the facility. One of the few unpopular decisions I had to make was to reassign Harry Armbruster to Edmonton. Harry had done too good a job of making the facility efficient. A contractor operated the quail facility with cost recovery funds. Summer staff picked up the workload during the busy spring and summer. Other priority programs in Edmonton lacked adequate manpower, and Harry reluctantly moved to Edmonton where he has made valuable contributions to caribou, swift fox, Piping Plover, and other conservation programs.

The cost recovery funds for captive-raised falcons also allowed the breeding facilities of David Bird at MacDonald College, McGill University, and Lynne Oliphant and Patty Thompson at the

University of Saskatoon to get funds to operate. Although these two facilities produced fewer young than the Wainwright facility, they supplemented the number of young for release in critical years of mass hacks and diversified the number of captive breeding facilities with *anatum* genes during the years when the wild population was still fragile. (Protection of the gene pool was a goal of the recovery plan.)

The 1985 audit initiated because of Operation Falcon (see Chapter 5) accounted for all eggs, young, and adults that had ever been at the facility. The audit proved unimportant to the operation of the facility and to staff management but used significant amounts of time and energy that could otherwise have been devoted to the primary purpose of the program.

While the improvements to the breeding facility were being implemented, other administrative improvements were underway that would benefit the Peregrine program throughout Canada. In the mid-1980s, the Western Raptor Technical Committee drafted the *anatum* Peregrine Falcon Recovery Plan. Canada did not have a national program of recovery teams, even though the species had been classified at risk for many years. Under the leadership of Chuck Dauphine and Tony Keith and with the authority of the Federal-Provincial Wildlife Directors, a recovery program was being developed, ultimately called RENEW (Recovery of Nationally Endangered Wildlife). At the 1986 directors' meeting, the recovery plan was not approved because of concerns about the implied commitments and expenditures it carried. A disclaimer was added stating that no one had to do anything! The plan was finally approved at the directors' meeting in Tuktoyutuk in June 1987, the first such plan in Canada. But what good was a plan without a team to implement it?

At the 1986 International Ornithological Congress in Montreal, an informal meeting of Peregrine enthusiasts, chaired by Tony Keith, discussed several issues, including the composition of the yet-to-be-formed recovery team. Some government biologists felt that only government representatives should be present. Joseph Hickey appropriately stated that the Peregrine recovery demanded that we gather all the interested people and resources possible, and that ultimately "them that pays, plays." Everyone who contributes should be a team member. One sore point was the ability of nongovernment biologists to criticize government actions publicly. The point was made that "them that plays" have to be and act as team players. If they do not like something, tell us, bring it to the meeting, but lay off

the counterproductive external criticism. The contentious issue at the time was the presence of Gyrfalcons, which along with Prairie Falcons were valuable as foster incubators at Wainwright. While some agencies saw any production of Gyrfalcons as a threat to private breeders, others believed the Gyrfalcons should be encouraged to produce as many young for falconers as possible. Team meetings were the place to resolve such differences, not the media.

The first recovery team meeting was hosted by David Bird at MacDonald College, McGill University, from 15 to 17 October 1986. Since Richard Fyfe had decided to retire, I chaired the first meeting; but Richard's absence was felt by all, and the team sent Richard a telegram to thank him for his efforts and leadership. The recovery team's task was to recover the *anatum* Peregrine Falcon in Canada by implementing the recovery plan. The plan's stated goals were to have 10 pairs of Peregrine Falcons producing 15 young annually in five of six "management zones" by 1997. The overall strategies of the plan were to identify management problems, recommend solutions, prioritize annual actions, and identify responsibilities and costs for the actions.

▲ **Figure 7.3** Pop, a captive-bred tiercel released in downtown Winnipeg, Manitoba, in 1986 (see family tree on page 121).

▲ **Figure 7.4** Madame on the edge of a nest box on the Delta Winnipeg Hotel (now Radisson Hotel Winnipeg Downtown), 2001.

Because the 1985 survey showed that relatively few pairs had established themselves in southern Canada, the team agreed to change the release strategy. Before the team meetings, falcons were distributed as equitably as possible to provinces that requested them. Although some large numbers had been released at a few sites, on average fewer than five young had been released per site per year. With a 10.5% return rate, many releases never had a falcon return, and about half of the sightings of returned falcons were of single falcons, which appeared never to find a mate. The team also recommended that releases focus in rural areas rather than higher-profile urban sites. In part, the low population in the 1980s was the result of a dispersed release strategy and the movement of Canadian released falcons to the United States. One example of the frustrations of those years is this account in the 1 July 1989 *Globe and Mail* newspaper by bird columnist Peter Whelan: "After lingering in Toronto all winter, a female falcon flew off—home to Detroit where she had been released in the campaign to revive Peregrine populations . . . the female from Quebec drove off the Detroit female, who then moved to Toledo, Ohio, where an Ontario female was in residence." Peregrines had been released in Ontario, and others had wintered there, but relatively few bred in the province.

On 25 June 1986, George Finney, then regional director of CWS-Atlantic Region, met with Monte Hummel, President of World Wildlife Fund Canada (WWFC), with a request that it help fund large-scale releases on the Bay of Fundy. The following day, Hummel, in his typically efficient manner, sent a fund-raising proposal to corporations requesting their support. True to form, the following year WWFC cosponsored releases near

the Bay of Fundy in New Brunswick and Nova Scotia, coordinated by Bruce Johnson of CWS.

Earlier mass hack releases in eastern Ontario and adjacent Quebec, organized by Iola Price, Chuck Dauphine, Michel Lepage, and others, had resulted in a cluster of nesting Peregrines in the St. Lawrence and Ottawa Valleys. Additional hacks, organized by Ted Armstrong, were continued to bolster this small population. Naturalist groups such as the McNamara Naturalists provided funding and manpower support to assist these releases. David Bird's facility at McGill University produced fewer young, but David was a master at ensuring that the entire city of Montreal was aware of the pairs that did nest there. His regular TV and newspaper columns made the public aware of many wildlife conservation issues.

In Manitoba, tireless Bob Nero released small numbers of Peregrines from buildings in Winnipeg and nearby cities. He was rewarded with a nesting pair that eventually grew in 1995 to four urban pairs, which were often successful.

In Saskatchewan, Lynne Oliphant and Patty Thompson successfully bred Peregrines at the University of Saskatoon and supplemented the large releases across Canada. In addition, they successfully established a pair of Peregrines in Saskatoon and Regina.

By 1992, the mass hacks had ended in the Maritimes, and Alberta had geared up to accept more young falcons. Both the declining levels of DDT/DDE and an assessment of prey populations in southern prairie Alberta indicated that this region of high plains was now ready to accept the return of the Peregrine. From 1992 to 1996, 223 captive-raised falcons were released in southern Alberta by a provincial recovery team led by Steve Brechtel, Alberta Environment. By 1996, 15 pairs

Manitoba Peregrine Family Tree

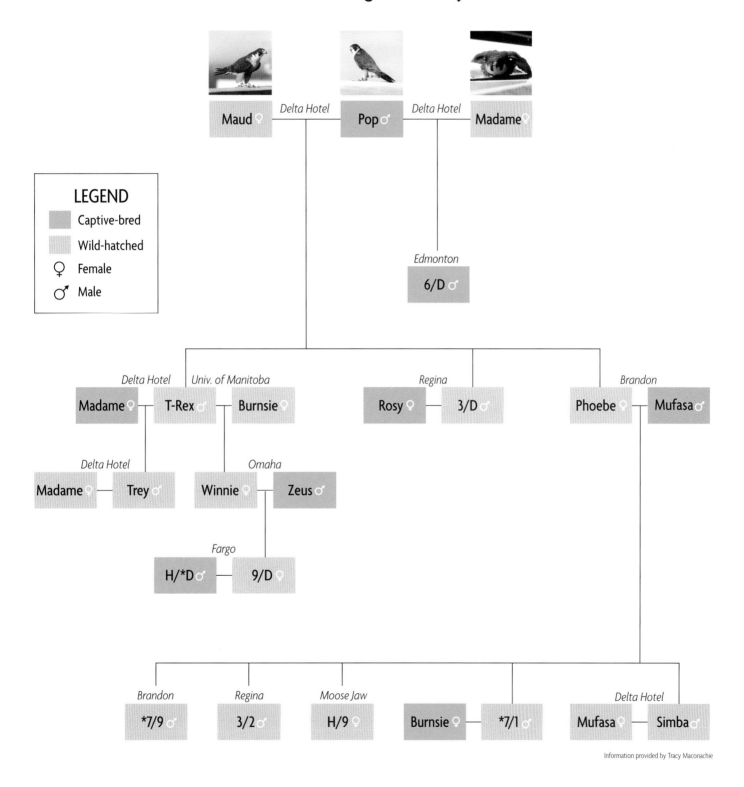

LEGEND
- Captive-bred
- Wild-hatched
- ♀ Female
- ♂ Male

Delta Hotel   Maud ♀

Pop ♂

Delta Hotel   Madame ♀

Edmonton
6/D ♂

Delta Hotel   Madame ♀   T-Rex ♂   Burnsie ♀   *Univ. of Manitoba*

Regina   Rosy ♀   3/D ♂

Brandon   Phoebe ♀   Mufasa ♂

Delta Hotel   Madame ♀   Trey ♂

Omaha   Winnie ♀   Zeus ♂

Fargo   H/*D ♂   9/D ♀

Brandon   *7/9 ♂

Regina   3/2 ♂

Moose Jaw   H/9 ♀

Burnsie ♀   *7/1 ♂

Delta Hotel   Mufasa ♀   Simba ♂

Information provided by Tracy Maconachie

▲ **Figure 7.5** Family tree showing progress of Peregrine restoration in Manitoba, Canada, beginning with the release of Pop in 1986.

Figures 7.6 and 7.7 T-Rex as ▶ a juvenile on the Delta Winnipeg Hotel in 1989 (right) and at the University of Manitoba in 1990 (opposite page). One of Manitoba's more charismatic Peregrines, his nickname reflects his fierce protectiveness of his chicks.

Robert R. Taylor

of falcons had established themselves in southern Alberta, and that year half of the adults were from captive-bred falcons. The other breeders were fledged from wild nests, fostered, or of unknown origin. By 2000, 23 territories were occupied.

In British Columbia, Peregrines appeared on the Gulf Islands, but their origins were unknown. Lingering concerns about high DDE levels in the Okanagan Valley precluded consideration of releases until later in the decade, when a nonprofit group headed by Mary Krupa released captive-raised falcons from buildings in Kelowna. Sightings of falcons in 2000 and 2001 indicate that these releases may reintroduce the species to south-central British Columbia, one of the last regions in Canada to be reoccupied by Peregrines.

David Peakall, a toxicologist with CWS in Ottawa, proposed to the team that we support a 1990 special issue of *The Canadian Field-Naturalist* on Peregrines. That 1990 issue (Vol. 104, No. 2) summarized Peregrine conservation topics to that time: the status of the population to 1985, toxicology levels, and issues to date. The issue profiled the Peregrine and became a core reference for conservation work on Peregrine Falcons in Canada.

The recovery team continued to meet annually, moving its meetings among most of the provinces to encourage local involvement. The minutes of the team meetings are not exactly prime reading, but they do reflect the issues that involved team members through the 1990s. They reflect the activities promoted in the recovery plan but often do not reflect the same priority listed in the plan. In addition to monitoring populations, protecting the *anatum* gene pool through three captive flocks, and conducting releases, the plan promoted other activities to ensure the Peregrine's recovery.

Education was always a busy topic as each agency had cultured public interest in the recovery of the falcon through mass media, posters, buttons, teachers' manuals, education kits, videos, and eventually websites. Closed-circuit monitors were put on a Peregrine nest in 1987 in Edmonton by Cam Finlay, then of Edmonton Parks and Recreation. The video fed into office lobbies in Edmonton and Calgary. The plight of the Peregrine was put in context. This was a human-caused problem; the result of naive use of a persistent pesticide as presented in Rachel Carson's book *Silent Spring*. But if we wanted to keep Peregrines, we also needed to conserve healthy wetlands for their prey and keep nest sites secure and undisturbed.

In the 1980s studies by Richard Fyfe and Ursula Banasch of DDT contamination in Peregrine prey species in Latin America found the highest levels in Peru and Ecuador. However, David Peakall and Gordon Court published reports that showed declining levels of DDT/DDE in Peregrines across

Canada and in Alberta, respectively. Peregrine eggshells were thicker, and broken eggs were a thing of the past. The team's emphasis on toxicology declined with retirement of Richard and David and the lower levels detected in salvaged eggs. Gordon and fellow Alberta biologists have continued to analyze unhatched eggs and to confirm the declining trends in DDT levels.

The goal to protect Peregrines from disease and disaster was implemented by maintaining a list of veterinarians who had experience with injured wild falcons and were willing to assist in the recovery of individual falcons. When dead falcons were found, a protocol for shipping the carcasses for necropsy was also prepared and circulated.

One high-priority activity that was only partially addressed by the team was the protection of foraging habitats. Protection of nesting sites was relatively easy, and provincial agencies had no-entry, no-disturbance zones around nest sites. Ontario produced guidelines for forestry operations around nest sites. Foraging habitats were more problematic. Although some data were collected on Peregrine prey, no telemetry studies were conducted to determine where nesting pairs foraged. Other programs such as the North America Waterfowl Management Plan (NAWMP) did protect wetlands; but the focus was on enhancing duck populations, and focal areas were far from nesting falcons. Although it can be argued that

NAWMP protected wetlands where migrating falcons hunt, there were no programs to protect foraging habitats in the breeding season or in winter. Of all the goals of the recovery plan, habitat protection was the least implemented.

High-priority activities were not always done because of lack of funds. Authority for RENEW is the Canada Wildlife Act, which is enabling, not mandatory, legislation. No new funding came with the growing concern about endangered species conservation. In addition, the Peregrine Falcon is not listed in the Migratory Bird Conservation Act of 1917. Thus the species was a lower priority for Environment Canada managers, despite its high public profile. Amazingly, the recovery effort proceeded despite the bureaucratic impediments. The recovery was accomplished because a wide array of professionals committed energy, time, and resources to the Peregrine's conservation needs and used all possible resources for the cause.

Significant amounts of funds were spent on Peregrine Falcon conservation. From 1988 to 1998, a total of $2.7 million and 67 person-years were contributed to the conservation of *anatum* Peregrine Falcons in Canada. Although this may seem like a lot, it is trivial compared with other wildlife programs such as the NAWMP. Also, the annual amount declined dramatically after 1996

Protection of nesting sites was relatively easy, and provincial agencies had no-entry, no-disturbance zones around nest sites.

123

with the end of large-scale captive-breeding and release programs.

Surprisingly, shooting was a frequent concern at the team meetings. Although the "bad" raptor was a thing of the past, fish and wildlife agencies reported Peregrines shot during most years. In 1991, two Peregrines were shot in Manitoba. In 1992, a Peregrine was shot near Atikokan, Ontario, and the shooter fined $25,000. In a 1995 review paper of raptor rehabilitation, Pat Redig and Gary Duke identified shooting as the fourth top cause of injury to 2,129 raptors, including 55 Peregrines, that were handled by 32 centers in the United States during 1994. One respondent to their questionnaire reported that shooting accounted for 70% of their admissions. In 1992, Lynn Oliphant canvassed Saskatchewan falconers

Ted Muir

▲ **Figure 7.8** Maud investigates researcher Robert Nero's offering on the roof of a building near the Delta Winnipeg Hotel nest site. She mated there with Pop and successfully produced three wild young.

Figure 7.9 (next page) ▶ Maud with her first chicks—the first wild offspring produced by the Peregrine Falcon Recovery Project in Manitoba since its inception in 1989.

and reported 10 falcons shot in 15 years; one falconry bird was shot for every 450 hours of flight, a worrying statistic if it represents the risk to wild falcons. In 2001, two falcons were shot in the Maritimes in midsummer, reflecting some residual, misguided attitude that raptors are "bad" and should be destroyed. These data led the recovery team to explore news releases, notices in hunting guidelines, magazine articles, and provincial announcements about the shooting of falcons.

Disturbance was also a concern as Peregrines established nest sites in southern Canada. In May 1989, Quebec had contracted with the Centre de Conservation du Mont Saint-Hilaire to monitor the breeding site established on the mountain, a popular climbing site. Chris Shank published an article in the annual magazine of the Alpine Club of Canada to alert climbers to the return of the Peregrine and encouraging climbers to stay away

from cliff faces with active nests during the breeding season.

Cooperation with the U.S. recovery efforts was always evident. The captive-breeding facility staff were in frequent contact with The Peregrine Fund staff most years to compare results, problems, and successes. Breeding stock was exchanged to enhance genetic diversity at both facilities. I visited The Peregrine Fund in 1992 to discuss the upcoming recovery effort in southern Alberta. The Peregrine Fund matched that effort with releases in eastern Montana. In Ontario, Ted Armstrong and his reintroduction and monitoring program to the north of Lake Superior had a great deal of support from the Midwest recovery program with identifying nest sites and banding young.

Annual management reviews of the federal captive-breeding facility continued despite approval of so-called five-year plans. Strapped for cash and staff, and with many other pressing conservation needs, all programs were reviewed regularly, and the falcon program was no exception. For example, in April 1993 I wrote to managers, at their request, about the impact of closing the facility within six months. However, the regional director had requested such a review of every project, not just the falcon program. Needless to say, the captive-breeding and reintroduction program survived until it had completed the task of returning Peregrines to southern Canada.

The 1990 and 1995 national surveys showed that Peregrines were reestablished across southern Canada and had stable numbers in the western boreal region of the Yukon and Northwest Territories. An estimated 400 pairs nested in the north, whereas in southern Canada the number of territorial pairs had grown to 105 in 1995.

Mass hacks were terminated in Canada in 1996, and that autumn the adult falcons from the Wainwright facility were dispersed free of charge to falcon breeders across the country. Although the recovery of the Peregrine and the end of the need to hack were a time of celebration, the closing of the captive-breeding facility was the end of an era in the CWS's Peregrine conservation story. In typical fashion, the Trefrys hosted a giant party complete with an outdoor play organized by Julie Ishida and the Wainwright Wildlife Society. The Trefrys' impact on the community was obvious as their many local and provincial friends gathered to congratulate them on a job well done. Only the roasted pig gave more for the celebration. The Trefrys moved to Upsanddowns, a farm near Edmonton. Phil took an early retirement so he could continue to breed falcons privately, although most of the young were provided to small releases and foster projects. Helen continues to work for CWS, spending most of her time on the conservation of Burrowing Owls and an annual trip to the Arctic to trap eiders.

Although the facility closed and staff were relocated, the legacy of the captive-breeding facility lives on. The Wainwright and District Wildlife Society continue to prosper. The Wildlife Society hosts meetings in town, is a steward of the local David Lake Natural Area, developed a local nature trail in town, and developed an extensive bluebird box trail. For two-and-a-half decades summer students received their first biology jobs at Wainwright. Many are now practicing biologists, all with a soft spot for falcons, and their friendship is a testament to the hospitality of the Trefrys, who always had fresh baked goods and refreshments available for staff and visitors alike.

CWS and the Edmonton Natural History Club cohosted a Peregrine evening in 1997 to celebrate the success of the Wainwright facility and the recovery of the Peregrine in Canada. CWS Director Gerald McKeating, who incidentally organized the first mass hacks in Algonquin Provincial Park, Ontario, presented each of the staff with awards from Environment Canada for their service to wildlife conservation.

In 1999, with relatively few pairs in southern Canada, the recent end to large-scale hacking programs, and the uncertainties of the proposed "harvest" of passage falcons in the United States, COSEWIC took the relatively infrequent step of disagreeing with the status report author and did not classify the Peregrine as at risk. The endangered status was improved to threatened. The 2000 national Peregrine survey showed continued increases in the number of Peregrines in southern Canada and stable numbers in the Mackenzie Valley and much of the Yukon. The decision to close the Wainwright facility was vindicated. A new status report will recommend a further improvement in the status designation.

In 2001, a new recovery strategy was drafted to guide the management of Peregrines after the proposed down-listing to Species at Risk. These species may have management plans, but the future of Peregrine management is somewhat uncertain. In Alberta, newly hired biologists bode well for management there. In Ontario, the Canadian Peregrine Foundation has taken a growing role in education, monitoring, and research in satellite telemetry. *Anatum* populations are monitored annually in some jurisdictions, every five years in others.

The *anatum* Peregrine recovery in Canada is the result of a 30-year odyssey by many dedicated staff, both at captive-breeding facilities at Wainwright, Saskatoon, and Montreal and across the country in virtually every province and major city. These people's dedication to the single purpose of returning this falcon to the wild was successful. As we continue with concerns with other endangered species, we can only hope we are as successful.

My thanks to Helen and Phil Trefry and Ursula Banasch for comments on this article.

> Although the facility closed and staff were relocated, the legacy of the captive-breeding facility lives on.

Geoff Holroyd *is a research scientist with the Canadian Wildlife Service, Environment Canada in Edmonton, Alberta. He is chair of the National Recovery Teams for Peregrine Falcons and Burrowing Owls and an adjunct professor at the University of Alberta.*

Chapter 8

Peregrine Falcon Restoration in the Rocky Mountains/Northwest

William Burnham

*P*eregrine recovery is a story about people and birds. This chapter documents the accomplishment and recalls the names and events of the Peregrine restoration in the Rocky Mountain/Northwest region of the United States. Unfortunately, space limitations mean only a small portion of those individuals who participated in this truly Herculean effort can be mentioned. The hack site attendants are listed in Chapter 14.

Prior to the mid-1960s few surveys were accomplished and only limited knowledge existed about Peregrines in the West. Bond (1946) provided what he called a "gloriously wild guess" that there were an estimated 750 pairs (including *pealei*) nesting in western North America with less than half in the United States. In the Rocky Mountains and Great Basin the species was considered "rare" (Enderson et al. 1988). Most known Peregrine nesting locations were along roads, in national parks, or other places people frequented (Burnham et al. 1988). The men contributing most importantly to the early knowledge of the Peregrine in the West were Richard M. Bond and Louis W. Walker. Both men were falconers and spent a great deal of time in the outdoors. Dick Bond was a trained scientist and graduate of Yale University who worked for the U.S. Soil Conservation Service. Lou Walker was a knowledgeable naturalist affiliated with the San Diego Natural History Museum. Neither man played a role beyond the survey and publication.

◀ **Figure 8.1** *Ready for Flight—Peregrine Falcon* ©Robert Bateman. Reproduction rights courtesy Boshkung Inc. and Mill Pond Press.

Jim Enderson

File photo

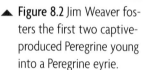

▲ **Figure 8.2** Jim Weaver fosters the first two captive-produced Peregrine young into a Peregrine eyrie.

Figure 8.3 Jerry Craig ▶ places captive-produced Prairie Falcons in a Prairie Falcon eyrie on Pawnee National Grasslands, Colorado, 1974.

In 1964 Jim Enderson carried out the first systematic survey of known Peregrine Falcon eyries in Alberta, Colorado, New Mexico, and Montana. He visited 51 sites, locating 15 pairs and four lone Peregrines (Enderson 1969). Other biologists and falconers, including myself, began searching for breeding Peregrine Falcons by the late 1960s, but we found very few pairs as the population decline continued. In 1979, of about 160 historical Peregrine Falcon breeding territories known in an area of about 4,000,000 sq km, including portions of Colorado, Idaho, Kansas, Montana, Nebraska, North Dakota, Oregon, South Dakota, northern Utah, and Washington, only 12 were found to be occupied by Peregrines. Use of DDT was banned in Canada in 1969 and the United States in 1972; probably because of the high level of DDT that remained in the environment and the few surviving Peregrines, however, population increases in Peregrines were not obvious until the mid-1980s when released falcons began breeding (Enderson et al. 1988).

Although the foundation was laid earlier, the restoration effort in the western states did not really begin until the early 1970s. In particular, 1973 was an important year. That spring Jim Enderson propagated the first three low-latitude *anatum* Peregrine Falcons at his home near Colorado Springs, Colorado (Cade 1988a). The next year, two Peregrines produced at The Peregrine Fund's Cornell facility were brought west by Jim Weaver and placed in an eyrie at Royal Gorge, Colorado, after the falcon's thin-shelled eggs broke. That was the first-ever release by fostering

of captive-produced Peregrine Falcons. Both young successfully fledged, and in a 25 July 1974 letter to Tom Cade, Jim Enderson reported, "Both are excellent fliers. I thought you should have seen them. Great to see!" (Cade 1974).

Also during the spring and summer of 1974, Prairie Falcons produced at Cornell were sent west for release. In the early years, the more common nonendangered Prairie Falcon proved a valuable surrogate for Peregrines. Jerry Craig and Jack Stoddart fostered the captive-produced nestlings into wild Prairie Falcon eyries, and Tom Smylie and Frank Bond hacked three Prairie Falcon fledglings from a "traditional hack house" near Tom's home at the foot of the Sandia Mountains in New Mexico (Cade 1974).

Colorado Days

In the fall of 1974, with the help of Jerry Craig, Wayne Sandfort, and Bob Tully, an agreement was struck between the Colorado Division of Wildlife (CDOW) and The Peregrine Fund in which The Peregrine Fund took control of a former research station near Fort Collins. The station had substantial facilities but was seldom used. Only a maintenance person who was preparing to retire was in residence, and one exiled, socially difficult biologist had an office there. Under Jim Weaver's direction and with $20,000 from the National Audubon Society (NAS) through a special grant from the trustees of the estate of Captain George Whittell, Jim began construction in October of the first "falcon barn" from which falcons would be produced to recover the western Peregrine population. We later were told Captain Whittell believed he would be reincarnated as a bird and his funds could go only to establish homes for feathered creatures. His dollars could have served no better purpose!

Helping with the construction of the first falcon barn was Jim's brother, John Weaver, as well as Bob Martin, Eric Strahl, and Willard Heck (then a Cornell student). Additional "barns" built in the following years were under Bob Martin's supervision, with the help of Bill Heinrich, Steve Tully, Tom Ray, Jerry Craig, and others. Martin left his hammer mark in the floor of one barn as a reminder of his work for us. Over time, Peregrines lived and bred in all 64 chambers of these five barns. After a visit by National Audubon Vice President Charlie Callison with co-workers Gene Knoder and Bob Turner, funds for the second barn again came from NAS, whereas Mrs. Cordelia Scaife May funded the third. Other donations also began to arrive. The first federal agency to participate financially was the Bureau of Land Management (BLM; thanks to Butch Olendorff) which, with the help of Bill Huey, Director of the New Mexico Game and Fish, helped encourage the U.S. Fish and Wildlife Service (FWS) to contribute $5,000 the next year. In the 1980s, at the direction of Congress, the contribution from the FWS was substantially increased. Following Butch's lead, others in BLM (Ed Roberts, Alan Thomas, and Mark Hilliard) continued to make the funds available. The first corporations to become actively involved were Exxon Company USA, Boise Cascade Corporation, and the J.R. Simplot Company.

On Christmas Eve 1974, Bill Mattox, with Jim Weaver and pilot Mike Sayers in an Ohio Division of Natural Resources airplane that Bill had somehow organized, arrived in Fort Collins with a cargo of falcons from Cornell for the newly completed barn. Telling his wife Joan he would be back in a little while, Bill went to the Ohio airport to deliver milkshakes and hamburgers to Mike and Jim while they refueled on their way from Cornell to Colorado. The next Joan heard from Bill was many hours later when he called from Kansas City where the plane next stopped to refuel. He arrived back home on Christmas Day. Peregrine restoration could be rough on spousal relationships!

Also on that Christmas Eve, I joined The Peregrine Fund as the western program's first and only employee, and Pat Burnham became the first volunteer. Our home was a three-room apartment above the garage and workshops at the CDOW facility. I was (we were) to raise the falcons and

Figure 8.4 Monument recognizing the donation from the Captain George Whittell estate and National Audubon Society to construct the first two falcon barns.

Figure 8.5 Mike Sayers and Bill Mattox unload their cargo of falcons for the new Fort Collins facility.

their food, provide round-the-clock security, maintain and clean the facilities and property, and "do anything else needing done." That quote was later to become part of every job description for the organization. The apartment came complete with chipped white enamel kitchen cabinets and a single gas burner for heat, plus toilet paper stuck in the cracks in the broken window glass to keep the winter winds and snow outside (later the CDOW provided funds for renovation). Despite the rather rustic conditions, we could not complain as Jim Weaver and Phyllis Dague lived upstairs in the Cornell hawk barn in a single room with not even a window and with the toilet downstairs.

A few days after Pat and I arrived at Fort Collins, Jim Weaver said goodbye and left for Cornell. As he departed he mentioned he had ordered two Roll-X incubators for me and good luck on the coming falcon breeding season. So much for my introduction to falcon propagation and The Peregrine Fund. Fortunately my background with birds of prey, electrical construction, and various other practical experiences helped me

Growing Up with Peregrines

Kurt K. Burnham

Growing up in The Peregrine Fund and with falcons was the greatest experience of my life. When I was three weeks old I saw my first Peregrine when it was set in my crib beside me. The Peregrine had hatched as I was being born; my father had been on the phone at the hospital explaining to my uncle how to help it along. That was in mid-May of 1975, and the young Peregrine was also named Kurt.

In grade school I was the only kid who knew 100 different ways to kill a Coturnix Quail. When friends came over to visit I never understood why they freaked out when I opened the fridge and there was a pile of stiff, lifeless quail next to the orange juice. In addition, I completely understood all about the birds and the bees, heck, not just the birds and bees but even artificial insemination (AI). I thought all kids liked to grind quail mush and that vacation was always getting to go to Padre Island to trap Peregrines or to grouse camp to hunt with falcons. These were just a few of the thrilling things a kid learned and got to do while growing up with Peregrines and The Peregrine Fund.

Looking back at the Peregrine Falcon's recovery in the western United States and The Peregrine Fund, I can recall many amazing memories and stories. What always seems to stick out the most, though, are the people and what they each added in their own way. In particular Cal Sandfort, Bill Heinrich, and

Bill Burnham

I thought all kids liked to grind quail mush and that vacation was always getting to go to Padre Island to trap Peregrines...

Pat and Bill Burnham, all of whom I have known for as far back as I can remember. I have been lucky to grow up around this tremendous group of people who have probably had more influence on my life than anything else.

During the 2001 falcon breeding season I helped out on a growth study on Peregrines in Cal's lab. Every morning for about 30 days I would go down to the lab and take measurements on young Peregrines and spend time talking with Cal and pestering him with questions. I was amazed at how many hours a day he spent in the lab feeding young and managing eggs and in the barns doing AIs. He seemed to be in the lab or barns from well

before dawn to well past dark; I am still not sure when he slept or if his family even knew he was alive. These types of hours for about 120 Aplomado Falcons amazed me. I cannot even comprehend the time it took him to hatch and raise over 2,000 Peregrines. In addition, he seemed to know each chick individually, and from my plethora of questions I quickly learned that hatching and raising falcons is an art, of which Cal is the greatest master of his time.

In October 2000 I was fortunate to have Bill Heinrich's help operating a fall trapping station on the west coast of Greenland. During that period Bill and I spent endless days trapping falcons and

untold nights drinking Aquavit and talking of falcons, life, and Bill's escapades releasing Peregrines throughout the western United States. It was the first time I ever had a chance to really understand Bill's deep-felt passion, commitment to his work, and sacrifices he had made in his life, all for the Peregrine. I gained a true appreciation of how important it is not only to have a job you love, but to also put everything you have into something and follow it through to completion. It is a great thing to see someone who not only is passionate about his job but also believes in what he is doing.

The little things are the glue that make work and life either go smoothly or fall apart, and Pat Burnham is epoxy. Working with and being around Pat has given me a chance to see how important it is to be willing not only to do your job but to always be ready to help out when someone else needs a hand and to pay attention to detail. I could list a thousand small things that by themselves do not amount to much, but added together these are the adhesive that bonds us together and enables us all to perform at a higher level.

Then there is Bill Burnham. My leader, my friend, and my father. Ever since I can remember, everything he has done has been for Peregrines. To this day I still think his ultimate drug is getting high off "sniffing" wildcaught falcons. His dedication has simply been amazing, and his attitude can be summed up by his answer to the question "What was one of the worst days of your life?" Bill's response, "I have never had a bad day." One of the things I pick up on fastest is how Bill is always positive and looking for the good things and a way to make them happen. As he says, paraphrasing someone else, "find similarities between people and their differences will be less important." I hope there are many similarities between Bill and me, as the greatest compliment I could ever receive is for someone to say, "You're just like your father."

I am truly grateful to be able to count these esteemed individuals among my best friends, and in one way or another they are all family. Knowing them has made me a better person, and I know I have learned a great deal from each of them. It can all perhaps be summed up by spending an evening with the two Bills. As the night grows long and the bottles of wine become empty and hollow, I watch as their eyes glaze over and they drift off to another world and begin talking about the days of trapping "beach birds" and of falconry birds from the past. Nowadays my eyes glaze over, too. I drift to the tundra of Greenland or the sands of South Padre, and it is still there—the addiction to the touch, the sound, and the smell of Peregrines.

Biographical information for Kurt can be found at the end of the sidebar, Dundas, in Chapter 14.

Bill Burnham

◀ **Figure 8.6** Pat Burnham—Peregrines were a part of everyday family life.

▼ **Figure 8.7** The first captive-produced Peregrine at the Fort Collins facility, 1975.

Brian Walton

File photo

▲ **Figure 8.8** Roger Smith (right) organized the first hack site in Colorado, although with captive-produced Prairie Falcons rather than Peregrines, and with convicts as hack site attendants, near Florence, Colorado, 1975.

figure out what needed doing and how to build and rebuild the equipment and do the hundreds of other things the job required. I was also grateful that Jim was there to answer questions and help out by telephone. We never saw each other during the falcon breeding season but did manage several times to go hunting together in the fall and winter with Gyrfalcons Jim had produced.

Probably in part because of the geographic separation, the eastern and western Peregrine programs developed somewhat differently within The Peregrine Fund. Jim and I each had our own way of doing things, and the demands on each program were somewhat different. For example, we dealt with wild-laid Peregrine eggs and fostering of young into eyries as well as captive-produced eggs and hacking.

In the spring of 1975 we had very few captive Peregrines but several pairs of Prairie Falcons formerly held at Cornell. Fifty-one eggs were laid, of which 12 were Peregrine (four fertile) and the remainder Prairie Falcon. Of the 37 fertile Prairie Falcon eggs, 30 hatched, but more importantly, two *anatum* Peregrines were hatched from Pat's and my falcons, Old Lady and Ratinsky (see Chapter 19). Their first egg hatched on 23 April 1975. Pat and I produced an offspring of our own, born the same day the second Peregrine hatched—18 May. Pat's brother Bill was attending the hatching egg with my direction from the hospital delivery room. Our son is now a biologist himself and manages The Peregrine Fund's work in Greenland, and Pat is The Peregrine Fund Administrator. Without Pat's skill, hard work, and dedication to the Peregrine and

The Peregrine Fund, the level of success we have enjoyed would not have been possible.

The incubation of eggs and brooding of young falcons occurred in the apartment the first spring. The incubators were next to the bed, an arrangement that simplified hand turning of the eggs every other hour, including during the night. Also, having the downy eyasses in the kitchen allowed for use of the sink to prepare falcon food. A further benefit was that Pat could look after both eggs and young when she got up at night to feed Kurt, whose room was a large closet we refurbished. Again with the help of her brother, Pat also took care of all the falcons and hatched 5,000 Northern Bobwhite Quail eggs (donated by CDOW) and raised the 1,000 day-old chickens for falcon food while I went to Greenland for over a month that first summer. Kurt "helped," accompanying her in a backpack.

Two interesting side notes for 1975. First, six of the Prairie Falcons were released by hacking on cliffs near the Colorado Penitentiary Work Farm under the direction of falconer Roger Smith and with convicts serving as The Peregrine Fund's first hack site attendants. Second, we gave a few pairs of the Prairie Falcon young to a fellow named Brian Walton so he could gain propagation experience. Years later, we followed up by providing him Peregrines and then funds for his organization and facility—the Santa Cruz Predatory Bird Research Group (SCPBRG)(see Chapter 9). To make space for more Peregrines, we either returned all the adult breeding Prairie Falcons to individuals who loaned them to us or gave them away.

Another event of 1975 was the appointment by FWS Director Lynn Greenwalt of two "recovery teams" for the "American Peregrine Falcon" (new terms FWS created): one team was for the eastern states, the other for the West. The FWS later appointed additional teams for Alaska and for the West Coast. The Rocky Mountain/Southwestern Peregrine Falcon Recovery Team then became responsible for developing a recovery plan for our initial region of interest, although later we added Oregon and Washington to our release areas. As directed by FWS, and under Jerry Craig's leadership, the recovery team developed a thorough species recovery plan. The first meeting was at our facility, and I participated in developing the captive propagation portion and helped otherwise as requested.

The original team members included Frank Bond, Jerry Craig, Jim Enderson, Al Heggen, Gene Knoder, Joel Kussman, Morley Nelson, Dee Porter, and Dale Wills. The plan, all 183 pages, approved 3 August 1977, represented a large amount of time and effort by these men and pro-

Memories

Patricia Burnham

How can I possibly take that portion of my life involved with restoring the Peregrine and boil it down to a brief portion of a book? It seems like all my life has been involved with Peregrines, and there are so many vignettes that flash before my eyes. A lab filled with incubators holding Peregrine eggs and Bill, Dan, or Cal turning them carefully by hand. A pan full of young chicks with their beaks open waiting for food, their heads colored to identify each one. My young son driving his toy fire engine through the room where we raised chickens. Taking him in his backpack as we fed the birds in the barns. Sitting in a large chamber watching the year's Peregrine Falcon young playfully interacting. Visiting release sites in the rugged Rocky Mountains of Colorado and watching Bill take a hack box up the side of the mountain, or hiking out to a box near Durango and getting a literal bird's eye view. Trapping and banding migrating falcons along the Texas beaches. The amazing feeling of holding a bird and imagining where it had come from and where it would return to as I released it to continue on its way. And finally, knowing that this bird is back.

Bill and I were married young—18 years old—and struggled to put first me and then him through college. But I knew from the beginning that falconry and birds would be an integral part of our lives. Early dates included trapping Prairie Falcons or hunting for pigeons under

bridges. Since I knew Bill's feelings for his falcons, I could not believe him when he told me that a man in New York named Tom Cade was asking falconers to give up their birds for captive breeding. When Bill achieved the ultimate of getting his own Peregrine Falcon, I could not imagine him ever letting it go. But fortunately he and others like him realized that the only way this bird would survive would be not only to provide their birds for captive breeding, but to dedicate their lives to seeing this magnificent bird once again flying free in self-sustaining numbers.

The vignettes continue, and a succession of faces flash through my mind. Perhaps the best part of being so involved with the Peregrine restoration was the opportunity to meet the people. Those I knew best were of course those with The Peregrine Fund. But I feel the reason the effort was such a huge success was the many, many people who worked together to make it happen. Many of them spent time with us, or we visited them, either at their facilities or at release locations. There were the private breeders and the Canadian contingent. Friends were found everywhere—in corporations, government, and foundations. People who sent small donations and large donations. For years at Christmas one woman sent us money to feed the birds and cookies to feed the people raising the birds. There were hundreds of hack site atten-

Bill Burnham

Pat Burnham received her B.Sc. and taught school in Colorado and Utah for six years. Upon "retiring" after having her son, she became the first volunteer for The Peregrine Fund's Rocky Mountain Program. Later she became an employee, and she continues with the organization to this day, now serving as the administrator.

dants who traveled briefly through our lives as they helped the birds adjust to life in the wild. And then there were the falconers who pitched in with time, money, and moral support. It was this group who built the barns on our dry, dusty hill here in Boise during a hot summer and who provided the funds to purchase this same property. It would be impossible to name everyone who helped, but they are all apart of it and can take pride in knowing the accomplishment. Friendships grew out of this effort that will last our lifetimes.

For me, however, the best part has been seeing the dedication Bill brought to the project. It has truly been his life work and one that has been shared by our son, Kurt, and myself. I count myself honored to have been a part of it.

> . . . *I feel the reason the effort was such a huge success was the many, many people who worked together to make it happen.*

The Eyrie

William R. Heinrich

In thinking back over the years of our Peregrine restoration work, thousands of memories always come to mind. I cannot help but think about many of my colleagues who ultimately became some of my best friends. The hundreds of hack site attendants setting out on a new adventure with eager expressions, new backpacks, and minds filled with bewilderment and wonder, often questioning, "How did I ever get myself into this mess?" We must have hiked several thousand miles throughout the Rocky Mountains and Pacific Northwest over the two decades it took us to accomplish our mission. I often wonder how we ever had the energy to hike from sunup to sundown, drive hundreds of thousands of miles from release site to release site, from eyrie to eyrie, and always remain committed and enthusiastic. I guess there is only one real reason to explain it all, and that was our love and admiration for the falcons themselves.

For me, some of the most satisfying and rewarding memories come from the climbing experiences I had involving pulling thin-shelled eggs from eyries, and fostering young Peregrines back in. Every time I found myself hanging several hundred feet over the edge of a cliff, rappelling down to an eyrie, I knew I was on a special mission. And each time it was the most important mission of my life. Doing something to help restore the failing Peregrine population was all that mattered, and without question it was worth the risk of continually putting myself in dangerous situations. In that special vertical world I was always alone, but for the cry of the falcon and the wind always trying to push me into a place I did not want to go. Finally, after what often seemed like an eternity, I would reach the eyrie and get that first special glimpse into a place I always felt guilty looking into. Would there be three eggs or four? Would they be cracked or broken? Would I be able to swing in under the overhang so I could safely remove the eggs and replace them with the artificial eggs in my foam-rubber padded box?

Every time I found myself sitting in an eyrie and looking out at the vistas beyond, I always knew I was looking at one of the most beautiful scenes nature can provide. The cliffs, the incredible views over another spectacular river drainage, and the sky itself would all have lost a special meaning without the presence of the Peregrines. It was a thought I would never consciously consider; none of us could, because the task before us was too great, and the thought of failing never crossed our minds.

> *In that special vertical world I was always alone, but for the cry of the falcon and the wind...*

Preparing to construct Wolf Creek hack site.

File photo

Bill Heinrich *is a native of Colorado, where his interest in raptors developed through falconry. He has actively worked with birds of prey for 38 years. His professional career began in 1975 when he worked as a seasonal raptor biologist for the Colorado Division of Wildlife. In 1976 he joined The Peregrine Fund and over the years became responsible for the organization's Peregrine Falcon, Aplomado Falcon, and California Condor release programs and in that capacity hired and managed over 800 seasonal employees. Bill has also studied raptors in Bahrain, Mexico, Colombia, Greenland, Guatemala, Italy, Panama, the United Kingdom, and Zimbabwe.*

vided an excellent literature review and organization of current knowledge and thought. Unfortunately, recovery plans are static, not dynamic, documents, and most become outdated even before FWS's final acceptance, which usually takes many months. This plan was no exception. I never opened the plan again after its writing.

After passage of the 1973 Endangered Species Act (ESA) prohibiting "take" of Peregrines from the wild, developing the captive-breeding population from the remaining wild *anatum* race was impossible. Also, no breeding Peregrines were known to remain east of the Rocky Mountains in the United States, and very few existed in the West (see Table 8.1). The few pairs known in the West were laying thin-shelled eggs, and in the mid- to late 1970s we were just learning how to manipulate breeding pairs and to artificially incubate and hatch their eggs successfully (Burnham et al. 1978). Permission was requested but denied by FWS to obtain *anatum* Peregrines from the wild. Great skepticism existed in FWS as to the potential to breed Peregrines in captivity predictably. FWS's own breeding project at Patuxent Wildlife Research Center in Maryland was producing no positive results with wild-trapped falcons and eventually failed completely. In 1979, however, we were authorized to keep for breeding a limited number of young hatched from thin-shelled eggs we collected. The number was based on a formula related to number of young released. If non-*anatum* Peregrines had not been propagated for release in the eastern states, freeing the few captive-bred *anatum* Peregrines for use in the West, the restoration program for the West would have been severely diminished and recovery delayed for many years.

In 1975-1976 Jim Enderson placed all but one pair of his captive Peregrines with us for breeding. That one pair came later via Ed and Charlotte Freienmuth, to whom Jim had loaned them. Later we also received two pairs owned by Tom Smylie and one pair from Frank Bond that had been held at Cornell. These falcons, plus the Burnham pair, formed the foundation of the captive-breeding stock for recovery of the Peregrine in the western United States. The names of some of these Peregrines were Lil, Blue, Spock, Little Bird, Porgy, Bess, and Frank. Many birds had been taken from the wild with falconry in mind and then unselfishly placed on loan to the recovery program. These falcons represent a story needing told in themselves (see Chapter 19). Of special note was a bird of Jim Enderson's named BC, an acronym for "beer can," which the bird played with as an eyass. When Jim gave us BC, he and we thought the falcon almost

▲ **Figure 8.9** Jim Enderson with box of two downy Peregrines.

Table 8.1 Number of eyries by state known to have been occupied by pairs of Peregrine Falcons, historical–2001.

Year	CO	N. UT	WY	MT	ID	OR	WA	Total
Historical	27	29 (all of UT)	18	23	17	39	12	165
1973	10	0	0	0	0	0	0	10
1974	7	0	0	0	0	0	0	7
1975	7	0	0	0	0	0	0	7
1976	7	0	0	0	0	0	0	7
1977	11	0	0	0	0	0	0	11
1978	8	0	0	1	0	0	1	10
1979	9	0	0	1	0	0	0	10
1980	9	0	0	0	0	0	5	14
1981	7	0	0	0	0	0	5	12
1982	8	0	0	0	0	0	5	13
1983	13	4	0	0	0	0	5	22
1984	14	3	1	1	0	0	7	26
1985	14	3	1	1	1	0	7	27
1986	21	9	2	2	1	0	7	42
1987	27	5	4	3	1	6	9	55
1988	31	9	6	3	2	10	9	70
1989	35	10	11	5	3	10	11	85
1990	41	16	14	6	9	16	14	116
1991	53	8*	14	8	9	26	20	138*
1992	56	8*	21	10	10	26	22	153*
1993	61	8*	29	10	14	27	25	174*
1994	67	10*	32	13	13	37	32	204*
1995	71	7*	32	15	13	37	31	206*
1996	84	10*	40*	15	17	**	37	203*
1997	86	11*	40*	17	15	42	46	257*
1998	86	11*	42*	18	17	51	45	270*
1999	93	8*	50*	27	21	54	59	312*
2000	108	7*	55*	29	23	65	57	344*
2001	115*	8*	46*	37	19*	**	72	251*

*Incomplete surveys of known nest sites.

**Some surveys conducted but data not available.

Historic numbers by Enderson et al. 1988; state numbers by Colorado–Jerry Craig and Jim Enderson; Northern Utah–Don Paul; Wyoming–Bob Oakleaf; Montana–Arnold Dude and Dennis Flath; Idaho–Wayne Melquist and Ed Levine; Oregon–Charlie Bruce; Washington–Hayes and Buchanan (2002).

Bill Heinrich

▲ **Figures 8.10 and 8.11**
Four young fostered
into an eyrie (inset) near
Las Vegas, New Mexico.

Bill Heinrich

Table 8.2 Peregrine Falcon production by The Peregrine Fund at Colorado (1975-1984) and Idaho (1985-2000) facilities. Captive-bred and (hatched in laboratory from wild-laid eggs).

Year	No. Hatched	No. Survived
1975	2	2
1976	17(4)	14(3)
1977	16(15)	13(13)
1978	34(24)	28(24)
1979	58(24)	53(19)
1980	106(11)	92(8)
1981	73(16)	46(16)
1982	97(20)	85(19)
1983	99(19)	95(19)
1984	116(18)	113(18)
1985	147(16)	147(16)
1986	116(24)	110(24)
1987	155(12)	153(12)
1988	185(19)	182(19)
1989	183(10)	182(11)
1990	153(17)	152(16)
1991	151	148
1992	156	152
1993	155	150
1994	130	128
1995	98	96
1996	97	90
1997	52	52
Totals 1975-1997	2396(249)	2283(237)
Survival Rates 1975-1997	-	95.3% (95.2%)
Totals	2645	2520

useless because he would have nothing to do with other falcons and only responded to humans. With Les Boyd's help and Bill Heinrich's persistence, and following Les's example in use of human-imprinted falcons as voluntary semen donors, BC went on to father many, many Peregrines. Peregrines were also loaned to us by Clayton White and Tom Ray. Tom's falcon was named Kai. Although she was paired with a male for several years, she never laid and was returned to Tom. Clay's Peregrines were *pealei*, and their young were sent to the Cornell facility for release in the East.

With the additional falcons, our Peregrine production took a big jump, and we successfully raised 14 young in 1976. Five of those were from Pat's and my pair, the remainder from Jim Enderson's Peregrines. We even raised the first F_2 *anatum* Peregrine. As the young falcons matured, the captive production rapidly increased (Table 8.2).

Also in 1976, Bill Heinrich joined us as the second full-time paid employee. By now Pat had become the first unpaid full-time employee. Bill had worked with Bob Martin to build falcon breeding barns. Bill's first assignment was raising falcon food, which was where every newcomer began back then. Later he assisted in raising falcons, and in 1977 he assumed responsibility for falcon releases. Since then, Bill has managed the release by hacking of 2,122 Peregrines, in almost 400 separate releases in eight states. Eighty percent of those birds became self-sufficient and dispersed naturally from release sites. To say this was an extraordinary achievement is a great understatement.

The hack sites were manned by 680 hack site attendants that Bill hired and supervised over 22 years. Bill is an exceptional person, and he also attracted and hired great site attendants plus some exceptional supervisory seasonal assistants who

Barbara Jenny

Jeannie Konkel

worked for many years. The hack site supervisors included Jim Willmarth (who worked for 11 years), Brian Mutch (10 years), Dan O'Brien (six years), Shane Davis (five years), Matt Erickson (five years), Barb Franklin (three years), and Ritt Enderson, Ed Levine, Jack Oar, Jim Spohn, and Doyle Brown (two years each) (see Chapter 14). Beyond their devotion to the Peregrine, another reason many of these people returned year after year may have been Bill's home-brewed beer and his wife Susan's cooking, as most of these people spent a great deal of time at the Heinrich home. In leaving this dedicated group I wish to add that we were fortunate to be able to hire one, Brian Mutch, as a full-time staff member and as Bill's assistant for release of Aplomado Falcons and California Condors.

An additional 266 Peregrines were fostered into wild eyries by Jerry Craig, Dan Berger, Jim Enderson, and Bill Heinrich with similar success and effort (see Chapter 17). I even got involved in the early days. Fostering of Peregrine young into wild falcon eyries is a difficult task, but it was a way to salvage the thin-shelled eggs, most of which could be hatched artificially, and greatly enhance wild Peregrine reproduction (Burnham et al. 1978, Burnham et al. 2003). To accomplish the fostering, first the stage of breeding of each pair had to be determined so the eggs could be removed during the proper time of incubation. Unless there were young falcons (14-21 days old) ready to be introduced, dummy eggs had to be given to the Peregrines so they would continue incubation until there were young available. On some occasions, because of lack of availability of young, it was necessary to delay by removing eggs within the first two weeks of incubation and not replacing them, causing the falcons to renest and lay another clutch which also had to be collected. Young Prairie Falcons were also temporarily placed with wild adult Peregrines to keep them occupied until downy Peregrines were ready. Therefore, eyries

were entered at least twice and sometimes four or five times. Many of the cliffs on which the Peregrines nested were huge, some nearly 1,000 ft high, and in remote locations. The challenges were many, and at times so were the dangers. A constant worry was falling rocks striking a biologist climber or severing the climbing rope. Dan Berger suffered a shoulder injury from a falling rock that required extended therapy, but no further accidents occurred. Their greater fear was for the Peregrine eggs or young.

In 1977 we accomplished the first cross-fostering experiment with Peregrines by placing three downy Peregrines in a Prairie Falcon eyrie in the Snake River Birds of Prey National Conservation Area, Idaho. The Prairie Falcon young were removed and later placed in other Prairie Falcon eyries. The adult Prairie Falcons immediately accepted the Peregrines, and the young all fledged successfully. Monitoring this release were Dan Konkel and Nell Newman (the daughter of Paul Newman and Joanne Woodward). We repeated the experiment additional times in Idaho, Colorado, South Dakota, and Nebraska but discontinued using that release method because of high mortality and the worry that young Peregrines reared by Prairie Falcons would attempt to hybridize. Results from hacking young to the wild were more predictable. Some years later Peregrines cross-fostered by SCPBRG were located breeding with Peregrines (see Chapter 9).

With Bill Heinrich handling Peregrine releases, Dan Konkel joined the team first to raise falcon food, then falcons. For the first weeks Dan lived out of the back of his pickup and we later learned he ate cold spaghetti out of the can for almost every meal. Dan and Jeannie Konkel contributed importantly to the Peregrine restoration program. In 1984 Dan moved to Wyoming and continued propagating falcons for use in falconry.

With Dan's departure, his assistant, Cal Sandfort, became responsible for propagation. Since

Mother Giant: Cross-fostering Peregrines into a Prairie Falcon Eyrie

Dan Konkel

*I*t is 6:00 a.m. and I have already been in the lab weighing eggs and feeding baby Peregrines for an hour. I am tired because it has been a long night. I had finished my usual 10:00 p.m. feeding, and when checking the hatchery there were two eggs starting their breakup. Two hours later the two chicks were safely out and I went to bed at midnight, only to return at 3:00 a.m. to check all the incubators, hatchers, and baby Peregrines. This is the life of the falcon propagation specialist at The Peregrine Fund.

Pat Burnham calls me into the office to talk to Bill Burnham. I know the second I enter Bill's office that he is sick because he looks very pale. I'm informed that because of his sickness he cannot go to the Snake River Birds of Prey National Conservation Area in Idaho to cross-foster young Peregrines into a Prairie Falcon eyrie as planned and I must go instead. I must leave in two hours. This sounds exciting to me, as propagation guys are seldom let off the place.

"How big is the cliff, Bill?" I ask.

"Well, you know how Heinrich picks release sites," he says.

"Yeah, I know. He likes the biggest cliff within 40 miles."

Bill informs me that it is the 150 m cliff known as Mother Giant. I inquire about the 150-m rope we have, only to find out there is none and that I have to jumar (ascend with special equipment) back up the cliff from the eyrie.

File photo

Dan Konkel *was born in 1953 in Denver, Colorado. He had his first falcon, a kestrel, at the age of 12 and has continued to have falcons ever since. He received a B.Sc. from Colorado State University. He worked for The Peregrine Fund in Fort Collins, Colorado, from 1976 through 1983 when he moved to Sheridan, Wyoming, and started a falcon breeding facility of his own and continues to raise falcons for sale. Dan and his wife, Jeannie, along with their two sons, Erik and Joe, reside in Sheridan. Falcons are still the focus of the family's lifestyle.*

"Bill, there's only one problem. I don't know how to jumar," I offer feebly while convincing myself I can do this. Five minutes later I am climbing the 10-m tall Division of Wildlife building as Bill gives me a 10-minute lesson on how to jumar. One hour later the falcons and I are on our way to Boise in a plane piloted by Jim Enderson.

Within minutes of landing safely in Boise, the young Peregrines and I are rushed off by the Bureau of Land Management (BLM) personnel to the release site. I walk to the edge of the cliff and look over it with John Testa and the BLM personnel.

"Wow! It's a big one," I exclaim. Far below I see tiny specks moving around on the other side of the river. "What are all those people doing over there?" I ask. "They look like ants scurrying." I find out it's a big party with all the important Peregrine people and government people and they are there to watch me go down and up the cliff to put the young Peregrines into the Prairie Falcon eyrie.

Climbing down the cliff and then switching the eyass Peregrines for the young Prairie Falcons go fairly easily. The climb up scares me nearly to death as this is my first time jumaring and I'm hanging on a rope 100 m up on Mother

Giant! After what seems like an eternity of struggling on that rope and shaking with fear, I finally reach the top. I've never been so happy to be back on level ground.

I look around and everyone is leaving. John Testa, the site attendant, has to go observe the Prairie Falcon eyrie to make sure the parents accept the baby Peregrines. The BLM people race off with the baby prairies to put them in alternate nest sites. I suddenly realize that in all the rush that morning, we overlooked transportation plans for me. I hitch a ride to the road across the river where I'm left to fend for myself. I hike down to where the party had been watching me on the cliff, but all the party goers are gone so I start walking up a desolate dirt road toward the highway.

Finally, after a long walk out of the canyon, a car comes up the road. Tom Cade and Morley Nelson pick me up. I'm so excited to be with these two important guys. These two guys know everything about birds of prey! They ask me where I want to be dropped off and where I'm staying, and I'm thinking, "Nowhere, no plans, no motel reservations as far as I know. I'd really just like to hang out with you two cool guys." Much to my disappointment they drop me off at the first motel and are gone.

I'm in a motel at the end of a long, physically and emotionally difficult day, and I'm thinking about how I just risked my neck and I ask myself, "For what?" I then know the answer. It is to be a part of the Peregrine's recovery, and climbing that big cliff was nothing different than what Heinrich and others do daily during the reintroduction season to help save the Peregrine. I feel great satisfaction in knowing that what I did today really did matter and that I am doing my share to help save the Peregrine Falcon.

The next morning as we're leaving for home, I look down from Jim Enderson's airplane at the Snake River canyon, and I can't help but wonder how my baby Peregrines are doing.

Now, 20 years later, my wife, Jeannie, and I have wild Peregrines nesting only 5 mi from our home, and just this morning the haggard female came in and gave us a beautiful show chasing my homing pigeons all over the sky. Yes, the Peregrine really is back, and I'm glad I helped!

File photo

▲ **Figure 8.14** Cal Sandfort feeding a very young Peregrine.

then, Cal has hatched over 2,000 Peregrines and successfully raised an amazing 98%. Please consider the magnitude of that accomplishment in that about half of those birds were produced from artificial insemination, and all those eggs, plus a similar number of infertile ones, were incubated in the laboratory by Cal and weighed and candled every three days. Then each fertile egg hatched under his supervision, and he fed and cared for each young for several days before fostering them under adult Peregrines to be raised until they went to the release site. The job, more accurately the lifestyle, required year after year of working long days, seven days a week for several months and with no time off. An incredible accomplishment (see sidebar, The Magnitude: What It Takes to Raise and Release a Peregrine, this chapter)! Assisting Cal through the years has been another volunteer, Machel Sandfort, and in more recent times, on occasion their daughters Amy and Kristin.

Over the years we had a congenial and mutually beneficial relationship with CDOW, its Director, Jack Grieb, and others in the organization, but no relationship is without problems. In the winter of 1978-1979, because of increased funding and an expanded "non-game program," we were informed that CDOW wished immediately to

File photo

▲ **Figure 8.15** Fort Collins, Colorado, falcon breeding facility, 1983.

▲ **Figure 8.16** The prospectus eventually establishing the World Center for Birds of Prey.

reclaim use of the area where we incubated falcon eggs and raised young and certain other parts of the facility. We had moved the incubators and brooders from the Burnhams' apartment into a vacant office area which was immediately below in the same building. We purchased a used office trailer and loaned it to CDOW, but that did not solve the situation, and we had to move from the building.

This demand could not have come at a worse time, and neither CDOW nor any other agency offered to assist. By then we were raising too many young to move the operation back into the apartment, and there were no other facilities on the property we could use. Explaining our plight to private supporters, we were able to piece together enough money to purchase two trailers, and recovering the one on loan to CDOW, we joined all three with a small central room with counter space for preparing falcon food, a wash sink, and storage cabinets. One trailer, a new double-wide, became the Burnhams' home, another the incubator/brooder lab, and the third an office and video monitoring room. The central room's large stainless-steel wash sink was on the opposite side of the wall and looked through a small window onto the house kitchen sink. By joining the buildings it remained convenient to monitor eggs and young night and day. Dan and Jeannie Konkel and Bill Heinrich, and later Cal and Machel Sandfort, lived in trailers strategically located for security purposes elsewhere on the property.

It was mid-January by the time the site was mutually agreed to with CDOW for location of the trailers and a new storage/shop/imprint fal-

con building. The site had no power, water, or sewer, and the ground was frozen nearly 5 ft deep with temperatures hovering around 0°F. Getting the backhoe to start meant tenting it at night with a tarp and lighting a kerosene heater set under the engine block three or four hours before dawn. We could not even break the ground's surface with a backhoe and had to hire a D-7 Caterpillar with a ripper tooth to make a shallow ditch which we filled with wood and ignited. By repeatedly firing the ditch, then scraping the thawed ground out, we finally had a deep ditch and installed the utilities and moved the trailers into place just before the first egg was laid. The new imprint barn was finished a month later, and its falcon chambers looked out on the front yard of the Konkels' trailer, conveniently allowing for falcons to see their human surrogate mates. In the summer we added a small used portable building for Pat's and my office.

The physical change, although problematic at the time, proved operationally more convenient. We centralized our activities and reduced maintenance and security responsibilities for the entire research station with CDOW's greater presence. At the same time, the control and isolation we had enjoyed for housing and breeding falcons were reduced. Even a small disturbance in the spring could result in setting off a pair of defensive Peregrines. And if one pair began to scream, so did others, like tossing a ping-pong ball in among a bunch of mouse traps. Quickly all the falcons were no longer incubating or brooding small young but instead vocalizing and flying about the chambers in excitement.

World Center for Birds of Prey

It seemed that no sooner were we resettled than new demands for use of other areas of the property arose. CDOW even suggested we consider purchasing adjoining property and moving part of our operation onto it. Continuing the Peregrine Falcon propagation at the facility would be possible but not easy or enjoyable.

About 1981 we began discussing the long-term future of The Peregrine Fund. When Tom Cade founded The Peregrine Fund, he never intended to continue beyond recovery of the Peregrine Falcon, but we were now working with other species nationally and internationally. There was an obvious need for a group with our interests and expertise, and Peregrine restoration was far from done, so why not continue? The idea for creating a World Center for Birds of Prey was emerging. In October 1982 Tom Cade and I printed a "Prospectus on a World Program of The Peregrine Fund,

A Life Style, Not a Job!

Cal Sandfort

I have worked for The Peregrine Fund most of my adult life, and the Peregrine Celebration in 1999 made me realize how many people I met and worked with through the years. Each face was a friend and reminded me of a story.

Like all of the early employees, I started in the quail production facility. Before long I was working with Dan Konkel raising the Peregrine Falcons. Most of the stories associated with Dan are amusing, but none can be told here (we must protect the guilty). Bill Heinrich was either coming or going from release sites in "who knows which" western state. You could always count on a party when he was home. Bill and Pat Burnham's house was attached to the laboratory trailer; in fact, the kitchen faced the sink where we washed our hands before entering the labs. If you didn't talk to Bill or Pat in the office or labs, you could chat while they ate dinner. In those early days everything was new and had to be developed. The Peregrine Fund's need to answer the endless questions and reach the goal of restoring the Peregrine Falcon provided endless opportunities to meet many people who came from diverse backgrounds, but with the same goal. There were also endless opportunities to learn new skills.

The organization had learned that Peregrine Falcons could be bred in captivity, and the goal was to breed lots of them. In the 1980s the number of falcon eggs increased, making it difficult to calculate the necessary weight loss by hand accurately and in a reasonable period of time. Initially, Colorado State University provided time on a mainframe computer for data collection, but connection time was limited or nonexistent. The next data-crunching phase was a Vic Commodore with a cassette tape drive. Now we were making progress. Thankfully, the personal computer became available and lots of egg calculations motivated me to learn how to write computer code. The result was a comprehensive computer program implemented in 1988 for acquisition of propagation and release data. Not only were the data more accurate, but the time required to weigh the eggs was reduced by two-thirds.

The number of captive Peregrine Falcons increased to numbers that made it difficult to monitor each pair. Bill Burnham and Dan Konkel traveled to the Canadian Wildlife Service Peregrine program in Alberta and saw a small video monitoring system. Soon after that we installed a video and audio monitoring system that allowed one person to view all the breeding falcons. Eventually the video system was expanded at the World Center for Birds of Prey and required 19 miles of video and audio cables. It also provided Jeff Cilek the opportunity, while describing the video system to the press one day, to say, "We don't want to disturb the birds, we just want to watch them breed."

Before long came the opportunity to learn about nutrition and investigate the quality of the diet we were feeding the falcons. This required a new group of collaborators and soon-to-be friends. Nutrition studies began in the mid-1980s and continued with the Peregrines to the end of the restoration program. This resulted in higher fertility, hatchability, and healthier falcon chicks. This information has been carried forth to other species of interest and has been used by facilities worldwide.

Through the years I have spent most of my time at the propagation facility thinking about the day-to-day operation of the program. I have been happy to have a career working with the falcons I care so much about. The Peregrine Celebration reminded me of all the people I have gotten to know and all the things I have learned along the way.

> *In those early days everything was new and had to be developed.*

© W. Perry Conway

Cal Sandfort has been a falconer for over 30 years. This interest led him to employment with The Peregrine Fund in 1979. In 1983 he became a raptor propagation biologist and assumed direction for propagation of the anatum Peregrine Falcon and later the Aplomado Falcon and Harpy Eagle at the World Center for Birds of Prey. He obtained a B.Sc. in biology from Boise State University. Cal and his wife, Machel, and two daughters, Amy and Kristin, live in Boise, Idaho, where Cal continues to learn about birds of prey and their eggs.

Machel Sandfort *is a computer instructor for St. Luke's Hospital in Boise, Idaho, and continues to help Cal. They still have their "dates," but now with Aplomado Falcon eggs and young, not Peregrines.*

Life with Peregrines

Machel Sandfort

When Cal began working with The Peregrine Fund, we were flying falcons, going to school, working, and still wondering what we would do when we grew up. I was excited that Cal had this opportunity—it seemed the perfect job for him. I always admired Cal's passion for falcons and thought it inspiring and unique. I was surprised to find there were so many others with similar passion. The energy of the group was contagious. Cal's job evolved to be more like a lifestyle for us both. I found it easy to fill much of our time together with the work of saving the Peregrine. Over the years I have had many unique experiences and learned some skills. I can hold a bird without getting bitten or footed (usually). I have helped with artificial inseminations and feeding chicks—lots of them. A few times I got to let a bird copulate on my head. I have felt the rush of excitement and relief during the

many successful breeding seasons. I have also felt the disappointment and helped with the hard work of the few trying times. I watched Cal learn and become excellent at something he loves.

Falcon propagation has dictated a life for us that is a little different than most. Our children were born into this unique life that is so closely related to the biology and needs of the birds. Our daughters understand this biology, and I believe their experiences growing up surrounded by falcon propagation will enrich their entire lives. I try to explain to them what a fantastic accomplishment they have witnessed.

For years Cal and I have joked about our 10:00 p.m. dates during the egg incubation and baby-feeding season. Our dates were mostly time spent together. We were doing Cal's job, and participating in a meaningful endeavor that makes me deeply proud.

Inc." Analyzing our existing situation and facilities at Cornell University and Fort Collins caused concern for continuing long term at either location. Even trying to bring in a pair of Gyrfalcons to the Fort Collins facility had resulted in an argument with CDOW, which felt we should only have Peregrines. Stringent CDOW (and FWS) permit stipulations, and reporting apparently designed to control us, were stifling.

In the early 1980s both production of young falcons and the number released to the wild rapidly increased (Tables 8.2 and 8.3). At least for propagation and release of Peregrines, we had now proceeded from the experiment to the production phase. The Peregrine restoration program was well on its way. The number of wild breeding pairs being located was also on the increase (Table 8.1). The results being achieved in Colorado and the Greater Yellowstone Ecosystem were particularly encouraging (see sidebar, Peregrine Restoration in the Greater Yellowstone Ecosystem, Chapter 17).

In 1982 CDOW introduced me to individuals representing a corporation that was considering constructing a major facility nearby, and they wanted to speak about the potential impact on our propagation of Peregrine Falcons. Months later, after they had an option to buy property and many other details had been resolved, we learned the Anheuser-Busch Companies, Inc. wished to construct a large brewery across the interstate highway and a mile north from the research station. Although the brewery was not a problem, it would be necessary to build a highway off-ramp cutting through a corner of the property. Discussions then began in earnest with Anheuser-Busch while we considered our alternatives which, with their potential help, included relocation. I made a trip to their headquarters to explain what we did and discuss opportunities for short- and long-term cooperation. They were unwilling to agree to anything other than a one-time settlement. The final meeting occurred in an airline lounge at the Denver airport. Anheuser-Busch had several people present, and I represented The Peregrine Fund. Negotiations probably took an hour, ending with a contribution of $450,000 to relocate our facility. Those dollars transformed the World Center for Birds of Prey from concept to reality.

Tom Cade and I had already begun exploring possible locations for the World Center for Birds of Prey. As word of our expanded program interest spread, potential opportunities arose at Cornell University, the University of California at Santa Cruz, the University of Texas, and in

Florida, Oregon, Idaho, and San Diego, California. The CDOW was kept abreast of our discussions with Anheuser-Busch and our desire to develop a World Center for Birds of Prey but seemed disinterested. The exact opposite occurred in Boise, Idaho.

Idaho Governor John Evans, Boise State University (BSU) President John Keiser, Idaho State BLM Director Clair Whitlock, Boise Mayor Dick Eardley and the City Council, and others very much wanted us in Idaho. Their enthusiasm was ignited by Morley Nelson, Idaho's long-time bird of prey expert and a board member of The Peregrine Fund. Further, we had been releasing Peregrines in Idaho and had developed relationships with several corporations and agencies, and we had made many friends. They invited us to hold our next board meeting in Boise and provided every consideration, including a reception hosted by Governor Evans.

Several incentives became apparent if we would relocate to Idaho: (1) the City of Boise would return 280 acres to BLM which would then sell them to us at a 90% discount off the current appraised value. The cost would be about $20,000, which falconers later donated through the North American Peregrine Foundation. The land, outside the city limits, was part of the Flying Hawk Reserve, a probable future open spaces area. (2) BSU offered to establish a Raptor Research Center at the university and with our help develop a master's degree program in raptor biology, the first anywhere. (3) Boise architect Hal Maxey and engineer Walt Gallaher agreed to develop the architectural plans and construction drawings and specifications for the facility as a donation. (Since then Hal Maxey has produced and donated every architectural drawing required by our organization.) (4) The Terteling Company agreed to donate the use of heavy equipment we would need for construction, as we planned to do much of the work ourselves. (5) Idaho Power Company donated sufficient funds to pay for substantial electrical power installation fees. (6) Boise Cascade Corporation agreed to provide construction material at their cost, and the Trus Joist Company donated all the trusses needed. Even the Idaho Department of Fish and Game offered total cooperation.

As I was the one who would oversee construction and operation of the new facility, I was essentially given the majority vote by the board as to where the World Center would be built, but Tom and I and most others were already in agreement. The decision was Boise, Idaho. Because of its limited population and somewhat remote location, Boise was not the ideal place for the headquarters of a nonprofit, but it was certainly a great place to live and raise a family. Idaho's western style "can do," friendly "you get what you see" approach was also a good match with The Peregrine Fund's way of working. We had found a home.

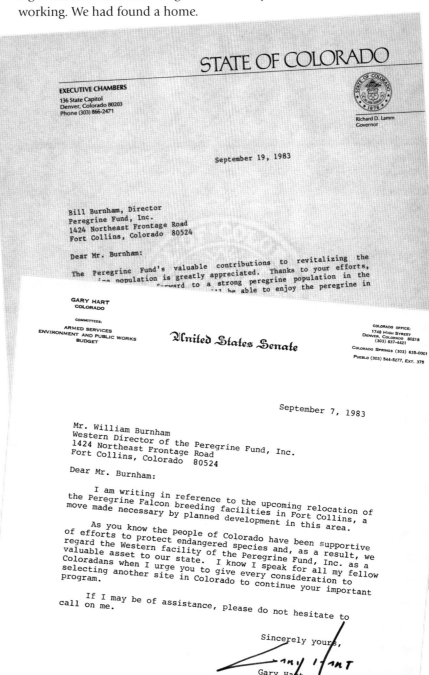

<figure>▼ Figure 8.17 Letters from Colorado officials expressed regret about The Peregrine Fund's relocation.</figure>

▲ **Figure 8.18** Site dedication for the World Center for Birds of Prey, 12 May 1984. Behind and to the side of the crowd gathered for the ceremony can be seen the many poles for the falcon barns.

▲ **Figure 8.19** Inset: On stage at the site dedication were (left to right): Jack Cooper, Director, Boise Park System; Richard Myshak, Regional Director, U.S. Fish and Wildlife Service; Morley Nelson, Board of Directors, The Peregrine Fund; John Keiser, President, Boise State University; Major General Tom Aldrich (USAF Ret.), Vice President, Anheuser-Busch Companies; Tom Cade, President, The Peregrine Fund; John Evans, Governor of Idaho (speaking); William Burnham, Executive Vice President, The Peregrine Fund (master of ceremonies); Ann Dore McLaughlin, Under Secretary of the Interior; Edward Freienmuth, North American Peregrine Foundation; Cecil Andrus, Former Idaho Governor and Secretary of the Interior; Dick Eardley, Mayor, City of Boise; Larry Woodard, Associate State Director, Bureau of Land Management; Rex Thomas, Bushnell Sports Council; Jerry Thiessen, Chief, Bureau of Wildlife, Idaho Department of Fish and Game; and Ernest Day, Western Vice President, National Wildlife Federation.

After Jack Grieb at CDOW was notified of our planned relocation in August 1983, he and the head of the Colorado State University Wildlife Department responded with a "good deal of distress." Colorado Governor Richard Lamm then called and we received letters from Senator Gary Hart and others asking us to reconsider. Too-little, too-late appeals and no real offers. We were determined, however, to ensure the Peregrine recovery program would not be damaged in any way or falter. We propagated falcons in Fort Collins in 1984, but the Idaho facility had to be ready to receive the entire captive-breeding population in the fall.

On 12 May 1984 we dedicated the site for the World Center. Many dignitaries gave speeches, and I was master of ceremonies. The sun shone, the weather was beautiful, and courting Long-billed Curlews flew overhead. Behind the speakers' stage to the north rose the majestic Boise Mountains, but more importantly, to the east was a forest of tall falcon barn poles pointing skyward from the ground and the beginning of a 10,700-sq-ft brick building—the future home of the captive Peregrine population and headquarters of The Peregrine Fund. Unfortunately we remained considerably short on the funds needed for the construction.

Jim Weaver had a mostly volunteer crew constructing three 50- x 100-ft, 20-chamber falcon barns and a smaller 19-chamber barn for behaviorally imprinted falcons, all for the Fort Collins Peregrines. A fifth 20-chambered barn would be added the next year for the Cornell Peregrines, which would also be moved there. Jim's crew lived in tents and a semi trailer Boise Cascade had donated. There was no running water, sewer, or electricity. Melissa Rogers, with daughter Andy as a helper, was the camp cook, and when the Rogers family left, Trisha Pineo took charge. Each day they prepared the hearty meals for all working on the barns, including Ralph and Scott Rogers and Doug Pineo. Other crew members included, once again, John Weaver plus newcomers Ron Ahrens, Frankel Bond, Craig Campbell, Bryan Dague, Leslie Daniel*, Harlan Doty, Dan Fenske, Jim Hatchett, Douglas Jennings, Dan Kelly, Walt Lowery*, Alberto Palleroni*, Machel Sandfort, Debbie and Ken Sterner, and Jim Willmarth. Most of these people were falconers. An asterisk indicates those who helped throughout essentially the entire construction. Everyone did an incredible job under difficult conditions, and their contributions will always be remembered.

Figure 8.20 Pouring a sidewalk are architect Hal Maxey (right), Alberto Palleroni (left), and Bill Burnham senior (lower center).

Figure 8.21 Falcon barns take shape.

Figure 8.22 The finished buildings, with crew members (left to right) Trisha Pineo, Doug Pineo, Jim Weaver, Debbie Sterner, Ken Sterner, John Weaver, unidentified, Harlan Doty, Walt Lowery, and Jim Willmarth.

Figure 8.23 (Behind) X-ray of Doug Pineo's femur with 16-penny nail. The nail missed crucial points in his knee and he was back on his feet in a few days.

Figures 8.24–8.26 Melissa Rogers (left) served as camp cook during much of the long summer. The hand-lettered sign says "No boids in here." Center: John Weaver. Right: Dan Fenske.

Excitement that hot dusty summer was pretty much limited to Doug Pineo driving a 16 penny nail through his femur with a nail gun (Figure 8.23) and to Joe Terteling bringing out cases of soft drinks. There was little time for anything but work, which lasted 12 hours a day and seven days a week. The self-imposed deadline for moving the Peregrines was fast approaching. We wanted to ensure that the falcons were all relocated in the early fall so they could settle in over the winter and that breeding would not be negatively affected or number of young for release reduced.

While Jim Weaver and crew built the barns, I oversaw the other construction, raised funds (which continued in short supply), and began preparing to move the falcons from Fort Collins to Boise. After the breeding and release season was complete, Cal Sandfort came to Boise to help while Bill Heinrich stayed in Fort Collins to make preparations on that end for moving the equipment and trailers and salvaging what we could. We traded the imprint and shop barn to CDOW for a tractor and other equipment, gave one barn to Don Hunter (another falcon propagator, who disassembled it and reassembled it in South Dakota), and sold the other three to a person who removed them from the property although we were never paid. In the end, all that remained marking our past presence were the imprint barn and the stone mon-

Figure 8.27 Clockwise from left: Jim Weaver, Bill Burnham, Douglas Jennings, Alberto Palleroni, Walt Lowery, Leslie Daniel, Jim Willmarth, Andy Rogers and her cat Kipgen, Melissa Rogers, Doug Pineo, and a Peregrine.

▲ **Figures 8.28–8.30** From left, John Testa (left) and Jack Stoddart load falcons in one of the rented vans in Colorado for transport to the plane, and a fork truck loads 6,000 pounds of frozen chickens and quail into a DC-3 before the falcons arrive. A Boise Cascade truck with its cargo of falcons nearly unloaded and Bill Burnham in the foreground, helper Kurt Burnham trailing behind.

Figure 8.31 Dave Belke (left), Jim ▶ Willmarth, Cal Sandfort, and Jerry Craig unload boxes from the truck.

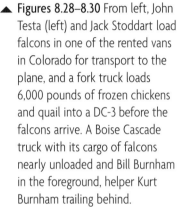

ument we had built recognizing the donors for the first two barns.

Early on 13 September 1984, at our Fort Collins facility, 119 Peregrines were awakened by being placed in a specially designed box and transported to two waiting U.S. Forest Service (USFS) DC-3 aircraft. After loading and a four-hour flight, the falcons and 6,000 lbs of frozen falcon food arrived safely in Boise where a Boise Cascade truck and a one-of-a-kind trailer and team of volunteers awaited. The trailer was designed to haul lumber and wood chips but also functioned well for transporting falcons. This was no small feat and required a great deal of preparation and perfect timing. That entire effort was another example of why the Peregrine program succeeded so well—cooperation among many people and organizations of various backgrounds, unselfishly working together for the benefit of wildlife.

The move meant that transporting eggs from Colorado Peregrine eyries to our labs and transporting the young to eyries and hack sites was not quite as easy. Jim Enderson, also a pilot, agreed to fly the eggs from Colorado to Boise and the young from us to Colorado and other locations as needed, solving the problem. In many cases it was easier than it had been when all the transportation was by automobile. Jim, in his Bonanza, moved hundreds of falcons around the West and never cracked an egg or injured a Peregrine (see Chapter 4).

With the falcons and staff settled at the World Center, the Peregrine restoration effort progressed. After a brief nutritional problem caused by a new source of quail food, under Cal Sandfort's direction that problem was solved and all aspects of Peregrine propagation were substantially improved. Each year became better than the last, and more and more Peregrines were released to the wild. Cal's assistants over the years included Glen Eitemiller, Ed Levine, George Carpenter, Lyle Kradolfer, and Dale Mutch.

◀ **Figure 8.32 and 8.33** Aerial views of the World Center for Birds of Prey in 1984 (above) and 2003 (below).

A disaster occurred on 9 June 1996 when a fire occurred in our barn holding behavioral imprinted Peregrine and Aplomado Falcons. I was awakened by a late-night phone call from Machel Sandfort saying "the imprint barn is on fire and it is terrible." It only took minutes to reach the facility. As I raced up the hill the sky glowed orange and flames roared hundreds of feet into the night sky. From the time the fire was discovered in a storage room on one end of the building, it spread the entire length of the barn faster than our biologists could run around the outside to gain access to the other outside door and the falcon chambers inside. If anyone had entered they would have certainly died in the few moments it took for the entire building to ignite. In the previous days the building had been cleaned and all the chamber walls received a fresh coat of linseed oil. It was like lighting an oil-soaked torch. Days later the fire investigator discovered the melted and charred remains of two nested plastic buckets in the storage room. In between the buckets had been left an apparently linseed-oil soaked rag which had ignited from spontaneous combustion. By the time I arrived on the scene that night there was nothing any of us could do, including the fire department which arrived minutes later, other than watch and ensure the fire did not spread to other buildings. We had carefully spaced all our falcon barns and other buildings to prevent that very event. We were fortunate no human fatalities occurred, but to all of us it was almost as if there had been. The falcons that died were old friends whom we had hand-raised and daily interacted with for years. After the fire, the dollars we could never raise for a fire system and sprinklers for the falcon barns and facility quickly became available. Thanks to those donors, every building now has fire sprinklers and nearby hydrants.

Patterns from returning released falcons showed that the best results in establishing breeding pairs were gained by releasing the maximum number of young in the fewest number of years and within a limited area. We therefore tried to concentrate releases, and once we felt sufficient falcons were released in one area, we moved to another location. After our first success with cross-fostering of Peregrines into a Prairie Falcon eyrie in Idaho, there was interest by South Dakota and Nebraska to use that technique to restore Peregrines in those states. There were a few historical Peregrine eyries reported for each state. Working with those states we cross-fostered Peregrines, but after a few tries further releases were terminated because of high mortality and lack of focus for

File photo

▲ **Figure 8.34** Destroyed barn where imprint falcons once lived.

release of falcons. As there was great interest by many states for Peregrine releases, decisions on where releases were to occur resulted in a few arguments and some hurt feelings as we guided the recovery program.

Because returning territorial falcons at hack sites prevented further releases and because of the geographically shifting release emphasis, Bill Heinrich and co-workers were constantly building new hack sites. In the early days the disassembled hack boxes, 300 or 400 lbs of pea gravel, tools, and camping equipment were carried to the top of cliffs for placement. After a herniated disk for me, bucking horses and mules scattering pieces and parts along mountain trails, and other problems, Bill began organizing USFS- and BLM-leased fire and other helicopters to lift entire hack boxes into place. A great improvement! Bill's leadership was crucial.

By the latter part of the 1980s most aspects of Peregrine Falcon release were resolved, although the unexpected continued to arise at every turn. A marmot appeared at a hack site just after the young were released, scattering them in all directions before they could find their way back, and other problems arose. Most problematic were Golden Eagles, Great Horned Owls, and returning territorial Peregrines. No matter how carefully

We were fortunate no human fatalities occurred, but to all of us it was almost as if there had been.

The Devil's Garden

Brian D. Mutch

Like a favorite hunting or fishing location—that special place where things seem to go just right. Where you draw from old memories, like they occurred yesterday. Events, unexpected, and in places so spectacular we relive them almost daily. A silver salmon taking your fly on a lonely Alaskan river, or the falcon you have hunted with and enjoyed for 14 seasons taking a grouse over Montana prairies, pointed by the two setters you have enjoyed for years as well. As with these special places and events, most of us who worked with Peregrines had that one special eyrie, and given any chance, and some extra time, we traveled there as often as possible to simply spend a day watching Peregrine Falcons and create memories to last a lifetime.

After awakening early from a spectacular storm, complete with over an inch of rain, I was pleased to find blue sky and the most beautiful and rugged granite spires I had ever seen, glowing red from the morning sunrise. These towered directly above the glacially carved valley where Jim Willmarth and I had arrived during the night and storm. I had no idea what to expect at the head of this valley as we wearily wound our way up for the last 15 miles of this 600-mi trip in the middle of the night. This was an area in Montana I had never been to before. Fortunately, Peregrines have been the catalyst for travel to many of these out-of-the-way, hidden, and

Brian Mutch was born and grew up in Missoula, Montana, hunting, fly-fishing, and hunting with falcons and English setters with his brother Dale. He surveyed for Peregrines in several Utah national parks in 1985, then became a Peregrine hack site field supervisor in 1988 for The Peregrine Fund. After graduating from the University of Montana in 1993, he joined the organization full time, working on Peregrine restoration and then, with its completion, the California Condor, Aplomado Falcon, and other Peregrine Fund projects, including research in Greenland. Brian lives in Sheridan, Wyoming, with his wife, Ruth, and her two boys, Travis and Zach.

amazingly beautiful areas throughout the Rocky Mountains and Pacific Northwest. This valley, with its spectacular cliffs and waterfalls, put it at the top of that list for me.

The date was 12 June 1988. We were meeting a helicopter that morning to fly a hack box approximately 2,000 ft above the valley floor to the half-way point of the boulder field and cliffs, later known to us all as The Devil's Garden. Jim had picked out an impossibly small ledge for all of this to occur on. I hooked the loads to the helicopter in the valley below while Jim had made the two-hr hike to "his" ledge earlier to unhook these loads. When the hack box, tools, and 300 lbs of gravel sat piled on the ledge, the pilot departed for Bozeman, smiling and shaking his head. But he gave me a thumbs-up as he departed, approving, I felt, of the lengths we all were going through to help recover this falcon.

This was the first of many hack boxes I was to place during the 10 years I worked with Peregrines. In my heart it was, and still remains, the most special site. Just two weeks later, Bob Oakleaf, the nongame biologist for the Wyoming Game and Fish, and I placed my second hack box on a much less spectacular cliff near the South Fork of the Shoshone River. Unlike the first, not a breath-taking site; hot, dry, and a 50-ft cliff sitting in a sage brush cattle pasture. However, many Peregrines were successfully released into the tremendous surrounding habitat during the five years we used the site. I now knew the extremes and flexibility when picking release sites in the future on my own.

We released a group of five young Peregrines from The Devil's Garden that summer. It was an exceptional place for the young falcons to learn to fly and for our attendants to watch them mature and

become independent and for me to fall in love with this job we called Peregrine reintroduction. The five young falcons did well, and as the time came for this site to close for the year, the falcons had been joined by three different adult Peregrines, all banded, which had been released in previous years from hack sites scattered throughout the West.

The following spring, during routine visits to each site, Matt Erickson and I located a returning pair of Peregrines here; a banded adult male paired with the yellow-banded female released from this site the previous year. In all the years that have followed, this site has been occupied by Peregrines. Unfortunately, I think because of its elevation and severe exposure to spring storms, it has not been the most productive eyrie in Montana. Nonetheless, 10 young Peregrines have fledged here since 1989. The aerial display from the adult Peregrines was nothing short of spectacular. Seeing hunting flights performed or simply watching Peregrines fly by at eye level in this Rocky Mountain backdrop was more than worth any trouble involved in getting here. On the occasions when this pair was successful and had young to feed, their hunting activity increased exponentially, as did the duration and quality of the show they provided.

My brother Dale, Ed Levine, and my girl friend, Ruth, now my wife, have made the difficult trek to our viewing area countless times over the years to witness this show. Granite boulders, some the size of a small house, are the first obstacles that take you up the first 1,000 ft of elevation. Then you lose about 300 ft of elevation as you traverse down an avalanche chute and cross a small stream directly below a 50-ft waterfall. I do not know the source of this stream; springs and snow melt, I guess, from much higher up in the cliffs and mountain. It is always flowing. It does not have a name, and surprisingly we never gave it one. However, we have all enjoyed drinking from its cold water and showering under the spray of the falls, cooling off after a hot summer hike. From here it is another 1,000 ft up an avalanche chute of loose soil and small boulders, the kind that easily slides so that three steps forward is actually only one or two steps of uphill progress. From the top of this chute you traverse back out toward the valley on a small shoulder ridge which is extremely exposed on both sides. At the end of this small ridge is an incredible view of the valley below, as well as everything on all sides and far into Montana's Beartooth Wilderness. This is the

In my heart it was, and still remains, the most special site.

site where the hack box used to perch. The just-completed hike is one our hack site attendants had to make every day in any weather for seven weeks, bringing food for their falcons and recording notes on their falcons' progress. It was unusual when one, if not every one, was not bleeding when the trip was finished.

It is here we would spend the day or any part of it we could spare. The female Peregrine used several different ledges over the years but always one that could be observed from this location. In 1991 her scrape was located directly across from us at the same level, on the "Number One Spire." We could watch her incubating eggs and feeding her young. It was a wonderful view of wild Peregrines.

With the success of the Peregrine Falcon behind us now, I do not travel to these special places much anymore. It is not by choice and has not been an easy adjustment. For me, no other project will ever compare with this one. I worked with many of the greatest people I have ever known, all inspired by this one incredible species. This was not work to us but a deep passion to try and help a falcon we all truly loved. I know we all still travel, whenever possible, to that special eyrie, and if not physically, then in our daydreams.

It is spring now, and I know the Peregrines are back from wherever their winter travels have taken them. I will try but may not find the time to visit them and this favorite eyrie of mine. As clearly as if I were there, though, I can hear their calls echoing from thousand-foot granite walls and see them hunting together in this magnificent Montana valley that a few of us came to know, love, and now miss.

File photo

▲ **Figure 8.35** Helicopter delivering a hack box on the long sling below.

hack sites were selected, and how hard attendants and biologists worked, an eagle, owl, or aggressive Peregrine could kill or prematurely disperse newly fledged Peregrines. A hack site with 100% success one year could be a total failure the next when one or more eagles appeared daily until they killed every Peregrine. Great Horned Owls would do the same but at night. Experience, hard work, vigilance, determination, cooperation, and luck were all critical ingredients to picking a hack site and a successful release of Peregrines.

Bill Heinrich and his hack site supervisors established the hack sites, provided overall direction, and were present when falcons were placed in and released from the box. Usually they also helped to close the site, but it was up to the hack site attendants to do the rest. In the West, many hack sites had names such as Death Canyon, Grave Point, Storm Castle, Devil's Kitchen, and Suicide. Before Bill Heinrich figured out easier yet equally successful methods, Peregrine hack site attendants were becoming the Navy SEALS or Army Rangers of biologists. The hack sites in the early years were typically set high on a mountain with the hack box located on the face of a cliff hundreds of feet above the ground. Climbing ropes and equipment were required to access the box. Water, food, and everything else had to be packed miles and hours upward through rough terrain. Hack site attendants were rugged, self-

continued on page 152

The Magnitude: What It Takes to Raise and Release a Peregrine

Cal Sandfort and William Heinrich

From egg to independence takes less than four months for a Peregrine, but it requires a full year and thousands of hours of human care and preparation. The investment of time, money, and human commitment for each bird we successfully released into the wild was incredible.

To Raise a Falcon

The "breeding season" at The Peregrine Fund's World Center for Birds of Prey begins not in the spring but in August, when we give the captive adult falcons a health examination and thoroughly clean chambers and ready them for fall and winter. Part of the exam involves the collection and analysis of a small amount of blood to determine the falcons' levels of vitamins and minerals. If changes in diet are required, they must begin in the fall to achieve proper nutritional levels by spring and development of the first egg.

Even before August, sufficient falcon food has been raised for the fall and winter months. In September and October we clean and repair every piece of equipment and the entire food production facility, from ceiling fans to floor drains. Nothing goes untended, for the success or failure of captive breeding depends on the food produced. By November we start raising domesticated Coturnix Quail for spring breeding and summer releases of falcons.

Christmas and New Year's include recleaning breeding chambers and reexamining all falcons. Video cameras and sound monitors are checked

▲ The science of raising and releasing Peregrines was refined to an art over many years. One- to three-day-old chicks with heads color-marked for identity gather around a warmer and beg to be fed.

and adjusted so careful observation of pairs can be accomplished as courtship and breeding begin. This is the final time we disturb the birds before breeding. Access to the falcon barns is reduced to an absolute minimum, and we guard against all outside disturbances. Peregrine feeding schedules continue at first light as days lengthen.

Before falcons lay their first eggs, we have repaired, cleaned, and tested dozens of incubators and brooders required for raising their young, and laboratories are cleaned and disinfected. Observation of pairs now occurs from first dawn to dusk. Biologists increase interactions with falcon males that have been raised to produce the semen so critical for artificial insemination (AI) of females that do not copulate. Almost half of the young will be produced from AI.

The entire breeding facility and its staff are now ready. Falcons lay their first eggs in March, and the race to August

begins. Time becomes almost meaningless as days become weeks and weeks become months, with our sole purpose of producing the most and best possible young falcons for release to the wild.

We monitor each pair carefully and record eggs noted as laid; AIs are made as required. Close management of every falcon pair maximizes the chance of producing young. Eggs may be taken as laid from one falcon and placed under another already incubating to increase production, or left under the laying female for one week. Giving each egg several days of incubation by a falcon increases the chance of hatching over those placed in an incubator throughout their entire growth. The first time an egg is handled it is coded, measured, and weighed. Once the egg is in an incubator, weighing and examining occur every three days, and the incubator conditions are adjusted to maximize the chance of hatching that egg. The incubators' tem-

peratures and humidities are monitored hourly.

About two days before hatching, the embryo breaks a hole in the shell (pips) and begins to breathe outside air in preparation for hatching. We count the hours from pip to hatch in case the bird should need assistance in hatching. Finally the embryo begins to rotate in the egg, breaking a line and creating a cap around the large end of the egg, which it pushes off as it hatches. The wet hatchling is examined, weighed, and placed in a warm brooder with other newly hatched chicks. Feeding begins in a few hours and continues every three to four hours until the young is introduced to its foster parents for rearing and later removal for release. Biologists must monitor all parents to ensure they are properly brooding and feeding the young.

With some occasional loss of blood and skin (on the part of the biologists, not the falcons), we remove the month-old young from the chambers, then band and place them in specially designed travel boxes for their trip to the release site. The last young leave the World Center in late August, just in time for the beginning of next year's "breeding season."

From 1985, the first breeding season the World Center for Birds of Prey was in operation, to 1997, when the final Peregrine releases occurred in the West, a total of 1,840 Peregrines were raised there. Those came from a total of 4,021 eggs laid, of which 2,425 were fertile. All eggs were incubated for a minimum of three weeks, meaning 36,189 egg weighings and candlings occurred. Of the fertile eggs, 1,115 were from pair copulations and 1,182 from 1,709 AIs. To obtain the semen for AI, about 9,334 copulations by imprinted Peregrines occurred with their surrogate mates/biologists wearing semen collection hats. Once the eggs hatched, a total of about 64,400 hand feedings of young occurred, requiring about 32,610 quail to be processed and ground. To support the breeding and release effort during this period, we raised 1,219,890 quail and 106,057 chickens, requiring over 2,652,000 lbs of quail feed and 732,000 lbs of chicken feed.

To Release a Falcon

To release a falcon successfully requires expert supervisory biologists, a suitable location, dedicated release attendants, a variety of equipment from four-wheel drive trucks to small radio transmitters, a group of young falcons and their food, and a measure of good luck.

Before a release site is selected, the location must be examined carefully for predators or other potential problems and to ensure prey is

available for the young falcons to chase and eventually begin to capture and eat. This selection occurs a year or more before the use of a location, with a recheck the spring before the young Peregrines arrive.

Once the site has been selected, and after most of the winter snow melts at mountain sites or mud dries in the flatland locations, biologists drive, hike, pack by horse, or helicopter to the site to build a release hack box. The box is prebuilt at the World Center, transported complete with gravel for the floor, and assembled and anchored to the cliff or attached to a tower that the biologists may also have built. When the box is in place, the camp for the hack site attendants—a tent, lantern, stove, and spotting scope—may also be delivered.

Hack site attendants are responsible for care and feeding of up to six Peregrines from their delivery at the site to the falcons' independence about six weeks later. Attendants range in age from 18 to 80 and from students to retirees. They camp for weeks in terrain ranging from remote mountain regions to marsh areas and have to deal with bears, mosquitoes, blizzards, and wildfires. Like the hack sites, these hearty souls must be found months ahead of the release, and dozens are required.

The first falcons arrive at hack sites in May, and the last become independent of human care in September. A nonstop whirlwind of needs, demands, and emergencies, release is independent of days of the week or hours worked. It begins a year before the falcons arrive at a site and does not end until they are all independent of

Once the breeding season commences, biologists (Shane Davis shown) watch and record each pair's activity.

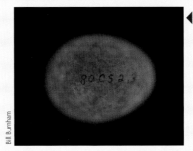

Eggs are incubated and periodically candled to determine if they are fertile. The lettering on the egg indicates it was laid in 1980 by pair CS in the second clutch and was the third egg.

Embryos are monitored and assisted to hatch as necessary.

Once at an appropriate age, young falcons are transported to and placed in readied release sites.

human care and the equipment has been retrieved.

The Peregrine Fund released a total of 2,122 captive-produced Peregrines to the wild in the Rocky Mountain Northwest by hacking between 1978 and 1997 during 338 hacking attempts at 103 different sites. The hack sites required construction of 22 towers and 108 hack boxes and the selection and employment of 680 hack site attendants. As each hacked Peregrine eats about 100 quail from the time we place it in the box to independ-

ence, a total of 212,200 quail were used. Equipping the hack site attendants required about 676 lanterns, stoves, and tents. To release the falcons and manage the people, over 1.5 million miles were driven.

Considering the above, remember that this was only about half of the total Peregrines propagated, two-thirds the number released to the wild by The Peregrine Fund, and half of all Peregrines released in North America. The magnitude of the total effort was incredible.

Cal Sandfort hatched and raised 1,969 Peregrine Falcons before the Peregrine was delisted while also supervising the raptor food production at the World Center for Birds of Prey.

Bill Heinrich supervised the release of 2,122 Peregrine Falcons to the wild and had responsibility for all The Peregrine Fund hack sites in the western United States.

Table 8.3 Peregrine Falcons released by The Peregrine Fund and cooperators, 1974-1997. Released by hacking or (fostering) or [cross-fostering]. R = number released. S = number survived to independence from hacking and to fledging from fostering/cross-fostering.

Year	CO**	WY	UT	MT***	ID	OR	WA	NM	NB	SD	Total
1974 R	(2)										2
S	(2)										2
1975 R	(5)										5
S	(3)										3
1976 R	(5)										5
S	(5)										5
1977 R	(12)				[3]			(8)			23
S	(9)				[3]			(8)			20
1978 R	5(20)				[5]		(10)				40
S	4(15)				[2]		(8)				29
1979 R	10(15)[8]		5		[3]		(10)		[3]	[3]	57
S	10(14)[3]		4		[0]		(0)		[0]	[2]	33
1980 R	12(16)	11	11							[2]	52
S	12(13)	9	7							[0]	41
1981 R	13(21)	8	10	4		(2*)					58
S	13(15)	6	8	4		(2*)					48
1982 R	23(26)	14	6	8	8	3*(2*)	3*				93
S	13(20)	9	3	6	8	1*(2*)	2*				64
1983 R	25(27)	19	8	8	12	3*	3*[2*]				107
S	23(21)	18	7	4	9	3*	3*[2*]				90
1984 R	32(28)	21	13	12	14	3*	[2*]				125
S	27(25)	20	10	10	13	3*	[2*]				110
1985 R	35(18)	30	10	25	20	5*	3*				146
S	24(15)	25	6	22	15	5*	3*				115
1986 R	20(6)	17	9	13	9	4,3*	3*				84
S	14(6)	10	3	12	3	3,1*	1*				53
1987 R	22(17)	25	19	23	18	8(2*)	5				139
S	19(16)	20	16	18	13	5(1*)	5				113
1988 R	33(12)	39	5	36	34	10[2*]	5				176
S	26(10)	33	3	32	29	8[2*]	5				148
1989 R	31(3)	30	9	39	38	16	14				180
S	25(3)	22	7	36	32	14	8				147
1990 R	15	31		36	32	21	15				150
S	12	27		27	30	19	8				123
1991 R		25		37	32	25	21				140
S		23		32	29	22	13				119
1992 R		32		47	22	19	11				131
S		26		33	18	18	9				104
1993 R		34		64	12	16	21				147
S		30		43	10	15	20				118
1994 R		26		47	27	13	11				124
S		25		36	23	12	5				101
1995 R		24		49	5	10	6				94
S		21		31	3	2	6				63
1996 R				57			5				62
S				47			4				51
1997 R				41			6				47
S				23			2				25
Total R	276(233) [8]	386	105	546	283 [11]	159(8)	132[4]	(28)	[3]	[5]	2187
Total S	222(192) [3]	324	74	416	235 [5]	131(5) [2]	94[4]	(16)	[0]	[2]	1725

Survived: Hacked = 79.16%; fostered = 79.18%; cross-fostered = 51.61%; total = 78.78%.
* Peregrine Falcons released by Santa Cruz Predatory Bird Research Group.
** Colorado Division of Wildlife fostered Peregrines and in 1988-1990 operated several hack sites.
*** Includes 30 Peregrine Falcons released on Missouri River in Montana by Ralph Rogers.

Bill Heinrich

▲ **Figure 8.36** Dave Stevens, biologist, Rocky Mountain National Park.

reliant individuals who could deal with most anything from black or grizzly bears to a marauding moose. At one location the USFS offered metal culverts for attendants to sleep in so they would not be bothered by a problem grizz. Falcon food at a hack site back then was live quail, which always attracted other predators, and the enclosures were either encircled with electrified wire or hoisted high in a tree. See Chapter 14 for some of those attendants' own stories.

What occurred in the western states would have been hard, if not impossible, to accomplish without the federal land management agencies and state wildlife departments whose assistance included financial support. Many releases occurred on BLM lands, national forests, national parks, and even wildlife refuges. State-managed lands were used as well. We also released falcons on many private properties, including in Idaho forests owned by Boise Cascade. The Boise Cascade release site was our most successful in fledging young—39 released with 95% survival. Listing all the key people and specific locations involved is not possible as there are just too many. They all, however, were important to the ultimate success we achieved.

I do wish to mention certain key individuals and their affiliations. A partial list of participating state biologists includes Bob Oakleaf, Dan Stevenson, Dale Mutch, and Bill Long (Wyoming Game and Fish Department); David Anderson, Lee Stream, and Harriet Allen (Washington Department of Fish and Wildlife); Mark Henjum and Bill Haight (Oregon Department of Fish and Wildlife); Al Heggen, Phil Wagner, Don Paul, and Bob Walters (Utah Division of Wildlife Resources); John Cada, Dennis Flath, and Arnold Dude (Montana Department of Fish, Wildlife, and Parks); Dick Norrel, Justin Naderman, Wayne Melquist, and Ed Levine (Idaho Fish and Game Department); Jerry

◀ **Figure 8.37** Mountain hack site near Hermosa, Colorado.

Ed Freienmuth

Craig and Dan Berger (Colorado Division of Wildlife); and Ross Locke (Nebraska Game and Fish Commission). Biologists and administrators I wish to include with the federal agencies are Olin Bray, Rob Hazlewood, Chuck Peck, Rich Howard, and Ron Joseph (FWS); Dan Hinckley, Eric Brekke, Doug McVean, Jim Roscoe, Mike Kockert, and Larry Rau (BLM); Bob Wood, Dave Stevens, Steve Petersburg, Joel Hogan, Jeff Connor, Joe Alston, Larry Hayes, and Terry McEneaney (National Park Service); and Tim Schommer, Ralph Anderson, Marion Cherry, Sally Orr, John Ormiston, Jina Mariani, Bill Ruediger, Trichia O'Conner, Bruce Smith, John Weaver, Keith Gierzentanner, and Mike Rath (USFS).

Another important group comprised the spouses and families of the individuals who participated in the restoration program. It was they, through their support, who made it possible for the spouse, daughter, or son participating in the restoration effort to give his or her all in restoring viable populations of wild Peregrine Falcons. Every person who actively participated and all who enjoy seeing a Peregrine in the wild owe these families their gratitude.

Before ending I wish to address a final topic. I want to thank the donors, both in the private and public sectors, who made this work possible. Every one of you who gave your personal dollars, who helped direct or move foundation, corporate, or public funds to this project, or who contributed through in-kind gifts made this accomplishment possible. One person I wish to highlight is Jeff Cilek, now Vice President for The Peregrine Fund. I first knew Jeff when he directed the Senate subcommittee for Interior Department appropriations. As staff director Jeff annually added on funds to restore the Peregrine Falcon. Those dollars were critical and were matched annually by other contributions. Jeff, and all who directly contributed or helped to have dollars contributed, were just as important as those of us doing the hands-on work with the falcons. Without them, nothing could have happened. They have my sincere gratitude, now and always.

Bill Heinrich

Bill Burnham grew up in Colorado, spending as much time as possible in the outdoors. His initial interest in Peregrines developed through falconry. He began searching for eyries in the late 1960s and made his first trip to Greenland in 1972 just before graduating from Southern Colorado State College. He joined The Peregrine Fund/Cornell University in 1974 after completing an M.Sc. at Brigham Young University. He later earned a Ph.D. from Colorado State University. Bill was The Peregrine Fund's first employee in the West and developed its restoration program for the Peregrine in the Rocky Mountains. He was elected to The Peregrine Fund Board of Directors in 1977 and as a Founding Member in 1982. He was vice president for the organization from 1979 to 1985 and assumed its overall direction in 1985, first as executive vice president and then as president in 1986, and he has continued as such since then. Bill has managed his administrative responsibilities to allow for his continued involvement in fieldwork from the Arctic to the tropics. He also maintains his interest in falconry, hunting, fishing, and other outdoor activities while living with his wife, Pat, and their son, Kurt.

Fostering three downy Peregrines into an eyrie near Foxton, Colorado, 1976.

Restoration of the Peregrine Population in California

Brian James Walton

The Peregrine recovery efforts in California have been a lifelong source of research, inspiration, and personal joy for a large number of people.

They have resulted in population recovery, a great deal of additional knowledge concerning the species, and unique and powerful friendships. This chapter describes the personal events that led to the development of the program and follows that with current ecological information on the species.

When I graduated from high school, only one pair of Peregrines was known to nest in California. The nest was on Morro Rock, so I moved there and enrolled in the local college. By then I knew of the work of Tom Cade at Cornell and had made friends with Jim Weaver and Frank Bond through falconry activities. A big day in my life occurred at Morro Rock in 1973. My friend John Edmisten and I were observing the falcons, and several were flying about with an intruding adult, causing a lot of commotion. We were looking up in our binoculars, trying to figure out who was who, and I identified what I thought was a female

flying above us, then out over the bay. I heard a voice correct me, saying it was a tiercel. I glanced down from my binoculars and was stunned to see Tom Cade looking through his binoculars. Everyone quickly agreed it was indeed a tiercel. I had secretly dreamed of going to graduate school at Cornell as Tom's student.

By the end of that day, Tom had me thinking about breeding and releasing falcons with a project in California. Tom's enthusiasm was infectious. So at age 22 I decided to skip graduate school and breed Peregrines in California.

Tom had corresponded with James C. Roush, II, a veterinarian in Santa Cruz. I ended up meeting Jim and hearing his dreams of a California project. Jim's associate was an old college friend of Tom Cade's, the late Kenneth S. Norris, then professor of natural history at the University of California, Santa Cruz (UCSC). Ken was a lot like Tom. Both went to the University of California, Los Angeles (UCLA) and studied under George A. Bartholomew, both were leaders in their fields (Ken was a marine mammalogist), and both made you think anything was possible with perseverance. Both went against the normal academic grain, and both had fun in life.

Jim and Ken said they would help get things started but needed to get back to their regular

◀ **Figure 9.1** Painting by John Schmitt. Reproduction rights courtesy Brian James Walton.

Carl Thelander

Phyllis Dague

▲ **Figure 9.2** Ron Walker and Phyllis Dague place Peregrine chicks at the Morro Rock nest site in 1977. These were the first to be released on the West Coast.

▲ **Figure 9.3** View of Morro Rock from the east, 1977.

Figure 9.4 Warning sign ▶ at Morro Rock, 1977.

Phyllis Dague

lives as soon as possible. Thus, the Santa Cruz Predatory Bird Research Group (SCPBRG) was born. I got some *anatum* Peregrines from Bill Burnham, who has since become a generous and loyal lifelong friend. Other *anatum* falcons came from friends Dave Jamieson, Steve Baptiste, and Frank Bond and from wild, thin-shelled eggs we hatched. Most importantly, SCPBRG benefitted from the generosity of Louis Davis, who had a breeding passage *anatum* Peregrine named Nugget. We were given many of her young to mate with other *anatum* Peregrines we possessed. They proved to breed readily in captivity and were a highly productive family of birds.

Concurrent with these actions, we had a great field program going in California. Steve Herman had laid the groundwork. He was trained at the University of California, Berkeley and was a good influence. Steve collected historical Peregrine information, including data from Richard Bond from the 1940s, and had done the 1970 census. My then brother-in-law, Carl Thelander, documented that near-statewide extinction had occurred by the time of his work in 1974–1975. Following their work, Dave Harlow, Sandy Boyce, Merlyn Felton, Monte Kirven, Geoff Monk, Lee Aulman, Jeep Pagel, Brian Woodbridge, Brian Latta, Jeff Sipple, and Craig Himmelwright all helped chart the recovery. I am proud to know these people and praise their field-research efforts.

All of this work was made possible by leadership from our allies in agencies, including the late, great Butch Olendorff, Dean Carrier, the late Harley Grieman, Dave Harlow, Ron Jurek, and Robert Mesta. They deserve the highest praise accorded to government employees.

Along the way, a varied group of individuals have assisted SCPBRG with Peregrine recovery. We were fortunate to have a good historical record based on egg collections throughout the state, largely under the care of Lloyd Kiff and the late Ed Harrison at the Western Foundation of Vertebrate Zoology (WFVZ). Some members of the falconry community have aided SCPBRG. Artists John Schmitt and Hans Peeters and photographers Frans Lanting and the late Galen Rowell made significant contributions to our institutional longevity and financial resources. Nothing would have been as easy with breeding and release if we had not been able to follow the lead of Tom Cade, Jim Weaver, Bill Burnham, Willard Heck, Dan Konkel, Cal Sandfort, Steve Sherrod, Jack Barclay, and Bill Heinrich of The Peregrine Fund. We also had help from Wayne Nelson, Steve Baptiste, and Dewey Savell to increase the success of our breeding efforts.

Veterinarians such as Diana Bowen, Jim Roush, Pat Redig, and Mike Murray were invaluable.

An historic moment marked the start of Peregrine recovery in California. In 1977 the nest at Morro Rock failed, and two young Peregrines were flown from the Cornell facility and released at Morro Rock by Phyllis Dague. The wild foster parents accepted them as the first released falcons on the West Coast.

We hatched and released nearly 1,000 more Peregrines in Washington, Oregon, Nevada, and largely California between 1978 and the present. After the important, early pesticide work of Robert Risebrough and many others, and the bold leadership and announcement in 1972 by William Ruckelshaus of the Environmental Protection Agency (EPA) that DDT was restricted from use in the United States, our efforts sped up the rate and range of Peregrine recovery in the West. Where there were two known nests in California in 1970, by the year 2000 there were over 200 active territories in the state.

I cannot say how important my co-workers, especially Tery Drager, have been to our program. I get wild ideas but insufficient funding, and Tery, who has been with me from the start, made my dreams for recovery a reality. Janet Linthicum and Grainger Hunt have added significantly to the professionalism and publications of SCPBRG. Over the years SCPBRG has had an excellent, well-motivated, underpaid, and overachieving staff. All of them deserve to be remembered for their dedicated work.

We were privileged to have Bob Risebrough and Wally Jarman conduct our pesticide research. Lloyd Kiff handled eggshell projects, stimulated our creative process, and made meetings and work more fun.

As a part of UCSC the SCPBRG could not have a board of directors, friends' group, or membership. It was saved at least once each by the leadership, support, or friendship of Dan Brimm; the Newman family; the Jarman family; Cam Cooper; Donal C. O'Brien, Jr.; Ann Harvey; Yvon Chouinard; Ron Yanke; and Bill Burnham. The often timely or long-term support of ARCO, the Storer Foundation, Pacific Gas and Electric, the California Hawking Club, and The Ahmanson Foundation provided the core of support that let us have long life.

I am proud of all of the undergraduate students, recent graduates to whom we gave first jobs, and graduate students who have passed through our program. Over 100 have far exceeded my level of success or professionalism. All were invaluable and deserve credit in the Peregrine recovery.

Brian James Walton

Bill Burnham

We built a breeding facility in the lower quarry on the UCSC campus. It served as home for our falcons and my family and the center of SCPBRG actions for 15 years. We built it with volunteer labor and donations of funds and a large amount of gifts-in-kind. Some people questioned why a third facility in the United States might be needed. In California, DDT use in pounds per acre was among the highest applied anywhere. We had the largest manufacturing plant and some of the largest dump sites reported. The falcon population of the West Coast was once large but remained near extinction in the late 1970s. Since we wished to speed recovery, the resources of the then Fort Collins facility of The Peregrine Fund would have been spread too thin if California and initial Washington and Oregon releases had been included. With hindsight, the development of a third facility was the appropriate action.

We had a large, cooperative group of people working on the recovery goal. It was a common goal, and many people worked with us for a variety of personal reasons. I tried to get the most out of everyone and steer them in the direction that

▲ **Figure 9.5** Bucky, an immature female Peregrine, incubates fostered eggs.

▲ **Figure 9.6** "The Quarry," the Santa Cruz Predatory Bird Research Group facility.

▲ **Figure 9.7** Climbing to an eyrie in Yosemite National Park.

Figure 9.8 Merlyn Felton ▶ fostering young falcons into the eyrie of a Peregrine laying thin-shelled eggs.

would best aid the recovery effort. It was impossible to keep everyone happy, but we kept the effort up until Peregrine recovery goals of our community were fulfilled.

Finally I want to thank my family, who have always been supportive, from my honeymoon/ Peregrine survey to fall trapping trips on Padre Island, Texas, with my son. All of us have similar stories and support that make the work more enjoyable and productive. I have had the occasion a few times to take a serious look at what is important in life. I am happy that the Peregrine has recovered and cherish the friendships that joint interests and efforts have generated. I feel very lucky to have been able to work with a large variety of people from all over and all backgrounds, and I am also grateful to this community for that aspect of life.

Current Ecological Information

The American Peregrine Falcon (*Falco peregrinus anatum*) occurs as a nesting species throughout California except in the driest desert areas. SCPBRG observations and trapping of Peregrines in fall and winter show that the nesting population is augmented by Peregrines from other regions. These include winter visitors from American Peregrine populations surrounding California. In addition, dozens of winter resident Peale's (*F. p. pealei*) and migrant Arctic (*F. p. tundrius*) Peregrines occur (Anderson et al. 1988). The three subspecies are difficult even for experts to distinguish in the field owing to overlap in size and plumage. Most breeding Peregrines in California are richly colored, with a black back and head, reddish breast, and brilliant yellow feet and cere; however, observations of wild

Peregrines and specimens housed at WFVZ indicate plumage variation is considerable in the breeding population, and extremely light or dark individuals are not unusual.

Observers have documented that most breeding Peregrines in California are year-round territorial residents. Band returns and observation of banded individuals show that most immatures remain in California, or if fledged near the border of the state, they may move slightly into adjacent states and Baja California. There is a large floating population of adults as evidenced by rapid replacement of adults in territories when deaths occur. Same-day replacement has occurred frequently. It is not unusual to observe a Peregrine anywhere in California at any time of year.

Radio-telemetry studies in California have described defended territories. Territory size and density vary greatly. Six nests in the Long Beach/ Los Angeles Harbor area are less than 2 km from their nearest neighbor (C. Thelander and P. Bloom pers. comm), and two nests on Morro Rock are less than 500 m apart. In contrast, dozens of pairs in California reside many kilometers from the nearest adjacent nest site.

Breeding Peregrines are generalists that prey on birds and bats they catch in the air. Some Peregrines focus on pigeons, other flocking species, or specialize in winter on larger prey they cannot carry. Most remain generalists. Virtually every native or exotic prey species below the size of the

Mono Lake Peregrines

D. Lee Aulman

Mono Lake hack site— I think it was 1983 when we first hacked Peregrines from the top of a nunatak formation (glacial uplift rock pile) at about 7,000 ft elevation above the lake. We released one female and two males in an area thick with eagles and haggard, hunting Goshawks. After a couple of tense weeks defending the site from these predators, things calmed a bit for my wife, Sheree, and me, and the falcons began to develop rapidly. Eventually the female and one of the males appeared to "sibling-bond" and became almost inseparable. The other male, though compatible with the others, was more of a loner. The site proved successful, as the birds dispersed after about eight weeks.

Randy Wilson

In early 1984, prior to our arrival for a second hacking season, the owner of the property, Dallas Burger, and an Audubon group including David Gaines, head of the Mono Lake Committee, observed a Peregrine land on the rocks near the hack box. Shortly thereafter a second, smaller second-year Peregrine flew in carrying an American Avocet which he deposited to the wailing female, which immediately began plucking the prey. With high-powered spotting scopes, those watching excitedly observed blue release bands that coincided with the bands on the sibling-bonded pair from the prior season's release! Remember, this was at the height of the "water wars" between the Mono Lake Committee, which was trying to save the

ecological integrity of a unique lake, and the Los Angeles Department of Water and Power, which was drying up the entire area, including the Owens Valley. Every endangered species that occupied or used the lake environs was more ammunition for the committee and their fight to save the lake. At about that time there had been numerous sightings of Peregrines, including pairs chasing phalaropes and shorebirds at the lake, documented by the committee researchers.

Later that season we successfully released six Peregrines, including four females. About three weeks after the release, we were watching the six birds together down low on a moraine trying to catch Green-tailed Towhees when a seventh Peregrine cut through them heading toward the hack site. The second-year

male landed in a snag next to the box and was eventually surrounded by four hunger-screaming females, with the two young tiercels flying nearby with curiosity. The second-year falcon had a release band on the same leg as the "loner" male from the first release. From then to the end of that hack season, he took quail from the box, aggressively defended against eagles, and even courted one or more of the females, which was a perfect scenario for a hack attendant.

One day as I was watching the second-year bird through the spotting scope, I noticed two people walking toward me on the road. One was David Gaines and the other David Desante, the astute birder from Point Reyes Bird Observatory. Desante had been a critic and doubter of the captive-breeding and reintroduction program and even

in publications had said something to the effect that reintroduced falcons wouldn't be "real" Peregrines. As they approached I told Gaines to look into the scope. After a few seconds he exclaimed, "It worked!" and he told Desante to look in the scope. After what seemed to be 10 seconds Desante looked down from the scope and shook his head and said, "I guess you are right, Dave." We went on to talk about the ramifications of Peregrines being back at the lake and the idiosyncrasies of *Empidonax* identification, among other things of avian interest. What satisfaction!

Lee Aulman *began work with the Santa Cruz Predatory Bird Research Group (SCPBRG) at the height of its Peregrine Falcon management activities in 1981 and continued full time for the organization until 1992. Lee now lives in Santa Barbara County and represents SCPBRG on projects in southern California.*

largest gulls or ducks has been observed in predation attempts or in over 5,300 prey remains collected in nests. To date, John Schmitt and field observers have identified 190 different avian species as prey of Peregrines in California (SCPBRG unpubl. data).

California Peregrine Habitat

California is a large state with a tremendous variation in climate, elevation, terrestrial habitats, and avian species. The terrestrial features in Peregrine territories are highly variable. The crucial element in territories, the aerial environment, is difficult to assess. Unlike most predators, Peregrines use air space for hunting and only need the terrestrial environment for roosting and for laying eggs. Despite the variety of habitats or degree of human development and habitat alteration, the common element in Peregrine territories is a large number of available aerial prey. If prey availability is sufficiently high, Peregrines in California will lay eggs on a variety of cliffs, buildings, and snags. In areas where ground predators are limited, Peregrines even nest on the ground.

Nest ledges in California are located from sea level to over 3,500 m in river canyons of the mountains (e.g., 1,100-m El Capitan cliff in Yosemite National Park). The Channel Islands support territories where Peregrines nest on the ground or on various inland or coastal cliff ledges. There are over 1,000 km of marine coastline on the mainland that support territories on volcanic plugs such as Morro Rock or smaller dirt and sediment sea cliffs. The largest number of territories occurs in coast range foothills in chaparral, grassland, or forested habitat with small (15 m) to medium (120 m) cliffs that provide nest ledges. Peregrines lay eggs on ledges of manmade structures such as buildings and bridges (some in non-urban areas). Emergent snags in forests are also used for nest sites. When food is particularly abundant, Peregrines nest in unusual situations such as under a barrel in San Francisco Bay marshlands, on the ground in Channel Islands gull colonies, in a stick nest in a prune tree adjacent to brackish marshland, or on a 2-m high cliff overlooking a guild of nesting tern colonies.

Historical Peregrine Territories

No population surveys or statewide searches for nesting territories were conducted in California before 1970. There are several sources of historical information on territories. As part of his California Department of Fish and Game (CDFG) job, D. D. McLean traveled around the state for several decades. Because of his personal interest in Peregrines, he documented 20-plus nest locations (R. Bond unpubl. data, SCPBRG unpubl. data). Some local naturalists documented territories in their personal notes (WFVZ, UC Berkeley Museum of Vertebrate Zoology, and California Academy of Sciences unpubl. data). Throughout California local egg collectors discovered nearby nests and obtained the richly colored red eggs for their collections. Although the total number collected was only a few hundred sets over a 60-plus year period ending in the 1950s, those sets document a large number (75+) of historical territories. Before the real rise in popularity of falconry that occurred in the late 1960s and 1970s in California, Peregrines became very rare. Hence, no more than 65 nestlings were ever taken from nests for training by falconers (SCPBRG unpubl. data). Falconers were a source of 20-plus historical nest territories not previously documented by egg collections.

For the SCPBRG database, historical territories are sites we have been able to confirm from a reputable source such as those listed above. We define a nesting territory as a site where Peregrines resided at least one year and where breeding progressed at least to the egg stage. Most historical sites were occupied repeatedly and produced fledglings.

When R. M. Bond (1946) assessed the Peregrine population in western North America, he collected anecdotal information. Bond attempted to use these sources rather than a statewide search to determine population size and density. Steve Herman obtained Bond's records and collected addi-

Kurt Stolzenburg

▲ **Figure 9.9** Lucy defending her eyrie.

The largest number of territories occurs in coast range foothills...

tional information on historical territories through 1970. In the early 1970s, Herman conducted a survey of historical territories and additional Peregrine habitats for the first large-scale California study (Herman 1971). Despite all efforts, vast areas of the state were never visited specifically to discover Peregrine territories until after 1971.

The actual number of territories that were used in any year before 1970 was never determined. Most members of the Peregrine community accept that the minimum number of occupied territories in the state exceeded 120 annually, although most of the state was not represented by historical information. Significant changes to prey populations, habitat, and culture or shooting ethics of the public have occurred since historical territories were documented. Most of the current territories have no pre-1970 historical record. For these reasons, attempts to speculate on historical population size and comparisons of the anecdotal historical record to the current or future population of Peregrines in California have little value. In virtually all areas where recovery has progressed in California, the historically documented number of territories has been exceeded (SCPBRG unpubl. data), indicating that most of the early recovery goals clearly underestimated the potential for current occupancy.

The Peregrine Population Decline

Bond (1946) and others (Newton 1979, Ratcliffe 1980) have documented that not all territories in a species' range are occupied in all years. Widespread shooting and persecution of predators in general may have contributed to a lower overall potential for territory occupancy before protection of predators in the 1960s and 1970s. A worldwide decline in Peregrine numbers was observed beginning in the 1950s (Hickey 1969). Falconers in California noticed a rapid loss of territory occupancy in the 1960s, but no obvious cause was determined until DDT was implicated (Ratcliffe 1967,1970,1980; Hickey and Anderson 1968; Risebrough et al. 1968a, b).

There have been a multitude of mortality factors documented for California Peregrines (SCPBRG unpubl. data). Fatalities caused by egg collecting, falconry, and museum-specimen collection affected a few individuals over many decades but had no impact on the Peregrine population. DDT was the only mortality factor common to all Peregrines at one point in time. None of the other factors have been associated with widespread population declines. Except when heavy DDT

Brian James Walton

contamination occurs, most Peregrines die as a result of territorial conflicts and accidents.

DDT and its breakdown product, DDE, accumulated in the fat of all California Peregrines. DDE causes eggshell thinning and loss of productivity. DDT was heavily incorporated into the Peregrine's ecosystem in California because of its use as a household pesticide, mosquito abatement agent, contaminant in the pesticide Difucol, agricultural and forest insecticide, and environmental pollutant near manufacturing and waste-dumping areas. Eggshell thinning in California began in the 1940s and continued after the EPA's 1972 restriction on DDT use. DDT and DDE remain in California as residual environmental pollutants in the air, water, and sediments near areas of agricultural runoff or manufacturing dump sites (Risebrough 2000). By the late 1990s, however, it had become a mortality factor affecting individual birds and territories but no longer limiting productivity of the entire California population (Walton 1998, 2000).

▲ **Figure 9.10** Eyass *anatum* just before release.

Paying Bills and Peregrines: Making the Ends Meet

Tery Drager

Researchers would bring a bird into my office and offer to buy me lunch if I could identify it. It was a pretty safe bet for them.

I was never a birder and barely passed high school biology, so spending 22 years working for people whose lives revolve around the Peregrine Falcon was quite a challenge. Researchers would bring a bird into my office and offer to buy me lunch if I could identify it. It was a pretty safe bet for them.

In the late 1970s Brian Walton was arranging for permits, funding, birds, money, and staff to start a breeding facility. He had a contract with the California Department of Fish and Game for $19,995, and given his knowledge of budgeting, I am sure he thought we could save the species in California for that amount. Eight million dollars later, we got the job done.

Over the years I cleaned chambers, cut the heads off mice, made a lot of birthday cakes, and had a few dinner parties. But what I did best was make sure the bills got paid. Agencies wanted $40,000 worth of work for every $20,000 they gave us, and that is where my skills became important. With a little creative bookkeeping, the inside track on how the university accounting office works, an ability to cut through red tape, and soccer pals strewn around campus in critical positions, I spent my time making sure everything got paid for even if there was not enough money in the contract.

The staff was patient with my lack of knowledge relating to "the real stuff," and they trusted me to make the right decisions about how to pay

SCPBRG file photo

them—was it travel or a stipend?

Over the years we grew to know 380 attendants and sent them to 228 different sites—many of them named "Castle Rock." After obtaining 86 different permits, we handled 3,258 birds of 28 species. I never knew who was going to what site, where the sites were, or how long they would be there—but I could get blue corn chips to them if they needed them.

In 1978 when someone called with a Peregrine sighting, the entire office would empty. The whole group would drive hundreds of miles just to catch a glimpse of this "new" bird. Now when someone calls in with a sighting, the phone message gets circulated around the office for days before anyone

responds to it. We must have done something right!

We have gone from carbon paper to computer chips, endangered species to pest species. I have met a lot of wonderful people and had unbelievable opportunities and experiences. If I had it to do over, I would change only one thing—I would pay a little more attention in biology class.

Tery Drager *joined the University of California, Santa Cruz staff the year the campus opened, in 1965. For 25 years, she was the management service officer at the Santa Cruz Predatory Bird Research Group (SCPBRG). Tery's depth of experience with university policies and administrative procedures makes her an important member of the SCPBRG team. Tery retired in 2001, and she and her husband, Wayne, moved to northern California from where she still helps SCPBRG make ends meet, but now only part time.*

Brian James Walton

▲ **Figure 9.11** Peregrine with her eggs.

Shell fragments or whole eggs of over 1,300 eggs have been collected from Peregrine nests in California. They were all measured by Clark "Sam" Sumida and are stored in the WFVZ. The California samples showed that the population's eggshell-thinning level averaged over 17%, a level associated with population decline or extinction (Peakall and Kiff 1988). In recent years, groups of territories in regions with DDT sinks or near historical DDT dump sites have continued to experience eggshell thinning above the 17% level. Peregrines in the other areas of California still experience some, but more moderate, eggshell thinning (SCPBRG unpubl. data).

Annual Peregrine Surveys

The 1965 Madison Peregrine Conference (Hickey 1969) documented a worldwide decline of Peregrines and stimulated research across North America. Then in the early 1970s, the combined events of restriction of DDT by the EPA, passing of the federal and state Endangered Species Acts (ESA), and Steve Herman's Peregrine survey pointed out the need for Peregrine monitoring in California. Herman (1971) could only locate two pairs of Peregrines and suggested there had been a 95% reduction in the number of occupied territories in California.

Informal Peregrine surveys were begun in conjunction with statewide Prairie Falcon, Bald Eagle, and Golden Eagle surveys conducted for the CDFG from 1971 to 1974 (Garrett and Mitchell 1973; Thelander 1973,1974). Then in 1975 and 1976 Carl Thelander conducted a statewide Peregrine survey (Thelander 1975, 1976, 1977). Clearly, a major decline had occurred as no more

than 11 active territories could be located in the state. Planned recovery actions were needed to avoid extirpation in the state (U.S. Fish and Wildlife Service [FWS]1982).

From the 1970s through the 1990s, numerous researchers participated in ground surveys to canvass the state and map territories. In the late 1970s, I conducted helicopter surveys as Navy training missions on the Channel Islands. Sandy Boyce, Clayton White, Lloyd Kiff, Carl Thelander, and I made helicopter surveys over U.S. Forest Service (USFS) lands throughout the state (Boyce and White 1979,1980; Thelander and Walton 1980). Dave Harlow, Monte Kirven, and Geoff Monk conducted helicopter surveys of the northern Coast Ranges for the FWS and the Bureau of Land Management (BLM) where a remnant population persisted (Monk 1979–1982, Kirven 1982–1987, Monk and Harlow 1984). When population management efforts began in earnest in the late 1970s, an annual statewide effort to monitor the California Peregrine population was instigated by Richard Olendorff of BLM and coordinated by Geoff Monk, Monty Kirven, and SCPBRG researchers (Kirven and Walton 1988–1992, Monk and Walton 1989, Monk et al. 1989, Walton 1998). Jeep Pagel and Brian Woodbridge monitored Peregrine territories in the same region in the 1980s and 1990s for USFS (Pagel 1991). Other state survey areas were coordinated by SCPBRG biologists Merlyn Felton, Rob Ramey, Lee Aulman, Matt Nixon, Craig Himmelwright, and Brian Latta.

The results of these surveys included territory locations, productivity of territorial pairs, analysis of eggshells and egg contents, and collection of

Figure 9.12 Number of territorial Peregrine pairs in California (known to 1992, known and estimated 1993–2000).

The estimated minimum number of territories used annually in California currently exceeds 175.

prey remains. Various physical features of the territories were analyzed by Geoff Monk and SCPBRG. The information is managed as a computer database by Janet Linthicum of SCPBRG.

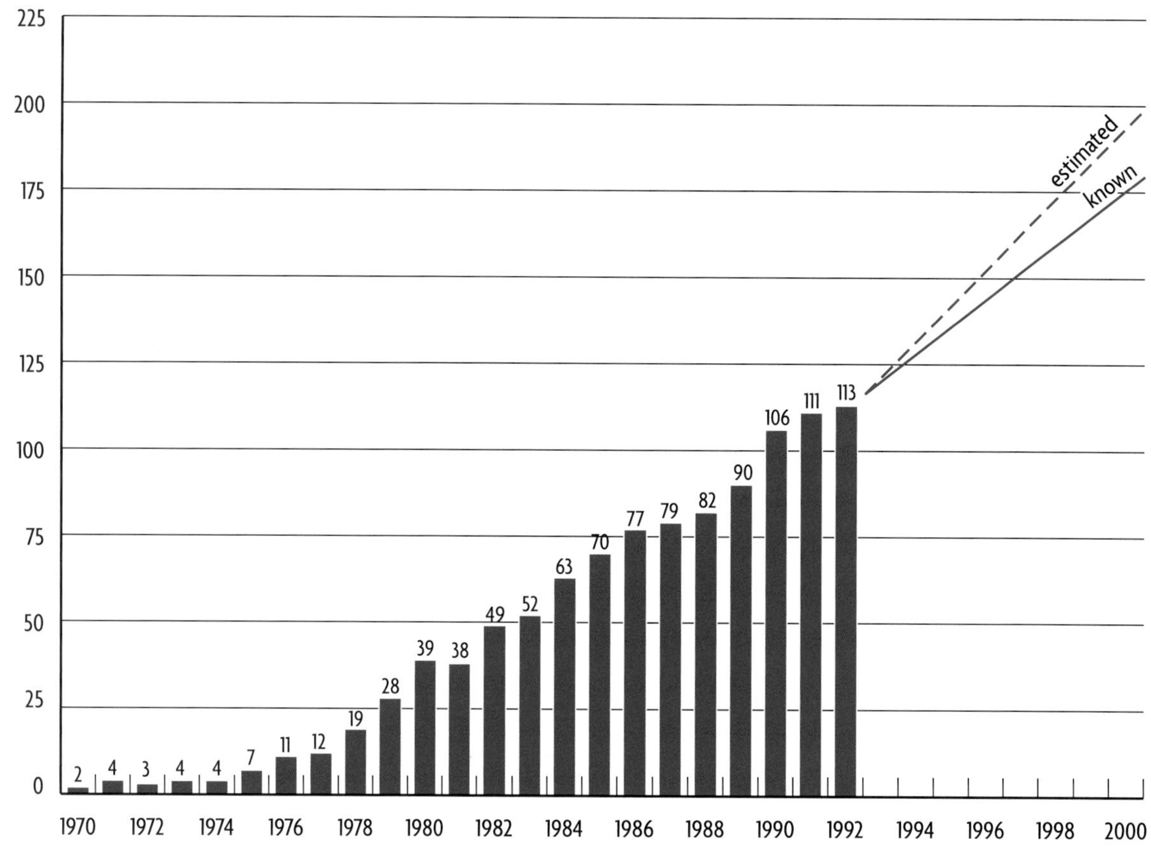

Figure 9.12 illustrates the increase in the number of known territorial Peregrine pairs in California from 1970 through the 1992 breeding season. The increases in the first 10-year period include discovery of some sites that may have been active for the entire period. The increases from 1980 to 1992 reflect a real three-fold increase in the California Peregrine population. By 1992, the California population reached the recovery goal of 120 pairs needed to trigger removal from the federal endangered species list (delisting). The emphasis of government agencies switched to other species. It became clear that future survey funding would not allow discovery of a high percentage of the actual pairs that nested in the state.

The numbers shown in Figure 9.12 from 1993 to 2000 are estimates, which I made, of the population increase. The population was too large to allow for complete statewide surveys each year. During this period, there was no evidence of multiple losses of previously known active territories, but there was consistent location of newly occupied territories each year. Between 1992 and 2000, over 60 new territories were incidentally discovered. The estimated minimum number of territories used annually in California currently exceeds 175.

Peregrines have become a commonly observed raptor. Many remaining historical sites have been reoccupied, and new territories with no previous history were documented in the 1990s. Although new pairs are commonly observed, not all of the state is surveyed, and most new pairs are not being monitored regularly. The current number of territories probably exceeds 200, and one could argue for 250 based on the large area of California not being surveyed. There appears to continue to be a huge potential for growth of the known population as new territories are discovered each year in areas previously surveyed.

Restoration Management Efforts

Many actions occurred to restore Peregrines starting in the late 1970s. A Pacific States Recovery Plan (FWS 1982) was written by a recovery team set up by FWS. The team included members of government agencies and was later combined with the Rocky Mountain team to form a Western Peregrine Falcon Recovery Team. The various protections afforded by the federal and state ESAs and the state's Fully Protected List were enforced. Consultations by FWS and CDFG personnel were required for actions concerning Peregrines or their

Too Many Peregrines?

Brian Latta

While still in college back East, my then girlfriend and I decided to drive across the country to California. She wanted to look at schools. I needed a break and some direction. One day we found ourselves at a small café overlooking the outrageously scenic Big Sur coastline. A hulking bulge of rock rising several hundred feet out of the pounding surf dominated the view from our outdoor table. Upon determining the object of my fixated stare, our chatty waitress informed us that the sea cliff in question was the home of a pair of endangered Peregrine Falcons. She further informed us that every spring, biologists from the University of California, Santa Cruz climbed to the Peregrines' eyrie, removed their thin-shelled eggs, and left a chick behind for them to raise. I think I said something to the effect of, "Wow, what a cool job!" Well, it was 1981. Meanwhile, a little bell was ringing in my subconscious: "Foreshadowing, foreshadowing..." How was I to know then that it would become my job to rappel into that very same eyrie over a decade later?

Ever since I was a little kid I have been obsessed with birds of prey. And ever since reading Jean Craighead George's *My Side of the Mountain*, I have been obsessed with Peregrine Falcons. "... I heard a cry in the sky. I looked up. Swinging down the valley on long pointed wings was a large bird. I was struck by the ease and swiftness of its flight. 'Duck Hawk,' she said." I too have been struck by the ease and swift-

Mitch Siemens

ness of its flight ... literally ... repeatedly ... it hurts! But when I was a kid growing up on the East Coast, I thought I would never get to see one. The last Peregrine had disappeared from my region a few years after I was born.

I became involved in the restoration of California Peregrines rather late in the game. Through a series of circumstances, however, I was able to participate in almost every facet of the recovery effort, building on the good works of those dedicated individuals who went before me. In 1990, 10-year veteran George Patracuola threw his back out and had to retire for the year. Fortunately I was in a position to take over his shift, caring for the captive birds and working with Janet Linthicum to raise a season's worth of

Peregrine, Aplomado Falcon, and Harris's Hawk chicks. The following year, Lee Aulman stepped down as lead climber and field coordinator, and again I was at the right place at the right time. Treading on the same worn cliff-top paths as Lee, Matt Nixon, Craig Himmelwright, Merlyn Felton, and others, I was given the privilege of rescuing thin-shelled eggs and delivering Peregrine chicks to some of the same eyries and running the same hack sites they had.

Since then I have had the pleasure of helping document the phenomenal increase in the number of pairs, reoccupied eyries, and newly occupied territories. I have seen Peregrine pairs battle Prairie Falcons and reclaim their historical nest cliffs. Most recently it has been my task

to abate the one downside of our collective unprecedented success. That is to capture and translocate hatch-year and second-year Peregrines that have been foraging at Least Tern and Snowy Plover colonies, both of which are listed species. Having grown up in a world where there were no Peregrines, I never dreamed there would come a day when there would be "too many." Thanks, Tom. Thanks, Brian. It has been a privilege.

Brian Latta *joined the Santa Cruz Predatory Bird Research Group field team in 1989 and became lead field biologist in 1991. He continues to participate in work with Peregrines, Bald and Golden Eagles, and other raptors of concern in California on a variety of projects.*

"I've found living proof . . ." —Bruce Springsteen

Janet Linthicum

In 1983, graduating with a degree in Environmental Studies from the University of California at Santa Cruz and feeling qualified to wait tables (a job I had never held), I found an ad in the paper for "Peregrine Nest Site Attendant." Although my interests tended toward evolution and animal behavior, I had a proclivity for raptors, and this sounded like a perfect job. A friend drove me back the 350 miles from Los Angeles for my big interview with Brian Walton, as I had no car and no driver's license. I found Brian in a dusty trailer, feet up on the table, and his only question for me in this all-important interview was, "Can you be in Santa Rosa April 1st?"

Well, sure, all I needed was a license and a car. I saw my first Peregrine in the company of Monte Kirven and Geoff Monk. A Peregrine owns the air like nothing else I have ever seen. I spent that El Niño spring "guarding" one of the few eyries on the West Coast at the time, although given the rain, that amounted to reading *The Brothers Karamozov* three times through in a week. I learned where ticks are found, and not to be the person sitting near a reputed rattlesnake den when the sun finally comes out.

I have been privileged to be involved in the recovery of Peregrines on the West Coast ever since, from following tandem hunts through a Questar after White-throated Swifts down the 3,500-ft face of El Capitan to following eggs from early embryogenesis out the door to take their chances.

▲ Janet Linthicum with Harpy Eagle chick.

Having no particular interest in falconry, my passion has always been wild Peregrines. I used to drive north up the coast from Santa Cruz in the hope of seeing a Peregrine during the winter and early spring. Over the years, my sightings increased. There was one crucial day in my experience. It was probably February or March. I picked up a juvenile male coursing the coastal cliffs north of Santa Cruz, owning the wind. I leap-frogged him for a few miles, where he encountered a previously unknown territorial pair and a floater female. I briefly had four Peregrines in view. Coincidentally, Bruce Springsteen was singing, "I've found living proof . . ."; an apt description of the experience. That day, I let go of the recovery of Peregrines. Fair winds to you, and all of your $F_{n\,=\,?}$ generations.

"Earthquake-proved, and signatured By ages of storms: on its peak A falcon has perched."

—Robinson Jeffers

There are so many stories to tell: Craig Himmelwright announcing to the Yosemite Park biologist, and everyone else in the park with a radio, that the former had "just missed a great copulation." Or Lee Aulman . . . , or Merlyn Felton . . . , or Matt Nixon . . . , or Jeep Pagel . . . , or . . . oh well. These are the guys who actually suspended themselves in the air for Peregrines.

I recently returned from a fishing trip with my husband, Brian Latta. We traveled through such stunning vistas as Flaming Gorge and the Frying Pan River canyon. I have no idea how many Peregrine cliffs we passed. The amazing thing is that we did not stop to scope out one of them. Did not have to. We just knew the Peregrines were out there.

Janet Linthicum *began work at Santa Cruz Predatory Bird Research Group (SCPBRG) in 1983, doing fieldwork with Peregrine reintroduction. Several years later she became a principal staff member of the Group's laboratory during its most productive years for raptor propagation. She continues with SCPBRG and participates in current raptor issues in California.*

habitat. Habitat protection measures, including buffer zones around nests, were applied.

The restriction on DDT use in 1972 made Peregrine restoration possible. The remnant population persisted at a small vulnerable size. Extirpation had occurred in large areas of range. The decision was made to develop a captive-breeding population and conduct releases to supplement remnant Peregrines until DDT levels in the environment diminished.

The budget of the Pacific States Recovery Plan went largely unfunded. Through the efforts of Robert Mallette and Ron Jurek of CDFG, Dave Harlow and Robert Mesta of FWS, Dean Carrier and Harley Grieman of USFS, and Butch Olendorff of BLM, government funds from a variety of sources were provided as seed money for hands-on recovery efforts. Fortunately the Peregrine is a charismatic species loved by many, and the public and corporations generously provided additional funds. The real fuel of the recovery, however, was the tireless volunteer effort of hundreds of people who worked diligently for two decades to keep the Peregrine increasing. The leadership of Tom Cade and The Peregrine Fund had shown that restoration was possible, and a nationwide effort resulted and continued until the bird could be delisted in 1999.

The surveys from 1980 to 1990 formed the basis for planning recovery strategies and release locations, to increase the rate of Peregrine population growth and range recovery in California. Peregrines disperse from the nest from which they fledge and when mature breed in other distant territories. We have found dispersal distances in California to be 10 to 485 km (median 150 km) for females and 13 to 670 km (median 90 km) for males. For thousands of years the only way to enter the breeding population, which likely occupied all available habitat at capacity, had been to replace breeding adults. To establish birds with natal origin in regions where Peregrines were extirpated and outside the dispersal distance from existing nests, releases were conducted to stimulate range recovery. In areas where only a few birds remained, releases were designed to provide birds as future replacements for breeding adults and to bolster productivity of existing adults that were still suffering from eggshell thinning.

A captive breeding population was established on the UCSC campus by SCPBRG with *anatum* breeding stock from falconers and The Peregrine Fund. Some young for release were provided to SCPBRG by private falconry breeders. Eggs were removed from wild nests with a history of failure from eggshell thinning. With laboratory incuba-

Kurt Stolzenburg

Figure 9.13 Peregrine at its eyrie along the Big Sur Coast. Note the eggs at lower left.

tion, some productivity was salvaged from eggs thinned to a degree that loss in the wild was likely (Burnham et al. 1978, Peakall and Kiff 1988). Those young were used for breeding stock and also for release.

Developing a breeding facility, perfecting breeding methods, daily care of breeders, rearing of food supply, and the intense effort each spring to hatch, rear, and release young falcons were a major undertaking. Although the many friends of the Peregrine provided significant funding, the number of volunteer hours, long days and nights, and stress of parenting can only be appreciated by those who participated in the achievement.

Releases for Population and Range Recovery

Once DDT restriction occurred, efforts to repopulate California began in earnest. The first management took place before a recovery plan was completed. In later recovery actions, we used annual release supplements written by me and adopted by the FWS and the California Peregrine Falcon Implementation Plan (Monk and Walton 1989). The development of techniques for captive breeding, wildlife management, and release of

The real fuel of the recovery… was the tireless volunteer effort of hundreds of people who worked diligently for two decades to keep the Peregrine increasing.

Remembrances of Peregrines Past

Cheryl C. Walton

My history with falcons started in the 1950s when a kestrel captured a Mourning Dove on our patio in Paradise Valley, Arizona. Years later, I met Carl Thelander and his best friend from high school . . . someone named Brian Walton. The college I attended, Cal Poly, San Luis Obispo, was their choice because it was near the

2:00 a.m. in the morning after Brian and Carl retrieved them from a friend who had illegally removed them from the nest. Later Captain Hugh Thomas arranged the "okay" for Brian to put the babies back into the nest. I guess that was the first California "reintroduction." May and Vern Davies were the nest observers, making sure all

Brian James Walton

"famed" Morro Rock Peregrine eyrie. Attending school was a sideline to our weekend trips out to "the Rock," the Carrizo Plains, or the Cholame Flats looking for Prairie Falcons and other raptors.

Falcons, falconry, and field work became a way of life. In 1972 my sister Linda and I had the Morro Rock babies on our living room rug at

went well that year. Later, my dear friends Johnny Glassburn and Merlyn Felton watched over Morro Rock for many years.

Once out of school, Brian and I got married, traveling the northern California coast to Fort Bragg on our honeymoon to check for Peregrines.

Ironically, the first job I had out of school was work-

ing at Stauffer Chemical Company, lab-testing the efficacy of potential pesticides and preparing environmental reports for the Environmental Protection Agency on the safety of the chemicals. Of course, one benefit was the two-week vacation I got. So off we would go, packed to the gills in our Volkswagen squareback, (with our English setter, Grimes) to visit as many of our friends as we could who were starting Peregrine breeding projects or were deeply involved with everything Peregrine . . . Les and Nicka Boyd in Washington, Wayne and Alora Nelson in British Columbia, John Campbell in Alberta, and Bill and Pat Burnham and Ed and Charlotte Freienmuth in Colorado. So many wonderful visits—such hospitality!

Brian started the Coast Range Biological Research Institute which evolved into the Santa Cruz Predatory Bird Research Group (SCPBRG) after Brian connected with local veterinarian Jim Roush and University of California, Santa Cruz (UCSC) natural history professor Ken Norris. We started out small with incubators, eggs, and babies in our bedroom and then with lots of volunteer help (too numerous to name here), developing our home and the facility on the university campus. Having friends like Frank Lepori, Rick Kline, John Schmitt, John Moran, Hans Peeters, John Baumlin, and Bob Katona, blessed with the artistic talents to engineer gorgeous renditions of nature's finest specimens, was

amazing. Many donated their crafts to auctions held to raise money for SCPBRG Peregrine work. The auction highlight was Steve Martin's "bird show" where his trained crow flew out to collect checks from the audience.

Over the years, I filled in where I could be supportive to the cause. There were many highlights where Peregrines enriched my life. I drove baby falcons up to remote California locales to meet Merlyn to exchange the babies for an incubator full of eggs to be hatched at the lab to start the cycle all over again.

In contrast, I joined Bob Risebrough and Wally Jarman at the Bodega Bay Institute to work endless hours on pesticide analyses of Peregrine eggs. I had a variety of office jobs, my favorite inputting over 5,000 entries of prey species data that had been collected by Merlyn, Jeep Pagel, Brian Latta, and others and identified by John Schmitt. I visited waterfalls, canyons, towering cliffs, vistas of splendor, all reminding us that when we are at Peregrine nests we are in God's country. I loved scouting the Big Sur coast while having gray whales frolic in the surf below—mothers and their calves. A great family memory was having Brian's mom, all 95 pounds, hanging onto the car-door handle for dear life at "Hurricane" Point. We once airlifted a hack box by helicopter up to Chimney Rock with Bill Burnham in Colorado; and also hand-carried another one piece-by-piece across the top of a narrow promontory at Muir Beach in California.

A scary driving story (don't we all have one?) was driving along the top of a steep ravine on an extremely narrow dirt road (barely wide enough for one rickety truck) in Durango, Colorado, while Ed Freienmuth told tales of Peregrines past, all the while gesturing wildly with both hands off the steering wheel. Then there was trapping on South Padre Island, Texas, riding all-terrain vehicles and finishing off the day with an unbelievable shrimp feed prepared by Randy Townsend.

In 1982 Lloyd Kiff scheduled a month-long excursion to check out various egg collections for the Western Foundation of Vertebrate Zoology around the International Ornithological Congress meeting that was being held in Moscow . At the last minute, Lloyd had to back out of the trip, and Brian and I were allowed to go in his stead. We first went to Finland to visit a museum's collection, then Moscow where Bob Risebrough delivered his paper in Russian and Fran and Fred Hamerstrom and Bill and Pat Burnham joined us in Red Square. We went to Ireland (where Ronald Stevens had a meal prepared on our behalf that was like no other—especially after having been in Moscow for a week

where portions were extremely small), then London (where we met Ian and Halina Newton and Derek Ratcliffe and went out to Ian's study area where he was radio-tracking European Sparrowhawks), and lastly to New York where we did eventually rendezvous with Lloyd and Julie Kiff before heading back to sunny California.

It has always been an "open-door" policy with SCPBRG and the Waltons, so we have shared many wonderful experiences with people from all over the world as well as being treated to many great occasions of homespun hospitality and generosities, all through the common thread of the Peregrine Falcon. Everything came to a crescendo with the gala in Boise, Idaho, and the removal of the Peregrine from the endangered species list.

Needless to say… work still continues, while capturing more and more people in its wake. I am glad to have been a part of it.

There were many high- lights where Peregrines enriched my life.

Cheryl Walton *graduated from California Polytechnic State University at San Luis Obispo, California. She married fellow biologist Brian Walton in 1974. One son, Neil, is 19 years old and plays baseball for California State University, Fullerton. Currently Cheryl works for Alternative Family Education, her local school district's Homeschool Program. Cheryl is an avid moviegoer and scorekeeps and attends as many of Neil's baseball games as she can in her spare time.*

▲ **Figure 9.14** Yvon Chouinard, founder and owner of the Patagonia company, was one of the many volunteers who helped with rock climbing and other project needs in California. With Tom Cade he climbed into one of the last occupied Peregrine eyries in southern California in 1954.

Peregrines was in its infancy in the 1970s, and all of the initial efforts were experimental. Fortunately The Peregrine Fund's biologists were a few years ahead of SCPBRG and had established some basic protocols. California releases began in 1977 with two captive-bred young from Cornell being fostered at Morro Rock. In 1978 we released the first captive-hatched young from wild eggs. The following year the first young were released by hacking. Cross-fostering began in 1982.

By 2000 we had released 309 young by fostering. Fostering was conducted by releasing two 14- to 21-day-old, captive-hatched, parent-reared nestlings into existing Peregrine nests. Fostered young replaced dummy eggs that had been switched earlier with thin-shelled wild eggs. Parent falcons accepted the young in all cases.

We released 508 young by hacking. Hacking was conducted by releasing small family groups of captive-hatched, five-week-old, parent-reared fledglings in areas where breeding pairs no longer existed. Young were placed in hack boxes on cliffs or towers and fed by unseen attendants until the 10-week-old young dispersed.

We released 115 young by cross-fostering. Cross-fostering was conducted by releasing two 18-day-old Peregrines into Prairie Falcon nests. We used captive-hatched young that were reared by Peregrines before release. We selected nests for cross-fostering in areas where Prairie Falcons occupied former Peregrine territories. Parent Prairie Falcons accepted the young Peregrines in all cases. Many Prairie Falcon nests contained four or five young that were translocated to other

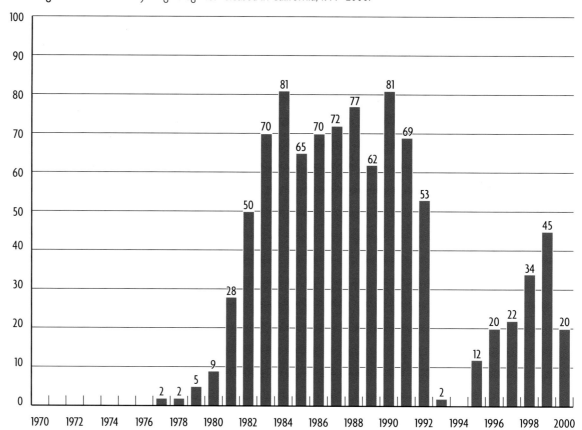

Figure 9.15 Number of young Peregrines released in California, 1977–2000.

Prairie Falcon territories and replaced with Peregrines. Since the Prairie Falcons often had their brood size reduced when two nestling Peregrines were cross-fostered, the survival of Peregrine young was very good. Only one cross-fostered Peregrine did not fledge. Despite extremely limited ability to follow or identify these birds, six cross-fostered Peregrines were later observed breeding normally with wild Peregrines. No Peregrine/Prairie Falcon courtship interactions have been observed in any regions of the state. We believe parent-rearing to age 18 days by Peregrines, and the instinctive ability of Peregrines to recognize age plumage dimorphism (an adult Peregrine from an immature Peregrine or the similar Prairie Falcon), later led to successful breeding of cross-fostered Peregrines.

We used fostering in areas with remnant pairs of Peregrines where eggshell thinning continued to depress productivity. Hacking was used in areas where nesting falcons had been eliminated to increase the rate of range recovery in California. Cross-fostering was also used in areas where adult breeders had been extirpated in order to increase the rate of Peregrine productivity. We know of examples where released birds mated with birds released by all three techniques and with wild-hatched birds.

A total of 932 Peregrine young were released to bolster productivity and increase the range of the once severely endangered Peregrine. When releases began, we expected a high first-year mortality, approximately 70%. Although we could not determine how many released birds survived, clearly first-year mortality was lower than anticipated. All three techniques worked well, producing more birds that later entered the breeding population than we expected when releases began. In the 1980s and 1990s, our blue-banded release birds were commonly observed as breeders throughout the state.

Figure 9.15 shows the number of young Peregrines released by all techniques. Releases from 1977 to 1993 were specifically designed to meet recovery goals for delisting the species. Starting in 1995 the release strategy was altered, and releases involved salvaged young we translocated to reduce high mortality of fledglings at urban or bridge nest sites. Some additional Peregrines were translocated from territories where fledglings and adults would consume nearby nesting California Least Terns and Snowy Plovers. Finally, additional birds were purchased from captive breeders and released because of FWS requirements that a bridge retrofit could only continue without delay if three Peregrines were released by hacking, guaranteeing the overall population would not suffer from resulting potential reduced productivity from nest disturbance. If bridge disturbances were actually known to occur to breeding Peregrines, young were removed from the eyries on bridges and also then hacked.

When releases began, the production of wild fledglings in California was low. By 1984, we were releasing 70 to 80 young a year and wild production of young totaled 50. We more than doubled the number of fledglings. By 1992 our captive adults were aging, and we were releasing 50 to 60 young a year. Wild productivity exceeded 100 that year. We were only increasing young fledged by 50%, and it was clear that our contribution would diminish as the recovery continued. The economics of continued captive breeding were no longer justifiable after 1992, so we closed our facility and moved our breeders to other programs.

Once the wild population had reached delisting goals for total number of territories, captive breeding was discontinued. In 1992 the population exceeded 120 pairs, but they were not distributed in the manner required in the recovery plan (FWS 1982) to reach the goal of each recovery management unit. Figure 9.15 shows how the recovery has continued through 2000 and that the goals have been exceeded in all recovery management units.

Conclusion

With increases in eggshell thickness in most regions of California, continued restriction of DDT use, and unexpectedly low levels of juvenile and adult mortality, the increase in Peregrines continues to occur, and management may only be necessary to complete recovery in areas of continued high contamination of DDT. Those areas are now supported by dispersal of young

from other areas of increasing productivity. Removal from the federal ESA occurred in 1999, and discussions have begun concerning the potential for delisting under the California ESA. Although it may be several years before the population stabilizes, it is clear that early criteria for recovery underestimated the potential for number of territories. The restoration effort was successful in eliminating the threat of extinction in California, increasing the rate of recovery of the population size, and increasing the return to full range of the species in California. The Peregrine remains a rare bird in California compared to most avian species; however, the Peregrine Falcon has returned to the prominent role on top of the avian food web in most of the ecosystems it originally occupied in the state.

▲ **Figure 9.16** Tom Cade (left), John Harrigan, Chairman and CEO of Union Bank, and Brian Walton in John's office where he had a television to monitor the activities of the Peregrines nesting on the building.

Brian Walton *received his Bachelor of Science degree from California Polytechnic State University, San Luis Obispo, in 1973 and his Master of Science degree in biological sciences from San Jose State University in 1978. He is a research specialist with the University of California, Santa Cruz, Division of Natural Sciences, and Coordinator of the Santa Cruz Predatory Bird Research Group (SCPBRG) at Long Marine Lab. He has been active in managing birds of prey since 1971 when he studied Prairie Falcons as a field biologist for the California Department of Fish and Game.*

Brian became the founding coordinator of SCPBRG in 1977, over time managing captive breeding of Peregrines, Aplomado Falcons, Bald Eagles, Harris's Hawks, and Elf Owls. While managing region-wide field operations for threatened and endangered bird populations, he has worked closely with biologists of state and federal agencies to craft strategies for the recovery of raptor populations. He served on the California Bald Eagle Working Team, California Peregrine Falcon Working Team, California Condor Recovery Team, and as a research associate of the Western Foundation of Vertebrate Zoology and consultant to various other conservation efforts. Brian also served two eight-year terms on the Board of Directors of The Peregrine Fund and is a former vice president of the organization.

Late in life Brian discovered he was good at coaching high school baseball. He has enjoyed that sideline in addition to his raptor work since 1998. His wife, Cheryl, assists him with his work while his son, Neil, continues to show an interest in baseball in college.

CE 88/90   Robert Bateman

Chapter 10

Peregrines in the Midwest

Harrison B. Tordoff and Patrick T. Redig

The pioneering work of The Peregrine Fund in eastern states made it easy to start the restoration effort in the Midwest.

Techniques for breeding Peregrines in captivity and for releasing them to the wild were handed to us, fully developed and tested in the field. The Minnesota Department of Natural Resources provided reliable annual funding from the Nongame Wildlife Program, courtesy of Carrol Henderson, which made up about a fifth of the cost of the Minnesota releases. The remainder came from generous donations from private sources, ranging from a few dollars to $5,000 annually. More than 150 individuals, corporations, and private foundations contributed to the Minnesota project. We estimate that the total cost per bird released was about $2,500. The 180 falcons released in Minnesota from 1982 to 1989 therefore cost about $450,000. Funding for the project in the other Midwestern states and provinces was independently raised. In the entire Midwest, 1,188 Peregrines have been released, at a cost of $2,970,000. By any standard, this is a lot of money but still only about a tenth of the cost of one F-16 fighter plane, currently selling new for $28,000,000. If the per-bird cost of $2,500 is a reasonable estimate for

the entire project, the total cost of the 7,000 Peregrines released continent-wide was about $17,500,000, still a bargain compared with the price of an F-16.

When other Midwestern states expressed interest in Peregrine releases, we decided to coordinate the entire effort, purchasing falcons from 36 private breeders, all falconers, checking the health of the birds and banding them at The Raptor Center at the University of Minnesota, then selling them to the various state and private agencies doing the actual releases for enough return to cover our costs. Our role as Peregrine wholesalers may have been unique. We wanted to eliminate the possibility of a dozen states bidding against each other for the limited supply of young falcons. Because we handled almost all of the birds at the University of Minnesota's Raptor Center, we were able to maintain a central database, recording pedigree information from the propagators and post-release data from the regional cooperators. With this information, we prepared and circulated annual reports, finder lists for identifying individual falcons, nesting outcome reports, progress reports twice monthly through the nesting seasons, and research papers on various topics.

Cooperation from the leaders in the 13 Midwestern states (North Dakota, Minnesota, Wisconsin, Michigan, South Dakota, Nebraska, Iowa,

◀ Figure 10.1 *Peregrine and Young* ©Robert Bateman. Reproduction rights courtesy Boshkung Inc. and Mill Pond Press.

▲ **Figure 10.2** The authors, Pat Redig (left) and Bud Tordoff (right), band a falcon at the Mayo Clinic hack site in 1987.

Table 10.1 Peregrine population growth and productivity in the Midwest, 1982–2000.

Year	Hacked young	Terr. pairs	Nesting pairs	Success pairs	Young fledged	Young/ terr. pair	Young/ nesting pair	Young/ success pair
1982–86	105	4	2	0	0	0	0	0
1987	73	6	4	1	3	0.5	.75	3.0
1988	87	13	8	6	16	1.2	2.0	2.7
1989	124	16	12	9	22	1.4	1.8	2.4
1990	103	23	16	13	33	1.4	2.1	2.5
1991	117	30	22	17	36	1.2	1.6	2.1
1992	107	37	32	23	68	1.8	2.1	3.0
1993	38	53	43	33	87	1.6	2.0	2.6
1994	66	62	51	41	116	1.9	2.3	2.8
1995	54	67	53	43	118	1.8	2.2	2.7
1996	33	77	58	48	127	1.6	2.2	2.6
1997	35	90	69	58	167	1.9	2.4	2.9
1998	55	99	84	74	205	2.1	2.4	2.7
1999	63	107	89	76	214	2.0	2.4	2.8
2000	32	130	101	84	248	1.9	2.4	2.9
Total	1092	814	644	526	1460	1.8	2.3	2.8

Illinois, Indiana, Ohio, Kansas, Missouri, and Kentucky, plus southeastern Manitoba and western Ontario) was excellent, and the falcon propagators supplied, in addition to birds, valuable information on the subspecific background of the falcons they produced. Our database was enhanced by the fact that about 80% of the pairs in the Midwest nested on manmade structures, mostly in cities, making it easier for an army of observers to keep track of daily falcon activities and to identify the individual birds involved.

Demography

The general demographic traits of Peregrine populations in various parts of the world are fairly well known. Our analysis of the demography of the Midwest population produced no surprises even though ours was the first report on a population that was predominantly urban. Our conclusions were based on larger samples than have been available for most other studies. Table 10.1 summarizes the demography of this growing population (Tordoff and Redig 1997, Tordoff et al. 1998b).

Age of first breeding: Usually two years, but many females and a few males nested at age one in the early stages of population growth (Table 10.2). As the population began to level off, finding a place to breed was more difficult, and some individuals were as old as five or six when first found breeding, as replacements in established territories. We have no proof, of course, that these older birds had not nested elsewhere, but it seems unlikely given the usual Peregrine fidelity to territory and our close monitoring. In recent years a sharp decline in the proportion of females breeding at age one and an increase in first breeding by four-year-old females have occurred. As the population has grown, the percentage of one-year-old birds in the breeding population has declined steadily (Table 10.3).

Dispersal: Mean dispersal distance (from fledge or hack site to adult territory site) of females (354 km, n − 67) is about twice that of males (174 m, n = 73), a pattern found commonly in raptorial birds (Newton 1979).

First year survival: Although difficult to determine, our best estimate is about 40% (Tordoff and Redig 1997). Using a hypothetical example, assume 50 pairs of nesting Peregrines, producing 100 young in one year. With first-year survival of 40% and subsequent annual adult survival of 87%, 100 fledged young should produce about 35 survivors at age two. With a similar 87% annual survival of breeding adults, annual loss will be 13 of the 100 original adults. These 13 can be replaced from the 35 survivors, now breeding age, leaving 22 survivors to join a floating population, potential future replacements of lost breeders. In the Midwest, we have records of about 286 individual breeding falcons, 1987 through 1999, derived from about 1,772 birds hacked or fledged wild in the period 1981 through 1997 (to allow two years before breeding). (The Midwestern Peregrine population is not a closed population. We assume that emigration and immigration with the eastern U.S. population are about equal.) In other words, it takes roughly six young birds, fledged or hacked, to produce one breeding adult. The discrepancy between 35% survival to age two (and thus potential breeders) versus the 16% of birds fledged that actually became breeders reflects the fact that survival is not enough; it is still necessary to find a mate and a territory to become a breeder. From the standpoint of maintaining a given breeding population, Peregrine reproduction produces a surplus of adults above recruitment needed to replace lost adults. This floating population permits rapid replacement of territorial adults when they die, sometimes within hours or a few days. As discussed below, the floaters not only serve as replacements but

Table 10.2 Age at first known breeding, Midwestern Peregrines.

	Years	Number	1 year	2 years	3 years	4 years	5 years	6 years
Males	1987–95	67	9%	48%	19%	16%	4%	3%
Males	1996–98	25	8%	40%	20%	20%	4%	8%

$\chi^2 = 1.46, df = 5, P = 0.92$

	Years	Number	1 year	2 years	3 years	4 years	5 years	6 years
Females	1987–95	53	26%	53%	19%	2%	0	0
Females	1996–98	31	6%	58%	19%	16%	0	0

$\chi^2 = 9.75, df = 3, P = 0.02$

Table 10.3 Juvenile Peregrines in the breeding population.

Years	Nesting pairs/ breeders	No. of juveniles	Percent juv.
1987–92	87/174	20	11%
1993–95	123/246	13	5%
1996–97	126/252	6	>2%
1998–99	172/344	6	<2%
2000	101/202	2	1%

◀ **Figure 10.3** Egore inhabited the first modern nest site in Indiana, under an elevated expressway in East Chicago.

◀ **Figure 10.4** Suzy Q defends three chicks and an unhatched egg at a nest site at U.S. Steel in Gary, Indiana. She was one of the longest surviving females in the Midwest, last nesting in 2000 when 12 years old.

also sometimes create vacancies through fights with territory holders.

Adult survival: In recent years (1995–1998), territorial males and females have had similar annual survival (91%, 86%, not statistically significant) (Table 10.4). When the Midwest population was growing rapidly and breeding males averaged younger (1987–1995), survival of males was significantly lower (79%) than for females (93%). Wayne Nelson suggested that higher mortality of young breeding males may be a result of increased energetic costs of breeding before foraging skills are fully developed. The decline in annual survival (not statistically significant) of territorial females from 93% to 86% may be a result of mortality in fights over territories. In a saturated Peregrine population, nonbreeding adults may equal or exceed the territorial adults (Newton 1988). There seems to be no way to measure the annual survival of these surplus birds, although Ratcliffe (1980) thinks it is likely to be lower than for territorial adults, because floaters must cope daily with unfamiliar surroundings. It has been suggested, however, that floaters may survive better than breeders because they avoid the energetic costs of territory defense and nesting and have access to a widespread prey base (Hunt 1998). Perhaps floaters on the watch for territorial vacancies do not wander daily into new places but instead patrol an area large enough to include several territories, yet not too large to become familiar.

▲ **Figure 10.5** Lisa, fledged in Detroit, Michigan, in 2000.

Judith M. Yerkey

. . . *if differences exist in fitness for Midwestern life among the five subspecies released there, they are not yet apparent in the new population.*

Table 10.4. Survival of territorial Peregrines in a growing population in the Midwest, 1987–1992.

	Years	Territory years*	Number lost	Annual survival
Males	1995–1998	117	10	91%
	1987–1995	115	24	79%
	Totals	232	34	85%
			$\chi^2 = 5.25, df = 1, P = 0.02$	
Females	1995–1998	141	20	86%
	1987–1995	136	10	93%
	Totals	277	30	89%
			$\chi^2 = 2.70, df = 1, P = 0.10$	
Sexes combined	Totals	509	64	87%

Survival of an individual from end of one breeding season to start of next.

Success of Different Subspecies

The suitability of the various Peregrine subspecies for life in the East and the Midwest was the subject of much early speculation. Arguments were made that only birds of the original race, *anatum*, should be released (as was done in the western United States and Canada), ignoring the fact that *anatum* Peregrines that might be available for release would be different from the original eastern and Midwestern stock (debate summarized by Barclay and Cade 1983). Others argued that birds of the subspecies *pealei*, from the cold northwest Pacific coast, would be poorly adapted for life in the Midwest. In the end, we released what was available and found, after the fact, that the representation of subspecies in the breeding population was essentially identical to that in birds released (Tordoff and Redig 2001). In other words, if differences exist in fitness for Midwestern life among the five subspecies released there, they are not yet apparent in the new population. Perhaps selection merely needs more time for its results to be measurable. Future selection must act on traits imbedded in a population of mostly hybrid Peregrines, some already with ancestors of four or five subspecies.

The mix of Peregrine subspecies released in the East (Temple 1988) was somewhat different from that in the Midwest (Tordoff and Redig 2001). In the Midwest United States, the contributions of the various subspecies to the gene pool of 921 Peregrines released were *anatum* 57%, *pealei* 27%, *peregrinus* 6%, *brookei* 6%, and *tundrius* 4%. In contrast, 758 captive-reared Peregrines released from 1975 through 1985 in the eastern United States were *tundrius* 46%, *anatum* 18%, *brookei* 18%, *pealei* 9%, *cassini* 4%, and "others" 5%, but the proportion of *anatum* genes increased in later years (T. Cade pers. comm.). Bear in mind that these percentages represent the genotypes released in hybrids as well as pure individuals. For example, no pure *tundrius* were released in the Midwest, only some individuals of partly *tundrius* ancestry.

Migration and Subspecies

Tom Cade recalls that when the first releases were made in the East in 1974, no one knew whether Peregrines of Arctic ancestry, for example, would fly to the Arctic when free, driven by their genes. Translocation experiments with other bird

Figure 10.6 Three young banded in 2001 on Lake Superior at Corundum Point, Minnesota.

Figure 10.6 Three young banded in 2001 on Lake Superior at Corundum Point, Minnesota.

Jacquelyn Fallon

species suggested that control of migration would be neither purely genetic nor purely environmental. Instead, some compromise between nature and nurture usually prevailed, and this also seems to be the case with Peregrines. A clear tendency has occurred in Midwestern Peregrines of non-migratory subspecific ancestry—*pealei, peregrinus,* and *brookei*—to be year-round residents once settled on a territory. Falcons of migratory subspecific ancestry, *anatum* and *tundrius,* tend to migrate more often and farther, especially in their first year, than birds from nonmigratory subspecies (H. Tordoff, M. Martell, P. Redig, G. Septon, and M. Solensky pers. obs.).

Once territorial, some adult Peregrines from migratory ancestors remain on their territories year around. Other individuals, however, continue to migrate long distances as long as they live, even if their home territory is in a city rich with pigeons and starlings for winter food. For example, a male *anatum,* 54T, that nested at age five in Omaha, Nebraska, in 1994 was trapped and released by Tom Maechtle at Paracas, Peru, 200 km south of Lima, in early February 1995 and returned in April to nest again in Omaha. Another *anatum* male, Calvin 48T, resident in summer on the State Capitol in Madison, Wisconsin, 1992 through 1996, departed each autumn for points south, judging by his capture on 14 April 1990 on Padre Island, Texas, and returned in the middle of April, when other falcons in the Mid-

west were already incubating. However, a female of predominantly nonmigratory ancestry (50% *pealei,* 25% *peregrinus,* 25% *anatum*), Algoma 77V, nesting on a cliff overlooking Lake Superior, 1993 to 2000, was trapped on Padre Island, Texas, by Tom Maechtle on 7 March 1999, with "such a large crop she couldn't see her toes." The Peregrine prey base around Lake Superior in winter is poor; migratory behavior of individuals nesting there appears to be appropriately flexible, regardless of subspecific ancestry. Midwestern urban Peregrines that leave their territories in winter often must fight newcomers to regain their territories on return in spring, suggesting that migration is maladaptive for these urban birds.

Cliffs, Buildings, Smokestacks, and Bridges

In the Midwest, Peregrines fledge the most young, on average, when they nest on smokestacks (see sidebar, Peregrine Recovery and the Role of Power Plants in the Midwest, this chapter) and buildings, somewhat fewer on bridges and cliffs (Table 10.5; Tordoff et al. 1998b). However, that is only part of the story. Mortality of young in the first weeks after fledging is highest for buildings and probably lowest for cliffs, with smokestacks and bridges in between. Eggs and nestlings in well-situated nest boxes on buildings, smoke-stacks, and bridges seem almost immune to pre-fledging losses to weather and predators, whereas young on cliffs are vulnerable to both, but particu-

Peregrine Recovery and the Role of Power Plants in the Midwest:
A Brief History and Current Status

Greg Septon

▲ Nest box being hoisted into place at We-Energies Pleasant Prairie Power Plant, Pleasant Prairie, Wisconsin, January 1991.

It was in 1986 on a visit to the former East Germany that I first encountered a Peregrine nest on a smokestack. The nest was an abandoned crow's nest on a grated catwalk just below the top of the stack which was spewing thick brown smoke. Reports were that Peregrines had attempted nesting there but that the nest had failed.

Returning home, I began wondering whether Peregrines might someday nest on smokestacks here in the states. In the meanwhile, Bob Anderson, Peregrine breeder and Director of the Raptor Resource Project in Minnesota, had already initiated the placement of a nest box on a smokestack in his home state, and in 1989 the first Peregrine nest box was installed at the NSP King power plant in Bayport, Minnesota. In the ensuing years, Bob continued his diligent efforts installing nest boxes at electric power plants throughout Minnesota.

Although Peregrine recovery efforts began here in Wisconsin in 1987, it was not until 1990 that a concerted nest box program got underway. In that year, the Wisconsin Peregrine Society initiated the "Lakefront Plan" which called for the placement of nest boxes on every suitable, tall manmade structure along a 200-mi stretch of the western shore of Lake Michigan, a well-known raptor migration route. Today these tall structures include five buildings, two grain elevators, and six power plants which have come to play an important role in Peregrine recovery in the Midwest. Before defining this role, however, I believe it is important to describe briefly the status and extent of current nest monitoring activities as well as define the consequent parameters in which I have presented my findings.

As the Midwest population has expanded, it has become increasingly difficult to document nesting activity accurately at each and every site. Therefore, to avoid the uncertainty of some nesting reports and remain consistent, I have based my information for this essay on known successful sites, i.e., those at which eggs or young were produced. Although some additional territories had falcons present, some nest sites failed and others probably went undetected. By staying within these defining parameters, I can present analysis based on known verifiable data, most of which stem from banding activities.

It has been well documented that the Midwest population expansion has been mostly urban in nature, with over 70% of nest sites located in or near cities. Although most of these nest sites are located on buildings, numerous power plants also serve as nest sites and have come to play an important role in Peregrine recovery in this region. The following summary of current nesting reports clearly shows just how important this role has become.

In 2000, for example, in Wisconsin we had a total of 11 successful nests that collectively produced 39 young. Seven (63%) of these nest sites were located at power plants where a total of 24 young (62%) were produced. Similarly, in Indiana eight urban nest sites produced a total of 23 young; 10 (44%) were produced at three power plants. In Ohio and Illinois, where efforts to install nest boxes on power plants have been less of a focus, one pair in each state nested at a power plant, with each pair fledging four young.

Looking at the big picture in the Midwest for the year 2000, 82 pairs of Peregrines successfully nested, producing a total of 199 young. Twenty (24%) of these pairs nested at power plants where 67 (34%) young were produced. The majority (90%) of these power plants were located in Minnesota, Wisconsin, and Indiana. In each of these three states where concerted efforts were undertaken to install nest boxes at power plants, two things have resulted. First, pairs established at power plants became a significant portion of the breeding population. And second, the young produced at these sites each year became a significant portion of the total annual production.

The role power plants have played in the recovery of Peregrines here in the Midwest has consequently been quite significant. By their very nature, power plants offer security, limited disturbance, corporate support, employee interest, and plenty of "structure," i.e., numerous levels, ledges, smokestacks, parapets, and catwalks, as well as various architectural nooks and

178

Nest box mounted to the side of a smokestack at the 300 ft level at We-Energies Oak Creek Power Plant, January 1991.

Greg Septon

Judith M. Yerkey

▲ Figure 10.7 Tiercel Kenny was wild-produced at the River Rouge across from the Detroit Edison Power Plant in 2002.

crannies where Peregrines can seek shelter. Power plants are often located along shorelines of rivers and lakes that provide cooling water for the turbines and also attract Peregrines. These factors have collectively contributed to high site occupation, high production, and consequent high fledge rates.

One concern regarding Peregrines nesting at power plants in the Midwest has been whether or not falcons nesting at these sites are being adversely affected by contaminants produced by the burning of fossil fuels. To address this concern, the Electric Power Research Institute sponsored a heavy metals study. The study aimed to determine whether suspected contaminants were present in Midwestern Peregrines nesting at these plants. Preliminary findings of this study indicated no elevated levels of suspected heavy metals. These findings have also shown no significant difference in contaminant levels between Peregrines nesting at fossil-fuel or nuclear generated power plants and city nesting falcons, results that should help alleviate concerns about the health of Peregrines nesting at power plants.

For me personally, it has been very rewarding to work with the electric power companies here in Wisconsin over the past 10 years. Their financial support and active hands-

on involvement with efforts to bring the Peregrine back from the brink have been exemplary and should be commended. During the early years of my life, I thought I would never see a Peregrine nest. But from where I sit now in my downtown museum office, I can look out the window and see not one but two nest sites here in Milwaukee. Spanning the Lake Michigan shoreline are seven more nests, with five of them located at power plants.

In the years to come, as our world becomes even more urbanized and opportunities to experience nature become less available, we can only hope that corporate stewardship from the electric power industry as well as that of many generous nest site sponsors continues, and that Peregrines will remain a part of our urban landscape.

Greg Septon *served as Director of Natural History Outreach at the Milwaukee Public Museum and is founder and chairman of the Wisconsin Peregrine Society. In 1987, he initiated Peregrine recovery efforts in Wisconsin. He served as Leader of the State of Wisconsin Peregrine Falcon Recovery Team and continues to manage the urban nesting population of Peregrines in the state.*

Greg Greer

larly weather. At fledging, young Peregrines typically fly out, circle, lose altitude, and make a clumsy landing. From cliff nests, they are usually still on the cliff and can sit there safely until they are ready to fly again. In cities, the too-frequent outcome of that first flight is to land in the street or crash into a perchless vertical wall or window. From bridges, an unintended and sometimes fatal swim may result. Considering all factors, natural cliff nests do well, despite the security afforded by urban sites to eggs and nestlings. The small differences in productivity from different kinds of sites may not matter much, since the number of young fledged is less important to population health than first-year and especially adult survival. All categories of nest sites in the Midwest, natural and manmade, produce enough young to guarantee a surplus of adults.

Effect of Brood Size on Survival to Breeding

Hacked Peregrine young consistently survive better in the first year than wild-produced young (Tordoff and Redig 1997), suggesting that wild young may sometimes be below optimum weight at fledging or when they attain independence. Weight at fledging has been shown to be positively correlated with survival in many species of birds. If provisioning of broods by adult Peregrines is not invariably optimum under some circumstances, for example in areas or seasons of scarce prey, young fledged from smaller than average broods might be fed better and therefore have increased chances of survival.

We tested the relationship between brood size and survival to breeding for Peregrines fledged from 139 unaugmented (no food or young added by humans) wild broods from 1987 through 1995

▲ **Figure 10.8** Zenith, a long-time Cleveland resident, takes flight. She raised more than 30 young in 10 years.

Table 10.5. Midwest Peregrine Falcon productivity at different nest locations, 1987–1998.

Nest site	Nests/ % of total	Successful nests/ % of total	Young fledged/ % of total	Young/nest
Building	224/56%	185/83%	540/60%	2.4
Smokestack	44/11%	42/95%	111/12%	2.5
Bridge	37/9%	28/76%	66/7%	1.8
Cliff	92/23%	73/79%	185/21%	2.0
Total	397	328/83%	902	2.3

No. successful nests, $\chi^2 = 0.64$, df = 3, P = 0.89; young/nest, $\chi^2 = 3.21$, df = 3, P = 0.36

Table 10.6. Relation between brood size and survival to breeding of Peregrines in the Midwest, 1987–1995.

Brood size	No. of broods	No. of young fledged (% of fledglings)		No. of breeders (% of breeders)	
1	18	18	(5%)	1	(2%)
2	35	70	(18%)	8	(19%)
3	55	165	(44%)	18	(42%)
4	29	116	(31%)	15	(35%)
5	2	10	(3%)	1	(2%)
Totals	139	379		43	(11%)

Chi-square 1 sample test, $\chi^2 = 0.77$, df = 4, P = 0.9

(Table 10.6; Tordoff et al. 2000). These 139 broods included 379 individuals, of which we identified 43 that survived to become breeders and for which the size of the brood from which they fledged was known. We assumed that brood size at fledging was the same as at banding, unless we knew otherwise.

We concluded that the probability of an individual Peregrine in the Midwest surviving to become a breeder was not related to size of the brood from which it fledged. No significant difference existed between the observed proportion of breeders from different brood sizes. The 43 breeding adults have come proportionally from broods of all sizes, including one adult from a brood of five young. One might speculate about advantages for young falcons in small broods, such as less sibling competition for food, or in large broods, such as more efficient huddling for warmth and increased social interaction and play opportunities, but the evidence from Midwestern Peregrines indicates that if such effects exist, they are not detectable with present information.

Fights and Population Regulation

Most kinds of birds defend some sort of territory, usually as vigorously as their physical equipment allows. Peregrine fights over territories are well known to be frequent, vigorous, and often lethal, because these falcons are adapted to kill birds their own size in routine foraging (Cade 1960). When populations reach carrying capacity, fights may be a frequent way to secure a territory.

We analyzed 16 Peregrine fights in the Midwest where we knew the identity of both combatants and the outcome of the fight. Incumbents (previous owner of the territory) won in seven cases, challengers in nine cases. By sex, female incumbents won in five cases, challengers in five; male incumbents won in two cases, challengers in four. There were 10 fatalities in the 16 fights, eight females (five incumbents, three challengers), two males (both incumbents).

In the 12 fights where we could estimate size by subspecific ancestry (admittedly a dubious procedure), large birds won over smaller birds in four cases; in eight, the participants were about the same size. No smaller birds won over large birds (males avoid fights with females). Remember, however, that our criterion for size was only marginally better than a guess.

Considering age, older birds won in six cases, younger birds in seven; in two fights, both birds were three years old.

Conclusions that might be drawn from this sample of 16 fights are that incumbency and age do not necessarily confer an advantage in territorial encounters that escalate to a physical fight. Whether size matters may depend on sex: large females should have an advantage in fights that end in a battle on the ground; small males might have an advantage in fights that remain aerial, but probably not if grappling on the ground ensues.

A sample of fights, however, is not a representative sample of territorial encounters, in which incumbents usually prevail because most encounters never escalate to fights. Only determined challengers press matters to a physical battle, perhaps often because they sense that their adversary is vulnerable. In several territorial replacements in the nesting season, incumbent females were killed or ousted during or shortly after egg-laying, when their energy reserves were likely low.

In 1999 in the Twin Cities, Minnesota, 10 pairs of Peregrines held nesting territories, four on buildings, three on smokestacks, and three on bridges. All 10 pairs nested and nine succeeded, fledging 25 young. At three of these territories, five Peregrines were killed in fatal fights, three at one site. Fatalities from fights over territories may be a density-dependent effect of the floater-to-breeder ratio in saturated Peregrine populations, but they do not influence the number of breeders. Further, fatality of adults is only the most visible cost of fights; loss of potential young because of interference with nesting must also be considered as a factor reducing individual fitness.

Fights between males are probably more frequent than fights between females, given the more conspicuous role of males in territorial establishment and defense. However, male-versus-male fights tend to be more aerial and perhaps less dangerous to the participants than fights between females, which more often grab each other, fall to the ground, and battle there with clawing and biting. One such fight at the Colonnade in Minneapolis between two females lasted two hours, during which the two birds were continuously locked together (Tordoff and Redig 1999). Here, the two birds appeared to be about the same size; and the loser was both the incumbent and older, but necropsy showed that she was in poor condition—weight 750 g, no fat, decreased pectoral muscle mass, and heavily parasitized with flukes and tapeworms. Even with these handicaps, severe facial injuries from the fight, including loss of an eye, and a clear defeat in the physical battle, she returned the day after the fight and sat in the nest box for two hours, unchallenged by the "victor," which departed the moment the "loser" came on the scene. The old bird seemed to have won the psychological battle, even if defeated physically. However, two days later she was found too weak to fly and was euthanized because her wounds were not repairable.

Return to the River Cliffs

When Pat Redig wrote the original recovery plan for the Peregrine in the Midwest over 20 years ago, we expected that the restored population would live in the same places as the original birds, namely on cliffs. The subsequent success of Peregrines nesting on skyscrapers and other man-made structures was gratifying but did not erase disappointment over their failure to reoccupy the cliffs along the Mississippi and its tributaries. Peregrines of the new Midwestern population have nested on cliffs around Lake Superior since the 1980s. In 2000, however, Peregrines nested successfully on cliffs along the Mississippi River for the first time since the original population was extirpated in the 1950s. Five pairs held territories on bluffs along the Mississippi—one in Iowa, two in Minnesota, and two in Wisconsin. Three of these pairs nested, and all succeeded, fledging eight young. The two pairs that did not nest, both in Wisconsin, each included a one-year-old female, probably not yet ready to nest because of immaturity.

Across their original range in the eastern United States, many Peregrines nested on lowland river cliffs. Here in the Midwestern United States, the river pairs likely made up more than half the total population. It is easy to understand the intense interest in the delayed return of the new population to these traditional nesting cliffs, not only along the Mississippi and its tributaries but also the Hudson, Susquehanna, and other lowland rivers in the eastern states. What were the circumstances leading to reoccupancy of the river cliffs? Was 2000 really the first year? Where did the cliff birds come from? Why 2000, instead of 1999 or 1998? Here is some history.

We began releases of Peregrines at Weaver Dunes, near Kellogg, Minnesota, in 1982 because about a dozen cliffs used by the falcons historically were within 20 miles of the hack site. Those releases of 40 young falcons resulted in eight nesting attempts on nearby cliffs in 1986, 1987, and 1988. All failed. At three cliff nests where adults or young were killed, evidence showed that Great Horned Owls were the predators. At a fourth nest, raccoons might have been involved.

At Weaver Dunes, predation by owls on the released falcons was low; one Peregrine was killed in 1982 and one in 1983. None of the 23 young released in 1984 and 1985 were lost to

▲ **Figure 10.9** Fight documented on the Terminal Tower FalconCam, which tracks Peregrine activity at an urban nest box in Cleveland, Ohio, and broadcasts images on the internet.

▲ **Figure 10.10** Female Peregrine at eyrie, Maiden Rock, Wisconsin. Her young were banded in June 2001.

owls, perhaps because of owl control measures. The Weaver Dunes hack site was abandoned because an adult Peregrine from an earlier release returned and attacked the young falcons on their first flights from the hack towers. We then shifted our releases to cities and cliffs in northern Minnesota.

We were probably too impressed with the potential of owl predation. The loss of one of the first five Peregrines released at Weaver Dunes in 1982 seemed a disaster at the time. Earlier, two of three falcons were killed by owls in an experimental hack by The Peregrine Fund at Jayhawk Bluff, south of Nelson, Wisconsin, in 1977. When the first eight cliff-nesting attempts failed, owls seemed to be a formidable problem indeed. We now speculate that the owls, unchallenged by Peregrines on the river cliffs for 25 years, needed reeducation to the proper state of humility required for coexistence with Peregrines. This surely has been happening over the past decade, as owls along the river have encountered Peregrines with increasing frequency. The cliff nest at Lansing, Iowa, in 2000 fledged four Peregrines in sight of a nesting pair of owls on a neighboring cliff. No one expects owls and Peregrines to live together in complete harmony. Abundant evidence from throughout North America indicates that Great Horned Owls will continue to prey on Peregrines and that Peregrines will continue to harass and occasionally kill the owls, but events in 2000 show that they can once more coexist on the Mississippi bluffs, as they did in the past.

To sum up, the return of Peregrines to the Mississippi River cliffs in 2000 appears to have been

the result of a strong Peregrine presence along the river caused by successful nestings on power-plant smokestacks along the river and the hacking of substantial numbers of young Peregrines from river cliffs in Iowa, plus the simultaneous production from wild nests of good numbers of Peregrines seeking nesting places in a region where the best sites in urban areas were already occupied. Given adult falcons seeking territories and lots of Peregrine activity along the river, those river bluffs, with their many good nest sites and a fine food supply, became irresistible (Cade et al. 1989).

Why 2000, instead of earlier? Growing population pressure, fewer unoccupied suitable breeding locations, and an increasing river presence of Peregrines—these all came together in 2000.

Might Peregrines have been nesting on these cliffs undetected for several years? One would not expect that the first step back to the river cliffs would involve five pairs. Why not first one or two, then a gradual buildup over the years? There are convincing reasons to conclude that 2000 was really the first. For starters, the best (for Peregrines, best usually means biggest) cliffs seem to be used first. If Peregrines nested along the river north of Iowa in recent years, they would probably have been at Maiden Rock in Wisconsin, or at Queens Bluff or John Latsch State Park in Minnesota, the tallest cliffs in that stretch of the river, and probably would have been detected by the many good birders in the area, as they were in 2000. Further, nine of the 10 individuals on river cliffs in 2000 had a known history; the tenth was not banded. Two were only one year old. Four were just two

Peregrine Falcons in the Lake Superior Basin

Brian Ratcliff

The Lake Superior Basin has some of the best habitat for Peregrine Falcons in eastern North America. The lake is ringed by hundreds of cliffs. Although many are less than 50 m high, many are spectacular, some towering more than 200 m at Sleeping Giant Provincial Park.

Historical records of nesting Peregrines on Lake Superior date back almost 200 years. In the early 1800s, lighthouse keepers observed nesting falcons at Grand Island, Michigan. The first recorded nest in Ontario was found on St. Ignace Island during the Louis Agassiz Lake Superior expedition of 1848.

Recovery efforts to reestablish Peregrine Falcons to Lake Superior cliffs were initiated by hacking young falcons in the mid-1980s, first in Minnesota at historical nesting sites in 1984 and soon after in Michigan and Ontario. The releases ended in 1996, and during that period 261 young falcons were hacked around Lake Superior.

The releases of young birds paid off; the first nest documented post-recovery was at Palisade Head, Minnesota, in 1988. The population has continued to grow—two nests plus four territories in 1990, 10 nests plus two territories in 1995, an amazing 26 nests plus 13 territories in 2000 (see map). Most of the nests (88%) are on cliffs, but the birds are also using three bridges and a building. Two birds have made a major contribution to the repopulation of the basin. A female (Fridge) hacked at

Minneapolis, Minnesota, in 1986, nested at Palisade Head from 1988 to 1996. During these nine years, Fridge fledged 21 chicks. The male at Devil's Warehouse Island, Lake Superior Provincial Park, was hacked in 1990 at Five Islands, Nova Scotia, and from 1996 to 2000 produced 17 chicks. This bird has very distinctive plumage, and it is believed that he has been at this site since 1993 and has probably produced 24 chicks.

In an effort to understand the dynamics of this growing population, 188 young Peregrines were banded at wild cliff nests from 1988 to 2000, in addition to the 261 hacked falcons. Banded birds from the Lake Superior basin have been reported from as far south as Cuba and Texas, and some birds have also returned to breed at Lake Superior nest sites.

Prey remains have been collected at 33 Ontario nest sites on Lake Superior since 1996. Of the 36 species of birds and two mammal species identified, the five most common species have been Rock Dove, Ring-billed Gull, Evening Grosbeak, Cedar Waxwing, and American Crow.

The data from the Canadian five-year surveys show that Peregrines have made a remarkable recovery on Lake Superior. The future of these birds looks extremely promising, as there are still many cliff sites not being used. We look forward with great expectations to the 2005 Peregrine Falcon Survey.

Brian Ratcliff *is the coordinator of Project Peregrine, Thunder Bay Field Naturalists, Thunder Bay, Ontario.*

▲ Peregrine nest, Pie Island, Ontario.

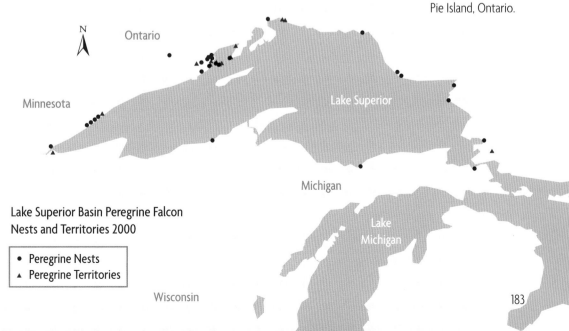

Lake Superior Basin Peregrine Falcon Nests and Territories 2000

- Peregrine Nests
- ▲ Peregrine Territories

183

Figure 10.11 Zenith arrived in Cleveland in May of 1993 and was killed in a fight with another female in 2002. ▶

Figure 10.12 Ohio Division of Wildlife officers fend off Zenith during an attempt to band her young. ▶

get to his former site at Alma, just four miles downstream. His one-year-old mate fledged in 1999 at the Colonnade, in Minneapolis. The two adults at Lansing, Iowa, nested in 1999 on a smokestack just yards from the cliff they used in 2000. A nest box placed on the cliff enticed them to move. At Queens Bluff, both birds were hacked in 1998, one from a cliff at Effigy Mounds National Monument, Iowa, and the other from a building in Mason City, Iowa. The pair at John Latsch State Park included an adult male, not banded and therefore wild-produced, and a two-year-old female from the Ford Parkway Bridge in Minneapolis. At Maiden Rock, the male was two years old, fledged in 1998 from the nuclear reactor containment building at Northern States Power at Prairie Island, Minnesota, and the female fledged in 1999 from the Firstar Bank in Cedar Rapids, Iowa. An interesting mixed bag of birds, crossovers from various types of fledge sites to nesting on cliffs.

So, we can regard the river-bluff pairs with the satisfaction of seeing the last of the objectives of the Midwest recovery plan met, after years of frustration and argument about possible solutions.

Names versus Numbers

It is generally considered bad form by scientists to give human names to individual birds. They are not little feathered people, despite a human tendency to consider them so. In the Midwest, biologists in Iowa, Missouri, Manitoba, and Ontario identified their Peregrines only by their color band designations. Elsewhere, names were usually given at banding, or in some cases, when an unnamed bird became territorial. Peregrines in cities, in particular, attract general public attention. Most city pairs also attract people, usually not biologists, who become deeply involved in the daily activities and welfare of "their" birds. For these people, names for the birds are almost essential. Some names chosen seem inevitable for individuals of a species saved from extirpation. Phoenix ("rising from its own ashes"), for example, was given to five Peregrines in the Midwest before we called a halt on grounds of confusion. Six were named Orion. The majority of birds, however, were named after children, spouses, and girlfriends, followed closely by patriotic names (Glory, Liberty) and cosmic names (Lightning, Thunder, Star).

Belligerent Individuals and Building Management Concerns

Peregrines nesting on manmade structures usually require some adjustments of human behavior. These may range from the provision of

years old, the most frequent age of first breeding. The other three were older birds that in 1999 were known to be nesting on smokestacks along the river. To argue seriously for other cliff nesters in 1999, for example, requires either that they all nested on secondary cliffs and vanished in 2000, or after nesting on the best cliffs, all either died over the winter or were evicted by the 2000 residents; none of these possibilities seem plausible.

One of the three older cliff nesters in 2000 nested in 1999 on the smokestack at Alma, Wisconsin. In early spring of 2000, he was injured in a fight with another falcon, treated in a rehabilitation clinic, and released at La Crosse, Wisconsin, 50 miles downriver from Alma. He then took up residence at Jayhawk Bluff, about as close as he could

a useable substrate for nesting in the form of pea gravel to installation of a nest box and alteration of building maintenance. The adjustments needed are increased if the individual falcons are aggressive toward humans. Most Peregrines circle and call in protest of human intrusions near their nest, some dive and come close, but a few strike humans at every opportunity, often some distance from their nest. These aggressive birds can be a serious problem. No one likes head lacerations from Peregrine talons, but even more serious damage, such as the loss of an eye, is possible.

The most frequent targets of aggressive Peregrines are their most frequent visitors: building maintenance people, particularly window washers. Peregrines often seem to learn that window washers can be ignored, and window washers, in turn, usually accept and even enjoy the risk and excitement of Peregrine attacks. Perhaps this is not surprising, considering the personality types likely to make a career of washing windows on skyscrapers.

From the Peregrine's perspective, each encounter with humans is a success, in that the falcons protest or attack, the people leave, and the nest remains intact. This positive reinforcement leads to gradual escalation in aggressive behavior by individual birds as they get older. Several individual Peregrines, all on manmade structures, are so aggressive it is nearly impossible to visit their nests without being struck. Among these superaggressive birds, females outnumber males, but not by much. So far, no Peregrines of the new population nesting on cliffs in the Midwest have struck people.

Getting Rid of Nuisance Peregrines

We do not tolerate savage dogs in our cities, or wolves on livestock farms. Even the most committed Peregrine enthusiast probably will admit that there are situations where the presence of a nesting pair may not be acceptable. In Hyde Park, Chicago, for example, Peregrines moved into a nest box placed on a plush apartment building overlooking Lake Michigan. To take advantage of the view, each apartment has its own balcony. The Peregrines resented human presence on these balconies, for which the humans paid a handsome rent. Peregrine attacks soon made the birds unwelcome. The nest box was removed before the 1996 season, and the Peregrines were found nesting unaided in 1997 in a niche on a nearby church, where they have remained ever since. Solving this problem was easy, but not the next.

At the Colonnade building in Minneapolis, Peregrines nested in a box on a 15th-floor ledge over some slanted skylights. The nest box was viewed at arm's length through a lightly-tinted window wall by the office workers inside. Over seven years, panels in the skylight were cracked, apparently by pea gravel kicked off the nest ledge. Replacement of three damaged panels cost $21,000. We moved the nest box around the corner, where falling gravel would cause no harm, but the building management by then had decided that the birds were a nuisance and must go. We pointed out that removing the box would not guarantee the immediate departure of the birds, but this changed no minds. The box came down in late March 2000. Predictably, the adults continued to scrape on the bare granite ledge where the box had been. In time, an egg was laid, rolled off, and was pursued to the ground by the diving male, all in sight of the horrified loyal Peregrine fans inside. A tense confrontation between upset building tenants and adamant building management ensued, finally resulting in an article and photos in the local newspaper. Angry citizens thereupon complained by letters to the editor, phone calls to the local chapter of the National Audubon Society (NAS), and even by anonymous phone calls to the home of the building manager. Someone finally realized that the building was owned by TIAA-CREF, holders of retirement accounts for groups in education and research, including, happily, the NAS. Quickly the situation was resolved in high-level talks in New York City. At the direction of the building owners, a nest tray was placed where the box had been. Meanwhile, four eggs had been laid, rolled off, and smashed. Before the scaffold used to put the tray in place on 1 May had reached the roof, the female Peregrine was scraping in the new tray. She laid an egg the next day, followed by two more. All three hatched and fledged. Clearly it will not always be easy to make Peregrines give up a nest site, particularly when it involves not just the birds but also their human advocates.

Peregrines as Pigeon Control

Building managers and health departments dislike pigeons on city buildings because of the mess

▲ **Figure 10.13** In 1987, a hack box was installed on the lower level of the Mayo Building, part of the Mayo Clinic complex in Rochester, Minnesota. In 1987 and 1988, 32 falcons were released from this site.

Midwest Peregrines: Propagators and Leaders

Mark S. Martell and Harrison B. Tordoff

Peregrine restoration in the Midwest began with two small experimental releases by The Peregrine Fund and the University of Minnesota from cliffs in Wisconsin along the Mississippi River. These attempts failed because of predation by Great Horned Owls. Further releases were deferred in favor of releases in the East at sites judged to be predator free. By 1982, private Peregrine propagators, all falconers, began producing enough birds to make possible releases independent of falcon production by The Peregrine Fund. As a first step, Pat Redig and Bud Tordoff agreed with Lynn Oliphant to fund operating costs of Lynn's breeding facility in Saskatoon, Saskatchewan, in return for half of the falcons produced. Teaming up with The Nature Conservancy (TNC) and the Minnesota Falconers Association, this arrangement resulted in 40 falcons hacked in Minnesota by 1985. When other Midwestern states expressed an interest in joining the effort, Redig and Tordoff coordinated the joint effort by buying the falcons from the propagators; banding, bleeding, and color marking them at the University of Minnesota Raptor Center; then distributing the birds to the various agencies for release. Records, databases, and reports were handled by The Raptor Center and the Bell Museum of Natural History, University of Minnesota. Eventually 13 states (upper right) were involved in the project. Peregrine restoration efforts in southeastern Manitoba and western Ontario with birds from the Canadian Wildlife Service (CWS) were included in the Midwestern

database because Peregrine populations there were biologically inseparable from the rest of the region.

None of this could have been done without the Peregrines produced by the 38 propagators; we are pleased to recognize them here (lower right). Production of young falcons for release was essential, but just as important was the effort given to releasing them in circumstances favorable for survival, monitoring their success, and managing the restored population. Each state and province had many cooperating citizens, hundreds in all, some involved in hacking and many more contributing essential funding, under the leadership of state and provincial coordinators (upper right). State and provincial natural resource agencies, U.S. Fish and Wildlife Service, U.S. Forest Service, National Park Service, CWS, Milwaukee Public Museum, Chicago Academy of Sciences, TNC, Raptor Resource Project, Wisconsin Peregrine Society, Minnesota Falconers Association, and Great Lakes Falconers Association all played important roles in Midwestern Peregrine restoration, which was only one part of a continental effort unmatched in conservation history.

Provided by Mark Martell

Leaders of the Midwest Peregrine Restoration

Illinois	Victoria Byre, Mary Hennen, Vernon Kleen, Mark Spreyer
Indiana	John Castrale
Iowa	Robert Anderson, Kim Bogenschutz, Jaime Edwards, Bruce Ehresman, James Haack, Laura Jackson, Pat Schlarbaum, Lowell Washburn
Kansas	Joanne Brier, Jerry Horak
Kentucky	Laura Burford
Manitoba, SE	Robert Jones, Bill Koonz, Tracy Maconachie, Robert Nero
Michigan	Bob Hess, Tim Payne, Joe Rogers, Ray Rustem, Judy Yerkey
Minnesota	Carrol Henderson, Mark Martell, Pat Redig, Matt Solensky, Bud Tordoff
Missouri	Laurie Brown, Mike Cooke, Walter Crawford, John Meyer
Nebraska	John Dinan, Ross Lock, Chris Thody
North Dakota	Wick Corwin
Ohio	Sara Jean Peters, Dave Scott
Ontario, Lake Superior Basin	Ted Armstrong, Harold Kish, Brian Ratcliff
South Dakota	Eileen Dowd-Stukel, Victor Hardaswick, Don Hunter, Tim Keyser, Charles Patterson
Wisconsin	Charlene Gieck, Pat Manthey, Greg Septon

Breeders Supplying Peregrines for Midwest Restoration

Breeders	Number of falcons supplied	Breeders	Number of falcons supplied
Robert Anderson	199	Brad Mitchell	4
David Baker	1	Greg Moore	1
David Bird	2	Lynn Oliphant and Paddy Thompson	119
Mark Bolton	20		
Les Boyd	18	Jack Oar	25
Canadian Wildlife Service (all released in Manitoba or Ontario)	205	Alberto Palleroni	2
		The Peregrine Fund	5
Lance Christensen	2	Michael Peterson	3
Larry Cottrell	3	Edward Pitcher	3
Miles Coussens	4	Alan Pollard	1
James Cowan	4	George Richter	1
Walter Crawford	115	Charles Robinson	2
James Doyle	4	Ralph Rogers	5
Gerald Geiger	3	Dewey Sevell	1
Richard Graham	41	Steve Sherrod	36
Bruce Haak	27	South Dakota Raptor Trust (Victor Hardaswick and Don Hunter)	295
Robert Hollister	5		
David Jamieson	4	Daniel Thee	9
Peter Jenny	7	Skip Tubbs	3
Burt Loessburg	2	Pete Widener	47
		Ric Wood	1

Mark Martell *was Coordinator of Conservation Programs at The Raptor Center, University of Minnesota, and coordinator with Bud Tordoff for the Midwest Peregrine restoration effort.*

Bud Tordoff - *For biographical information see the end of this chapter.*

they make and the diseases they may transmit. When they hear that Peregrines eat pigeons, thoughts of pigeon control, even pigeon disappearance, dance in their heads. Biologists understand that predators do not eliminate their prey, and may not even reduce prey numbers much if the prey base is broad, as it is for Peregrines. Even though elimination or major reduction of pigeons by Peregrines is only a dream, urban Peregrines do have important effects on the behavior of pigeons. When Peregrines reside on tall buildings, pigeons stop frequenting the upper stories, reducing debris from nests and droppings, although the Peregrines substitute some mess of their own in bird parts and liquid droppings. The exchange satisfies most building managers. The Minnesota highway department, MN DOT, welcomes Peregrines on its bridges and is ever ready to help out by installing boxes if needed and by supplying a snooper for banding young falcons. Bridge nests of Peregrines are usually on girders or beams under the roadway, often on debris from old pigeon nests. Most of the Midwestern bridges with nesting Peregrines are nearly pigeon free. On others, the pigeons may persist, but uneasily and in smaller numbers.

Letting Go

It is always hard to quit an activity that has been enjoyable, consuming, and rewarding. Peregrines no longer need help to survive in North America, beyond the protection provided by existing laws. Even if every nest box or tray vanished, the result would be only a diminished population, not disappearance. But as the Minneapolis Colonnade incident demonstrated, people have come to cherish their urban Peregrines and are unwilling to let them fare for themselves. With the first nesting in 2000 of Peregrines on the river cliffs of the Midwest, the last objective of the recovery program in this region has been met. Still, active management goes on. Hacking of young birds continues, to fill local gaps in distribution. People agitate for nest boxes in new locations, and even for installing boxes on cliffs that have plenty of natural nest sites. Perhaps some will one day view Peregrines as just another raptor, no more special than a red-tail. But for those of us who have devoted years to their recovery, they are more special.

Acknowledgments

Falconers led the Peregrine restoration, providing the expert knowledge needed for captive breeding and hacking of their favorite bird. A brigade of Peregrine admirers did the releases, paid the bills, and kept track of the new population. We thank these people, who are also acknowledged elsewhere in this volume, for the success of this unprecedented project. Only a remarkably charismatic bird could have inspired such an effort!

. . . people have come to cherish their urban Peregrines and are unwilling to let them fare for themselves.

Jacquelyn Fallon

Bud Tordoff *was born in Mechanicville, New York, in 1923. His undergraduate work in biology at Cornell University was interrupted by World War II where he flew the military's closest equivalents to Peregrine Falcons, P-47 Thunderbolts and P-51 Mustangs. After the war he did graduate work at the University of Michigan. Then followed seven years on the faculty at the University of Kansas, 13 years back at the University of Michigan, and a move to the University of Minnesota in 1970. In 1976 and 1977, he helped with early Peregrine releases by The Peregrine Fund on Mississippi River cliffs in Wisconsin. These failed because of owl predation. In 1982, young falcons began to become available from private breeders, so Tordoff and Pat Redig launched the Midwestern Peregrine releases, independent of but cooperating with The Peregrine Fund. Tordoff retired in 1991 from teaching, faculty meetings, and committees but continues to work enthusiastically with Peregrines in the Midwest.*

Provided by Pat Redig

Pat Redig *was born and raised in the iron mining district of northern Minnesota in 1948. His interest in raptors developed during childhood, nurtured in high school by Fr. Henry Mehr, Crosier Seminary, Onamia, Minnesota, and developed into a professional career through undergraduate work at St. Cloud State University and finally the College of Veterinary Medicine, University of Minnesota. During this time Pat also developed a keen interest in falconry that has continued. He and Gary Duke formed The Raptor Research and Rehabilitation Program, now called The Raptor Center, of which Pat became director in 1986. With Bud Tordoff, Pat developed the restoration program for the Peregrine Falcon in the Midwest. Pat coordinated acquiring falcons from breeders, developing release sites, and distributed Peregrines to nine Midwestern states while managing health and injury problems of falcons and assisting in developing a founder population database. With the completion of the Peregrine work, he refocused his efforts on teaching and veterinary-related research on raptors, although he maintains a keen interest in Peregrine Falcons.*

Chapter II

Peregrine Falcons, Naturalists, Scientists, and Biologists in Alaska, 1900 to 2000

Robert (Skip) Ambrose and Robert J. Ritchie

Alaska, "The Last Frontier," was indeed one of the last places in the United States to be explored by naturalists.

Almost 75 years after Lewis and Clark explored the western United States, Americans began biological surveys in Alaska. Because little was known of the flora, fauna, and geology of the Alaska Territory, and because logistics were extremely difficult, most of these early surveys were general in nature. In most accounts from these early explorations, however, one finds references to Peregrine Falcons.

In interior Alaska, for example, both naturalists and geologists frequently referred to Peregrine Falcons and often gave hints as to their relative abundance and wide-ranging distribution. In the early 1900s, Wilfred Osgood and Louis Bishop found Peregrines on bluffs approximately every 10 miles along the upper Yukon River, densities similar to those Tom Cade found in the 1950s. Following Osgood and Bishop were Olaus Murie, who described Peregrine sites that still are regularly used today on the Tanana River; Lee Raymond Dice in the upper Kuskokwim; and F. C. Hinkley, who described this falcon as common on rugged bluffs along the middle Kuskokwim. Similarly,

◀ **Figure 11.1** *Tundra Glow* © Rod Frederick. Reproduction courtesy of The Peregrine Fund.

early investigators in northern Alaska recorded Peregrines but noted a sparser population than in interior Alaska. Many of the early naturalists who visited Alaska spent much of their time along the coast, where Peregrines are both year-round residents and migrants from interior and northern Alaska. Alfred Bailey and Joseph Dixon were examples of early coastal researchers who regularly recorded Peregrines.

Interestingly, some of those first scientists' observations were doubted because they described Peregrines as common in areas that were considered peripheral habitat, such as upland cliffs and tors in the Yukon-Tanana Uplands. For example, Eliot Blackwelder, a young geologist, traveled through interior Alaska in 1915 and noted that "Duck Hawks were common wherever suitable nesting sites are available among high crags. . . . especially in the White Mountains," a mountainous area north of Fairbanks. Few ornithologists trusted these

observations, and most thought he was probably seeing Gyrfalcons, not Peregrine Falcons, in these alpine areas. As the recovery of Peregrine Falcons advances, however, and as Peregrines now occupy those rocky crags, many of these old accounts take on new meaning.

In the early 1950s, a student at the University of Alaska in Fairbanks began a lifelong affair with Alaska raptors, the Peregrine Falcon in particular. As an undergraduate at the University, Tom Cade floated the upper Yukon River between Dawson, Yukon Territory, and Circle, Alaska, in 1951 and surveyed Peregrines along the way. In the late 1950s, Tom was back in Alaska, working on his Ph.D. on Peregrines and Gyrfalcons. Tom worked throughout the state but focused primarily on the upper Yukon River in interior Alaska and on the Colville River in northern Alaska. Surveys on the Colville River, begun in 1952, continued into the 1960s; during these years, Tom often worked with Clayton White. The work of those two men, surveying and writing alone and together, provided the basis for much of the later research in Alaska.

By the mid-1960s, concern for declining populations of Peregrine Falcons in lower latitudes reached Alaska, which had long been considered pristine, secure, and far from the threats of more populated areas at lower latitudes. Surveys were initiated in the mid-1960s and were conducted primarily by Tom Cade, Clay White, Jim Enderson, John Haugh, and Jerry Swartz. These scientists regularly surveyed parts of the Yukon, Tanana, and Colville Rivers to assess the influence of contaminants on Peregrine Falcons in Alaska. They also visited more remote tributaries of these rivers, including the Chandler and Anaktuvuk Rivers in northern Alaska and the Fortymile and Porcupine Rivers in interior Alaska.

▲ **Figure 11.2** Tom Cade on the lower Colville River, July 1967.

▲ **Figure 11.3** Ted Swem, also on the lower Colville River, 1989.

Figure 11.4 Colville ▶ River, northern Alaska.

Initial surveys in the 1960s reinforced the notion that northern areas were safe: population levels appeared to be similar to those observed during early biological surveys in the early 1900s. Unfortunately, these similarities were misleading. The purposes of the early surveys were to examine all flora and fauna, not to focus on individual species such as the Peregrine. As a result, counts from those early surveyors probably were often incomplete and hence underestimates of the real population size. The similarities in numbers found in the 1960s with some historical counts (e.g., along the upper Yukon River in the early 1900s) were reassuring; however, by the late 1960s it was clear that a decline was underway (Cade et al. 1971). Recent surveys from index study areas such as the upper Yukon River have revealed numbers of nesting pairs three to four times higher than levels once considered "historical, pre-DDT." These findings suggest that either a decline was well underway by the time systematic surveys were initiated in the 1960s, or that current numbers are higher than pre-DDT numbers. We believe the former is most likely. Regardless, by the early 1970s populations in interior and northern Alaska were well below all previous known levels and historical estimates.

In 1973, the Endangered Species Act (ESA) became law in the United States. Because of declining numbers throughout North America, both the American and Arctic Peregrine Falcons (*F. p. anatum* and *F. p. tundrius,* respectively) were included in the list of threatened and endangered species. With passage of the ESA and inclusion of both subspecies on the list, the U.S. Fish and Wildlife Service (FWS) appointed a recovery team for American and Arctic Peregrine Falcons in Alaska, and a recovery plan for these populations was prepared. This was one of the first recovery plans completed under provisions of the ESA. It laid out directions for research and recovery actions in Alaska. Also at that time, as required by the ESA, every federally permitted activity in the United States was reviewed to ensure that the proposed activity did not negatively affect Peregrine Falcons. Thus, the few nest sites that remained in the contiguous United States, as well as those in Alaska, received special protection from disturbance and destruction.

In the mid-1970s, FWS, along with the Bureau of Land Management (BLM), National Park Service, Alaska Department of Fish and Game, and several private organizations, initiated surveys for Peregrines throughout Alaska. Many individuals participated in the surveys, but those most involved included Mike Amaral, Michelle

Ambrose, Dan Benfield, Peter Bente, Mike Britten, Lance Craighead, Jim Curatolo, Bob Dittrick, Bruce Durtsche, Janey Fadely, Jeff Hughes, Penny Knuckles, Robin Hunter Long, Fran Mauer, Carol McIntyre, Dave Mindell, Kathy O'Reily-Doyle, Harry Reynolds, Dave Roseneau, Phil Schempf, Jeff Shryer, Jim Silva, Alan Springer, Chris Todd, Ted Swem, Steve Ulvi, Van Waggoner, John Wright, and ourselves, Robert Ambrose and Robert Ritchie. All of those listed could probably thank many additional individuals, for probably more than 100 people altogether helped with surveys in Alaska.

From the mid-1970s to the present, research and recovery efforts in Alaska have continued. As more was learned about local populations, surveys were refined to include specific index areas, and more detailed research efforts were undertaken, such as contaminant studies and banding efforts to improve information on migration and population turnover. With the direction provided in the recovery plan and the cooperation of so many interested parties, researchers were able to monitor these populations and collect data to support the delisting of both subspecies in the late 1990s.

continued on page 197

▲ **Figure 11.5** Ice break-up on the Yukon River.

Alaskan Peregrines—Their Comings, Their Goings, Their Comings

Clayton M. White

It was June 1962. I was in the car's back seat. My mentor, William Behle, and his wife, Dorothy, sat in front as we headed for Ithaca, New York, to attend the International Ornithological Congress. I was excited for many reasons. First, I had been told of some Ph.D. student from Yale who worked in the Middle East and was to be there and had described a new subspecies of Peregrine from some island. Second, I was

reading my copy of Tom Cade's published dissertation, "Ecology of the Peregrine and Gyrfalcon Populations in Alaska." I hoped to finish it during the long drive and also that Tom would be in Ithaca so I could ask him about his statement that, "Alaska is a meeting grounds of these various subspecies and geographic variants of the Peregrine, and a serious student of the subject would do well to gather material from

▲ Sagavanirktok River, northern Alaska.

this region." I wanted to immerse myself in a study of the populations Cade had written about. And to study a population, I reckoned there should be many falcons. Little did I realize that the populations he saw had already declined from some higher but unknown level. I thought that Peregrine populations in Alaska would still be pristine,

and why not? Was not Alaska pristine territory?

Enter now early autumn 1962; I was at Fairbanks, Alaska. I was naive but nonetheless surprised not to find Peregrines where Cade mentioned them, a dozen years earlier, at such prominent landmarks as Chena Bluff. Nor were they at several places along the Tanana River; I thought that just coincidence, not significant. Then came winter.

As the ice broke and snow began to melt, heralding spring, birds by the scores returned to Fairbanks, especially at Creamer's Dairy where dark cow manure accelerated snow melt. My first Peregrine sightings there were in the last week of April. By my count on one day there were an adult male and two adult females, or perhaps it was only one that moved at enormous speeds from one end of the field to the other. The fields were a mass of bird life, primarily waterfowl, gathering in ponds and on the ever increasingly exposed ground.

I patiently sat in a cold car hoping to see a Peregrine leave its perch and attack a bird or do something. They were more patient than I, however. After a few days, the falcons left for what I presumed to be their breeding sites as silently as they had arrived. I never knew where they were headed, but at least there were several Peregrines. I was "coming" into a world of Peregrines.

A year later, working out of the "village" of Umiat, on Alaska's North Slope, I had

the opportunity to travel with several oil company geologists as they tooled from cliff to cliff in a helicopter. Sure enough, the cliffs Cade mentioned on the Colville could be easily identified. Unlike on the Tanana, at least one pair of Peregrines occupied each cliff exactly as Tom had written. My spirits were lifted. Perhaps there were just more Peregrines here, or they were easier to find than in the Yukon drainage. However, to my surprise John Haugh and I found Peregrines in 1965 on the Yukon River at all the cliffs they had occupied in 1951.

I had mixed feelings, because by 1968 Peregrines were few on the Tanana but seemed to still be at what was thought to be baseline historical levels on the Yukon and Colville Rivers, even if not on many of their tributaries, and I did not understand what was going on. Reflecting back, I was witness to the uneven decline of Peregrines, with populations hanging on in core regions, probably those very areas where the last Peregrine would occur should they disappear everywhere else; I was seeing the "goings" of the peripheral populations.

And you know something is happening, but you don't know what it is . . . Do you Mr. Jones?
—*Bob Dylan,
Ballad of a Thin Man*

Over the next 10 years or so I worked on many projects throughout Alaska searching for Peregrines, often the species of principal interest.

For example, there were about 10 locations along the Sagavanirktok River, the mouth of which ends near the oil fields of Prudhoe Bay, where they were known to have bred, and we believed there might have been 15 breeding locations. By 1970–1971 only four pairs remained at such places as Franklin and Sagwon Bluffs, only two of which were usually successful. Along the remaining 700-plus miles of oil pipeline route to Valdez, few falcons were seen, although we passed many former Peregrine breeding stations. In 1973 Steve Sherrod and I assessed potential impacts on raptors of a proposed Yukon River Dam to be built at Woodchopper Volcanics. We started downriver from Dawson. On 18 June we passed Old Woman and Castle Rock, where fledglings were seen 5 August 1899. Falcons were there but not at many other likely localities. These two places were probably the crème de la crème of habitat. In 1974 I surveyed the Susitna River, where a dam was also proposed. Were there Peregrines there? Nope. Had there ever been many? Who knows?

In 1975 Tom Cade and I carried out an aerial and ground survey of the entire Colville watershed. We could only find 12 occupied eyries on the main river and six on tributaries.

The story was different in the Aleutians in the early to mid-1970s. The birds seemed never to have been gone. Buldir Island, a tiny speck of lushly vegetated jutting volcanic rock about 12 miles in circumference with 5,000 acres, housed five pairs—about one falcon per 270 acres of land when adding in fledged young and nonbreed-

ing floaters. At Amchitka a maximum of 21 eyries occurred along the 112-mile shoreline, plus an unknown number of nonbreeding subadults and adults. After fledging this means about one falcon per 612 acres of island.

15 July 1987. My pilot dropped me off at a Colville River bar a few miles above the Ipnavik River. I awaited Ted Swem, during which time I began rehoning the craft of mosquito swatting and practiced all the necessary vocabulary that went with it. Ted arrived. I asked, in a manner indicating I had full control of the situation, "Aren't the mosquitos a bit worse this year than usual?" "No, Clay," responded Ted. "You have just forgotten." And so I had, but I remembered that there had been between 30 and 40 pairs of Peregrines, depending on how much river was covered in the 1950s–1960s—now there were over 60 pairs. Peregrines were back.

And then, it was the first week of June 1991. At last I had a chance to get my wife, Merle, on the Yukon River. For me it was important because now what I felt and experienced could also be felt, on a personal level, with someone else in my family. All talk around the dinner table would not be just words. Skip Ambrose was taking us where I had not been for over 15 years, the upper Yukon River. Peregrines were everywhere. Inter-eyrie distances were less than a mile or so in some places. Where John Haugh and I found 17 eyries in 1966 there were now nearly 40. Some were on unthinkable and unimaginable locations; we could look into one eyrie from the river surface. All the places where we found them earlier were

Clayton White *received a B.A. in zoology from the University of Utah, did graduate work at the University of Alaska, and has a Ph.D. in zoology from the University of Utah. He is Professor of Zoology at Brigham Young University. He worked as a vertebrate ecologist for the U.S. Energy Research and Development Administration on issues dealing largely with Arctic oil development. Research includes ecophysiology of finches and ecology and natural history of raptors, primarily falcons. He has served on two U.S. Fish and Wildlife Service recovery teams for the Peregrine Falcon and two terms on The Peregrine Fund Board of Directors.*

occupied, some in the same ledge as in 1966; not an unexpected finding. Peregrines were back.

26 July 2000. Some six pairs of Peregrines nest between Fairbanks and Tok Junction along the highway's roadside in such places as roadway cuts through gravel hills and fractured stone faces where rock was quarried to get highway rip rap. Ted Swem, Bob Ritchie, Jane McDonagh, Laura Phillips, and I stood on the road's shoulder watching two fledglings about 50 ft back from the road. John Wright and Peter Bente have found some 23 pairs along the Sagavanirktok where we reckoned the maximum was about 15. The story is the same elsewhere in Alaska. Peregrines are back; we are watching their "comings."

Were there Peregrines there? Nope. Had there ever been many? Who knows?

Bill Burnham

193

The Colville River, Alaska

Tom J. Cade

▲ Tom Cade (driving), John Haugh (swatting mosquitoes), Clay White (reclining), and an Inupiat mechanic set off in old World War II "weasel," an amphibious tracked vehicle used for tundra exploration, 1967.

In 1949 the Territory of Alaska reached out in all its wild expanse to embrace me as I arrived in Seward, a steerage passenger on the steamship *Baranoff*, on my way to become a student at the University of Alaska in Fairbanks and to search for falcons in the Far North. George Willett, my first mentor in natural history and curator of birds and mammals at the Los Angeles County Museum of History, Science, and Art, had told me as a teenager to go to Alaska if I wanted to find lots of Peregrines. After a stint in the Army, I followed his advice, using my educational support under the GI Bill of Rights to help pay the way.

I soon learned from Urban C. Nelson, a waterfowl biologist for the Bureau of Sport Fisheries and Wildlife (FWS), that the Colville River, the largest watershed north of the Brooks Range, was a good place to find nesting falcons and hawks. His lead was emphatically confirmed in 1951 when John Buckley, one of my professors and the unit leader of the recently formed Alaska Cooperative Wildlife Research Unit, informed me that on an aerial waterfowl survey of the Colville River he had seen Peregrines, Gyrfalcons, and Rough-legged Hawks flying off their nests on the numerous cliffs lining the river for most of its length. That was enough. The next year found me on the Arctic Slope under contract with the Navy to conduct the first ornithological reconnaissance of the main Colville River valley.

At that time the Navy had control of a huge piece of land,

most of the Arctic Slope of Alaska, referred to as the Naval Petroleum Reserve No. 4 or simply Pet-4, which included most of the Colville River system and all of the land lying north of the river to the Arctic Ocean. In addition to supporting geological surveys and petroleum exploration, the Navy operated a large arctic research facility at Barrow, Alaska, the Naval Arctic Research Laboratory, which provided operational support and logistics for a wide variety of both marine and terrestrial scientific studies. It was my privilege to be associated with this outstanding institution in the 1950s, 1960s, and early 1970s. During most of those years the director of the lab was Max C. Brewer, who readily embraced my interests in falcons and other predators and always kept my associates and me well supplied in the field. In the 1950s I also worked with Frank A. Pitelka on his lemming project, but Frank also allowed me to spend much of my time studying raptors.

John Buckley organized the 1952 study through the Alaska Coop Unit and obtained a contract between the Office of Naval Research and the University of Alaska. Because I was only recently graduated from the university, I could not serve as the principal investigator of the project, a position the university handed over to a newly arriving assistant professor with a fresh Ph.D. from Cornell University, Brina Kessel.

As it turned out, the Navy had an absolute prohibition at that time against the pres-

ence of any female personnel on the petroleum reserve, so the responsibilities for carrying out the actual field investigations fell to me and a young assistant, who got assigned to the project at the last minute.

Recently graduated from high school in Missouri and 19 years old, he was a gaunt young man with an intense gaze, extremely exploratory mind, distinct German accent, which he had carried with him as an immigrant from postwar Europe, and utter disregard for personal comforts. We first met in the field at the mouth of the Etivluk River, an upper tributary of the Colville, where I had been waiting several days in camp for his arrival. When I noticed that he ate his oatmeal with a goodly amount of mosquitoes mixed in without comment, I knew he was somebody special and that we would travel together just fine. It was to be George Schaller's first natural history exploration.

We managed to save each other from serious accidents several times. Once, when George climbed down a cliff on a rope free-hand to take a baby raven from its nest, he somehow managed to get a coil of rope around his neck, and when his feet suddenly

slipped out from under him, he was left literally hanging and unable to take the tension off the rope. I had to climb up to cut the rope above him and let him fall a few feet into loose talus below the nest. George still got the raven. In later years I have sometimes mused about how much great natural history would never have been written if that incident had turned out differently.

We made two trips down the river that summer, each of us with a 14-ft collapsible canoe, and discovered an easily navigable river flowing down a spectacular valley cutting through the foothills of the Brooks Range to the Arctic Ocean and lined for nearly its full length by a series of rocky cliffs and earthen bluffs ranging from 50 to 300 ft high. We observed 62 species of birds and collected 178 specimens of 45 species. The cliff-nesting assemblage of birds was phenomenal, and in addition to numerous pairs of Canada Geese, we found 40 pairs of Peregrines between the mouth of the Kiligwa River and Ocean Point, four pairs of Gyrfalcons, more than 48 pairs of Rough-legged Hawks (not all pairs were counted), and about four pairs of Northern Ravens. The results of the trip were published later by the University of Alaska (Kessel and Cade 1958).

The uniqueness of the Colville River as a major landscape for arctic-nesting raptors, especially Peregrines, was evident from our initial study, and it has led to more or less continual annual monitoring of raptor populations to the present. Over the next decades I made more than a dozen excursions on the Colville, employing a variety of craft from Kalamazoo boats, the old U.S. Geological Survey standard, to motorized Avon rubber rafts and even an airboat once or twice for short trips in and out of Umiat. We once crossed the river in an amphibious weasel (Max, you never knew that), and in later years we often flew in helicopters and slow-flying fixed-winged aircraft such as the heliocourier.

I enjoyed these trips with a variety of great companions—Hal Webster, Jr., Morley Nelson, Clay White, Walter Spofford, Jim Weaver, Stan Temple, John Haugh, Paul Spitzer, Ken and Rebecca Riddle, Frank Bond, and Pete Sovalik, an inland Inupiat (Nunamiut) who was born in the Colville country. In later years, Ted Swem took over the annual raptor surveys for FWS and Bureau of Land Management (BLM) around 1981, after the petroleum reserve had been transferred from the Navy to the jurisdiction of the Department of the Interior. I made my last trip with him in 1989.

The Colville River region was, and to a large extent still is, true wilderness where few human beings are permanent inhabitants in a country measured in the tens of thousands of square miles (Cade 1970, White and Cade 1971, Cade and White 1976a). From the top of one of our favorite

cliffs (no. 41), facing the Oolamnagavik River, one can look 360 degrees in all directions and see unbroken expanses of riparian and foothill tundra where caribou, moose, wolf, grizzly bear, and wolverine still roam freely over the vast countryside, where in spring tens of thousands of wild geese and ducks, a great variety of plovers and sandpipers, and many other arctic-nesting birds such as Red-spotted Bluethroats, Yellow Wagtails, Arctic Warblers, and Northern Shrikes join with the hardy resident ptarmigan to breed in the continual daylight of the brief summer. Here, too, the Peregrine Falcon, Gyrfalcon, and Rough-legged Hawk, now more numerous than they were in the 1950s, still scream defiance to intruders at craggy eyries along fast-flowing arctic streams.

During the Navy's control of the petroleum reserve from the 1920s to the 1970s, access to the region was strictly limited. Even the inland Inupiat, except those at Anaktuvuk Pass, had moved to the coast, and there were few human activities to disturb the land and its wildlife—mainly geological survey teams and some exploratory drilling in isolated locations for oil and gas. All that changed with the flurry of conflicting interests in land uses and land ownership spawned by the Alaska Native Land Claims Settlement Act in the early 1970s and the discovery of a large reservoir of oil at Prudhoe Bay east of the petroleum reserve.

Since very little oil or gas had been discovered in the petroleum reserve itself, for a time consideration was given to the idea of converting Pet-4 into some kind of national arctic biome reserve or

wildlife refuge to preserve the major coastal plain and foothills region of northern Alaska. Unfortunately, that idea could not be sustained politically. The American public did end up with the protection of some magnificent wilderness mountains in the Brooks Range, but to this day the only part of the arctic coastal plain and foothills to receive protected status is the relatively small section in the Arctic National Wildlife Refuge, and it remains politically vulnerable to development.

To its great credit, after taking responsibility for the surface values of the renamed National Petroleum Reserve-Alaska (NPR-A) in 1976, the BLM officially recognized the Colville River valley as an area of special biological signifi-

▲ Later—amphibious vehicle sunk in wet sedge tundra.

cance because of its raptors and other wildlife and referred to it on maps as the Colville River Special Area. In the 1980s it was also listed as a "key raptor area" in BLM's habitat management system, along with the foothills of the Brooks Range, the Utukok River uplands, and the Sagwon Bluffs, more than 2,700,000 acres in all (Olendorff et al. 1989).

More recently during Bruce Babbitt's tenure as Interior Secretary, when the northeastern portion of NPR-A was finally opened up for oil leasing by private industry, some specific stipulations regulating oil development in the Colville River Special Area were established by order of the Secretary to protect raptor nesting habitat.

Still, the region is under constant threat of more development. Sadly, it appears likely that the stretch of unparalleled Peregrine nesting habitat that stretches virtually uninterrupted from Umiat to Ocean Point on the lower Colville will soon be trashed, but there is still hope that the upper Colville and its tributaries and the Utukok River can be spared, because oil and mineral deposits there

are too small and scattered to be commercially produced. It is not yet too late for our nation to establish a National Arctic Tundra Biome Reserve to protect the most ecologically valuable portion of the arctic coastal plain and foothills of northern Alaska.

For biographical information on Tom Cade, see Chapter 5.

Figure 11.7 Surveying for ▶
Peregrines on the Charley
River in eastern interior
Alaska.

▼ **Figure 11.6** Adult female Peregrine, nesting in 1993 along
the Yukon River, was the first to be tagged with a satellite transmitter. She wintered near Naples, Florida, and
returned to the same nest territory the following year.

▼ **Figure 11.8** The Yukon
River, with float plane
and canoe—new and
old means of access.

There are a few unique aspects of the work in Alaska that we want to mention. The Alaska Peregrine Falcon Recovery Plan was very specific, in that it identified both index study areas that had to be monitored and specific recovery criteria that needed to be achieved before delisting could occur. Since the mid-1970s, biologists have been surveying those areas and monitoring those criteria. Special thanks go to the members of the Alaska Peregrine Falcon Recovery Team for the guidance provided in the recovery plan. The index areas and recovery criteria were so well defined that research objectives and recovery goals were very clear. Consequently, the data collected were instrumental in the removal of American and Arctic Peregrine Falcons from the list of threatened and endangered species. The members of the Alaska Peregrine Falcon Recovery Team were Don Frickie (team leader), Jerry MacGowan, David Roseneau, Clayton White, Laun Buoy, James Larson, Steven Leskosky, and Louis Jurs.

Another unique aspect of Peregrine recovery in Alaska is that it was not influenced by releases of captive-bred birds or nest manipulations. In some areas of the lower 48 (contiguous) states, local Peregrine populations were completely extirpated, and captive breeding was the only practical way to restore these populations. Alaska, however, still had some nesting pairs. Peregrine populations in all of the lower 48 states were influenced to some degree by captive breeding and release programs, and increases in those populations were undoubtedly due to both the restrictions on the use of DDT and releases of captive-bred birds. The influence of release programs on the rate of recovery of local populations where some wild birds remained will probably never be fully understood. In Alaska, however, local populations began to rebound without artificial or supplemental support soon after restrictions were placed on the use of DDT in 1972. Populations in Alaska were too far away from release programs to be influenced, and our surveys were able to show the natural, unaided recovery of a Peregrine population.

Peregrine recovery continues today in Alaska, and the northern and interior populations of *F. p. tundrius* and *F. p. anatum* probably exceed 1,000 pairs. As some areas reach what appears to be carrying capacity, we are seeing behaviors we have never seen before. In recent years, we have observed frequent and intensive territorial defense (to the point of injury and possibly death of some adults) and an increase in the time both adults spend away from the nest site (probably in search of prey). We are seeing birds nesting in places we would never have imagined 10 or 20 years ago, including regular use of quarried areas along busy highways in interior Alaska and manmade structures in northern Alaska. Although recent declines in productivity of some "crowded" river populations seem to suggest the reaching of carrying capacity, we have much to learn about this species.

Many dedicated people have worked on Peregrine Falcons in Alaska. It seems that everyone who ever worked in Alaska on Peregrines was equally enthralled by the Great Land and its Peregrine populations. No one came to Alaska to work on Peregrine Falcons for fortune or fame or because of agency mandates; mostly, these were people dedicated to the species and this Great Land. Each shared the desire to see this species recover and fill the skies over Alaska's great rivers. Successful wildlife recoveries in our shrinking world of resources seem uncommon, but we are grateful for this one, and we hope it reflects other possibilities in conservation.

Photo provided by the authors

Robert Ritchie *(left) is a Senior Scientist with and cofounder of ABR, Inc., Environmental Research and Services, an environmental consulting firm with offices in Alaska and Oregon. He came to Alaska in 1972 and attended the University of Alaska in Fairbanks. He began working with Peregrines in 1973 along the upper Yukon River as part of his Master's degree. He has worked on Peregrines and other raptor species throughout Alaska and continues to conduct surveys in many areas of the state. His interests include managing his business for a "triple bottom line"— social, economic, and environmental profit.*

Skip Ambrose *(right) is currently a wildlife biologist with the National Park Service, working on Peregrine Falcons and acoustic issues in national parks. He began his career with the Endangered Species Program of the U.S. Fish and Wildlife Service in Alaska in 1979. He first worked on Peregrine Falcons in 1973, working with Robert Ritchie on the upper Yukon River in eastern interior Alaska. He has worked on Peregrines in many areas of Alaska and other states. His surveys along the upper Yukon River continue.*

The Greenland Peregrine Falcon Survey

William G. Mattox

Extirpation of the anatum Duck Hawk in eastern North America, and declines of Peregrine populations elsewhere,

have been discussed in other chapters of this book. The 1969 publication of Hickey's *Peregrine Falcon Populations* spurred interest in possible causes of this decline, among which chemically affected behavior seemed one possibility (Hickey 1969). At that time we thought studying a "normal" population could contribute to explaining the causes of the decline. Greenland was reported to have breeding Peregrines, but their status had not been determined through field studies.

Another meeting on the Peregrine question, organized by Tom Cade and held at Cornell University in November 1969, recommended a North American Peregrine Survey (under Cade and Hickey) and designated a group of "regional captains" who would be responsible for operation in their respective areas (T. Cade 2 December 1969 to World Wildlife Fund). Greenland would be covered by Finn Salomonsen, Curator of Birds at the University of Copenhagen's Zoological Museum and the dean of Greenland ornithology. Salomon-

sen encouraged such a study, and indeed supported our early efforts to locate the necessary funding. He had noted in his monumental *The Birds of Greenland* (Salomonsen 1950–1951) that the Peregrine "is a common breeding bird in the southern parts of the West-coast northwards to Nûgssuaq Pen." No reports of population declines in Greenland had been made, nor were any studies then in place to determine the status of the species. In fact, no species-specific work had been done at all.

Strong attempts by Cade in late 1969 and early 1970 to secure funding for a Peregrine survey in Greenland failed; and the Danes indicated they had no money for this activity, although they supported such a survey (Salomonsen pers. comm.).

I then tried and failed to get the needed support over a period of several years. In 1972, LTC Richard Graham, U.S. Air Force (USAF), and I scraped together money to buy basic equipment; and three college students succeeded in obtaining small grants: Bill Burnham (grant from Southern Colorado State College), and Jim Harris and Dave Clement (Mellon Fund grant from Dartmouth College). The first season of what came to be known as the Greenland Peregrine Falcon Survey began with shaky support in unknown territory, but with great enthusiasm.

◀ **Figure 12.1** Painting by George E. Lodge from the collection of Bill Mattox. Reproduction by kind permission of copyright-holder Tryon Gallery.

▲ Figure 12.2 Finn Salomonsen with Bill Burnham, July 1973, at crossing to Between Rivers cliff.

Figure 12.3 F. Prescott Ward ▶ atop saddle south of Ringsø (cliff in background), 4 August 1973.

Figure 12.4 Adult female and ▶ brood of four young at Ringsø, July 1990.

Details of those first years came out in brief field reports published mainly in the journals *Arctic* and *Polar Record*, in Jim Harris's Master's thesis (a shortened version published as *The Peregrine Falcon in Greenland* [Harris 1978]), and in Bill Burnham's book *A Fascination with Falcons* (Burnham 1997). After the first season, the U.S. Army, through F. Prescott (Scott) Ward, provided the real impetus for a long-term study through travel expense and per-diem payments to team members. From 1973 we were also able to travel to Greenland on invitational orders from the USAF arranged by Scott Ward. Ward's interest (through a notable prescience) centered not only on the species itself but also on the growing indications of environmental pollution. As everyone now knows, the Peregrine provides an unparalleled species to monitor pollution.

Graham and I had picked central West Greenland as the study area because a USAF base at Søndre Strømfjord received weekly flights from the United States (McGuire AFB, New Jersey) and maintained the usual well-stocked BX and Visiting Officer's Quarters, the so-called "Arctic Hotel." Our study could not have succeeded without this base and the friendly support of American and Danish personnel there. The base closed in September 1992, but the study has continued each year since. Although no native settlement ever existed at Søndre Strømfjord (now called Kangerlussuaq), Greenlanders showed interest in our project. They welcomed us to their country, and each team member recognized what a privilege it was to walk the hills of this foreign land and to carry out fieldwork in the wilderness of inner West Greenland.

Our first summer proved to be a tough one. We had maps, both Danish and U.S. military, but could not actually see our survey area from the air because the only available small aircraft were out of service. The USAF never stationed planes there.

After getting Harris and Clement established at two local falcon cliffs where they would carry out behavioral observations from a blind, Graham, Burnham, and I started out with heavy packs on a walking tour north of the base. We had marked our planned route on a map for the base security office. Soon after we started out, word had arrived at the base that Graham was needed back in the United States because of an emergency. When we arrived back at the base, the security search and rescue team was suited up and ready to head out to look for us. Our return at that point was lucky for them: they would not have found us easily, because our week's backpacking route turned out far different from the one we had marked on their map.

After Graham left for the States, Bill Burnham and I began backpacking trips of up to eight days, trying to locate breeding cliffs and band young. We occasionally visited the Harris/Clement camps. They had arranged with the air-base radio station to broadcast any messages, and were able to receive the local station's music, weather, and news broadcasts intermittently on a small portable radio. The station's cryptic announcement, "You've got mail!" meant something only to Dave and Jim at their camp, but now means another thing to Tom Hanks, Meg Ryan, and millions of E-mail recipients.

During our long, tiring walks across the tundra under heavy packs, we found eight Peregrine and three Gyrfalcon eyries, with 18 Peregrine nestlings and eight gyrs. We banded some of them and collected prey remains and addled eggs; we concluded after that first season that "Peregrine Falcons in West Greenland appear to be in a healthy state as evidenced by a high nesting density (1/100 sq mi) and a high production rate (2.25/eyrie)" (Mattox et al. 1972).

From that modest beginning, the survey grew in a real extent and scientific scope. Never in my wildest dreams could I have guessed that by 1998 the survey would have included over 90 volunteer participants who expanded the study area to over 1,200 sq mi with 126 known Peregrine territories. Nor, after banding those first 13 nestlings, would I have guessed that by 1998 we would have banded over 1,800 nestlings and 150 adults. For me, the greatest pleasure came from those 90 participants, who demonstrated a singular love of Greenland and the Peregrine Falcon. Without

Tom Smylie

that love, the countless miles of tough walking over the rugged Greenland terrain would not have been possible. This story of Greenland's part in the recent Peregrine restoration is the story of individuals who worked hard and came back for more. But of equal significance to me, Greenland's wilderness areas, which happen to be home for Peregrine Falcons, have incomparable worth. That tundra wilderness, in a world rife with development, is for us a Shangri-La of stark beauty, silence, and peace. Those wanting to intrude upon this arctic wilderness learn immediately that they face a serious challenge. We tried to change nothing and leave few traces of our intrusion, but that land surely changed us! For the better—and forever.

People studying Peregrine Falcons in Greenland, and elsewhere, require three main qualities: they must be rock climbers, wilderness survivors, and raptorphiles, including experience in banding nestlings. I learned that such outdoor people come mainly from the West in our country, and that they are strong, resourceful, and upbeat. They also take seriously the responsibility of carrying out scientific research in a foreign land, and they value the privilege they had been offered by Greenland, and by Mother Denmark.

▲ **Figure 12.5** Adult female at Taserssuaq.

"It was not lonely, but made all the earth lonely beneath it."

—Henry David Thoreau

Greenland Falcons

William Burnham

▲ Kurt and Bill Burnham, Thule, Greenland, 1998.

The stark beauty of the arctic landscape is unsurpassed in nature. Greenland is the unspoiled frontier for Arctic North America. Vast areas remain largely unchanged from time immemorial. In the late 1970s a positive change did begin, an increase in Peregrine Falcon populations within the large ice-free area to the north and south of Søndre Strømfjord and probably along much of the island's west coast. Thanks to Bill Mattox and his multitude of field biologists, we know a great deal about the Peregrine there and its expanding population.

I was invited to join Mattox in 1972, the first and then many following years of what became known as the Greenland Peregrine Falcon Survey. We walked hundreds of miles together in search of falcon eyries and shared many memorable experiences. The experiences were both enjoyable and formative. In 1998 Bill requested that The Peregrine Fund and I assume responsibility from him for continuing the work on falcons in Greenland. We were honored by his trust and reassured by the foundation of knowledge he had established and knowing he will never truly not be involved.

Rewarding were not only the experiences in search of eyries and studying the falcons we found, but the resulting friendships, especially with Bill Mattox. A further highlight was sharing the Arctic with my son, Kurt. In a single field season he also became infatuated with the Far North and has returned each year since. Spring 2001, as The Peregrine Fund's Greenland Projects Manager, he completed his 12th field season there. Working with him and other young biologists as the transfer of knowledge and responsibility are passed between generations, I become increasingly optimistic for the future of falcons and humanity.

Bill Burnham *For biographical information see Chapter 8.*

Those Lean Years

Burnham, Harris, and Clement all returned in 1973. Burnham and Clement walked the tundra (they also visited East Greenland but found no Peregrines); Harris spent time at one of his 1972 cliffs and, with me, visited Alan Jenkins who was studying nesting Gyrfalcons at two cliffs (Burnham et al. 1974). With us that summer was Scott Ward, who was to play a major role in that and future years, supporting our work and bringing a new technique to bear, in the form of plastic color bands. These red leg bands had large numbers which could be read at a distance through binoculars or spotting scopes (Ward 1975).

The following year two more students from Dartmouth, Thom Snowman and Ginger Cox, placed time-lapse cameras at two cliffs; Burnham and Steve Sherrod traveled north to Disko in search of falcons; and Jim Weaver pioneered the use of a two-man kayak, with me as field companion (Mattox 1975). After that 1974 season we had banded 55 nestlings and received our first recovery—Cape Charles Charlie captured at Cape Charles, Virginia, by Bill Clark's team (a hatch-year male banded at Dome in July by Burnham and Weaver).

It was obvious that we were involved in a numbers game and that we had to band more falcons in order to learn more about the locations of migratory routes and wintering areas. So in 1975, while Burnham hosted Peregrine experts Tom Cade, Jim Enderson, and Clayton White in our survey area, I attempted autumn trapping on the outer coast. With hawk trappers Dan Berger and Bill Clark, I traveled in September to southwest Greenland where the icecap narrowed to the sea. There we saw only a few Peregrines and caught one hatch-year male, which we instrumented with a microtransmitter for Bill Cochran. This effort, and a similar one with Steve Sherrod in 1976, did nothing to increase the number of Peregrines banded in Greenland, although we did band a number of Gyrfalcons. Steve had spent the summer in the survey area studying nestling behavior up to and following fledging. Those two summers saw only 22 nestlings banded, nine or more in 1977, and 17 in 1978 (Mattox et al. 1980).

In 1979, however, we banded 20, and in 1980 we reached 30. Of the 160 nestlings banded since the beginning, we had received but six recoveries. We did not realize it then, but we were seeing the low point of Peregrine populations in Greenland (Burnham and Mattox 1984). By 1983 we had increased the annual banding to 53 nestlings, and it was all up from there (Mattox and Seegar 1988).

W.S. Seegar

Figure 12.6 Bill Seegar with adult female tagged with Platform Transmitter Terminal (PTT), June 1994.

Adult Banding

By banding only nestlings we obtained little data about adult Peregrines, so in 1983 we began capturing adults at the eyrie. This operation was carried out at active eyries by the so-called Advance Team (known behind their backs as the "Backward Team!"—they were envied by the backpackers because they rode in a helicopter) led by Bill Seegar, who by then had taken over from Scott Ward the securing of funding for the project—a task he performed with outstanding success.

Bill Seegar and his regulars (most of whom stayed and walked the tiring survey routes like everyone else) captured over 200 adults (148 individual birds) over the 15-year period from 1983. From 1986 we used color alpha bands of blue anodized aluminum, which worked better than Scott Ward's red plastic bands because they were stronger and could not be removed by the bird. In all, between 1983 and 1998 we captured or read the alpha band of 403 falcons, which provided superb data on adult population dynamics: turnover, nest-site fidelity, loss, and individual longevity.

Larger Teams

All this time we were able to support larger teams who found more cliffs and banded more nestlings. From the 51 banded in 1983, we banded

68 in 1984, 102 in 1985, 99 in 1986, 112 in 1987, 159 in 1990, and a record 190 in 1991, a season fielding 22 team members. Team members peaked in 1992 with 24; in 1990 and 1991, we had begun to study Gyrfalcons, so we needed extra field people. The impressive numbers resulted solely from Bill Seegar's solid support through the U.S. Army Edgewood Research, Development, and Engineering Center. Our team members were volunteers, but we needed equipment, food, and travel money, plus many hours of expensive helicopter charter for the adult banding.

The work incorporated other activities beyond climbing to eyries and banding adults and young. From the early days, ancillary studies undertaken by the project included brooding behavior, trace element analysis of feathers, eggshell thickness and pollutant loading, embryonic abnormality (we found an unusual twin embryo egg), prey species density and distribution, radio-tracking of adult home ranges, ectoparasites, blood-pollutant analysis, nest-detritus analysis, blood parasites, and prey-species analysis. Some of these subjects formed the basis for graduate degrees by team members, or detailed studies by their faculty advisors.

The Personal Commitment

The survey attracted several stalwarts over the years, some of whom spent many summers in

We did not realize it then, but we were seeing the low point of Peregrine populations in Greenland.

Greenland Peregrine Falcon Research

Tom Maechtle

▲ Figure 12.7 All of Greenland is influenced by the huge icecap, which covers about 85% of the island's area. Note the backpacker walking alongside the stream.

Greenland. All their contributions cannot be detailed here because of space, but the dedication of a few must be recorded to underline the importance of their long-term commitments. And too often forgotten is the long-term support of their work by spouses and companions.

The pioneers of the early years returned to Greenland for only a few seasons, with the exception of Bill Burnham who surveyed for falcons up to 1979 and again for two years in the early 1990s. In the late 1970s the survey had the involvement of Peregrine friends who also would take an active role in the Peregrine restoration effort.

Although the Greenland study has no direct connection with Peregrine restoration, many people working in Greenland later participated in that effort in various ways. Jim Weaver, a Peregrine Fund director who participated early on, installed the time-lapse cameras at two cliffs for the Snowman-Cox effort in 1974. Peregrine

W hat I remember most, as I reflect upon 18 summers of Peregrine Falcon nest surveys in Greenland, is the haunting silence at most of the cliffs I visited during my first survey in 1981. My field companion, Jack Oar, and I walked and kayaked from cliff to cliff searching for Peregrines and were seldom rewarded. We spent hours at each cliff expectantly waiting for the "food wail" of an adult female—a transfer from an incoming male, and the food begging of nestlings. Time after time we left disappointed by negative results. When we did encounter a Peregrine, it was often a lone adult female. Hours of observation confirmed there was not a male in residence. Jack and I brainstormed for the reason why. Despite our relatively small sample size, we could not escape the fact that the females could shed accumulated loads of contaminants through the fats in their eggs. The males had no mechanism to eliminate chemical residues from their bodies. Were males still dying from toxins in greater numbers, leaving these females with no available mates? I suppose we will never know. Jack and I did find two productive nests that summer, and we banded

▲ Tom Maechtle and Jack Oar at Sunshine Point, Greenland, 1981.

My field companion, Jack Oar, and I walked and kayaked from cliff to cliff searching for Peregrines and were seldom rewarded.

three nestlings at one site. The others were too young to band. After 18 days in the field, we returned from our area and joined the rest of the team who also had spent weeks searching. We were elated to have set a new record of 33 nestlings banded, a result of five two-man teams searching long days and walking hundreds of miles throughout the tundra of Greenland.

As dramatic as the paucity of Peregrines in 1981, by 1983 the same cliffs showed signs of becoming one of the most densely occupied regions in our study area. Many of the sites silent in 1981 now had pairs in residence, and most were producing young. As the years passed, my partners and I worked faster to visit each cliff during the short window of time we had to band nestlings. Our only mode of transportation remained our kayak and traveling on foot. By 1986, we could expect to band 40 or more young falcons on this same route.

Today chances are when you visit a cliff in the Kangerlussuaq area you will find

Peregrines. Production is high, and it seems the only restriction to an expanding population is the availability of suitable cliffs and prey. These cliffs are no longer silent. Female Peregrines wail for food from males who busily search for prey in their territory. The nestlings reveal their presence at every feeding as they noisily scramble for their share.

In the final analysis, the primary reason we averted the extirpation of Arctic-nesting Peregrines was the restriction of DDT use. Peregrine reproduction in our Greenland study area grew dramatically in response to less contaminated prey.

Peregrines are adapting to changes they encounter in their winter habitat. As I write this during the spring migration on South Padre Island, Texas, there is a Peregrine visible from my window. Perched on a 10-story condominium, she faces the Gulf of Mexico, presumably waiting to prey on an exhausted migrant passerine, perhaps a warbler first hitting landfall after hours of uninterrupted flight

that may have started in the Yucatan. Tourists stroll on the beach below her, and cars pass by nonstop in her view. She appears unconcerned as she shares her manmade cliff in close proximity to thousands of people. In a few weeks, she will once again arrive at her arctic cliff, far from the dense human populations in parts of her southern winter territory.

I am honored to have participated in the Greenland survey. I made lifelong friends with those I traveled with and will always have a love for and miss what others consider an austere landscape. For me, my finest memories of Greenland will always be the sounds of Peregrines at their cliffs.

Tom Maechtle *went to Greenland first in 1981 and participated in the survey for 18 seasons. He made valuable contributions to all aspects of the project. His skills in falcon capture on cliffs enabled the adult study to begin successfully in 1983. He attached PTTs to several adult Peregrines.*

Joe Papp

▲ **Figure 12.8** The adult female at Ringsø, July 1990.

experts Cade, Enderson, and White have already been mentioned as early visitors to the study area (in 1975 with Bill Burnham and Bob Martin). Steve Sherrod did part of his Ph.D. fieldwork in the study area. Bill Heinrich (1977, 1978, and 1980) teamed with Jack Oar (13 seasons) and Dan O'Brien in those years, and even survived a piteraq wind (catabatic gale from the icecap) with Tom Smylie in 1978. Well-known medical researcher and raptor rehabilitator Pat Redig helped the effort with long trips in new territory (1979 and 1980). He also piloted a small plane for team resupply. Other veterinarians who helped us were Bob Whitney (three seasons), Bill Satterfield (three seasons), Ken Riddle, Tom Ray (1985), and of course Scott Ward.

In the late 1970s, several people began long field careers in Greenland: Bill Seegar (18 seasons), Bud Anderson (four seasons), and early Peregrine Fund employee Tom Maechtle began his 18-season string in 1981. Mike Yates began in 1983 with the new effort to capture adult Peregrines. He contributed significantly for 14 seasons. Sidebars in this chapter by Maechtle and Yates provide a different perspective on the Greenland experience. The six stalwarts—Oar, Seegar, Maechtle, Yates, Bob Rosenfield (13 seasons), and Joe Papp (10 seasons)—contributed a cumulative 86 seasons to the Greenland Peregrine study, evidence of an incomparable love of Peregrines and of Greenland.

In later years, other team members gave many seasons as well. Tom Nichols (four seasons), Ralph Rogers (seven seasons), Greenlander Kâle Siegstad (six seasons), Father Phil Vance (five seasons), Chris Schultz (four seasons), Bob Murphy (four seasons), Denis Case (four seasons), and Mark Robertson (four seasons) all made valuable contributions.

The study lasted so long that even a second generation of Greenland teams arrived: Scott Rogers in 1987, Tim Mattox in 1989, Kurt Burnham and Jeff Yates in 1991, William H. Seegar in 1994, and Brandon Fuller in 1996.

Early team member Mark Fuller (1977) pioneered remote sensing techniques and walked the tundra for eight seasons; he instrumented both Peregrines and Gyrfalcons and organized a wide-ranging habitat and prey-species study that continues to the present. He instrumented adult falcons to determine home range in 1992, and Colin Pennycuick picked up their radio signals during daily flights in his Cessna.

Bob Rosenfield and Joe Papp teamed to carry out valuable prey habit studies, in addition to their regular survey backpacking routes. One year

Adult Capture

Mike Yates

In 1983 we began capturing adult Peregrines for a new study on longevity and nest-site fidelity. Over the years, this involved travel by foot, kayak, and helicopter and used several different capture methods. Other individuals (most notably Mark Robertson) were involved, but the adult capture team was usually Bill Seegar, Tom Maechtle, and myself. Typically we would travel by Bell 206 helicopter and capture falcons at their nest ledge via noose gin over dummy eggs. Blood samples were taken and blue alpha-numeric bands affixed for subsequent identification of individuals by scope. In 1994 we first used backpacked satellite-received telemetry on nesting females to garner home range, migration, and wintering data.

Although we each performed all necessary duties at one time or another, our roles within the team became quickly defined. Bill was the spotter, below and facing the cliff. A talented multitasker, Bill could locate an eyrie, position climbers, read a band, catch a char, and pick up a pound of qiviut (muskox wool) simultaneously. Tom, the youngest and possessed of simian qualities uncommon in a man his size, was the default climber. Substantial yet cerebral, I became the backup climber and scribe. Tom and I often found it quickest to forego the search for a suitable anchor; a quick body belay from me would have him at the scrape in no time flat. I often mused that, when asked my occupa-

tion, "Maechtle's tie-off" would be the most proper response.

We saw and knew the whole of the study area like no others, save Bill Mattox. The challenge of flying a 206 in the manner required with three big guys aboard was daunting for our series of pilots, but most adapted well. There were close calls, such as the time we lost hydraulic control on takeoff. The pilot literally flew us onto the ground amidst a sea of emergency response vehicles, and we lived to trap another day.

Individual Peregrines became part of the fabric of our lives. We encountered falcons nesting in Greenland that we had banded on migration at Assateague and Padre Islands, and the reverse as well. There was the elation each year of seeing an old friend back at its cliff, and sometimes the disconsolate feeling when its absence was confirmed.

More years ago than I care to admit, I captured my first Tundra Peregrine at Assateague Island. Over 3,000 more have since followed in various locales worldwide. Yet in retrospect, it was the first falcon that captured me; my life since has been intertwined with this most remarkable and compelling of organisms. The Peregrine has given me so much. The strongest bonds of friendship in my life have been with fellow falconers and biologists. No one lacking the connection we have to the Peregrine can ever truly understand us or why we've spent the best

▲ Mike Yates in front of the Elisabeth Peregrine eyrie after capturing an adult.

Photo provided by Mike Yates

years of our lives trying to give something back to it. My 14 summers on the study passed all too quickly, and I will forever hear Greenland's siren call. In 1995 we last confirmed the presence at one cliff of a breeding adult male I had banded as a nestling 11 years earlier. In my thoughts and my hopes, he is there still. The view from his eyrie comes to me clearly, and I am with him once more.

Mike Yates *went to Greenland first in 1983 and was active through 1996, or 14 seasons. He worked with Tom Maechtle on the advance team capturing and tagging adult Peregrines. He found many new Peregrine territories on the ground and in small aircraft surveys.*

The pilot literally flew us onto the ground amidst a sea of emergency response vehicles, and we lived to trap another day.

Joe Papp

▲ **Figure 12.9** Joe Papp.

Figure 12.10 Kâle ▶
Siegstad and Bob
Rosenfield.

Bill Mattox

(1989) they set up a blind at the eyrie at Golden Child in T-South, and the following year used the same technique at Ringsø, with the help of James Schneider.

Marco Restani (six seasons) started a study of ravens (banding mainly at the Søndre Strømfjord dump, but also at the nest), helped by Rick Yates in 1993 and 1994 and Henrik Vang Christensen in 1995. Henrik had been with us the year before, when he placed his bird-banding camp near the "villa," and succeeded in banding thousands of small birds by working almost around the clock.

We made use of other rock-climbing experts, Terry McEneaney, Bob Meese, Mike Root, Tom Nichols, Mark Robertson, and Alberto Palleroni, gentlemen to whom even a rather hard technical climb always seemed to be described as a "walk-in."

The early 1990s saw larger teams, made up mainly of veterans, but each year had a sprinkling of new climbers and graduate students who have continued to present: Gregg Doney, Catherine Wightman, and Travis Booms.

Recoveries

Bird-banding (or ringing, in the rest of the world) allows us to glean many facts about the birds we study. This key activity of any study of birds consists of placing a small metal band on the bird's leg (tarsus). The large numbers can be easily read, and the words inscribed on this small band tell the finder where to send the recovery information. In recent years we have elaborated on this simple system by placing a second ring on the other tarsus. This ring, usually anodized a bright color and scribed with several large letters

or numerals, allows an observer to read the lettering with binoculars or spotting scope and thus identify the bird. This method elaborated somewhat on Scott Ward's original idea.

Our most exciting recovery in the early years was the first. In our third season we banded a male nestling at a local cliff called Dome on 27 July 1974. This male also carried a red plastic tarsal band (A-24). Banders at Cape Charles, Virginia, captured the bird on 13 October 1974. As of then, we had banded 55 nestlings but had no recoveries. So this was news heard around our Greenland project world!

Then, in what became one of the most fascinating recoveries, Bud Anderson banded four young at Between Rivers on 22 July 1979. The nestlings were 23 days old, three females and a male. Bud's photograph of that brood was published in Cade et al. 1988 and later in a review of that book in *Science*. The male, smaller than his sisters, stood proudly in front of the group. He wore a red plastic leg band (3A0). On 3 October of that year the Russian oceanographic research vessel *Belagorsk* had on board an American guest scientist, Dottie Holcomb. She spotted a Peregrine Falcon perched in the rigging; it left to catch and bring back to the vessel a Yellow-billed Cuckoo. The bird perched in the rigging for 36 hours, leaving the vessel once to make another catch. Holcomb noticed a red band on the bird's right tarsus and used her spotting scope to read the white letters 3A0. The bird left the vessel for good on 4 October, presumably to continue migrating. The vessel was then 120 mi at sea, east of Long Island, New York. Was the young male Peregrine blown off course, or was he heading south in normal fashion?

Upon return to the United States, Holcomb notified the Bird Banding Laboratory of her observation; the lab knew Scott Ward was developing tarsal bands and notified him of Holcomb's observation. So the fifth recovery on our list became known as the *Belagorsk* male.

Five years later, in July 1984, Bud Anderson climbed a cliff to band young at Mariann, 17 km southeast of Between Rivers. The resident adult male Peregrine defended the cliff in the usual fashion, got tired, and perched close to Anderson, who noticed that the male had a silver band on his left tarsus. This was duly noted, and no more thought about it until two years later (22 June 1986) when the trapping team captured the adult male at Mariann and read his band of 422585. They didn't know it at the time, but he was the *Belagorsk* male, probably the same bird observed there by Anderson in 1984. They added a blue alpha band to his right tarsus. He was identified at the cliff in 1985 and 1986 but was gone in 1987.

Recruitment

The *Belagorsk* male was our first "recruit," a bird hatched in the area and returned to breed as an adult.

In a study of natal recruitment in our study area, Restani and Mattox (2000) looked at the 583 broods (1,702 nestlings) banded during the 1978

to 1997 breeding seasons. At least one nestling could not be identified to sex in 56 of those 583 broods, so they calculated nestling sex ratio from the sample of 527 broods (1,566 nestlings). They found an overall sex ratio that approached parity (774 males, 792 females). They found that teams had documented the identity of 42 banded nestlings that were recruited into the study population. Of these 42, 35 were males, seven females, and they dispersed to breed about the same distance in the study area. But the unequal number of females indicated that they disperse farther in general. Indeed, we have received reports (Falk pers. comm.) that our colleagues Knud Falk and Søren Møller in South Greenland have captured two adult females we banded as nestlings in our study area 700 km to the north! And a third female banded as a nestling was videotaped by a Greenlandic sheep farmer in the same area. The blue alpha band is clearly legible in the videotape!

More on Recoveries

Banding birds gives us valuable information about migratory routes, wintering areas, longevity, nest-site fidelity, and much more. In the case of the Peregrine Falcon, a species in trouble, we hoped especially to gain knowledge about areas where the falcons might spend more time on migration or concentrate during the winter. Stud-

▲ **Figure 12.11** A cool, damp evening above the Arctic Circle, Kangerlussuaq, Greenland.

▲ **Figure 12.12** Søndre Strømfjord.

ies of their blood samples showed higher levels of various pollutants when returning on spring migration from Central and South America (Henny et al. 1996).

But band returns could not pinpoint exact wintering locations as was later provided by remote sensing techniques. We did learn, however, that the females rarely reached South America at the end of their autumn migration, whereas many males did. In fact, males migrated over twice as far as females to reach their wintering grounds. Why was this?

Information through banding has been augmented many fold through the use of microtransmitters attached to the falcon by a backpack. The radio transmits signals which are received by polar-orbiting satellites. This technique, pioneered by Skip Ambrose in Alaska and Bill Seegar in Greenland, has provided a wealth of data on migratory routes and wintering areas.

Through band returns we found that many falcons are still shot, despite modern awareness of the need to protect all species. But the shooting of all birds banded is still under 10%. Half of our recoveries were birds captured on migration by bird-banders at autumn and spring falcon staging

areas. Through our adult trapping project in Greenland we recaptured or read the bands of many falcons, including the 27 "recruits," nestlings returning to breed (Restani and Mattox 2000) mentioned above. From year to year we noted that a small number of adult females moved from one cliff to another (often close to the first), even returning to the original cliff to breed.

Support for a Dream Project

Words often fail us when emotions are involved. Words, expressed by rational thought, also might fail to convey, or seem to trivialize, important feelings.

The Peregrine elicits deep feelings in many people. Yes, emotions reign. Words fail.

The same holds true about Greenland, the tundra, Peregrines, and the people who have sought them out in the wilderness. Words cannot even approach my feelings about the field people on our Greenland teams. A special feeling binds us. It cannot be described, but it is there and everyone who has studied Peregrines in Greenland feels it.

I do not have to thank these people. The bond I feel for them suffices. Their bond with Greenland and the Peregrine provides a lifelong link to carry throughout good times and not so good. Their studies of Peregrines in Greenland, some for many years, have been unique in arctic work. But the unique aspect has not been limited to Greenland and the Peregrine. It has pervaded the lives of all of us, and we have been changed forever.

It has, of course, also pervaded the lives of those dear to us. Only the team members can fully appreciate the importance of support from home. But all too often, despite our deep feelings about this support, these feelings seem to go unstated, unacknowledged, and even forgotten in the rush to finish up one season and prepare for the next.

Acknowledging by name the many team members has been difficult enough because of space; to do so for all the supporters is out of the question. But some of them have been rewarded with trips to Greenland so they could see for themselves why the place elicits the emotion it does.

The Future

The Peregrine Falcon today thrives in West Greenland. In 1972 we found 10 cliffs occupied by Peregrines. Today within the study area we know of over 125 cliffs that are regularly occupied. We would like to continue monitoring to detect any changes, but resources are slim. The Peregrine Fund has begun a project to study Gyrfalcons and thereby will be able to note Peregrine nesting as well. Gyrfalcons vary in number cyclically over the years, with other arctic animals. They have not been studied in any great detail in Greenland, so promising projects abound. The excitement of the unknown, as we experienced with the Peregrine, awaits future researchers.

Participants in the Greenland Peregrine Falcon Survey, 1972 - 1998

Joelle Affeldt	Bill Heinrich	Scott Rogers
Bud Anderson	Paul Howey	Mike Root
Rita Apanius	Alan Jenkins	Bob Rosenfield
Tom Bain	Hal Jones	Carl Safina
Steve Belardo	Randy Knapp	Bill Satterfield
Ed Bender	Dan Konkel	Jim Schneider
Dan Berger	Julie Ann Lee	Linda Schueck
Bins Binswanger	Tom Maechtle	Chris Schultz
Travis Booms	Bob Martin	Bill Seegar
Bill Burnham (senior)	Bill Mattox	Jim Seegar
Bill Burnham	Tim Mattox	William Seegar
Kurt Burnham	Terry McEneaney	Steve Sherrod
Tom Cade	Richard Mearns	Kâle Siegstad
Denis Case	Bob Meese	Karen Smith
Janis Chase	Bob Murphy	Tom Smylie
Henrik Christensen	Gerry Myers	Thom Snowman
Bill Clark	Tom Nichols	Steve Taft
Dave Clement	Connie Oar	Mark Thwaits
Lisa Clepper	Jack Oar	Phil Vance
Ginger Cox	Dan O'Brien	Scott Ward
Jim Dayton	Alberto Palleroni	Jim Weaver
Gregg Doney	Joe Papp	Clay White
Jim Enderson	Jimmie Parrish	Bob Whitney
Brandon Fuller	Colin Pennycuick	Joyce Whitney
Mark Fuller	Arlo Raim	Catherine Wightman
Bill Gould	Tom Ray	Jon Wilde
Dick Graham	Pat Redig	Vince Yannone
Dick Gritman	Marco Restani	Jeff Yates
Mark Haley	Ken Riddle	Karen Yates
Jim Harris	Mark Robertson	Mike Yates
Willard Heck	Ralph Rogers	Rick Yates

W. S. Seegar

Bill Mattox *began studying Duck Hawks (Peregrines) in 1949 while an undergraduate at Dartmouth College. He went to Greenland for Gyrfalcons in 1951; surveyed Peregrine cliffs in Vermont and New Hampshire until 1953; and then went to Scandinavia on a Swedish government grant. He spent a year in Iceland researching the fishing industry for his Master's degree. After two years in Germany with the U.S. Army, he*

entered McGill University, completed his Master's, and worked as Assistant Professor and Director of McGill's Sub-arctic Research Lab in Schefferville, Quebec. He began research on the Greenlandic fishery in 1960. From 1964 to 1968 he did research and writing in Copenhagen as a Fellow of the Institute of Current World Affairs. His Ph.D. dissertation for McGill University was published in 1973 in the Danish arctic series Meddelelser om Grønland. In 1972 he began the survey of Peregrines in West Greenland, a project he led for 28 years. In autumn 1972, he joined the Ohio Department of Natural Resources (ODNR) and worked for 20 years in charge of water planning, groundwater mapping, floodplain management, and the state water data system. Upon retirement from ODNR in 1992, he joined his wife, Joan, full time in their environmental firm of Greenfalk Consultants to carry out an assessment of birds of prey in the Idaho Army National Guard's Orchard Training Area. He moved to Boise permanently in 1998 where he lives with his wife. He is President and a director of the Conservation Research Foundation and currently studies Swainson's Hawks and philopatry of wintering raptors.

Chapter 13

Research on Migratory Peregrines

William S. Seegar, Mike Yates, and Tom Maechtle

*T*undra Peregrines (F. p. tundrius) were in steep decline by 1970 according to nesting surveys in the Arctic

and accounts by banders at traditional migratory trapping sites. Concerned scientists sought the best method to monitor populations of this highly migratory subspecies that nests in remote areas in the Arctic and winters throughout the Americas in diverse and geopolitically sensitive areas. Jim Enderson advocated standardized surveys at known migratory locations. Counts at Cape May, New Jersey, Hawk Mountain, Pennsylvania, and Cedar Grove, Wisconsin, helped address this need for information, but Assateague Island, Maryland/Virginia, offered a unique opportunity because of the historical database that existed. Falconers Alva Nye and Bill Turner discovered the autumn concentration of Tundra Peregrines on Assateague Island in 1938, and trappers subsequently frequented the island each year. Falcons were captured and kept for falconry, but many more were banded and released. Because of the observed decline in Tundra Peregrine populations, falconers were no longer allowed to trap at Assateague after the 1969 migration. A three-decade legacy of detailed notes on dates, observations, captures, and weather was still available from such serious and credible naturalists as Al Nye, Jim Rice, Brian McDonald, Bob Berry, and Lou Woyce.

▲ **Figure 13.1** *Peregrine and Ruddy Turnstones* ©Robert Bateman. Reproduction rights courtesy Boshkung Inc. and Mill Pond Press.

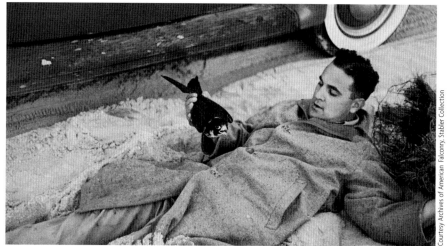

The Assateague Island Survey

In September 1970, F. Prescott (Scott) Ward and Bob Berry began a standardized study at Assateague, with assistance at times from Lou Woyce. Scott, a civilian scientist with the Ecology Branch at Edgewood Arsenal, Maryland, obtained operating funds through the Department of the Army's environmental programs to support the survey. Assateague Island is owned and managed by a consortium, which includes the Assateague Island National Seashore, Chincoteague National Wildlife Refuge, and Assateague State Park, Maryland. After the Tundra Peregrine was placed on the list of endangered species in 1970, full access to the survey area was difficult to secure and retain in the early years. Three decades of field research later, our program is now fully supported by the state and federal agencies involved, as well as by countless visitors who follow our activities through public talks and other forums. Bob Berry left the survey in 1976, and Mike Yates joined Ward in 1977. Bill Seegar made the duo a trio from 1981 through Ward's departure after the 1990 survey, and Jim Dayton came on board in 1995.

Assateague is a barrier island 60 km long, and it varies in width from 200 m to 5 km. A hurricane in 1933 detached Assateague from Fenwick Island, and a jetty was built to preserve the inlet and the newly formed island to the south. Assateague is separated from mainland Maryland and Virginia by a series of shallow bays and narrow inlets. Access to the island was by ferry until construction of two bridges, one in Virginia (1962) and another in Maryland (1963). During a normal high tide, the front beach varies from nonexistent to about 100 m in width along the length of the island. The beach backs naturally to a low, unstable dune line. A manmade dune line was created in the 1950s to protect "improvements" and is still maintained in some places. Behind the dunes lie vegetation, swamps, tidal flats, marshes, and forests. The public has access to the entire island during the study period by foot and boat, and to 26 km of beachfront by four-wheel-drive vehicle.

We have historically observed and captured migrating Peregrines on the beachfront, sand roadways, and tidal flats and have recorded Peregrine observations when traveling in areas not conducive to trapping. A database on all other species of raptors observed during the survey has also been compiled. Since 1970 we have conducted the study yearly in September and October, operating two research vehicles from dawn to dusk except in cases of vehicle breakdown, high winds (>25 kt), or dangerously high tides. The

▲ **Figure 13.2** (Above) Abandoned Green Run Hotel on Assateague Island in the 1930s. Falconers camped here while capturing Peregrines. Note hooded Peregrines on crude screen perch.

▲ **Figure 13.3** (Below) Al Nye emerging from the sand after capturing a Peregrine, 24 October 1940 (see Figure 2.4 for explanation of trapping method). The falcon was kept in falconry and later named Kokomo.

▲ **Figure 13.4** Nye later gave Kokomo to Bill Turner, shown holding her in 1942.

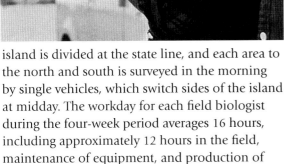

Courtesy Archives of American Falconry, Nye Collection

Bob Berry

Bob Berry

island is divided at the state line, and each area to the north and south is surveyed in the morning by single vehicles, which switch sides of the island at midday. The workday for each field biologist during the four-week period averages 16 hours, including approximately 12 hours in the field, maintenance of equipment, and production of extensive field notes.

The National Park Service (NPS) has provided quarters for the survey on the island since the inception of the program, initially at private dwellings that were acquired by the Seashore when it was established. Since 1983 we have been based at the historic Assateague Beach Station of the U.S. Life-Saving Service (later U.S. Coast Guard), built in 1875. Early on, the survey had a distinct U.S. Army flavor and an olive-drab color. Scott's vehicle was a canvas-topped military Jeep checked out of the Edgewood motor pool. Both doors were removed for access, visibility, and capture efficiency. This arrangement made for some cold, wet, and uncomfortable days on the beach; you may be sure that all who accompanied Scott were dedicated to the importance of the work. An open military trailer full of jerry cans to transport gasoline was periodically replenished off the island to keep the vehicles going. To sustain the researchers by day, Scott brought cases of C-rations. At night, we generally ate better. Few successful surf fishermen could resist Scott Ward's persuasive powers. Often he not only got the best of their

catch but also charmed them into delivering the goods to our headquarters so he would lose no beach time trapping falcons. During the early years that beach time could be brutally unproductive. It is much more physically and mentally exhausting to have spent 12 hours looking in vain for a Peregrine than to have been busy all day trapping a large number of them.

Although monitoring migratory Peregrine populations has been the primary objective of the survey, we also use the program to investigate many other aspects of the falcons' natural history and ecology. Color bands with alpha-numeric codes that can be read at a distance through binoculars or a spotting scope were deployed to enhance recapture data. This technique provided us information (without recapture) on the length of time falcons stayed on the island, and we periodically received returns on falcon bands read by others off the study area (Ward 1975). One of the most interesting sightings was a falcon that spent a day on the Russian ship *Belagorsk* off the east coast of the United States. The ship was doing a pelagic bird survey, and the falcon was clearly seen and the band read by several ornithologists on board. We conducted field studies on the prey species taken by Peregrines while hunting and resting on the island during migration (Ward and Laybourne 1985). Another research project involved the collection of small feather samples from captured Peregrines for trace element analysis. This work

◀ Figure 13.5 (Left) Brian McDonald and Bill Shinners banding a Peregrine, Assateague Island, 30 September 1963.

▲ Figure 13.6 (Above) Scott Ward and Bob Berry repairing falcon trapping equipment, an every day/evening activity when capturing Peregrines, Assateague Island, 1974.

▲ Figure 13.7 Relaxing on the beach to cocktails and steaks gratis Corny McFadden, Assateague, October 1964. Standing, left to right: Jim Rice, Sr., Max Berger, Jerry McFadden, Jim Gerlach, and Bill Mattox. Seated/kneeling: Corny McFadden, Jimmy Rice, Barbara Berry, and Carol Berry.

▲ **Figure 13.8** Hank Paulson prepares to release two adult Peregrines, Assateague Island, October 1978. In 1996 he became Chairman of the Board of The Peregrine Fund. He also became Chairman and CEO of The Goldman Sachs Group, Inc.

Figure 13.10 Migrating ▶ Peregrine being fitted with a radio telemetry device.

was directed at determining the natal origins of falcons captured on migration. Colleague Jim Parrish demonstrated that ratios of trace elements in the falcon feathers were unique within discrete geographic populations (Parrish et al. 1983). Accordingly, a migrant's natal origin could be determined if baseline data for that location were available. Developing technologies of this type was part of the Army research and development program and was directed at understanding how geographically discrete breeding populations of Tundra Peregrines were distributed in the flyway and wintering grounds. We color-marked banded falcons with dye to avoid recapturing individuals and also to generate information from sightings of marked birds south of Assateague before the color faded. During the late 1970s Bill Seegar and Tom Ray did standardized Peregrine counts by fixed-wing aircraft along the barrier island chain between north Assateague and Cape Charles to the south. In concert with Bill Cochran, we outfitted Peregrines with some of the early VHF radio transmitters. Cochran tracked them south by fixed-wing aircraft and learned about Peregrine migration dynamics along the eastern coastal zone (Cochran

▲ **Figure 13.9** Wendy Paulson releases an immature Peregrine after banding, Assateague Island, October 1973.

1985). Mark Fuller and Kim Titus assisted in a study using pulse-coded VHF transmitters on uniquely color-marked Peregrines. We were able to determine not only how long those migrants remained on the island but how likely we were to observe them during the normal course of the survey (Howey et al. 1984). Blood sampling has been a routine part of our protocol and was initially used to monitor pesticide levels of migrants (Henny et al. 1982). Later we used blood samples in collaborative genetics studies, and more recently we joined with the National Wildlife Health Center to investigate the Peregrine's possible role as a reservoir of West Nile encephalitis virus and a vector that could quickly spread this arbovirus into the Southern Hemisphere. We have provided a comprehensive file of Peregrine captures and sightings according to Global Positioning System (GPS) coordinates. When these data are integrated with the NPS Geographic Information System (GIS) database, resource managers can look at land use in regard to Peregrine distribution. We have hosted visiting scientists from the former Soviet Union, Russian Federation, Greenland, Mexico, Canada, and People's Republic of China in order to foster cooperative ventures benefitting scientists worldwide.

In 1981 we began a technical development effort that would take 10 years to achieve. Our goal was to develop a space-based system to track and monitor Peregrine movements anywhere on the surface of the earth. We started the effort with The Johns Hopkins University Applied Physics Laboratory, which at the time was one of the most experienced groups in the world in space tracking

▲ **Figure 13.11** Peregrines from many locations pass over Assateague Island.

Bob Berry

systems. Within the first year we identified the French Argos System, which had satellites in Low Earth Orbit capable of providing global tracking coverage. We were successful in developing a new Temperature Compensated Crystal Oscillator and a unique solar power source that allowed us to miniaturize then-current transmitter terminals from their 2- to 3-kg size to 180 g for use on large birds. The units on the birds, Platform Transmitter Terminals (PTTs), transmit signals at programmed intervals to orbiting satellites, and Service Argos computes PTT locations using Doppler Shift algorithms (Fuller et al. 1995). The accuracy of the location estimates is between 150 m and several kilometers. We fielded prototype PTTs on larger birds by 1984 and gradually achieved miniaturization of the units until we were able to track successfully a Gyrfalcon in West Greenland in 1990.

In October 1993 two adult female Peregrines were harnessed at Assateague with 30-g PTTs equipped with activity, temperature, and battery voltage sensors. One of the 1993 adults wintered in a unique wetland habitat, at 14,000 ft in the central Argentine altiplano. Members of our research team visited that area in February 1994 and made detailed observations on the wintering behavior of the falcon and 23 other species of birds. These included three species of Neotropical migrants sharing the same high-mountain wintering habitat. It was determined that an immature female Peregrine also wintered in this small wetland with the adult we tracked from Assateague Island (Seegar and Yates 1994).

Since that time we have continued to develop, miniaturize, and apply these technologies to unlock the remaining mysteries of the Peregrine's ecology. Migrating falcons were not only *tundrius*

Bill Burnham

but boreal forest *anatum* Peregrines. Studies by our group at both Assateague and Padre Islands have shown that contaminant levels attributed to the use of DDT have declined. Migrants may, however, still face toxic threats in their Central and South American wintering grounds from new pesticides or misuse of existing agricultural chemicals.

Satellite telemetry represents an invaluable tool in identifying critical habitats and in pinpointing and mitigating global sources of contaminants affecting Peregrines and the Neotropical migrants with which their life histories are so irrevocably intertwined. Future systems with improved electronics and new sensors hold great promise for the management of species on a local, regional, and global scale. Through this technology we now look into the most remote places on the surface of the earth, seeing relationships we could only imagine when we began this quest in 1981, between Peregrines, their prey, and their habitat.

The Assateague survey continues each autumn with private support from interested foundations and individuals.

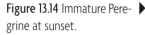

Figure 13.14 Immature Peregrine at sunset.

Figure 13.15 (Opposite page) Randy Townsend on North Padre Island, autumn 1985.

Tom Maechtle

The Padre Island Survey

The Texas Gulf Coast has been known as an autumn concentration point for migratory Peregrines since 1890, as described by Griscom and Crosby (1925) in a paper published in *The Auk*. This phenomenon did not receive much attention until one of the pioneers of North American falconry, the late Colonel R. L. Meredith, retired in the region and explored the beaches of Padre Island in search of migratory Peregrines during the 1950s. His observations and baseline notes brought attention to this concentration of falcons, and falconers who had a keen interest in the biology of the birds soon followed. These included W. Grainger Hunt, who studied the migratory Peregrines that visited Padre Island (Hunt 1966) for his Master's degree while a student at Sul Ross State College in the mid-1960s. Biologist and falconer Ralph Rogers also researched Peregrines at Padre while a student in the Wildlife Department at Texas Tech. The late falconer and naturalist Daniel Slowe worked with Rogers and Hunt in these first systematic surveys of migratory Peregrines in coastal Texas. Together they published in *The Canadian Field-Naturalist* (Hunt et al. 1975) the first details of chronology of migration, age and sex ratios, banding data, and predatory behavior of Peregrines using Padre Island.

The Texas surveys continued with involvement from the Texas Department of Parks and Wildlife. Most notably, Ken Riddle in 1973 began annual

▲ **Figure 13.16** Padre Island, Texas is a focal area for migrating Peregrines to pass before continuing south either along the coast or across the Gulf of Mexico.

autumn surveys on High, Matagorda, and South Padre Islands. In 1977 Mustang and North Padre Islands were added to the survey, and with support from the Ecology Branch at Edgewood Arsenal, Riddle was able to maintain systematic counts. In 1978, Ward discovered the springtime concentration of migratory Peregrines at Padre, and Riddle added a spring survey in 1979. Ward had looked for a spring focal point exhaustively, visiting Assateague in late April and May of 1972, 1973, 1974, and 1976, Panama in March of 1973 and 1974, and the Dry Tortugas, Florida, in early April of 1974. He had contractors make springtime visits to the Dry Tortugas in 1975, Cumberland Island, Georgia, in 1976, and Sandy Hook, New Jersey, in 1977 and 1978. All those efforts resulted in only 15 sightings and one capture.

It is important to note that all the initial surveys in Texas were restricted to the beachfronts of the barrier islands. There simply was no way to drive a conventional vehicle safely on the expansive wind-tidal flats that lie behind the dune barrier. It was not until the spring of 1981 that Riddle and his team had access to the flats by means of all-terrain cycles (ATCs). The advent of this vehicle was revolutionary in accessing the vast habitats and in encounters with Peregrines that were previously out of reach.

In 1981, the survey expanded to include not only the beachfronts of North and South Padre Island but also the wind-tidal flats of both islands. Riddle established a system of monitoring North Padre Island using a remote field camp that

Tom Maechtle

included tents to house the researchers. Equipment and ATCs were transported from South Padre via inflatable boat, or at times by helicopters from the Corpus Christi Army Depot. Teams of two or three individuals on each island would split their time between the North Padre field camp and a rented house located in the Town of South Padre Island. From these two stations, the team left before dawn and surveyed throughout the day on the respective islands, typically not returning until after dark. Because the ATCs had only a few pounds of air pressure in each tire, they were able to traverse the soft terrain without becoming mired, leaving little evidence of their passing. Wind and rain erased our tracks after each season, leaving a blank slate for the next survey.

In 1985, Tom Maechtle took over the operation of the survey from Riddle, proceeding with the continued support of Ward and Seegar at Edgewood. From 1985 through 1994 we ran surveys on both islands and benefitted from advances in ATC technology. The machines became four-wheeled instead of three, making them safer and more comfortable. During years when the survey covered North and South Padre Islands, it was not uncommon to drive 320 km a day on a land mass that stretched 130 km long and ranged from 1 to16 km wide.

Since autumn of 1994 we have concentrated our survey efforts on South Padre Island. This change in operation has decreased the overall volume of sightings and captures. Data collection using a smaller landmass remains, however, relevant to the detection of population trends and the collection of biological samples for analyses of contaminants, disease, and natal origin.

Today our survey consists of the 40 km long beachfront north of the Town of South Padre Island to the Mansfield Channel which separates the south and north islands. We also survey the wind-tidal flats west to the Laguna Madre. The landmass can vary daily because of wind-driven

Bill Byrne/Mass. Division of Fisheries and Wildlife

South Padre Island, 1965

Grainger Hunt

I was speeding 45 mph down the beach in a stripped-down (frame and windshield only) VW bug, a pigeon in one hand, steering wheel in the other, my attention focused straight overhead on a fast-moving, low-flying tiercel that refused to look my way. At mid-shout—to get his attention—my situation suddenly changed to smooth, rapid deceleration, a brief sinking, a second of quiet confusion, followed by a cold, excessive drenching from above.

It took seconds to realize I had planed out through the surf, sunk to my waist, and ruined, among many other items, the foolishly kind motel owner's brand spanking new pair of 10 x 50 binoculars. The 8-mi walk back included almost catching a passage female, just down from the high latitudes, and tame enough to follow a wet lure pigeon to my feet.

Grainger Hunt *For biographical information see sidebar, A Pile of Prey Remains, Chapter 4.*

219

Bob Berry

Pat Burnham

Barbara Jenny

▲ **Figure 13.17** (Above) Exquisite newly-captured immature Peregrine.

Figure 13.18 (Right) ▶ Halter Cunningham. With Brian McDonald, he developed the modern pigeon noose harness for trapping falcons that revolutionized Peregrine capture in North America.

▲ **Figure 13.19** (Below) Dave Remple releasing a Peregrine, South Padre Island.

tides on beaches and flats and rainfall that, along with high winds and lightning storms, can prevent our access to the study area.

Much of South Padre Island is privately owned, although The Nature Conservancy recently purchased a significant portion of the study area. It is now conserved in perpetuity, with management by the Laguna Atascosa National Wildlife Refuge (NWR).

During the course of our studies at Padre Island, we have taken blood samples from thousands of falcons which have been analyzed every six to 10 years by Charles Henny of the U.S. Geological Survey (USGS). We learned early on that Peregrines were becoming contaminated with organochlorine pesticides while wintering in Latin America (Henny et al. 1982). More recent blood analyses have shown that organochlorine concentrations in Peregrines captured at Padre are no longer the threat they were a decade ago (Henny et al. 1988, 1996). Our blood sampling

remains important not only for continued monitoring of contaminants but also for analyses of other threats (i.e., West Nile encephalitis virus, which appears to be spreading through migratory birds). Blood and feather samples have also played an important role in learning about the geographic origins of the Padre migrants.

All these tools assist in not only understanding the biology of migrant Peregrines but also in the ongoing conservation of Peregrines and other species of migratory birds on which this large falcon preys. The autumn and spring surveys at Padre continue today with private support from interested foundations and individuals, along with a legion of highly experienced and dedicated colleagues who donate their time to maintain this unusually long-term database.

Results

During the past 32 seasons at Assateague, the principals have spent 16,186 man-hours in the field, observing 14,550 Peregrines and capturing 4,110 (Table 13.1). Yearly sighting and capture totals have increased exponentially since the 1972 U.S. ban on DDT. Observations and captures at Assateague were at all-time lows of 41 and 8 that year, and a mean 10-man-hour period in the field produced only 1.26 sightings (Berry and Ward 1975, Ward et al. 1988). By 1998, observations and captures were 999 and 261 respectively, and that same mean effort produced 17.96 sightings (Seegar et al. 1998).

Since 1977 we have surveyed for Peregrines on Padre Island during 24 autumn seasons and 23 spring seasons; these 47 survey periods lasted an average of 30 days each. We spent 25,147 man-hours in the field, observing 33,452 Peregrines and capturing 6,905 (Table 13.2).

Analyzing the Padre data presents a more complex problem than at Assateague because of the increased number of personnel involved, the variety of routes driven during the survey, and the different capture methods used over the years with varying success rates. We have used trucks along the beachfront, fixed trapping stations, ATCs, and experimented with hovercraft. By far, the ATCs are most efficient since they can access the soft terrain of the wind-tidal flats where the majority of falcons are found. The use of ATCs quickly increased the sightings per 10–hr block from an average of three to eight sightings during the late 1970s. Fixed trapping stations are not as productive because Peregrines are not concentrated at any point along Padre Island. Trucks along the beachfront are useful but limited to the relatively small and linear landmass of the high-tide zone.

It is apparent from our data that even in a completely recovered population, yearly counts on a highly standardized study such as ours can vary significantly. Contributing factors are local and continental weather patterns, and also the timing of events that prevent full conduct of the study (vehicle breakdown, high wind and tide, flooding of inland flat by rain, etc.). Continental weather patterns play a major role in the overall number of Peregrines encountered at Padre. For example, in the autumn of 1993 alone we captured 696 Peregrines and observed 2,416 in 995 man-hours. Meanwhile, the Assateague survey had an average year with 192 captured and 595 observed in 593 man-hours. These confounding factors further illustrate the value of our long-term studies as such yearly aberrations are balanced and distributed over time and a more accurate index of populations emerges.

We know from band returns that migratory Peregrines throughout the North American Arctic can be encountered at Padre during autumn, although the majority are from the western and central Arctic. This distribution changes during spring migration, when Peregrines from all natal regions pass through Padre Island from their winter quarters in Central and South America, resulting in a natural concentration point for falcons traveling north to their breeding grounds. When analyzing data for detection of trends, we have been careful to consider only those dates for each survey for where we have multiple years of data; we have also considered spring surveys separately from those in autumn. Data have not revealed statistically significant trends that suggest a decrease or increase in Padre numbers since 1986 (Seegar et al. 1998).

A principal finding of our research identifies Padre Island as a major staging area for northward migrating Peregrines in this hemisphere. Our efforts to identify a springtime concentration of Peregrines on the East Coast have been unsuccessful. Captures of previously banded falcons on Padre Island and satellite tracking results reveal that autumn East Coast migrants wintering in Central and South America commonly appear at Padre Island on their way north and do not retrace the route they followed south. Therefore a high percentage of all migratory Peregrines pass through Padre Island in springtime. Conclusions drawn from our work there carry implications pertinent to the migratory Peregrine population as a whole.

Satellite Tracking— To date we have deployed 17 PTTs at Assateague and 21 at Padre Island. Through the use of satellite tracking we have been able to evaluate the migration strategy of

Table 13.1 Assateague Island Peregrine Falcon survey totals—1970-2001.

Year	Man-hours expended	Peregrine Falcons sighted	Peregrine Falcons sighted/10 man-hours	Peregrine Falcons captured	Peregrine Falcons captured/10 man-hours
1970	310.0	66	2.13	23	0.74
1971	222.1	120	5.40	35	1.58
1972	325.7	41	1.26	8	0.25
1973	360.7	136	3.77	47	1.30
1974	360.3	59	1.64	22	0.61
1975	332.5	186	5.59	40	1.20
1976	336.2	176	5.23	48	1.43
1977	468.2	209	4.46	75	1.60
1978	436.2	259	5.94	64	1.47
1979	427.4	598	13.99	127	2.97
1980	451.1	512	11.35	110	2.44
1981	564.7	347	6.15	89	1.58
1982	632.3	591	9.35	121	1.91
1983	637.2	562	8.82	116	1.82
1984	724.9	547	7.55	150	2.07
1985	683.0	483	7.07	147	2.15
1986	704.1	838	11.90	230	3.27
1987	607.4	327	5.38	112	1.84
1988	671.7	409	6.09	132	1.97
1989	601.2	813	13.52	203	3.38
1990	509.3	659	12.94	248	4.87
1991	630.3	743	11.78	227	3.60
1992	558.8	340	6.08	116	2.08
1993	593.2	595	10.03	192	3.24
1994	557.3	467	8.38	133	2.39
1995	485.4	525	10.82	139	2.86
1996	374.3	568	15.17	192	5.13
1997	516.5	889	17.21	254	4.91
1998	556.3	999	17.96	261	4.69
1999	504.3	560	11.10	179	3.55
2000	536.8	522	9.73	155	2.89
2001	507.3	404	7.96	115	2.27
Total	16186.7	14550	8.99	4110	2.54

The Scent of a Peregrine

William Burnham

Bill Burnham

Only the laws of nature govern her life, and the drive to survive and reproduce provide direction.

Struggling to escape the monofilament nooses and drag that are keeping her from flying, she turns toward me in defense. Defiance, not fear, shows in her dark eyes. Silent. She is perfect. Every feather exact, as if new. They almost are, as she only hatched in June or July and this is early October, but she has already flown thousands of miles. Picking her up, I am extra careful with her flight feathers which will not be replaced until next summer. Her ability in flight and to catch food will largely determine whether she lives or dies. Surviving to breed and replace herself with young is critical to ensure the future of her kind. With the first grasp, experienced hands and mind register she is in good condition. In particular, the feel of the breast muscles in relation to her keel bone tells she has been eating well. Changing my grip from two hands to one, I slip the hood on, keeping her calm so she does not struggle for the few minutes I need to band her. One hood brace in my teeth and the other between my thumb and fingers, tension closes the hood back, making it snug on her head but not touching the eyes or interfering with her breathing. My face next to hers, I catch the fresh scent of her breath—a further indication of good health.

She is unbanded. Where did she come from? Maybe an eyrie in the High Arctic of Greenland or from a river cliff in the taiga zone of Alaska, between tundra and forest. We will never know that, but now with the aluminum band she wears we may know where she reappears in the future. What has she already witnessed? What has she done without government telling her what she can or cannot do, or when. No thought of heaven or hell. No physical possessions to worry over or devices to depend on. Only the laws of nature govern her life, and the drive to survive and reproduce provide direction.

Loosening the hood, then shifting my grip back to two hands, I gently bury my nose in the feathers between her wings and sniff. There is nothing in the world that smells like a newly captured Peregrine. She smells like a mix of willow and birch of a green arctic tundra, the scent of pine as the rays of sun pierce the forest to dry the needles of the morning dew, the freshness of the golden prairie grass on an autumn day, and the fragrance of the sea breeze through marsh flowers. The Peregrine smells like freedom.

Goodbye; have a good life. You make ours richer by your presence.

Bill Burnham *For biographical information see Chapter 8.*

the Tundra Peregrine and fully establish the wintering range of this subspecies. Unlike bird bands, which yield a 2 to 3% recovery, satellite tracking follows individual sentinel animals in the population through time and space, collecting thousands of locations on the living bird. In the first 20 years of trapping and banding Peregrines on Padre and Assateague Islands, we received recovery information on or recaptured about 400 falcons. Most recoveries were of dead individuals, whereas recaptured falcons were usually encountered on the same beaches where they were banded. In 18 months of satellite tracking 40 Tundra Peregrines, we recovered thousands of independent location estimates on the birds and completely defined their range and migration routes in the Americas.

Perhaps one of the most interesting examples of Tundra Peregrine migration was an adult female we tracked off the Assateague beach in 1998. This falcon was released and flew normally down the eastern coastal zone to southern Florida, leaving the Keys on 22 October heading SSW. At the same time, Hurricane Mitch was building to the south in Central America. By 25 October Mitch was reaching full strength and hit land in Nicaragua. Several hundred miles off the Florida coast, the falcon sensed the presence of the hurricane dead ahead and flew west from her position into the middle of the Caribbean. On 27 October the falcon must have found refuge on a ship headed to Galveston Bay, an inference from the locations received on the falcon over an 18-hour period, all in a straight line and headed for Galveston harbor at approximately 9 kt per hour. The falcon sought refuge to the west of Galveston Bay in a well-known stopover spot for Neotropical migrants.

On 2 November the falcon took off at 0200 hours local time and headed out into the Gulf for a second crossing attempt. Mitch had hit Central America and swung northeast toward Florida. At this point the storm winds had subsided and the front was carrying a great deal of rain. For a second time the falcon headed straight into the storm, and this time ended up on a platform in the middle of the Gulf for two days, generating several locations showing her to be stationary. On 5 November Mitch passed Florida and headed out to sea; the falcon made landfall on the Yucatan Peninsula later that day.

Another revelation of our PTT tracking has been the confirmation that some Tundra Peregrines winter at more northern latitudes than had previously been known. One female outfitted at Assateague in October 1996 was captured and wintered on the

Table 13.2 Autumn and spring Padre Island Peregrine Falcon survey totals—1977-2001.

Year	Season	Man-hours expended	Peregrines sighted	Peregrines captured	Peregrines sighted/ 10 man-hours	Vehicles used
1977	Autumn	467	121	31	2.59	Trucks/beachfront
1978	Autumn	384	118	33	2.90	t/b(12) & PTS (21)
1979	Spring	154	58	8	3.77	t/b (8) & PTS (0)
1979	Autumn	420	377	89	8.98	t/b (41) PTS (24) ATC
1980	Spring	542	473	54	8.73	t/b-PTS-ATC
1980	Autumn	0	0	0	0.00	Hurricane Allen
1981	Spring	448	271	32	6.05	t/b ATC
1981	Autumn	602	599	152	9.95	t/b ATC
1982	Spring	950	781	92	8.22	t/b ATC
1982	Autumn	734	815	155	11.10	t/b ATC
1983	Spring	1150	1364	149	11.86	t/b ATC
1983	Autumn	986	1092	283	11.08	t/b ATC
1984	Spring	1240	906	88	7.31	t/b ATC
1984	Autumn	809	1171	196	14.47	t/b ATC PTS
1985	Spring	895	900	152	10.06	t/b ATC
1985	Autumn	409	451	128	11.00	ATC
1986	Spring	597	933	102	15.60	ATC
1986	Autumn	632	840	216	13.20	ATC
1987	Spring	828	1056	140	12.70	ATC
1987	Autumn	433	692	188	15.90	ATC
1988	Spring	770	1497	209	19.40	ATC
1988*	Autumn	656	953	296	14.50	ATC/began using dye in fall.
1989	Spring	864	1254	127	14.50	ATC
1989	Autumn	701	778	248	11.00	ATC
1990	Spring	817	1112	129	13.60	ATC
1990	Autumn	735	1341	298	18.20	ATC/TBF
1991	Spring	670	914	114	13.60	ATC
1991	Autumn	580	780	250	13.40	ATC/TBF
1992	Spring	578	624	89	10.70	ATC
1992	Autumn	114	210	64	18.00	ATC/TBF
1993	Spring	618	807	127	13.00	ATC
1993	Autumn	995	2416	694	24.20	ATC/TBF
1994	Spring	319	390	83	12.20	ATC/hovercraft
1994	Autumn	276	616	118	22.30	ATC/SPI only
1995	Spring	139	209	43	15.00	ATC/SPI only
1995	Autumn	192	313	84	16.30	ATC/SPI only/hurricanes
1996	Spring	54	92	19	17.00	ATC/SPI only
1996	Autumn	397	484	198	8.20	ATC/SPI only
1997	Spring	87	54	16	6.21	ATC/SPI only
1997	Autumn	328	440	183	13.41	ATC/SPI only
1998	Spring	164	252	44	15.37	ATC/SPI only
1998	Autumn	605	1152	309	19.04	ATC/SPI only
1999	Spring	160	326	78	20.38	ATC/SPI only
1999	Autumn	512	891	275	17.40	ATC/SPI only
2000	Spring	195	480	80	24.62	ATC/SPI only
2000	Autumn	400	790	151	19.75	ATC/SPI only
2001	Spring	251	544	105	21.67	ATC/SPI only
2001	Autumn	290	715	186	24.66	ATC/SPI only
Total		25147	33452	6905	13.40	

*From autumn 1988 on, all captured Peregrines had their breasts dyed. This allowed for easy identification of Peregrines that had already been captured and greatly reduced re-capture, improving efficiency.

Vehicles and locations used: truck = t, beachfront = b, Permanent Trapping Station = PTS, all terrain cycle = ATC, Truck Beach Front = TBF, South Padre Island = SPI

◀ Figure 13.20 A good day trapping. Ruth Mutch, South Padre Island, October 1993.

▲ Figure 13.21 Bob Berry and "an unassuming little body of water" on the Fox Hill Level, Assateague Island, 1971.

island's northernmost limits. She spent the summer of 1997 to the northwest of Hudson Bay and then returned to Assateague in the fall. We captured her (and removed the PTT) within a mile of the 1996 encounter. The same female was again captured on the same wintering spot in the fall of 1998, and each year through 2001 we have observed her wintering in the same area. In 1996 we outfitted eight nesting females in West Greenland with PTTs, and from this sample three wintered along the mid-Atlantic coast between Delaware Bay and Norfolk, Virginia. The coast of Tamaulipas, Mexico, immediately south of Padre Island, has also been identified as a winter area for Tundra Peregrines (McGrady et al. 2002).

Authors' Reminiscences and Perspectives—Mike Yates

In the early years Scott's partners most often used their own vehicles, and sometimes the results were not pretty. There is a classic slide of Bob Berry's Wagoneer on the Fox Hill Level, front end immersed in an unassuming little body of water. In 1978 I traversed that self-same level in a brand new Ramcharger just before dawn. It had rained overnight, and a "puddle" through which I drove turned out to be the rediscovered "Berry's Hole." Ramchargers, as I soon learned, do not float indefinitely. My companions (Hank Paulson and John and Kiku Hanes) scrambled out the tailgate to safety; still in disbelief, I went down with the ship. Once the water inside and out stabilized at chest level, I knew we'd struck bottom and reluctantly exited. A few days and a lot of dollars later, the truck was back at work. At the end of October I unloaded it to a wholesaler, and I still lose sleep thinking of the unsuspecting sap who became its next owner.

My quarter century on the Assateague study and work on the Padre spring survey since 1982 have enriched my life in countless ways. I have come to know these unique places like few others, and to witness and sometimes participate in natural dramas that amaze, amuse, dishearten, and inspire. I've been able to share it all with my wife, Karen, and with my kids from childhood through adulthood. I have forged the closest friendships of my life with the coauthors and some of the others acknowledged in this chapter. These men are my true brothers, and time and trial have not and cannot weaken the bond between us.

The principals of the Assateague survey have always been mindful of the rich history and lore of the pursuit of falcons on that beach. Our respect for those who came before us and showed the way with their energy and ingenuity is boundless. We enjoyed the participation of Nye and Rice before their passing and still have the continuing benefit of Woyce and McDonald's help. All were and are our good friends, and we are proud to have hosted celebrations honoring Nye and McDonald on their respective 50-year anniversaries of trapping at Assateague.

I captured my first Peregrine there for falconry in 1967 and am grateful I was able to participate briefly in that era. In my estimation, the success of the Assateague survey has been, in large part, due to the fact that most of the principals have been falconers. How many others would toil 16 hours daily for a month, without added remuneration, in such a cause? Only an ingrained affection and concern for the Peregrine, and the knowledge that we are giving something back to it, can possibly induce such an effort year after year. As like-minded people know, however, the opportunity to be with the Peregrine in its element is more than adequate compensation. I have myself become more like the object of my extreme affection as the years pass. When autumn approaches I am drawn to Assateague just as surely as a passager fresh from its Greenland eyrie. In spring I am only content on the vast wind-tidal flats of Padre Island. On arrival I feel as if a circle has been completed; one with which I have been involved for countless centuries. I feel at peace when those places first come in view because I know I am where I'm meant to be. If Peregrines could articulate such a thought, I'd like to think they'd feel the same way.

Authors' Reminiscences and Perspectives—Tom Maechtle

Peregrines inhabit places I find awe inspiring. From the open tundra of the Arctic to the relatively featureless flats of Padre Island, I have found myself at home and comforted by these sometimes austere environments that come alive with the presence of falcons. I have been fortunate to follow the Peregrine's annual journey from the breeding grounds in the Arctic through stopover points at Padre Island and southward into Mexico and South America, and then back again. I have shared a kinship with fellow enthusiasts that has developed into life-long friendships that can take up where they left off after months or years of separation. Padre Island will always be the central point of these life experiences for me, as it is with the falcons that visit there.

▲ Figure 13.22 (Above) Sunrise greets Assateague Island, October 1971.

▲ Figure 13.23 Jim Rice (left) and Scott Ward hold three migrating Peregrines caught at sunset on the north tip of Assateague Island, 4 October 1979.

Bob Berry

▲ Figure 13.24 Dan Hayes releases a Peregrine at sunset, October 1972.

It has always been about the falcons and their conservation, and the people who have made the journey memorable.

Authors' Reminiscences and Perspectives—Bill Seegar

Like many involved in the study of Peregrines, I came by my interest in this species at a young age. I was extremely fortunate early on in my career as a scientist to meet key people who enabled me to make a life pursuit from this interest. Scott Ward led the way with his enthusiasm and passion for life and his love of Peregrines. Bill Mattox took me to the Arctic, and Joe Wall believed early on, as did I, that we could harness space technology to find better ways to understand the tundra falcons. It has always been about the falcons and their conservation, and the people who have made the journey memorable. My wife, Janis, supported and shared all of this with me and together with my three sons, William, Tom, and James, made this life work possible. I have forged relationships with people during this quest who are now my family. They know who they are and mentioning names is not necessary. My career in this global endeavor has been all the better for my involvement with the military, which has supported me through the years. The lessons of organization, delegation, improvisation, accountability, and all the other qualities the military develops have helped immensely in our getting the job of conserving the Tundra Peregrine accomplished. Indeed, getting a job done or accomplishing a mission is key to inner contentment that makes life such a happy place. Those without a useful mission are missing a key to real contentment. For now my colleagues and I can feel the contentment of accomplishing a great task in furthering our ability to conserve this species, although I, for one, shall remain ever vigilant on behalf of the Peregrine which is such a great part of all our lives.

Acknowledgments

In addition to those already mentioned in the preceding text, we wish to acknowledge the following individuals for their participation and friendship throughout the years: Skip Ambrose, Bud Anderson, Carolyn Appleton, Bill Burnham, Tom Cade, Tom Cantella, Bill Clark, Lisa Clepper, Nancy Clum, Bill Cole, Michael and Steffi Colopy, Billie and Rachel Dayton, Gregg Doney, Jim Enderson, Scott Francis, Rod Friday, Steve Gatti, Rich Glinski, Chris Godfrey, Sherri Goodman, Peter Harrity, Willard Heck, Bill Heinrich, Blake Henke, Mike Hill, Steve Hoffman, John Hoolihan, Russ Jackson, Peter Jenny, Paul Juergens, Gretchen Knapp, Jack Kumer, Brian Latta, Seth Layman, Bill Lent, Donna Leonard, Sam Lindberg, Kathy and Ireland Maechtle, Jessica Maher, Mark Martell, Brent Metz, Betty Moore, Pete and Vicki Moore, Don Morizot, James Mussell, Ruth and Brian Mutch, Tom Nichols, Ron Nielsen, Geoff Nye, Connie and Jack Oar, Mel Olsen, Alberto Palleroni, Tim Pitts, Bob Ritchie, Mark Robertson, Tony Robertson, Bill Satterfield, John Schroer, Linda Schueck, Janis, William, Tom, James, and Jim Seegar, Rick Sharpe, Phil Shempf, Jeff Sipple, Brad Smith, Stewart and Jenny Somers, Rick Spaulding, Kevin Taylor, Randy Townsend, Sam Voss, Brian Walton, Jim Weaver, Nancy West, Bob Whitney, Catherine Wightman, Kirk Williams, David Williamson, Phil Willis, John Wright, Gordon Wood, Karen, Jeff, and Amy Yates, and Carl Zimmerman.

We are also grateful for the support of Earthspan, the Department of Defense's Legacy Resource Management Program and Strategic Environmental Research and Development Program, the U.S. Army Edgewood Research, Development and Engineering Center, The Ed Rachal Foundation, The Archie W. & Grace Berry Foundation, The Haldan Family Foundation, Assateague Island National Seashore, Chincoteague NWR, Assateague State Park, Maryland Department of Natural Resources, Virginia Department of Game and Inland Fish, USGS Bird Banding Lab, U.S. Fish and Wildlife Service Office of Endangered Species, North Star Science and Technology, The Johns Hopkins University Applied Physics Laboratory, University of Maryland-Baltimore County, Boise State University, Virginia Polytechnic Institute, The Grasslans Foundation, Texas Parks and Wildlife Department, Laguna Atascosa NWR, The Nature Conservancy, The North American Falconers Association, and Sausage Guy (California).

Editors' Note: The list of names provided by the authors, although extensive, represents only a portion of the many individuals who have participated in capture and banding of Peregrines at Assateague and Padre Islands and elsewhere in North America.

William S. Seegar *received his B.A. from the College of Wooster, Ohio, and his Ph.D. in pathobiology from The Johns Hopkins University, School of Hygiene and Public Health. Bill was the recipient of a National Research Service Award at Johns Hopkins; was a NATO Research Fellow at The Wildfowl Trust at Slimbridge and Oxford University, England; and received the Civilian Research and Development Award for development of space-based tracking and monitoring of wildlife while managing the Bird-Borne Program at The Johns Hopkins University, Applied Physics Laboratory. He is a founding member of Earthspan Inc. and is currently with the U.S. Army Soldier, Biological and Chemical Command.*

Tom Maechtle *is a raptor biologist working as a private consultant. He has participated in studies of Peregrines since his high school days and monitored several of The Peregrine Fund's early Peregrine reintroductions on the U.S. East Coast. Since then he has studied Peregrines in Greenland, Texas, Mexico, Russia, Alaska, and South America. Tom assists in studies with other species ranging from Ferruginous Hawks to Trumpeter Swans, focusing on tracking movements of wildlife with satellite-received telemetry. Tom lives in Sheridan, Wyoming, with his wife, Kathy, and daughter, Ireland.*

Mike Yates *is a raptor biologist working with Earthspan and the Raptor Research Center at Boise State University. A falconer since 1966, he has conducted studies on Peregrines and other raptors in Maryland, Virginia, Texas, Alaska, Nevada, Greenland, Canada, and Russia. He has captured and banded over 3,000 Peregrines and hundreds of other raptors. In addition to his ongoing Peregrine migration studies, Mike has projects in Nevada with other species of birds and mammals. Specializing in study design, capture, tracking, and data management, he has authored and coauthored numerous articles and scientific publications. A father of three, Mike lives in Minden, Nevada, with his wife, Karen.*

Robert Katona '71'
ANATUM PEREGRINE

Chapter 14

The Role of Field Personnel in Recovery and Research of the Peregrine

William Burnham, J. Peter Jenny, and Ed Levine

In this chapter the authors portray their experiences and insights gained while working with Peregrines.

They share a few of the thousands of stories and associated events that occurred during the two-and-a-half decades during which falcon releases occurred. From the regional leaders of the restoration program we requested the names of those who played a part in the field work and have listed them in the Honor Roll. We apologize in advance for omissions, as no doubt there are some because of the length of time over which the restoration program occurred and the large number of people involved.

The release of several thousand Peregrines to the wild and their monitoring required an army of field personnel functioning in a variety of important roles. The majority were involved in the release of Peregrines by hacking. A hack site required two dedicated people who were willing to work continually for six to eight weeks with no days or time off and many times under difficult living conditions. They were responsible for the feeding, care, and observation of typically four to six Peregrines from the time they were placed in

the hack box through release and until independence (Sherrod et al. 1982). Overseeing the hacking and assisting the hack site attendants at key times were the hack site supervisors. These men and women were former hack site attendants assigned responsibility for a group of hack sites by a release coordinator. The coordinator was responsible for planning the releases, hiring the necessary personnel, dealing with government agencies, selecting and establishing the release sites with the help of the supervisors, purchasing the necessary equipment from trucks to tents to camp stoves and lanterns, resolving all the logistics, and dealing with whatever was needed that others did not handle.

Another body of personnel was required for fostering of young Peregrines into wild Peregrine eyries. Fostering required removing clutches of wild-laid eggs and replacing them with young hatched in captivity, be they from wild or captive-laid eggs (Cade et al. 1996). Sometimes clutches of wild eggs were removed and not replaced with young (double-clutching), causing the falcons to renest and lay a second clutch, which could also be removed and then replaced by young falcons. If young Peregrines were not available for a pair of wild Peregrine adults, then eyass Prairie Falcon young were sometimes placed in an eyrie to

◀ **Figure 14.1** Drawing by Robert Katona. Reproduction rights courtesy of Lloyd Kiff.

occupy the adults until young Peregrines were available. To accomplish all of this required people first to survey potential sites where Peregrines breed to locate pairs. Then they, or others, would make observations to determine the status of a given pair of falcons in regard to when they laid their eggs and began incubation, because if eggs are to be taken, and particularly when double-clutching was planned, timing is very important. With accurate information available, the eyries, some such as El Capitan being huge cliffs, had to be climbed into and the wild-laid eggs removed and replaced with downy young falcons. Many times observers remained near the eyrie sites throughout the breeding season, watching the falcons, and at a minimum were there periodically to monitor results. For all eggs and young handled, people were needed to transport them carefully to and from falcon breeding facilities. Coordinating all aspects and overseeing the observation and fostering were supervisors and coordinators.

Accurate observations were important not only for hacking and fostering but also for monitoring Peregrine populations in temperate and arctic regions. The latter was accomplished by another small army of people who collected and reported information, including on city-nesting Peregrines. Many, if not most, of the people were unpaid and spent long hours watching pairs of Peregrines, and with luck their young, throughout the breeding season, then carefully reporting results. Many in this group are probably missing from the lists in this chapter but may be included elsewhere in this book. Congratulations and thanks to each and every person who participated in this critical aspect of Peregrine restoration.

◀ **Figure 14.2** Mt. Tom hack site, Massachusetts.

George Silk

Bill Burnham *For biographical information see Chapter 8.*

The Hack Site Attendants

J. Peter Jenny

▲ **Figure 14.3** Madison River hack site, 1983, in Yellowstone National Park, Wyoming. Mark Witmer (above) and Terry Hall were attendants.

*V*hen most people think of hacking Peregrines, they think of individuals like Jack Barclay, Steve Sherrod, Bill Heinrich, Jim Weaver, and others . . . selecting release sites, building towers, and transporting falcons to release sites.

There was, however, a larger, perhaps less well known, but equally important group of people who made an essential contribution to the recovery of the American Peregrine Falcon. They were known as hack site attendants. They were a veritable army . . . foot soldiers . . . an infantry of thousands of highly motivated individuals.

Who were these people? They were men and women. Many were college students with an interest in nature. Some were decidedly "Ramboesque" in appearance, whereas others were retirees, educators, and falconers. Some went on to pursue careers in medicine, obtain a variety of graduate degrees, and write books. Some became Directors of The Peregrine Fund, and one, Director of the U.S. Fish and Wildlife Service.

What was it like being a hack site attendant? For many it was their first opportunity to work under demanding field conditions. They had to be pragmatic and use common sense, and they often had to make decisions on their own. They had to learn to work together, around the clock, with someone they did not know or perhaps even like. But I would be lying if I did not admit that there was also a fair share of romances that were kindled. Perhaps the most difficult aspects of being a hack site attendant were weather, insects, and boredom.

In 1977 I shared a release site with Skip Tubbs. Our site on the Susquehanna River was hot and humid. In contrast, high-altitude sites in the Rocky Mountains were often bitterly cold. Being a hack site attendant meant camping out for an extended period of time. This often resulted in many interesting interactions with wildlife:

Brian Mutch was bitten twice in one year by rattlesnakes. One broke a fang off in his leg and the other became entangled in his pant leg.

Jim Willmarth was dragged uphill in his tent by a bear, and more than one hack site attendant had to sleep in a steel culvert to protect himself/herself from bears marauding their camp.

In addition to feeding quail to Peregrine Falcons, we also fed them to mink, fisher, bobcat, coyotes, racoons, vultures, and ravens.

Some hack site attendants were pushed out by forest fires, up trees by moose, and some . . . simply turned around and went home.

Suggested Personal Equipment

In addition to the tent, lantern, stove, spotting scope, telemetry equipment, and climbing gear provided by The Peregrine Fund, it is suggested that attendants have:

1. Additional spotting scope and tripod
2. Binoculars
3. Sleeping bag (one that will be warm to 32 degrees F)
4. Cot or comfortable foam sleeping pad
5. Cooking pots, pans, plates, glasses, utensils, etc.
6. Wash pan and scrub sponge
7. Cooler
8. Warm clothes (hats, gloves, etc.)
9. Rain gear
10. Good hiking boots
11. Tennis shoes
12. Necessary toilet articles (dop kit, etc.)
13. Lightweight folding chair
14. Extra propane fuel cylinders (16.4 oz) for standing single-mantle Coleman lanterns and stoves (two will be provided)
15. Sun tan lotion or sun screen
16. Plastic tarp
17. Water container
18. Water bottle or canteen
19. Reading material
20. Insect repellent (musk oil or Cutters work well)
21. Small shovel
22. Lightweight and heavy duty back pack
23. Flashlight
24. Matches
25. First aid kit
26. Extra twine or nylon cord for hanging food or to secure tent
27. Solar shower

It turned out that a favorite food of marmots and porcupines is plywood, and a constant battle was waged to keep them from eating our hack boxes. There was even a mountain goat that enjoyed standing on top of a hack box. Unfortunately, his presence was not appreciated by the falcons.

The Golden Eagle and the Great Horned Owl were, without question, our greatest source of concern, with the one carrying off our falcons by day and the other by night.

Some hack site attendants were pushed out by forest fires, up trees by moose, and some, on hiking into a remote wilderness site, simply turned around and went home.

The pay was subsistence, no more.

But in spite of the challenging working conditions, these were highly sought-after jobs.

Without exception, all the people I talked to told me how elated they were at being chosen for a position as a hack site attendant.

What did all these people have in common? They shared a passion. But even more, they were given a unique opportunity to help restore a species, to improve the world in some small way, to make a difference. And many years later, I think I can say for all who were hack site attendants, that we felt privileged to have been a part of this incredible restoration effort.

▲ Figure 14.4 A list of suggested supplies that was sent to newly hired hack site attendants.

File photo

Peter Jenny's *association with The Peregrine Fund began in 1970 when he accompanied founding board member Bob Berry to the eastern Canadian Arctic to collect some of the first Peregrine Falcons to be used for captive breeding. Once captive breeding was successful, Pete manned one of the early release sites located on the Susquehanna River, Pennsylvania. Peregrine Falcons produced by him at his breeding facility in Sheridan, Wyoming, were released and are successfully breeding in New York City and other parts of the United States. In addition to his work with Peregrines he pioneered The Peregrine Fund's involvement in the Neotropics with his research on the Orange-breasted Falcon and subsequently cofounded the Maya Project, Guatemala, with Bill Burnham. As Vice President of The Peregrine Fund, Pete divides his time between directing the management of species restoration efforts for the Northern Aplomado Falcon in the American Southwest and the Harpy Eagle in Central America, with overall program development. He is a member of the IUCN Captive Breeding Specialist Group, an active falconer and private pilot, and enjoys bird hunting and fly-fishing. Peter resides in Sheridan, Wyoming, with his wife, Barbara, and three children, Jacques, Helen, and Barkley.*

Bill Burnham

▲ **Figure 14.5** A hack box in Rocky Mountain National Park, Colorado, the first hack site in western North America.

The Release

Ed Levine

It seems wrong to talk about only one small link in the huge chain that is the story of the monumental task

that was the reintroduction program for reestablishing the Peregrine Falcon across much of the United States. This is the story of only one incident in the long line of activities by dedicated people who all pulled together to make this tremendous program successful. Yet in a symbolic and real way it was an important and fundamental event in this process. I am talking about the release, the moment when the bars or doors were removed from the hack boxes. That day when the young Peregrines, which had been so carefully hatched, raised, fed, transported, placed, cared for, and watched over, were finally set free and allowed to try and make it in the unforgiving and difficult world of the wild. Over the years I had the good fortune of sharing in this special day many times, with hardworking, committed volunteers we called hack site attendants. Attendants were charged from that day forward with the huge responsibility for the continued care of the then-freed falcons.

For me it started early in the spring of 1981. I

was standing in my camp in the backcountry of Rocky Mountain National Park (RMNP), Colorado. Buzzing along the rim of the large cliff formation above me were Bill Burnham and Bill Heinrich, riding in a helicopter that was bopping around in the gale-force winds like a dragonfly in a wind tunnel. They were checking cliffs for the first returning pair of Peregrine Falcons on Colorado's Eastern Front. I had been hired by them to watch this pair from the ground, and now this pair seemed to have gone missing. They were checking this cliff and all the others in the area. They may have also been checking on me, a little bit. A pretty big spring snowstorm had just blown through.

I waved to them as I stood next to my tent, lying flattened on the ground and buried under 8 inches of heavy wet snow. Everything I had all around me was soaking wet. It was cold, and the wind was whipping, but I was smiling. I knew this was the job for me.

That is where it all started, there in the mountains of Colorado. I was a young undergraduate in the wildlife biology program at Colorado State University in Fort Collins. The Peregrine Fund was located just out of town. I met Bill Heinrich while mowing weeds at the Colorado Division of Wildlife's research station where The Peregrine

Figure 14.6 Waiting for release day.

... opening the entire world to these anxious fledglings was a great honor filled with an overwhelming sense of responsibility and awe.

Fund facility was located. A while later he called me on the phone and asked if I had any interest in camping in RMNP for some weeks and observing a pair of wild Peregrines. Was he kidding? I think I was there before the phone hung up.

From RMNP that spring I headed up to the Tetons to a place aptly named Death Canyon to work a hack site with Bob Hollister, my college roommate. After all of that, I was hopelessly hooked on Peregrines, and they have woven their way into and through my life ever since. The Peregrine Fund was extremely generous to keep finding work for me.

But of all the wonderful jobs I have been fortunate enough to have within the world of this amazing recovery story, one of the most rewarding of all was being part of the release of the young falcons from the hack boxes. It had a powerful symbolic aura to it, but more importantly it also had the immediate, incredible feeling of the coming to fruition of an entire enormous chain of events. It was the culmination of a tremendous amount of effort, dedication, and sacrifice by many people, all focused toward this one goal. Pulling the cardboard away from the door and opening the entire world to these anxious fledglings was a great honor filled with an overwhelming sense of responsibility and awe. It was also a moment of truth filled with uncertainty and trepidation. Birds that had been under the intense care of so many people were now going to be set out into the world where they would have to fend for

themselves, and the hack site attendants and I were responsible for seeing that it was all done correctly. Each and every time I could feel the weight of this huge responsibility bearing down while at the same time feeling the elation of watching these young charges step out into the wide open world for the first time.

Though it was superficial and significant only in the artificial context of labels and timing, I have had the great honor of being a part of the last release of falcons in each of the states of Idaho, Wyoming, and Montana, as well as the last Peregrine ever released by The Peregrine Fund as part of the Rocky Mountain recovery program. Although I was lucky enough to be part of all of these symbolic milestones, one seemingly less obscure, routine release stands out in my mind above most others. To me it was an example of some of the hard work, emotional difficulty, and personal sacrifice individual hack site attendants made and what made up the flavor of this entire program and made up the fabric of what these Herculean efforts to reestablish Peregrines were all about.

This one particular story started in early July 1994. I was in Bill Heinrich's office at The Peregrine Fund facility in Boise. Bill, Brian Mutch (Bill's assistant), and I were discussing the happenings at the various release sites then underway. We were in the thick of battle and dealing with the usual sets of problems and crisis situations coming up during the release season. You see,

Lisa Langelier

young Peregrines have to go into the boxes at specific ages. They stay in for a set number of days and then must be released at another specific age, almost to the day. There is little room for contingencies. Time moves forward, birds grow, and releases must happen. No matter what, the show must go on.

However, this does not stop the onslaught of unknowns from constantly erupting and threatening to derail the whole process. There are all kinds of these mines in the field, such as powerful storms, fires, bears, Golden Eagles, Great Horned Owls, and blackflies, to name just a few. The entire show is constantly in motion, and all must be dealt with in some way as best as possible because the train never stops until the last young are out and released.

The conductor of this chaotic show was Bill Heinrich. He was the one who had to choreograph attendants, agency folks, private landowners, birds going out, birds going in, releases, and all emergencies, contingencies, and alternative plans along the way, be it with people, the falcons, or other creatures. It was an enormous task filled with uncertainty and complexities—one in which Bill found himself immersed year in and year out, but no matter what manner of disaster or chaos came at him, he always seemed to pull it off. It was akin to juggling knives and hand grenades. None of us envied that position.

So, this day in the office he was laying out plans for solving the particular crisis at hand while making sure all the other knives and grenades stayed in the air as need be. Several other of us reintroduction specialists, as we were called, were scattered around five western states handling the other simultaneous releases and emergencies. I was just back from one road trip and preparing for the next and being given my marching orders. Brian was listening in, and preparing for his upcoming trip to Texas to deal with yet more situations down there in the emerging Aplomado Falcon release program.

Bill was telling me I needed to leave right away to make the 10-hour drive to the Garden of the Gods release site in the Bighorn Mountains of Wyoming. I needed to go up to the box at that site and check on the birds. Blackflies had invaded the site and were attacking the young birds in the box. These blackflies are an insidious little menace of a fly. They are a biting midge and are not really black when you look close. They are tiny little things with transparent wings, a striped butt, and a terribly mean bite. They can bloody the cere and eye rings of confined young Peregrines, actually dehydrate them through blood

Hack Site Attendant Experiences

Jamie Rappaport Clark

On 20 August 1999, the Peregrine Falcon flew off the endangered species list, crowning one of the greatest comeback stories of the century. As Director of the U.S. Fish and Wildlife Service, it was a unique honor to have this momentous accomplishment take place during my watch.

For that privilege I am grateful to a great many people, especially to the hack site attendants who manned the front lines of the Peregrine rescue effort. I fully appreciate their contribution; as a 20-year-old wildlife biology student, I interned as a hack site attendant myself. To this day, that summer job remains one of the most rewarding and memorable experiences of my life.

Working at a hack site was a coveted job among conservationists, but it was far from glamorous. At Maryland's Aberdeen Proving Ground (APG), I spent long hours in a remote, isolated field, oftentimes in the heat and humidity of the mid-Atlantic summer or in unrelenting rain. At APG, The Peregrine Fund entrusted me with five fledgling falcons. Hack site attendants had limited contact with the birds because we did not want them to become accustomed to a human presence. For that reason, I held the Peregrine Falcon chicks only when they first arrived, as I cradled them atop a tall wooden tower before placing them in the hack box that would be their home for the coming weeks.

Nonetheless, a bond did develop between us. I named my charges after famous women from American history who inspired me as I grew up. I cared for them every day, feeding them, protecting them, and observing them. Over time, one by one, my Peregrines learned to fly. By the end of that summer, when the last falcon had spread her wings and left the hack site area for good, I felt a sense of pride, as much for them as for myself, but also a twinge of regret that our time together had come to an end.

During that summer, I truly believed the future of an endangered species lay literally in my hands. That sense of responsibility has been with me ever since. It is a responsibility that, while overwhelming at first, energized me for a lifelong career dedicated to saving wild things. As a hack site attendant, I released five Peregrine Falcons. All of us share a responsibility for saving species from the brink of extinction. Each of us doing our part, however small, can keep wonderful creatures like the Peregrine Falcon from disappearing forever.

Jamie Rappaport Clark *was Director of the U.S. Fish and Wildlife Service 1997–2001.*

Figure 14.7 Jim Willmarth ▶ packs in the roof of a hack box.

▲ **Figure 14.8** Brian Mutch builds a hack box at the Canyon Creek site in the Bitterroot National Forest in Montana after access by helicopter was delayed by two rainy days.

Figure 14.9 In some areas, ▶ hacking towers were built to elevate the young Peregrines away from predators.

letting, and make them so miserable and distressed that when you finally do open the box the birds fly away as fast as they can to parts unknown just to escape the torture. It is a bad deal, to say the least.

When the attendants at this site saw the flies and saw that the birds were cowering behind the hide to get away from these awful little things, they reacted immediately and did exactly what they were told to do. They made an hour-and-a-half drive to Sheridan, Wyoming, and found a hardware store and picked up screening, duct tape, staples, and a staple gun. They rushed back, hiked back up to the box, and screened it in, and in all likelihood saved these birds' lives, as this was a nasty infestation.

My job was to go there and assess the situation and see if a release was still possible. At the same time I was to meet attendants for another site in Montana about two hours away and put in their camp, wait for their birds to be driven over, and put them in. After finishing with that I was to go back and release the birds at the Garden of the Gods site if all looked okay. If not, we were going to come up with Plan B.

The second site where I was to put in the camp with the attendants and then the birds was a real bear. It was near the Big Horn Canyon in the Pryor Mountains. Because of a proposed wilderness designation, managers of the area required us to hike about an hour to the camp across some hot, dry country. From camp it was about 45 minutes straight up to the cliff, and then a short rappel down to the box which was placed on a lone pinnacle just barely large enough to hold the box. Attendants at this site certainly had their work cut out for them and probably were in for an experience of a lifetime. It was not for the weak at heart and probably represented everything in the "hard sites" we all told stories about. It had the potential to have it all: killer hikes, no water except what you carried on your back, very remote, dry country, wicked summer thunderstorms, fires, bears, biting flies. It had the full monty here, but with all of this hardship came the chance to camp in a gorgeous wilderness setting, release Peregrines into one of the wild places they should be, and experience a unique piece of the western landscape in a way few people ever do.

Now mind you it was late in the season. Falcons had been released already at many sites. Many other long drives and hikes had been made and other crises handled. I was probably feeling the strain and stood there just looking at Bill, letting this latest itinerary sink in. I think I just said, "Okay," and left to go gather the supplies I would need.

Blue

Ruth Rudner

My co-attendant, Stefania Strzalkowska, and I decided against naming our four Peregrines because we were concerned names might engender too personal an attachment to them. Determined to be objective and scientific, we referred to them by the color of their leg bands. The result was that Blue, Red, Green, and Yellow became every bit as much names as Ruth or Stefania. From the start, watching the Peregrines through the peephole in the hack box, it was clear how different each was from the others. There was laid-back Red, clumsy Green, gourmand Yellow. And then there was Blue. Bold, regal, he spread his wings with such majesty that you knew you were in the presence of no ordinary bird. He jumped from one perch to the other, jumped on the other Peregrines, jumped at the bars, at the box door. The box seemed too small for him, and he, so eager for the sky.

Upon release, Blue immediately jumped to the top of the box. Taking his time to check out the world around him, he was not the first to fly, but when he did, it was clear he understood flight. While Red, Green, and Yellow made short beginning forays, learning to take off and land, Blue soared in a bee-line toward the ridge to the east, flew behind it, and was gone.

He was really gone. He did not return that day, the next, or the next. We had been told a young falcon could survive four days without food if it

▲ A hack site attendant's view of young Peregrines inside the hack box, waiting for release day.

did not encounter an owl or a Golden Eagle, or did not land on the forest floor and get eaten.

Our telemetry picked up Blue's signal in one direction then, at once, in the opposite direction. The signal came weakly across what seemed great distances. It bounced along ridges. We hiked miles trying to gain a clear direction. By the third day we pretended calmness. By the fourth, we believed he must be dead. What skill could he have to survive so long on his own?

I searched the sky for him. In spite of the three Peregrines in the sky, the sky seemed empty. Some magic, glorious, soaring moment had disappeared. The more I mourned Blue's loss, the more he became, for me, mine. Continuing to watch the others, logging their every action in my notebook, I felt bereft. My Peregrine was gone.

In the late afternoon of the fifth day I sat at my scope in

the meadow 1,000 ft below the hack box cliff. A hot day, and the birds had spent it roosting in cool niches on the wall. Now, with the sun lower, they erupted into the sky. Four of them.

Blue was back! My beautiful bird was alive! He had gone far, and he had come back. Soaring, diving, tumbling through the air, four Peregrines filled the sky with the glory of falcons and the miracle of return.

Continuing to watch the others, logging their every action in my notebook, I felt bereft. My Peregrine was gone.

Ruth Rudner *has published articles in many prestigious publications, including a story in* The Wall Street Journal *on her experience hacking Peregrine Falcons. Author of eleven books, her two most recent are* A Chorus of Buffalo *and* Windstone.

237

▲ **Figure 14.10** The view from the Big Horn hack site in Montana's Pryor Mountains.

Ed Levine

We all loaded up our gear and hoofed it in. No matter how you slice it, it is a long, hot, dry hike to that camp.

Brian followed me out and we walked over to his house there at the project to talk about how to get this done. Brian had selected and placed the site in the Pryors near the Big Horn Canyon. It was a difficult site for many reasons, and besides himself and me, earlier that spring only one other reintroduction assistant had even been there. I was pumping Brian for information on how to do what I needed to and what he thought the best plan of action would be. We were going over the logistics and what it would take to get it done and he said, "I sure wish I could go with you on this one."

I said I sure wished he could, too, and I meant it. At that point I was not about to be proud, knowing that the task at hand was formidable. Finally, after we turned it over some more, Brian said, "Let's go talk to Bill and see if I can't go along, too. This might take two of us." I was all for it.

We walked back and talked to Bill. He probably was not too happy to see us both come walking in, knowing we had been trying to figure things out. Though he was shorthanded, as always, and did need Brian down in Texas, there seemed to be enough slack in the tight schedule, so he agreed and said, "Okay, both of you go and get it done." I was relieved.

We loaded our stuff and took off immediately. The drive was a grind as usual. We made it to Bozeman that night and headed out again in the morning. We arrived at the attendants' camp in the afternoon. We met up with attendants Diane Krahe of Missoula, Montana, and Patricia Stepaneck of Springville, California. We all made the 45-minute hike up to the box to take a look at the situation.

The attendants had done a fantastic job, and the birds looked great. They were all out from behind the hide, alert and content, but the black-fly situation did not look good at all. The screen over the barred front of the hack box was coated with a full layer of flies clamoring to get in and chew on the falcons. We knocked them off the screen more out of disgust than anything else, because we knew they would just come right back. Then we reinforced it with a few more staples just to be sure there was not even the slightest crack for these things to squeeze through.

We went back down to camp and discussed the alternatives with the attendants. We thanked them for saving these birds, and we let them know we needed to think over the situation and look at the alternatives before we could say whether or not we would try to release the birds here.

Next we had to go over to the other hack site, meet those attendants, take them to their camp, and get them set up. After that we were to come back for the release at the Garden of the Gods site. That was the original plan anyway.

Early the next morning we met the two young attendants, Jay Kolbe from Whitehall, Michigan, and Kevin Mitchell from Sun River, Oregon, at the Big Horn Canyon National Recreation Area main office. Brian and I introduced ourselves, showed them where the freezer was located with the quail for the birds, introduced them to the folks at the Recreation Area, lined things out with them, jumped back in the truck, and told these guys to follow us. The trailhead was about 10 miles away down a winding dirt road.

Brian and I were just talking and driving along, not really paying much attention. We could see one of the attendant's trucks following in the distance. When we got to the parking spot at the head of the two tracks where we needed to walk in, we stopped, got out, and started to gather some of the equipment the attendants were going to need for camp. After a little bit the first attendant showed up and pulled over behind us. A few seconds later a Ranger came flying in with his lights flashing and skidded to a halt. Brian and I looked at each other and started to walk toward the Ranger. He leaped out of his vehicle and shouted a question at us. "Are you missing anyone?" he asked in a rather loud voice.

We looked around and said yes, that there was another guy coming. He proceeded to tell us that he was coming all right after being left in the dirt and having no idea where he was. We did not figure this was too big a problem since there was only one road and one way to go down it. He would have arrived eventually, we were fairly cer-

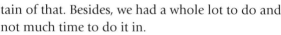

tain of that. Besides, we had a whole lot to do and not much time to do it in.

The Ranger was still agitated and thought we should be a little more concerned. Finally he blurted out, "You guys were driving like a bunch of stripe-id-assed monkeys, for Christ's sakes! This is a National Recreation Area. You can't go driving around here like that, so slow it down. Okay?" We both hung our heads a little bit, kicked around some, and said we certainly would.

He knew who we were and what we were up to. We apologized and then struck up a conversation. Finally our second attendant came bumping on in. The Ranger calmed down and was in a more friendly mood. Since he seemed to be in much better humor, I figured I would ask if we could drive the 3 mi along the two tracks to the camp instead of hiking in. He gave me a sideways look, stared for a few seconds, and then just said, "You know you can't drive in there. It's proposed wilderness."

"Okay," I said. "Figured it wouldn't hurt to ask." Brian walked around the back of the truck so he wouldn't laugh. We didn't want to make this guy mad all over again.

We all loaded up our gear and hoofed it in. No matter how you slice it, it is a long, hot, dry hike to that camp. We hauled in a bunch of gear for them, showed them where to set up camp, and then took off to head back out and over to Garden of the Gods.

It was late evening by the time we got to Lovell, so we got a room in one of the local, low-rent hotels. We were up early again and heading on our way.

We called Bill and told him the blackflies looked really bad and we were nervous about

releasing the birds there. We talked it over and all decided we should go and pull them from the Garden of the Gods site, drive them over to the Big Horn Canyon site, put them in there, and then release them after a day in that box. It seemed like the safest thing to do for the birds.

We arrived at the Garden of the Gods about midmorning. It was a warm, bright, sunny July day. Diane and Patricia were not in camp so we assumed they were up at the box watching the birds. We started up the hill, each carrying the boxes.

◀ **Figure 14.11** Peregrine hack boxes were often delivered by helicopter to remote sites.

▲ **Figure 14.12** Settled into a basket, downy Peregrines patiently wait to be carried down a cliff face, where they will be exchanged for thin-shelled eggs before meeting their new parents.

◀ **Figure 14.13** A western hack site. Note the feeding platform on top of the hack box, placed to prevent pine martens from stealing the falcons' food.

Brown and Black

Jean C. Ruhser and Gary G. Ruhser

▲ Jean and Gary Ruhser.

The release at CSKT Tower in Montana on 1 August 1992 did not go smoothly. There were two hack boxes on the tower, each with five falcons—a double, simultaneous release. A male, named Brown for the identifying color band on his leg, was first out of the hack box; he was startled into fledging 14 minutes later. Four more falcons, including Black, bolted into flight, each in different directions, early in the release, each landing at distances up to half a mile from the release site. None of these falcons, fledging so precipitously, had time to eat or take note of the outside appearance of the hack box, to which they needed to return to feed for weeks while learning to hunt.

After landing on the ground, Brown was stooped on by a Northern Harrier, and then a Red-tailed Hawk continued the attack until a release specialist ran close enough to flush the red-tail and ascertain that Brown appeared uninjured. Brown shied away from the tower after these experiences, finally returning on the fifth day, when he fed and drank repeatedly from the water pan provided because of the 90 to 100° temperatures common at the site. Brown was present on the tower only from the fifth day through the seventh day after release, then he disappeared; consequently we initially had to consider his fledging unsuccessful.

It was Black, another male, that especially engaged our efforts that summer. After bolting on release day, Black established a home base on a series of power poles located along the road a half mile

> *Four more falcons... bolted into flight, each in different directions, early in the release, each landing at distances up to half a mile from the release site.*

west of the tower. Although he flew well, when Black attempted on two separate days to return to the tower a week after the release, he was able to land only on the tower understructure, did not find any quail, and returned to the power poles. Thereafter Black flew with the other young falcons, but he did not appear to recognize the tower as a source of food. Beginning on the sixth day, quail were placed on fence posts and rocks near Black's chosen poles in an attempt to ensure Black's survival. During daily observations, we determined from quail remnants and his distended crop that he was eating and appeared fit.

After more than two weeks, Black again attempted to return to the tower, finally landing on the tower plat-

form on the 19th day after release. He seized a partially eaten quail and hunched protectively over it for five minutes before relaxing enough to eat. After four days of observing Black feeding at the tower, we shut down his "Power Pole Hack Site."

The following year we were delighted to learn from Peregrine Fund sources that both Black and Brown were believed to have returned to the hack site. The indomitable will to survive shown by these falcons inspired us. In 1996 we visited the same hack site and observed it being used by an adult pair and their recently fledged young. We were awed to imagine Black or Brown as one of the parents and to witness the fruition of our contribution to the work of The Peregrine Fund.

Jean and Gary Ruhser were born in 1944 and are residents of Wisconsin. Jean received an M.Sc. in biology and is a retired instructor of ornithology at the University of Wisconsin-La Crosse while pursuing her and husband Gary's interests in farming, birding, and camping. Her first hack site experience in 1990 so inspired her that she continued helping with seven more Peregrine releases, for a total of 65 Peregrines. She later helped with Aplomado Falcon releases in Texas and worked with Bald Eagles in Arizona, Sage Grouse and Ring-necked Pheasants in Colorado, and participated in the Wisconsin Breeding Bird Atlas project. She is currently involved in a five-year grassland bird project in Wisconsin.

Gary received a B.Sc. in engineering and went on to become a professional engineer with Allis-Chalmers and The Trane Company (retired) and also was an instructor at Western Wisconsin Technical College. He volunteered as Wilderness Ranger in Boundary Waters Canoe Area in 1990, then resigned from his engineering job in 1991 to partner with Jean reintroducing Peregrines. He worked at seven sites, helping release 60 Peregrines. Currently he is monitoring Sage and Sharp-tailed Grouse lek sites as a volunteer in a multiyear study.

About halfway up we met the attendants heading down. They were happy and both smiling. Diane asked as they greeted us, "Are you bringing us more birds?"

Brian and I looked at each other and looked back and just said, "No."

They knew immediately from our faces what was happening. It was a depressing moment. These two young women had spent a great deal of time caring for and watching these birds. They were serious about their job, and these birds meant a lot to them. They had named them all, saved them from certain death, and after all the time and effort they had put in we were coming to take them away. It was an awkward moment and not an easy thing to do.

The hike back up the hill was a quiet one. We explained why we had to do this and they understood, but it did not make it easier to swallow. We told them they were more than welcome to work the other site with the two guys and they should think about it before they made a decision. We asked if they would at least come to the site with us and help us put the birds in. They agreed to do that.

It is a bit of a scramble to the rock outcropping the box is on at the Garden of the Gods, and you have to use a system of anchors and cables to pull your way up and across to it. Neither of these women had ever climbed before, and neither was that comfortable with heights, but over the course of time they had been there, both had overcome this fear and were climbing up to the box like it was nothing, and they were proud of it, as they should have been. Just one more thing to add to the sting of this loss.

We went into the box and pulled out Josie, Kate, Virgil, Morgan, Wyatt, and Doc; two females and four males all about 40 days old. They were in terrific shape and not that happy about the intrusion. We put them in the transport boxes and headed back down the hill.

After hiking back to the trucks we loaded the birds into The Peregrine Fund truck and all headed out for Big Horn Canyon. There was nothing happy about any of this, except that we all knew we were doing what was best for these young falcons.

We arrived at the Big Horn attendants' camp early in the afternoon. Introductions were made, and then we all headed up the mountain to the cliff where the box was. We clawed our way back up through the devils club and thick brush. The trail more resembled a miniature avalanche shoot going straight up the side of these thick, overgrown hillsides. When you grab for something to

Carl Sanders

get a handhold, you get hands full of stickers. It was wet and slippery from recent afternoon rains, and we all ended up sweaty, muddy, and bloody by the time we got to the top with the birds. We had enough boxes to split the birds up for the rugged climb, and each of us carried a box. The climb was bad enough without carrying anything, let alone trying to haul an awkward, large box with precious cargo. Diane and Patricia both made it without any problem and did not complain once.

When you get to the top of this steep climb you first come out into a meadow a bit below and back from the cliff itself. In this meadow is a muddy spring. On close inspection you can see that many animals use it, but what you notice most are all the bear tracks, hair, smell, and other telltale signs. It is a classic, bona fide bear wallow. Just adds to the flavor of the place.

When you walk out to the cliff rim you look east and north to see a magnificent vista. Just east is the rim of the Big Horn Canyon itself, which yawns in the distance as a massive crack in the colorful landscape before you. It is a rolling, open dry land filled with a variety of textures and colors. You can see for miles and miles, probably all the way to Billings, Montana. Behind you the thick forests start and the Pryor Mountains roll to the west. It is an intensely rugged and remote piece of real estate. You are immersed in the feeling of being in a place not many humans ever go, let alone even see. Proposed or not, it feels like true wilderness. A precious commodity in the Lower 48.

This hack box at the Big Horn site is like no other I have ever seen. It has Brian Mutch written all over it. He picked the site, and all you need is one look at it and even from 3 mi away, you

▲ **Figure 14.14** Peregrines make the journey to the Lake Roosevelt hack site in boxes.

▲ **Figure 14.15** (Above) Attendants Barbara Douglas and Jodi Shippee kept watch over their charges in a camouflaged hack box at Lake Roosevelt, Washington.

▲ **Figure 14.16** (Below) Attendant Blair Larson kept food locked in a metal box to discourage bears near the Chief Joseph, Wyoming, hack site.

▲ **Figure 14.17** (Right) Live quail, kept as food for the fledgling Peregrines, were often hoisted between trees to discourage bears. Later, frozen quail were used, eliminating this need.

might guess he selected it. When you get a look at the box there is no question about it. I guess when they had the box helicoptered in and Brian was scrambling around this pinnacle where the box was being lowered down, Jack Oar, who was helping him place it, leaped over next to him, clipped a protective rope to his belt, and leaped back away. Jack is not known for being the overly concerned type, so for him to take such a drastic measure in an effort to protect someone from himself says volumes about this whole affair.

Anyway, the box is perched atop this pinnacle, rising like a stalagmite from a spot only 6 ft or so from the base of a massive cliff and running all the way to about 75 ft below its rim. It is an easy step/jump to the pinnacle, but you do not want to dwell too much on the amount of air under you when you make the step. The box clings to the top of this spire and barely fits; in fact, it does not really. The door where the falcons go in literally hangs out into space. You can barely scramble around three sides of this box on about an 8-in lip of rock. It is a good idea to be tied in with rope when messing around this thing. On top of all this, time and gravity have played a little with the anchors and the box tilts ever so slightly toward the door and the wide open spaces below. The anchors were solid, and the box was not going to fall off there, but it did not really look like something you wanted to tie yourself into and then swing out over to try to place angry, fighting, 40-day-old falcons into.

Brian and I had been there earlier in the year, replacing the front that had somehow fallen off

Figure 14.18 Brian Mutch climbs down to the hack box near Big Horn Canyon in the Pryor Mountains of Montana.

the cliff and smashed to bits hundreds of feet below. We knew the condition of the box and had already devised an alternative plan. We had hauled up a cordless drill and keyhole saw. We were going to cut a new door in the back of the box just big enough to put the falcons through. We had hinges and a hasp with us to close it back up.

We stood at the top of the cliff, boxes with birds in them ready to go, and everyone by boxes so the strong winds would not lift one off and carry away a boxed falcon. Brian asked the guys if they had ever rappelled before. One of the guys had just had knee surgery, and he was going to be able to get down in a week or so, but he passed for now. The other guy said yes, he had rappelled before and could rig up his own harness. We had a lot to do, and only a short period of time to do it in, so we obliged and let him go to it. Diane and Patricia took one look at this situation and said they would wait above and watch the boxes and help lower them to us.

I was getting things ready to go down and Brian was doing the same when I happened to look over at Jay, who said he knew how to rappel, and the way he had rigged himself up. I tapped Brian on the shoulder and told him he might want to go and take a look at that guy's setup because it looked to me like he was about to die. It was true. I have no idea what kind of setup he was trying to come up with, but it looked like it was going to be a one-way rappel, and a fast one. Brian was in a hurry so he just whipped the stuff off the guy and rigged it back up on him the right way. The guy was a little embarrassed but took it in good

humor. Brian said we would go over the right way to do all of this with him later.

When Jay did go over the edge he started to climb down and was not using the rope. You actually can climb down to the box here because it is not totally vertical, but there is a major pucker factor. If you slip you are not going to stop for quite some time, and when you do it will be a search and recovery, not rescue, effort. Brian was already down and I was watching Jay go. I finally yelled to him to either use the rope or climb down but not to try to do both. He decided to trust his rope and rappel the normal way. It was a little rough but he made it okay.

It is funny how this goes. It is just human nature to be scared in these situations because you can die if you screw up. Miraculously, nobody ever did, but you know for sure it is very possible. The first time or two attendants rappelled to the few sites that required it, most were scared to death and filled with trepidation. By the time we came back to release and check on how things were going, they were whipping up and down these sites like spidermen/women without a second thought. Just takes some getting used to, I suppose.

I am not much of a climber myself and do not think I ever did get to where I was not thinking second, third, and fourth thoughts. All I knew was I was very happy to have Brian along, who never seems to notice if he is five or 500 ft up and is incredibly competent to the point of making sure not only that he survives but that those around him do, too.

It is an easy step/jump to the pinnacle, but you do not want to dwell too much on the amount of air under you when you make the step.

243

A Dream Come True

Tom Smylie

Tom Smylie

▲ Almost ready for first flight.

Being a hack site attendant for the Peregrine has always carried a special meaning for me. In the early 1970s, Tom Cade came to my home in New Mexico and asked if I would be interested in loaning my two pairs of *anatum* Peregrines to his fledgling Peregrine Fund for captive breeding. A few years before, at the suggestion of the renowned Irish falconer and author Ronald Stevens, I had taken three pairs of eyass Peregrines from New Mexico eyries. Ronald had convinced me if I wanted to continue to fly Peregrines, I had better start raising my own. I had had limited success with one pair laying eggs, with one even hatching but dying soon after birth. Looking back I now realize I was in way over my head, but so was everyone else at the time. No one had gone where Tom Cade, Jim Weaver, and staff were about to go in breeding raptors.

When Tom told me of his vision for saving the Peregrine, I was impressed. I realized the possible survival of the species far outweighed my falconry needs; I gladly offered up my birds. It was not long before Jim Weaver came out from Cornell and took my two pairs, plus a pair I had given to Frank Bond in Santa Fe, to provide the "seed crop" for the Fund's endeav-

To an earthbound human, it was a feat of incredible courage and faith.

ors. It was a decision I never regretted.

After turning birds over to the Fund, I began silently to harbor the dream of one day being able to release their distant progeny into the wild. Looking back to those early years, who could have foreseen that by the summers of 1994 and 1995 I would be able to be a hack site attendant at some of the last releases before the species was delisted as an endangered species? Realizing the program was winding down, I took an early retirement as Assistant Regional Director of the U.S. Fish and Wildlife Service's Southwestern Region to fulfill my dream.

In the early summer of 1994, my wife, Cherie, our five-year-old daughter, Jamie, and I were attendants at a release site on the eastern foothills of Washington State's Mount Rainier in the William O. Douglas Wilderness. There, on a high cliff overlooking the valley of the American River, we released five female Peregrines at hack. What a magnificent site it was, with a river far below the snow-capped Mount Rainier as a backdrop.

I have flown and observed Peregrines for some 40 years, yet being a hack site attendant provided insight into the species far beyond my previ-

ous experiences. To open the hack box and see the release to freedom is forever embedded in my mind. Almost immediately the falcons were out running and hopping about the face of the escarpment with total abandonment. They would face into the wind while gripping tightly to the rocks and pumping their wings energetically, much like an airplane warming up before heading down the runway. It was not too many days later when they would pump their wings, release their talons, and drop off the face of the cliff. To an earthbound human, it was a feat of incredible courage and faith. Although at first the flights were awkward, followed by less than graceful landings, it was not long before the birds gained mastery of the air.

Although they were sometimes gone for a day or more before returning for food, they remained quite sociable. Often they spent hours lying together preening, sleeping, or birdwatching on top of the hack box, sharing food and being affectionate siblings.

However, after a couple of weeks their behavior suddenly changed into that of solitary, independent, and aggressive falcons. They would fly in, grab the food, and go off to some solitary place to eat. They now spent little or no time at the hack box, or even with each other. We saw them less and less over longer periods of time; soon they only returned for food. Eventually they were not to be seen at the box at all, and we could hope they had become "All That They Could Be" by becoming wild Peregrines.

We followed the summer of 1994 in Washington State with the summer of 1995 at another site near Pinedale, Wyoming, along the Green River at the foot of the Wind River Mountains. We were on a private ranch where the hack box was placed high above the ground on four sturdy power poles. The site was located near a bow in the river above a hay field. We fed the birds by canoeing across the Green River and observing them with a telescope from our travel trailer. We were most thankful to be using the trailer as a blind because of the horrendous hordes of mosquitoes.

We had two tiercels and three falcons for release at the site; however, we were soon faced with some unforeseen problems. First, when the birds first began flight, the three females, being less aerial than the males, tried landing on the willows along the swollen shoreline of the river. The limber willows would not hold their weight, and they fell to the water below. We spent hours splashing through the thick willows in thigh-deep cold water trying to find the birds before they drowned. Fortunately, we were able to retrieve them successfully and place them, soggy but healthy, back on the hack tower. They seemed to have learned their lesson, for we never saw them near the willows again. In the process, we were near exhaustion from splashing through the numbing waters, covered with mosquito bites, and somewhat unnerved from hearing moose splashing and snorting in front of us.

All went well for awhile, until one morning, while going to feed, I found a pair of Peregrine wings at the base of the tower. During the night a Great Horned Owl had killed and eaten one of the roosting falcons. Sometimes it's extremely difficult to accept nature in its entirety. Fortunately, it never happened again, since the experience convinced the remaining Peregrines to roost elsewhere.

I would be remiss if I were to confine our experience only to the hacking, regardless of how thrilling the experience. How special it was to spend the better part of two summers in some of the most beautiful places in the world with my family. To see beautiful sunrises and sunsets against the backdrop of mountains, carpets of wild flowers, cool clean air, and the pleasure of seeing an array of wildlife from mountain goats to moose and elk; from eagles to swans and grouse, to songbirds, and even wild Peregrines. For sure, it was not all peaches and cream. There were cold days and nights, snow flurries, thunderstorms, insects, heavy packs, dehydrated food, and long hours in a blind. But for those of us who embrace wild things, there can be no greater experience than playing a part in the recovery of one of nature's truly magnificent creatures. For us, the skies would be empty without them.

▲ **Figure 14.19** Franconia Notch eyrie, photographed with its resident Peregrine in 2003. In 1981, this was the first natural eyrie to be reoccupied in the East, one result of hacking many Perigrines in New Hampshire.

All three of us got down to the box and set about getting everything ready for the birds. We cut the new door in the back and got the birds into their new home without a hitch. The birds were happy to be done with the bumpy trip and be back in a roomy hack box and away from us humans. We were glad to have them in, too.

We hiked out and took Diane and Patricia back to their camp. We took them to dinner that night at a tiny place some miles down the road from their site. After dinner we parted ways. We thanked them for all their help and all they had done for the birds. It was sad and disappointing for them, and we felt bad. At least they knew the birds were safe at another magnificent site and soon would be released.

They chose not to work the site with the guys, and that was understandable. They had become attached to the birds and to the idea of doing the site themselves. They did not want to have to share that experience with two new people they did not know at a place they also did not know.

As an attendant you have to give up so much in order to live in these difficult places. It takes a great deal of sacrifice. You psych yourself up and rise to the challenge, and often the knowledge that you were able to meet the challenge and succeed helps you get through it. It would be difficult to have the entire dynamic change, have your birds move to another site, and then have to share those burdens with others besides your partner at a site other than your own. We understood.

Tom Smylie, *a falconer and raptor researcher, has been an ardent supporter of The Peregrine Fund from its inception, providing some of the first breeding Peregrines for the organization. Tom, his wife, Cherie, and daughter, Jamie, served as hack site attendants for two summers in Washington State and Wyoming. He was formerly Assistant Regional Director for the Southwest Region of the U.S. Fish and Wildlife Service and presently directs, produces, and performs the World Animal Encounter Shows at the Albuquerque Biological Park in New Mexico.*

▲ **Figure 14.20** Bill Heinrich ascends a rope with a basket of young Peregrines for the hack box at Chimney Rock, Colorado.

Diane lived in Missoula, and she did return after the birds were released to check on them and watch them all flying free.

Brian and I took the 4th of July off to rest for a minute, do some fly-fishing, and get ready for release day on the 5th back at the Big Horn Canyon site.

On the morning of the release we headed back up to the hack site. We met with Jay and Kevin at their camp, went over the release details for the day, and all hiked to the top of the cliff. We left the two attendants at the observation point in sight of the box, somewhat below the rim, so they could keep an eye on that side of the cliff and watch what happened when we opened the box and had to move away. Brian and I went on to the top.

We were going to have to do some creative thinking to come up with a plan to release birds from this box. We could not take the front off. We did not do that anymore because that requires shoving the birds behind the small hide, holding them in there with a piece of cardboard or something, then pulling it and running. After some years we figured out that we did not need to cram them in a small place together where they might hurt each other inadvertently or come blazing out just to get out of the cramped space. Instead we soaked them down with water, opened the door, and backed off. Worked a lot better. Besides, there was so little room in the front of this box it would have been really hard to pull the hide and get away without spooking the birds.

At this site we had two big problems. One was that the opening in front of the door went right into a 400-ft drop to the bottom of the spire. Not the best first step for a fledgling Peregrine. The second problem was that once you removed the door, you were not running anywhere. You had to scramble up about 75 ft of cliff before you could get out of sight. This would take even Brian more than a few seconds to do. If a Peregrine happened to come to the door right away, look up and see a human towering above and moving rapidly, it might tend to send the birds flying. Again, not a good thing.

We had thought this over on our day off while throwing flies around. You have to do something while you are fishing, and we came up with what seemed like a workable plan. In order to get the birds past the 400-ft drop, we would find a log and lay it from the edge of the main cliff where there was a good ledge, on over to the front edge of the door where there was a little lip of rock.

To solve the problem of removing the door and not being able to get away, we would use a piece of cardboard, like we used at towers for the same purpose, only this would be in reverse. Instead of standing on the ground and pulling a string attached to the cardboard taped over the door and running away, we would tape the cardboard over the door, climb to the top of the cliff with 100 ft or so of string tied to the cardboard, have the other end tied to a big rock, and heave it off the cliff and run away. Seemed like a plan to us.

When we got to the edge of the cliff above the box we put our packs down, got out a bunch of the equipment we would need, and started to get ready. I went to look for the ropes and other climbing gear we had stashed in bags and hung from trees. I thought we would need them to lower ourselves and the dead tree over the edge of the cliff. Brian went to look for a tree.

I was fumbling around with the rope, trying to sort out which end was which and laying things out, finding an anchor, and all that kind of stuff when I looked up just in time to see the end of a rather large snag disappearing over the edge of the cliff above the box. I looked around me again and yep, I had all the rope and climbing gear.

I could not believe it! While I was messing around with all this junk, Brian had torn down this 12-ft snag, hauled it over to the cliff, and then somehow climbed, freehand, down to the ledge across from the box with a tree over his shoulder. I ran over to the rim of the cliff whispering things like, "What the hell are you doing? Are you nuts?"

I had to whisper because we did not want to freak the birds out just yet. I looked over the edge with some apprehension, hoping that I was going to see Brian still there and not be hearing some horrible crash instead. He was there, no problem, standing on the ledge with his tree and propping it across to the tiny lip of rock just under the door. I just shook my head and went about getting the rest of the stuff down to him.

We were able to soak the birds down pretty well through the little door in the back of the box. Then Brian climbed on top of the box. I handed him the cordless drill and he leaned out over the edge to get at the hinges of the door. He was able to take the door off and slide the cardboard over the opening and tape it securely in place. We secured the log with some big rocks, put out the three days worth of quail, and I took the string and headed to the top of the cliff. Brian adjusted the tape and cardboard just right so it would pull away when the rock went by. He checked everything and made sure all was ready, then looked over to the attendants who were out on their observation point watching the whole thing. He gave them the thumbs-up and then climbed up the cliff to where I was.

▲ **Figure 14.21** Many hack boxes incorporated branches or rocks as perches for young Peregrines.

Chas S. Clifton

He asked if I was ready. I said yep. I stepped back from the edge of the cliff, and Brian crawled up to the edge to peer over so he could watch and see how it all went. I wound up and heaved the grapefruit-sized rock with the string tied to it out and away as far as I could.

The white string arced out in a long loop, following the bending trajectory of the heavy rock. The wind was blowing pretty good along the face of the cliff. As the string lifted upward with the momentum and arc of the throw, it pulled the cardboard away from the box just slightly and the wind held it there perfectly some 3 in from the opening of the door and it wobbled back and forth, vibrating like a big leaf in the stiff breeze. Brian said he could see a little Peregrine's face and beak as it stood there wide-eyed, watching the fluttering cardboard and crack of open sky behind it.

I could not help but look over myself as the string was now following the rock off and down into the abyss. The cardboard just hung there, suspended in space and time, and we just watched. It seemed like it took forever, but then in one sharp instant the string caught up with the rock, all went taut, and the cardboard was gone with a whoosh, falling away into the abyss with great speed, trailing behind the hurtling rock and string.

This left the young Peregrine standing there looking at nothing but a gaping hole where the cardboard had been. It had a really surprised look on its face. We ran away into the woods, laughing as quietly as we could and giving each other high fives. It had gone perfectly.

We ran around to our observation point on the opposite side of the cliff. We had to go through some trees, cross a gully, and then up to a second rim formation. Finally we came out into view and could see the box. The attendants were around the corner from us, and we couldn't see them, but we knew they had a good view of the door and the front of the box. We could see the log and the

continued on page 250

. . . the opening in front of the door went right into a 400-ft drop to the bottom of the spire. Not the best first step for a fledgling Peregrine.

247

Murder at Haystack Rock

Joseph Alston

I wish I had more to offer to the contents of this book than the macabre story that follows, but perhaps it will serve as a warning to the thousands of birders wandering through the backcountry only vaguely aware of potential dangers.

In January 1978, I found myself unemployed. I had enjoyed the previous summer as a river ranger at Dinosaur National Monument on the Green and Yampa Rivers in western Colorado. As the summer progressed I was asked to be a wrangler on a wild (feral) horse roundup on the high country of Douglas Mountain in the northeast portion of Dinosaur National Monument. The horse roundup ended in December as the last of the 700 horses were captured for adoption.

To occupy my newfound free time, I birded while my wife, Judy, taught first and second grades in the tiny and rough community of Dinosaur, Colorado. She tells the story of taking away chewing tobacco from one of her second graders and confronting the child's parents, who responded, "at least he won't get worms."

As the winter progressed, one of my heroes, Jerry Craig, the nongame raptor biologist for the State of Colorado and champion of the Peregrine Falcon's recovery, came to my rescue. Jerry hired me as a wildlife technician for the State of Colorado to monitor Peregrines in the Dinosaur National Monument region. Additional help came from

Steve Petersburg and Cecil Lewis of Dinosaur National Monument and Ernie Most of the Bureau of Land Management, providing housing, a vehicle, and a radio.

In March and early April, I hiked the region in a futile search for Peregrines. Heavy snows had impeded access to two known eyries in Dinosaur National Monument at Steamboat Rock near the confluence of the Green and Yampa Rivers, and Haystack Rock several miles up the Yampa River.

In early April, as the snow was beginning to melt, I made a few trips up the 25-mile dirt road to the rounded summit of Blue Mountain, where snow continued to block my access to the Yampa Bench Road leading to Steamboat and Haystack Rocks. Finally, after a few warm days it seemed the last large snowdrifts must have succumbed to the sun's warmth.

On the weekend of 8 April, Judy and I headed up Blue Mountain and were surprised to find tire tracks in the mud of the recently receded snowbanks. As we made our way to the Haystack Rock point we

found a pickup already there. In addition, there were wire, gas cans, a goodly amount of trash, and a large amount of juniper bark lying on the ground. At this point I wanted to talk to the owner of the truck about the mess he had made, but I could not find him.

Judy and I walked to the sandstone promontory of Haystack Rock to see if the birds were present. As we walked we could smell the distinct sweet smell of juniper smoke but could not locate its source. As we began to realize how odd all this was, we heard the truck start up and leave.

Feeling a bit uncomfortable, we continued on but were unsuccessful in our attempt to find any falcons. Sometime later, we decided to pack up and head downriver to Steamboat Rock for the night and check again at Haystack the next day. As we folded up the tripod and spotting scope and began walking back to our truck, I noticed a small bit of juniper bark on a finger of rock separated from the main sandstone monolith. I crawled out onto the finger, and lying on my stomach, looked over the 400-ft cliff. Judy asked me what I could see and I said, "A tire, a

gunnysack, some burned vegetation, and a body."

Several things became clear at that moment. The person in the truck was probably involved in more than littering, he had probably seen us and we had not seen him, and there was only one way out and that was the route he had taken.

We chose to follow him out rather than find ourselves dead-ended in Echo Park. We drove at considerable speed the 25 miles of dirt road to the small store and telephone at Elk Springs, 35 miles east of Dinosaur, Colorado.

Keeping the engine running and an eye on the road, we called park headquarters and they in turn called the sheriff's office and highway patrol. We soon met our neighbor and friend, highway patrolman Mike Kay, and a deputy sheriff. At their request, we reluctantly began to retrace our way back to Haystack Rock. Unfortunately, Mike Kay was called away to man a roadblock, leaving us with the deputy sheriff. As we came over the crest of Blue Mountain, I saw a one-way set of tracks heading off a small spur road. We stopped and the deputy ran up the road, spotting a truck that matched the description we had given him.

The deputy returned to our vehicles and handed me a rifle and said, "Let's go."

Against my better judgment, I followed the deputy. As we passed the truck, the deputy pointed for me to go one way and he'd go the

> *I aimed the rifle at him, I think I remembered to release the safety, and asked the suspect to remain where he was.*

Jim Enderson

other. My way soon led me to the suspect, a middle-aged man lying on his side under a tree, smoking a cigarette. He calmly spoke, "I thought I might see you again."

I aimed the rifle at him, I think I remembered to release the safety, and asked the suspect to remain where he was. A few minutes later the deputy returned to help me take the suspect into custody.

As it turned out, the suspect, a Mr. Ashton of Darby, Montana, had tried to dispose of the bodies of two young women at Haystack Rock, probably the year before. One of the bodies had become lodged on a shelf closer to the rim than he had intended. He had returned to the scene to try to dislodge the body with a makeshift bomb (which was contained in the gunny-

sack) or by burning the face of the cliff.

Judy reminds me from time to time about how stupid I was to leave her in the truck while the deputy and I chased the suspect. She asks what would have happened if the suspect had doubled back to her or she had heard gunshots, or what if there had been more than one bad guy? I don't have good answers to those questions except to say that fortunately it turned out alright.

Soon after this incident, a high-powered technical climbing team was brought down from Wyoming to recover the bodies. They were concerned about the poor quality of the rock and the difficulty of their climb. I found it somewhat gratifying to know that Jerry Craig and

his sidekick, Dan Berger, had made a more difficult descent at the same location the year before as a matter of routine to "double-clutch" Peregrine Falcons.

As a postscript, 10 years later, almost to the day, I was

Bob Barbee

birdwatching on the delta of the Gunnison River as it flows into Blue Mesa Reservoir in Colorado. As I looked through my spotting scope among the cranes and geese, there was yet another body; but that is another story.

Joseph Alston *continued his career with the National Park Service. He and his wife, Judy, have enjoyed assignments at Dinosaur National Monument, Yellowstone National Park (twice), Alaska (Regional Office and Glacier Bay National Park and Preserve), Curecanti National Recreation Area (Gunnison, Colorado), and Glen Canyon National Recreation Area (Page, Arizona). Joe is currently Superintendent of Grand Canyon National Park and remains interested in Peregrine Falcons and now also the reintroduction of the California Condor to the Grand Canyon.*

Figure 14.22 First view of freedom.

. . . he could see a little Peregrine's face and beak as it stood there wide-eyed . . .

Tom Smylie

back of the box plus our side of it. Between the two observation points we had a full 360-degree view of what was happening.

We really had no idea how this was going to work or even if it would work. None of the birds were out yet when we sat down and set up our scope, but not long after one of the males emerged, probably the one that had been standing there all along and watched his door fly away.

He stepped up onto the rim of the open door and hopped right to the log and stood there for a second. The wind was still blowing and he had to spread his wings now and then to keep his balance as he clung tight to the log with his talons digging into the dead wood.

After a second another youngster poked his head out the doorway to see what was going on, and the first bird started to move farther along the log. He hobbled out on unsteady legs until he was almost in the middle and started to waiver back and forth like a log roller. He looked just like a reluctant sailor forced to walk the plank. The wind was pushing him around and he needed to go forward or back soon before he was swept off into space, which would not have been a good thing. He decided to go forward and all of a sudden skittered his way unsteadily along and

hopped to the ledge on the main cliff. We both started to breathe again.

Brian and I were psyched! One bird made it so far. It only took a few minutes before the next one popped out, then the next, and the next. In fact, the next two jumped to the log at about the same time, and the one behind was pushing and messing with the one in front. We thought for sure one would push the other off but they made their way across the log, bickering and squabbling as they went, until they got to solid ground on the other side. Two more came behind and made it just fine. Now there was just one female left in the box. She was probably the shy one and not really ready to venture out yet. Eventually she came out, too, and made it across. We laughed and joked about how this had all come together. It had been a heck of a lot of stress and tons of flying by the seat of our pants, but in the end the birds had made it out of the box and were now safe on the big ledge of the cliff. We knew the attendants on the other side could see this as well and had to be happy too. So far, so good.

We settled in for a long day of watching to see how the first day would go but were really happy about how it had worked up to this point. Many dangers now awaited these young falcons, and so much would be out of anyone's hands, but it was a huge step for them both figuratively and literally to be huddled on this ledge, out in the wide open spaces, safely out of the box and paddling, preening, jumping, playing, and eating.

A few of the birds did not stay on the ledge too long and bailed off to take their first flights. Josie, one of the females, was the first of the group to fledge. She flew off toward us and landed on the rim of the cliff across the gully from where we were, crashing down lightly as she attempted her first landing. One of the young males flew off in the opposite direction, and after a while she went to join him and vanished from our view. Before long a second male fledged and landed somewhere over toward where the other two had gone.

After an hour or so Brian and I were kicked back just watching the world go by when we both spotted a falcon coming in high over the forest from behind the cliff and over the far ridge. We looked at it with our binocs and could tell it was an immature Peregrine. "Oh no," we thought, "here comes a subadult bird to harass these young birds." This will not be good. Of all the problems that can happen at a release site, returning or wandering Peregrines are probably one that is bittersweet trouble. It is a good indication that things are going right with the whole release pro-

gram when other Peregrines become more of a worry, but that does not help with the immediate situation at hand. Adult and subadult Peregrines can be a major problem, especially on or close to release day. The young are taking their first flights and can barely negotiate takeoffs and landings. Wild Peregrines can get quite aggressive in their play and interactions with newcomers to the neighborhood. It can be dangerous for these youngsters to have a skilled and experienced older Peregrine stooping and strafing them on their maiden flights. They can be driven into rocks or trees and get injured, or they can get scared and fly too far away and become lost and starve. It is a very real problem.

So we watched this bird, knowing all of the potential risks that were now soaring and diving in from above. We watched this dark anchor drop from high in the sky, race along the ridgeline, and then swoop down toward the trees. When it got near the treetops it threw its wings all the way out, put on full air brakes, and crashed into the top branches of a big fir tree.

"What the hell was that?" I asked, confused and a bit incredulous.

Brian said, "That's one of our birds! That's one of the birds that just fledged!"

It was unbelievable. Both of us had released a lot of Peregrines over the years but neither one of us had ever seen anything like this before. A bird that had only been out of the box for maybe two hours had flown way out over the ridge, gone up hundreds of feet, come soaring back over, then

stooped like she had been doing it all her life, and the only thing that gave it away was when she had to crash land in the tree like a wayward paratrooper. Unreal. This was Josie, the first to fledge, and obviously one heck of an athlete. This was a special bird for sure.

She hung out in the top of this conifer for awhile and then decided to try and get back down to the cliff about 500 yd below her. She took off, circled around the cliff to the side of the box we could not see, and then came up around in front of the box and landed again on the rim of the cliff right in front of us. That is when we were able to see for sure it was Josie.

She sat there for some time, then did another little flight and ended up relanding on the same rim, just a bit closer and almost directly across from us. What an awesome bird this female was. It made us feel even more satisfied about all we and the two groups of attendants had gone through in the past few days to get these birds out and on the wing. It was worth it no matter how any of the birds would perform on that first day, but to see this incredible individual out and about doing the things she was doing made it all that much more special.

We were excited about how all this had come together, and now this awesome show to top it off.

We were also exhausted. All the stress, hiking, climbing, and short nights were catching up. Both of us kicked back in our power loungers, and before long the warm midafternoon sun had us both dozing off.

▲ **Figure 14.23** Peregrines at hack.

Dundas

Kurt K. Burnham

When days grow long and the stress of life piles up on me, my mind must escape. I immediately think of Thule, Greenland, and a mountain called Dundas. When sitting on top of Dundas, nothing matters except for that moment. Most people would hate Dundas and consider it a cold and terrible place. Sitting on top of Dundas, though, it is just nature and me alone on the mountain.

Thule, Greenland, is one of the most northern permanent human establishments, in addition to being a U.S. air base. Thule is located 800 miles south of the North Pole and is a place few people ever visit or would want to visit. I have spent time in Greenland the past summers studying Peregrine Falcons. Dundas is home to a pair of Peregrines, so I was privileged to spend a very special time there on the mountain.

My view from Dundas is spectacular. A slight breeze almost immediately picks up and my body begins to shiver. In the distance I hear a great crash like the roar of a far-off lion. It is an iceberg breaking off from one of the many glaciers and plummeting into the ice cold waters below. Icebergs dot the water like army ants when they swarm. All different sizes and shapes of icebergs are present, taking on the appearance of other objects. One looks like an aircraft carrier, another like a plane. Some of them even have large holes

▲ Kurt Burnham with adult Peregrine, Kangerlussuaq, Greenland, 2003.

The sound of her wings slicing through the air reminds me of a piece of fabric being torn.

in them which look like picture windows.

Suddenly the silence is shattered by the high-pitched scream of a Peregrine Falcon. The Peregrine has come home to find a stranger on her mountain and is mad as hell. She rolls over onto her back and, tucking in her wings to stoop, drops from the heavens like a bullet. She makes stoop after stoop, screaming while coming closer and closer every time. The sound of her wings slicing through the air reminds me of a piece of fabric being torn. She wants to stoop down and unleash all her fury in one tremendous strike and drive me from her mountain. After a short while she wearies of this routine and flies off to tend to her

small chicks. They live on a nearby cliff and she must be careful not to leave them exposed to the environment for extended periods. What an incredible bird to be able to live here and raise young.

The dark and ominous clouds on the horizon make me realize it is time to put a coat on. White flakes begin to fall all around me. The snow hits my face and body. Summer in the High Arctic! With the snow and wind picking up, it is time to depart. My visit has been extraordinary and I feel renewed and invigorated. I run my hand over the lichen-covered rock I have been sitting on. Again I hear the high-pitched scream of the Peregrine. Unnoticed, the male has been observing me. My sudden movement has

caused him to rise and begin the defensive tirade all over again.

All around me live creatures that can miraculously survive and even flourish in this extreme environment. From this, I gain hope and I feel rejuvenated. I know I too can survive in my environment at home and succeed and feel comfortable with others. The best part is that Dundas and the Peregrines will always be here for me to return to, even if only in my mind.

Kurt Burnham *has participated in research on falcons in Greenland for the past 14 years, the first times as a teenager. He has a B.Sc. in biology from Albertson College of Idaho and is working toward a doctorate at Oxford University. Kurt is the projects director for The Peregrine Fund's research and conservation actions in Greenland.*

I was half dreaming about something, nodding in and out, enjoying the quiet when all of a sudden back in my mind I heard an awful sound that could only be one thing, and at the same time Brian woke up with a jolt from the same sound and started yelling, "Shoot! Shoot!"

I was up now and could hear a Peregrine cacking. Brian shouted again, "Shoot!"

My hand was frantically searching the ground next to me as I looked up and saw a large black delta hurtling straight down out of the clouds. I could hear the roar of the wind through tucked feathers and it was getting louder and louder as this object grew, heading straight for our gorgeous little Peregrine perched across from us. Finally my hand found what it was looking for and locked on the hard rubber of the .44 magnum's Pachmayr handgrip. I snatched it up and instantly started to fire the blanks into the air.

By now the huge form of this falling eagle was barreling right down on the young falcon with deadly intent. As the first shot rang out she simultaneously leaped off the rim of the cliff and both falcon and eagle hurtled together into the canyon below with the eagle closing fast. I kept on firing and miraculously the eagle hesitated and swerved off to the side. Even more miraculously, the young female Peregrine turned the opposite way, kept her head, and flew right back up to the cliff rim. Once again, this bird did something Brian and I had almost never seen from such a young bird in the face of certain death. In most cases a young Peregrine would have just kept right on going and either flown out of sight or around a corner, risking being lost from the site and its food supply, or worse yet, flown far enough that the eagle could have regained its wits about it and gone for a second attack, this time too far for us to have any hope of dissuading it.

Well, the adrenaline was flowing after that moment of terror, but this amazing young bird was once again perched across from us, seemingly safe and sound for the moment and all was quiet again. Needless to say, we did not doze off for the rest of the day, which fortunately was completely uneventful after that. No more visits from eagles. The birds flew and landed a little more but for the most part seemed content to sit, preen, stretch, and take stock of what was in front of them.

As late afternoon moved into evening, we knew it was time for us to leave. We packed up our stuff and started the long hike out. We climbed down and around to the attendants and came across Kevin perched on his own little pinnacle with a great view of the box and the cliff in front of it.

Bill Heinrich

© Carl Sanders

File photo

▲ Figure 14.26 Field glasses and a notebook are the constant companions of a hack site attendant.

▲ Figure 14.24 (Above) A fledgling Peregrine peers into its hack box after release.

▲ Figure 14.25 (Below) Much of a hack site attendant's day is spent observing the released Peregrines and keeping notes.

Figure 14.27 A fledgling
Peregrine crouches in the
safety of a hack box. Some
return to the boxes to nest in
later years.

Bill Heinrich

We talked a bit about all we had seen and what had happened that day. We answered some questions about the upcoming days and weeks, then thanked him for all he and Jay had done to help us out and wished them luck for the remaining weeks. We also told him to take care of that special female for us.

As we started to climb our way back down through the thorns, Kevin shouted out, "Hey, how old are you guys anyway?"

We laughed and told him, "Too old to be doing this stuff still." He gave us a thumbs-up and said, "Awesome, man. I hope I have half you guys' spunk when I'm your age."

Talk about feeling a little old! Oh well. It was a good day and a memorable release, that was for sure. Josie went on to dazzle the attendants for the rest of the release and dispersed on her own after about five weeks. I bet she is out there somewhere in one of those beautiful, wild places making babies to continue to dazzle the skies wherever they live.

Ed Levine *has been interested in raptors for as long as he can remember and a licensed falconer since 1979. He first began working with birds of prey while getting his BS in wildlife biology at Colorado State University. In 1981 Ed began working for The Peregrine Fund for a total of about eight years, primarily as a falcon propagation assistant but also raising quail, as a hack site attendant, monitoring pairs of wild falcons, and as a reintroduction assistant. In 1988 he returned to school for an MS in raptor ecology at Boise State University while studying Peregrine Falcon populations in the Greater Yellowstone Area. From 1991 to 2001 he worked for the Idaho Department of Fish and Game as a research biologist, studying Peregrines and other raptors. Currently he is part owner of a small radio-telemetry company called Merlin Systems, Inc. in Boise, Idaho, where he lives with his wife, Jules Mulholland, and their critters.*

Honor Roll

The Peregrine Fund • Peregrine Release Supervisors

File photo

A Peregrine defends her eyrie on a bridge.

Release Coordinators	Hack Site Supervisors	
Jack Barclay	Gian Basili	Brian Mutch
Marty Gilroy	Doyle Brown	Jack J. Oar
Bill Heinrich	Shane Davis	Dan O'Brien
Steve Sherrod	Matt Erickson	Jim Spohn
Stan Temple	Barb Franklin	Will Sugg
	Bert Harding	Glenn Thompson
	Brian Kimsey	Jim Willmarth
	Ed Levine	

The Peregrine Fund Hack Site Attendants and Field Personnel

Dennis Abbate
Nancy Abbate
Robin E. Abbey
Jesse Aber
Mark Abraham
Brook Adams
Steven Adams
Mindy Ager
Russell Joseph
   Albanese
Mikel Alfieri
Sharon M. Allan
Thomas A. Allan
Betsy Allen
Jeffrey Allen
Juanita Allen
Cela Alvarez
Leland Alverson
Heather Anderson
John Anderson
Katy Anderson
Robert L. Anderson
Barbara J. Andorfer
Susanne Apellaniz
Ed Appel
David Appleton
Louis R. Armstrong
Ed Arnett
Jim Arnzen
Janet Artley
Val Asher
Perry Atheneos
Dan Audet
Edward Backus
Whitney Bacon
Dean Bado
Thomas Baird
Vanessa Baird
David Baker
Stephen R. Baker
Scott Ball
Elizabeth S. Ballard
Bob Ballou
Nancy Ballou
Sean Ballou
Michael J. Banta
Jack Barclay
Michele Barclay

Kimberly Barcus
Stephanie Barday
Larry Barnes
Christopher Barr
Michael Barth
Ian Barton
Gian Basili
Brett Battaglia
Colleen Bauer
Elizabeth Bauer
Nina Baum
Karl Beard
Mark Beardsley
Leigh Ann Beavers
Matt Becker
Will Beecher
Todd A. Bennatt
Kathy Bennett
Tim Bennett
Lee Benson
Sue Benson
Lisa Benton
Michael P. Berman
Biff Bermingham
Louis Berner
John Berry
Rita Berry
Robert B. Berry
Kellyn Betts
Matthew Betz
Art Beyer
Brian Bieger
Marilyn Biever
Thomas Bills
Micheline Bisaillon
Barbara Blackie
Patsy Blackstock
Robert Blaes
Marcie Blanchard
Tracy Blashill
Jack Bobo
Bonnie Bochan
Hans Bodenhamer
Stephen Bodio
Todd Boettcher
Denise Boggs
Barbara A. Boileau
Jeff J. Bolln

Diane Bond
Keith Bonnlander
Lila Borge
Matt Born
Lisa Borta
Rosalie V. Borzik
Erica Bowman
Kelly Bowmnan
Richard Boylan
Katherine A. Boyle
Abraham D.
   Boynton
Patrick Bradley
Dana Bradshaw
Michael
   Brandenburg
Sherri Brauner
Daniel Brauning
Howard Brinkerhoff
Lori Brinkerhoff
Eileen P. Bristol
John Britt
Hallie Brooks
David Brown
Doyle Brown
Lois Brown
Timothy Brown
Tracy Brown
Richard J. Browne
JoAnne M. Brule
Daniel Brunetti
John F. Bruno
Rachel Bryant
Craig Bublitz
Andrew Buhl
Bonnie Burkhart
Bruce Burks
Biff Bermingham
Carolyn J. Burnett
Joe Burns
William Busby
Paul R. Cabe
Theresa Cabrera
Brian Cade
Drew Cade
Renetta Cade
Tom J. Cade
J. Calhoon

Richard Callahan
Pete Cameron
Sherry Campbell
Glenn Carlson
Jeff Carlton
Kent Carnie
Lila Borge Caron
Neita Carr
Janet Carroll
Jennifer Carroll
Jody Carter
JoEllen Carter
Ray Carter
Rudolph Cashwell, Jr.
Christine Cassidy
Aaron Chadwick
Cindy Chadwick
John H.
   Chamberlayne
Michael L.
   Chamberlin
Dwight Chapman
Robert Chapman
Stephen Chidester
Elizabeth Chipman
Richard B. Chipman
Lauryl Chorpenning
Alice H. Chow
Chris Church
Mark G. Churchill
April Claggett
David Clark
Helen Clark
Joel Clark
Kimberly Clark
Mary B. Clark
Laurie Cleary
Bert Cleaveland
Charlotte Clews
Charlotte A.
   Clifford
Curt Cline
Bobby Clontz
Ethan Clotfelter
Chip Clouse
Lindsay Cochran
Phil Cochran
Marcus Cole

Bob Coleman
John Coleman
Cherie Collins
Amanda Colombo
Tamara Colten
Amy Comfort
A. Marc
   Commandatore
Michael Conner
Christopher Cook
Caren Cooper
John Cornett
Amy Coulthard
Michele Counsell
Allison Cowie
Christina Craig
Gary Cress
Richard Crist
Brian Critcher
Robert R. Cross
Donna J.P. Crossman
Carol Crump
Yves Cuerrier
Todd Culver
Claire Currie
Tim A. Cwalinski
Daniel D. Dahl
Katherine A.
   Dantzler
Chris Dassler
Carla Dattilio
Scott Davies
Alani Davis
Brian Davis
Douglas S. Davis
Jeff Davis
Robert Davis
Shane Davis
Fenton Day
John Dean
Diane DeBiase
Jeffrey deCosta
Ben Deeble
Dinah J. Demers
Francis Demmerle
Martha Desmond
Beth Dickervitz
Joe DiDonato

Ian Dillner
Rick DiMaio
Jeff Dingle
Dana
   Doherty-Dahl

Kathy Bennett

Melissa Owen at Timpie Springs, Utah, site, 1984.

Debranne
   Dominguez
Alice Doolittle
Carol J. Dorff
Diane Dorman
Nancy A. Dorsey
Harlan Doty
Barbara Douglas
Carla J. Dove
Randy Downer
Wendy Heather
   Downs
Matt Drennan
Daniel E. Driscoll
Paul DuBowy
Peter Duley
Patrick Durham
Kelly Durkin
Scott Durkin
S. Duty
Anthony
   D'Alessandro
Gano Earl
Philippa W. Eckhardt
Kevin Eddings

Jim Edwards
Jeff Ehman
Mark Elder
Wilfred Emonts
Anne Enderson
Betty Enderson
Ritt Enderson
Mark Ensor
Brent Erdmann
Andrea L. Erichsen-
   Commandatore
Denise Erickson
Matt Erickson
Jeana Ernst
Janie Erxleber
John Fackenthal
Mark Fanning
Jerry C. Farley
Terry Farley
Brian D. Farrell
Shawn Farry
Jim Favreau
Rebecca Felknor
Jennifer Ferenstein
Holly Ferguson
Tammy Ferreira
Cindy Field
Christopher E. Filardi
Cheryl Fimbel
Chad Fisher

James Fisher
Eleanor Fitzgerald
Terry Flaherty
Craig J. Flatten
Andrew Fleckner
Salvatore Foglio
Shelby M. Fonley
Judith Ford
Nathaniel D. Foster
Laura Frasch
Mark Freeman
Tim Freeman
Edward Freienmuth
Scott Fretz
Rodney Friday
Kathy Fritts
Mark Fuller
Kathleen Fulmer
Hans Gabler
Rob Galbraith
Evelyn C. Gallagher
Sean P. Gallagher
John D. Gallup
Christopher S.
   Garber
Lori Garbus
James P. Garreau
Bill Garrett
Jennifer D. Garrett
Bret Gaussoin
James Gaynor
Bobbi Geise
Matthew Georgeff
Christine Gettys
Christopher
   Ghicadus
John Gilardi
Martin Gilroy
Lauren Gilson
Steve Godsil
Karen Gonzalez
Andrew G.
   Goodband
Chad Goodchild
Cecilia Goodrich
Greg Gordon
Annette Gosnell
Brandon Grabensk

The Peregrine Fund Hack Site Attendants and Field Personnel (continued)

Jenny Grant
Tom Grant
Brandon Grebence
Jim Greene
Terrence Greene
Gregory Greer
Letitia Grenier
Sara Griffen
Mike Griffith
Corey M. Grinnell
Roman Grochowski
Jane Gull
Scott Gustin
Joan Hagar
Donald Hagen
Charlene Hahn
Susan Hahn
Arthur Haines
Liz Hall
Steve Hall
Terry Hall
Alice Hallaran
Terry Hallaran
Bill Halpin
Margy Halpin
John R. Halsey
William Halstead

Ann Henry
Nancy Herrick
Brent Hetzler
Carey Hill
Dave Hill
Gene Hill
Todd Hillaker
Alan Hinde
Peggy Hines
Danile Hodges
Bob Hollister
Jon Holst
Christina Holstrom
Steven Holt
Melinda J. Hooker
Mary Beth Hoover
William D. House
R. Edgar Howard
Bill Howe
Tara Hridel
Richard Hughes
Brian Humphreys
Frances A. Hunt
Kathleen Hunt
Dave Huntimer
Mike Hurley
Charles Hutchins

Sue Tredennick at the Sheep Mountain site in Rocky Mountain National Park. Bill Rierden was her co-attendant.

Scott Hammond
Lisa Kern Hannon
John Hard
Bert Harding
Peter M. Hark
David Harlow
Al Harmata
Steve Harmon
Charles Harrington
Cathy W. Harris
Regina Harris
Peter Harrity
Eric Harrold
Robert M. Harshbarger
Patricia Hartt
Michael W. Hauser
Dayna Hawes
Shawn Hawks
Charlene Hawn-Shirrel
Betty Hayes
Daniel J. Hayes
Cheryl Hazelton
Priscilla Hearst
Leon Hecht
Hillary Hedges
Becky Hegmann

Michael Ingraldi
Norman B. Jaffee
Cathy Purchis-Jeffries
Frank Jeffries
Jeff Jeffries
A. Felton Jenkins
J. Peter Jenny
Joe Jensen
Barbara Johnson
Doug Johnson
Lyn Johnson
Minette Johnson
Steve Johnson
Veronica Johnson
Elizabeth O. Jones
John Jones
Katie Jones
Michael Hunt Jones
Monica R. Juhasz
Robin Jung
Lydia Kading
Jim Kaiser
Kathryn Kavanagh
Chris Kayser
Gloria N. Kearly-Kraemer
Sean Keenan

Barry Keister
Kent Keller
Quentin Kelley
Brian S. Kenney
Stuart D. Kent
Brad Kerstetter
Lisa Kerwin
Constance Kick
Jonel Kiesau
Charles Kilpatrick
Brian Minsey
Christopher S. King
Justin T. King
Manu Kingston
Debby Kirk
Brandon Kisner
Ann Klein
Bert Klein
Fred Klein
Lisa K. Klein
Glenn Klingler
Richard L. Knight
Aaron Knudson
Dale Kohlmoos
Jay Kolbe
Brian Koldyke
Mary Beth Kolozsvary
Dan Konkel
Mark Kopeny
Craig Koppie
Earl Kraay
Ed Kraay
Dale A. Kraemer
Diane Krahe
Huong Kuang-Ying
Edward Kucskar
Alis Gardner Kuhn
Kathy Kyle
Lisa LaFranco
William Lane
Susan Lansdel
Blair Larsen
Brett Larson
Paul LaStayo
Brian C. Latta
Jack Lauer
Robin Lawford
Aimee Lawrence
Doug Lawrence
Lori Laws
Sean Lawson
David Ledig
Julie Ledig
Julie Lee
Kevin Leftwich
Rom Leidner
Leslie Leo
Chris Lepisto
Ann F. Lettenberger
Ed Levine
Dana Levno
Jennifer Levy
David Licht
Harold Lindebo
Gail Lindeboluft
Bruce C. Lindsay
Kristi Link
Peter H. Liotta
Hank Lipps
Joan F. Lokker

Karin Looney
Sebastion Lousada
Garrett Lowe
John Luft
Anne Lund
M. Tryg Lunn
Maureen Lynch
Sarah Lynch
Maureen Lynce
Arabella Lyon
Trish Lysten
Amy M. Melendy
Jim MacDougall
Herbert MacMurphy
Lisa Machowski
Kelly M. Mackey
Dana Madsen
Tom Maechtle
Molly E. Malecek
Steve Malone
Donald Maloney
Thomas Maly
Carol Manganaro
Dru Marshal
Everett Marshall
Steven Marshall
William Marshall
Andrew Martin
Nancy Martin
Amy M. Martinez
Stephanie Matlock-Cooley
Margaret Elaine Mattox
Michael Matzko
Mike Mauer
John Mayer
Aspen Mayers
Sherry McAllister
Peter McBride
Lisa D. McCarthy
Brad McClain
Kathy McCracken
David McCullough
Harold McDaniel
Patrick McDaniel
Patty McDonell
Thomas McDonough
Bruce McElroy
Shiela K. McGowan
Mike McGrady
Liam McGranaghan
Carol McIntyre
Donald E. McIvor
Larry McMullen
Russell McMurray
Bob Meese
Jeffrey Mellman
Lisa Mellott
Ron Mellott
Russell Melton
Jim Menakis
Einar Mencl
Heinz Meng
Mary Merges
Grant Merrill
Alison Meyer
Penny Meyers
Jeremy Michaelson

James E. Milby
Gerald J. Millard
Julie Miller
Mike Milligan
Kevin J. Misiak
Donna Mitchell
Kevin Mitchell
Glen Mittelhauser
Christine Moen
Medhat Mohamed
Scott M. Monk
J. Montejo
Betty Moore
Kirsten V. Moore
Sean Morgan
John Morlock
Mindy Morlock
Larry Morrisette
Craig Morrison
Douglas Morrow
Clifford A. Moser
Gale Motter
Karl Mueller
Julie Mulholland
Mike Mulligan
Christopher T. Munch
Edward M. Muniak
Nicole Munkwitz
Chris Murphy
Brian Mutch
Penny Myers

Neal D. Niemuth
Egil Nilsson III
Michael Nix
Ernest Noel
Susan Noh
Barbara North
David North
Ted Norton
Greg Nottingham
Dan O'Brien
Kathleen O'Brien
Maureen O'Mara
Harry Oakes
Lindsay Oaks
Jack Oar
Andrew Okey
David Olson
Jane Olson
Beverly Oney
Jill Oppenheim
Sophie Osborn
Jeffrey C. Owen
Melissa Owen
Pat Oxsheer
Sara J. Pace
Kurt Papenfus
Margaret Parker
Megan Parker
Paul Parker
Kris Parrish
Kathleen Patnode
Jon Patz

Steve Potts
Nick Pouder
Robert Powell
Marion Pratt
Amy L. Price
Daniel Priser
Dave Priser
Jennifer Pultz
Cathy Purchis
Nayaret Quezada
Peter Quinn
Andy Radtke
Michael Raffaeli
Donna Rainboth
Robin Rand
Jamie Rappaport
Timothy J. Reese
Ruth Regier
Amy Reid
John Reilly
Dan Reitter
Jessica Reiss
Rosalind Renfrew
Carla Reynolds
Lou Reynolds
Amrit Rich
Jeffrey Rich
Russel Rickard
Cynthia Riegel
Bill Rierden
Amparo Rifa
Jim Rimsza

Mark Rohden
Daniel J. Rohlf
Nancy L. Rollins
Bill Roody
Donata Roome
Chuck Rosenburg
Mary Lou Rowland
Jon Rubright
Robin Rucker
Jeff Rucks
Ruth Rudner
Gary G. Ruhser
Jean C. Ruhser
Carolyn Ruos
Irene M. Rusnak
Jeffrey R. Sabol
Carl Safina
Scott Sagor
James E. Sailer
Gon Sanchez
Gregory Sanders
Julie Sanger
Anthony J. Savereno
Melissa K. Sayler
Gavin Schaberg
Becca Schad
Stephanie Schaeffer
Julie Schafer
Renee Schaufler
Karen Schik
John Schmertzler
Andrew Schmidt
Joel Schmutz
Matthew G. Schnurr
Ron Scholl
Tony Schreck
Christopher Schultz
Kate Schumacher
Mary Schwartz
Robert Schweager
Wendy P. Schweizer
Ben Scofield
John G. Scott
Hugo Searle
James Seegar
Nancy Segal
Kathleen Selig
John Senior
Nancy Sergeant-Abbate
David Sexton
Julie Shaffer
Tom Shanahan
Carol Shaw
Blair Shean
Mary Lou Shean
John Ann Shearer
Karen Shelley
Todd Shepard
David Sherman
Pam Shiao
J. Mark Shields
Jodi Shippee
Robert L. Shumate
Karen E. Simmons
Louise Skonier
Lowell Sliger
Dan Smiley
Christine Smith
Julie Linn R. Smith
Leslie Smith

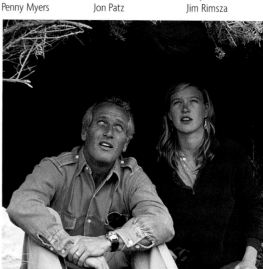

Attendant Nell Newman (right) observes a site with her father, Paul Newman.

Curt Mykut
Christopher A. Nadareski
Kelly Nauman
David Nauman
Sangita Nayak
Graham Neale
Andrew Neeb
Elisabeth Neely
Neal Neimuth
Ann Nelson
David Nelson
Laurie Ness
Karan Newman
Nell Newman
Rossi Newton
Amy Nicholas

Joanne Paul
Linda Pederson
Richard Peiffer
Brian Pendleton
William L. Penning
Gwyn Peterdi
Amy Peterson
Wendy Peterson
Melody Phillips
Anna Pidgeon
Kathy Pierce
Sean Pierce
Joe Pinto
Patricia Platt
Steve Platt
Kurt Popenfuse
Sara Possehl

Dale Rinkel
Betty Rist
Tom "Farley" Rivest
Martha Robbins
Mark Robert
Kevin S. Roberts
Randy Roberts
Jane Robinson
Penny Rodefer
Jon Rodine
Don Rodkey
Devin Roe
Andy Rogers
Melissa Rogers
Ralph Rogers
Scott Rogers
Timothy Rogers

The Peregrine Fund
Hack Site Attendants and
Field Personnel (continued)

Roger Smith
Scott Smith
Steve Smith
Jamelle Peregrine
 Smylie
Cherie Rife Smylie
Tom Smylie
Eleanor Lynette
 Snell
Gerald Snodgrass
Brad Snyder
Julie Songer
Kelly Sorenson
Laurie Sorenson
Robin Spahr
Beth Spanjian
Mark Spencer
Kyle Spendiff
Betsy Spettigue
Jim Spohn
Sandy Spon
Elizabeth
 Springborn
Michael St.
 Germain
Will Staats
Mark Stafford
Terri Stahl
Virginia Stahl
Airica Staley
Jim Stapelton
Heather Staszheim
Russ Stauff
John R. Stebbins
Jerry Steketee
Patricia Stepanek
David H. Stephens

Ted Swem
Ann Van Sweringen
Diane Taddiken
Steve Tanguay
D. Bryant Tarr
Christopher Taylor
Daniel Taylor
Jeannie Taylor
Lynn Taylor
Wes Taylor
C. Tejeda
Charles P. Terry
John Testa
Matt Testa
Glen Thompson
Dean Thompson
Heather Thompson
Jeffrey L.
 Thompson
Jay S.W.
 Tischendorf
John Tobin
Suzanne Tomassi
Mark Tomaszewski
Chet Tomlinson
Forest Tomlinson
John Townsend
Randy R. Townsend
Sue Tredennick
Thomas Trenchard
Shelley Gwen Trott
John Townsend
 Tubbs, Jr.
David H. Turner
Robert Glenn
 Turner
John Tyler

Ron Walker
Wade Walker
W. Patton Walkins
Kelly M. Wallace
Michael Walls
Kimi Walsh
Kristen E. Walther
Lon Waltman
Scott Ward
David Warner
Jason Watkins
Gail Watts
Rick Watts
Andrew J. Weaver
Joe Weber
Shana Weber
Eric Wegner
Margot Wegner
Evelyn H.
 Weinstein
E. Quentin Welch
Karen West
Mark C. West
Susan K. West
William Wham
Alden Whitaker
Alice Whitelaw
Jennifer June
 Whitford
Susan Whittemore
Kenneth Wiersema
Cheryl Wiescamp
Adelheid Wiese
Catherine
 Wightman
Scott Wilbur
Eric Wilcox
Seth Wiley
Hal Williams
James J. Williams
James Willmarth
Lisa Wilson
Michael Wilson
Michael Allen
 Wilson
Tim Wilson
Eric Winicov
Marge Winski
Mark Witmer
Keith Wittenhagen
Linda Woistman
Susan Wolfe
Kent Woodruff
Chris Woods
Laura F. Woods
Marie Worley-Myers
Michael F. Wright
Rob Wright
Jim Wyma
John J. Ybarra
Dale Yerger
Jill Yetman
Robert M. Young
Stephan Paul Young
David L. Yow
Betsy Zeigler
David Zucker

Ritt Enderson with attendants Forest
Tomlinson and Aspen Mayers in 1987 at the
Phillips Canyon hack site trailhead in Bridger-
Teton National Forest, Wyoming.

Glenn R. Stewart
Laura Stewart
Ruth Stewart
Charles Stock
Dorrey Stoley
Barbara Stone
Kristen Stram
Stefania
 Strzalkowska
Michele E. Studer
Andy Stump
William C. Sugg
Jay Sumner
Tobias Swank
Stacey Swearingen

William Wat Tyler
Theresa Ulm
Craig Underwood
Caroline Ungs
Randy Ury
Patrick Uhtoff
Sandra Vana
Bruce VanderLee
Laurie
 VanSteewalker
Eleta Vaughan
Carl Veilleux
David Vesely
Sandy Vissman
K.C. Walker

Midwestern Recovery Program
Hack Site Attendants and Field Personnel

Natalie Ames
Ed Anderson
Robert Anderson
Theresa Anderson
Ryan Andrews
Steve Aqualini
Eric Arnold
Steve Atherton
Brian Ausloos
Bill Balda
Linda Barbaris
Rosanne Barile
Dan Bartley
Lee Bass
Sally Baumgardner
Jim Bean
Dan Belknap
David Bernier
Irene Berry
Jeanette Bettinger
Laurie Birk
Gerette Bleam
Barbara Bloom
Diane Bond
Bill Bowerman
Bonnie Box Top
David Brinkman
Steven Brockway
Brett Brunken
William Brunner
Craig Bublitz
Gail Buhl (Johnson)
Eileen Bunker
Donna Burdick
Laura Burford
Vicki Byre
Jodeane Cancilla
Kay Carlus
Ellen Carpenter
Tony Childs
Jennifer Ciriacks
Pamela Claar
Dina Clark
Hal Cohen
John Coleman
Phillip Collura
Glen Conrad
Dave Conrads
David Conrads
Mike Cooke
Walter Crawford
Janet Creamer
Dorothy
 Cunningham
DeeCee Darrow
Simon Davies
Elna Davis
Andrew Day
Tom Deckert
Colin Deihl
Mary Derr
John Dinan
Dan Dinelli
Laurie Dinelli
John Dingley
Tom Doan
Brian Doherty
Roarke Donnelly

Peregrines have been successfully hacked from
power plant smokestacks in the Midwest.

Greg Septon

Didge Donovan
Terry Donovan
Laura Donson
Carol Dorff
Stephanie Dubs
Jim Duffy
Richard Dunn
Shelly Dunn
Dave Duvernell
Bruce Ehresman
Leanne Eis
Don Eisenmenger
Donna Eisenmenger
Reid Erickson
Jim Evans
Lisa Evans
Randi Faust
Sandy Fejt
Brad Fisher
Cheryl Fisher
Rhan Flatin
Mark Floersch
Mike Gabriel
Sue Galatowitsch
Antonella Gianni
Charlene Gieck
Matt Gies
Pat Gillet
Lauren Gilson
Kimberly Goffin
Vivian Grant

Melissa Grover
Debbi Gunther
Jim Haack
Joan Hagar
Cis Hager
Rich Hamilton
Jim Hansen
Robin Harding
Brian Hardiman
Daniel Hazlett
Mary Hennen
Ginny Herbst
Andy Hershner
Bob Hess
John Heusinkveld
Linda Hill
John Hillier
Peggy Hines
Joe Hoffman
Doug Hohman
Roger Holloway
Dan Holm
Jack Holt
Paul Holtzlider
Mary Beth Hoover
 (Garrigan)
Lynne Hubert
Jason Humble
Katherine Hunt
Pandora Hutchinson
Laura Jackson

Carol Johnson
Ross Johnson
Gwyn Jones
Vicky Jones
Russ Kamine
Sandy Kamine
Jim Kaney
Curt Kearly
Margaret Kelly
Brian Kenner
Dave Kester
Tim Keyser
Robert Kirkman
Charles Kirkpatrick
Rose Kirwan
John Kline
Bill Knittel
Jennifer Kolopus
Martha Konidaris
Yvonne Krebs
Donna Kuchapsky
Mike Lampe
Michelle Land
William Lane
Ora Lee
Ricky Lien
Walt Loope
Kathy Lucas
Rich Mallien
Brett Mandernack
Carol Mandernack
Jim Marks
Mary Maule
Jessie McCoy
Chris McCue
Suze McGearhart
John McGuire
Dave McIllrath
Jason McMeen
Jonathan Melk
Marilyn Merkle
Jeff Meshach
John Meyer
Valina Miksel
Cliff Miller
Jeff Moline
Tom Morrell
Jim Mussell
Andrew Neill
Debbie Nichols
Mary Ellen
 Novinger
Randy Nyboer
Mary Fran Oehler
Kieran O'Malley
David Ortiz
Mary Parisi
Leila Parts
Charles Patterson
Bobbi Perkins
Mike Perniciaro
Greg Peterson
Wendy Peterson
Angela Petrasek
Anna Pidgeon
Julie Plummer
Steve Pokorny
Irv Potts

Larkin Powell
Mike Pratt
Bruce Raine
Sara Ranney
Ginger Retz
Bill Riebe
Barb Rogers
Jeremy Rogers
Joe Rogers
Rodney Rovang
Wayne Russ
Melissa Schick
Karen Schik
Pat Schlarbaum
Laurene Schlueter
Mary Ann Schmidt
Sue Schultz
Herb Schultz
Eric Schwaberg
Jenifer Schwartz
Sarah Scott
Greg Septon
Karen Shiltz
Janice Siska
Patricia Skewes
 (Manthey)
Jim Small
Mike Specht
John Spoden
Mark Spreyer
Mary Spreyer
Susan St. Pierre
Christine Stenson
Tim Stephenson
Angela Tate
Dan Taylor
Rebecca Taylor
Mike Tenney
Steven Thompson
Ed Timper
Jerry Toll
Kirt Tomlinson
Bridget Touney
Roger Tucker
Bill Tweedy
Jan Underwood
Terry VandeWalle
Barbara VanHatten
Kristin VanRees
Peter Vaterott
Elaine Vercruyssee
Dave Vesely
Alice Wagner
Kenneth Wagner
Lowell Washburn
Mark Washburn
Andrew Weaver
Libby Wheary
Jeremy Whitted
Tom Wiese
Annie Wendt
Arthur Wheatley
Kristina Wilkes
Jim Wilson
David Yancy
Dana Yaw
Judy Yerkey

257

Santa Cruz Predatory Bird Research Group • Peregrine Release Supervisors

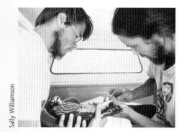

Sally Williamson

Release Coordinators
D. Lee Aulman
Merlyn Felton
Brian C. Latta
Brian J. Walton

Nest and Hack Site Supervisors
D. Lee Aulman
Gary Beeman
Craig Himmelwright
Monte Kirven
Matt Nixon
Glenn Stewart
Clara Weigant

Nest Manipulation Climbers

Victor Apanius
Werner Braun
Laura Brown
Yvon Chouinard
Mike Clark
Peter Croft
Dave Diegleman
Jamey Eddy

James Elias
Merlyn Felton
Scott Francis
Craig Himmelwright
Troy Johnson
Ron Kaulk
Brian C. Latta
Peter Leeming
Geoff Monk

Matt Nixon
Brian Norton
Jeep Pagel
Rob Roy Ramey III
Rick Ridgeway
Mark Robertson
Galen Rowell
Walt Shipley
Mitch Siemens

Jeff Sipple
Kurt Stolzenberg
Carl Thelander
Russell Tucker
Ron Walker
Brian J. Walton
Brian Woodbridge
John Yablonsky
Ken Yager

Santa Cruz Predatory Bird Research Group Field Personnel

Leif Abrell
Gail Ackerman
Elizabeth Adams
Donna Aitkenhead
Roger Aitkenhead
Gwen Alley
Ken Alley
Judy Ambrosini
Bud Anderson
Frank Arian
Jon Ashen
Sheree Aulman
Greg Austin
Bob Baker
BLM Personnel
J.A. Zak Ball
Branden Barber
Chris Barber
Larry Barnes
Kirk Bates
Matt Baxter
Cynthia Beck
Paula Becker
Doug Bell
Steve Benner
Carrie Bennet
Debbie Jo Bird

George Carpenter
Michael Charnofsky
Laura Cholodenko
John Cleckeler
David Clendenen
Wayne Coleman
Amanda Colombo
Angie Cone
David Cooke
Michael Coughlin
Kristin Covert
Christy Craig
Kim Cranston
Libby Creelman
Laura Creigton
Deborah Crooks
Kit Crump
Rebecca Cull
Craig Culver
Thom Curdts
Tom Cuthbertson
Peggy Cymerys
Todd Czerwinski
Sabrina Daniel
Bob Davis
Malia Davis

Craig Flatten
Clay Fletcher
David Foote
Holly Freifeld
Winifred Frick
Matt Fry
Joanna Fuentes
Bret Gaussoin
Steve Gellman
Nathaniel Gerhart
Tay Gerstell
Brian Gibson
Alan Giese
James Gilardi
John Gilardi
Marty Gilroy
Richard Glinski
Jerry Granger
Chip Greendale
David Gregoire
Gary Guliasi
Lee Gurreri
Guyere
Tamara Hamilton
Patricia Hampton
Bruce Handel
Wendy Hanson
Craig Harris
Jason Hassrick
Steve Hatchett
Jim Hatchett
Brian Hatfield
Shoshannah Hausmann
Steve Hawks
Shawn Hayes
Steve Henderson
Brent Hetzler
Doug Hirzel
Todd Hoitsma
Matthew Hora
Nathan Horn
Tom Howell
Mary Beth Hull
Tery Hunt
Grainger Hunt
James Hutton
Ted Illenberg
Jason Ingenthron
Clint Irwin
Mark Iverson

Ron Jackman
Chris Janowski
Jim Jennings
Lin Jensen
Linley Jensen
David Jesus
Lynne Jesus

Neil Rose

Kendall Jewett
Carl Johansson
Jan Johnson
Brett Johnson
Laurin Jones
Peregrin Jones
Vicki Jones
Andrea Joyce
Marceya Kagan
Tom Kaiser
Robert Kaler
Lisa Karpinski
Max Kauffman
Staci Kawa-Thompson
Sheila Kee
Ray Kemp
Caroline Kennedy
Ted Kennedy
Jeff Kidd
Chuck Kilpatrick
Jennifer Kranz
Kerry Kriger
Christopher Kuntzsch
Ross Laird
Suzanne Langridge
Nicole Lapuyade
David Lavorando
Dave Ledig

David Lee
Allison Leete
Bill Lehman
Randal Leininger
Colleen Lenihan
Joe Leonard
Marsha Lerner

Tom Leskovjan
Alex Lewis
Janet Linthicum
Don Lipoma
Bill Lockhart
Anna Locks
Dan Loughman
Roy Lowe
Sean Lydon
Martine Lynch
Trish Lysten
Julie Malcolm
John Scott Malvitch
Lucy Marcus
Derek Marino
Theresa Marsh
Tami Martinez-Harris
Jeff Maurer
Laural Mayall
Kevin Mazzocco
Robert Mazurek
Vir McCoy
Bev McIntosh
Rod McMannis
Kim Melody
Eric Meriwether
Robert Mesta
Linda Miller

Lisa Miller
Jason Minton
Betty Moore
David Moore
Stan Moore
Kevin Mozocco
Mathew Mullin
Bill Murphy
NPS Personnel
Nancy Nahstoll
Nancy Naslund
Gail Naylor
Cliff Neighbors
John Neilsen
Mari Newman
Bill Niehus
David Nixon
Jennifer Noone
Meighan O'Brien
Victoria O'Brien
Tina Odenbaugh
Alisa Ottman
Diane Patracuola
Mark Pavelka
Dale Payne
Johathan Pelky
Alexis Penn
Susan Perin
Elissa Pfost
Marshal Pickett
Becky Pierce
Sean Plunket
Manel Pomarol
Anne Marrie Preatzel

Penny Principe
Greg Rawlings
Arlo Reeves
Colleen Reichmuth
Sue Rennels
Howard Rhinehart
John Richardson
John Ringwald
Karen Jo Rippens
John Roach
Paul Roush
Laurel Sanborn
Dewey Savell
John Schmitt
Monty Schmitt
Steve Schubert
Wende Schwake
John Sciacca
Tom Scott
Claire Seminara
Dan Shepherd
Katie Siegler
Randolph Skrovan
Marvin Sleeper
Bill Slye
Gary Smith
Ashley Smith
Dawn Smith
Rachel Smolker
Scott Sokol
Steve Spangle
Rick Spaulding
Doug Stanat
Anthony Steenkamp

Rob Stein
Doug Stinson
David Stoner
Russell Stot
Chuck Striplen
Judy Sullivan
Sam Sumida
Jason Sutter
Ted Swem
Kent Swick
Kelly Taggert
Glen Tarr
Greg Tatarian
Trish Tatarian
Don Terry
Dean Thompson
Glenn Thompson
Lynn Thorensen
Mike Thorndike
Russell Thorstrom
Nick Todd
Tyson
USFS Personnel
Alistair Usher
Ellen Van Gelder
Dan Varland
Cathie Vouchilas
Jenny Waddel
Robin Warne Weathers
Sarah Weber
Jennifer Weeks
Adam Wells
Geoff Wells
Clive West
Clara Weygandt
Charlotte Wheeler
Amy Whitesides
Mike Whitsel
Andre Willie
David Willoughby
Heather Wilson
Randy Wilson
Jennifer Wiswell
Blair Wolf
Bill Wood
Paul Young
Ramona Zeno
Joe Zimmerman

SCPBRG file photo

Anastasia Bizieff
John Blanchard
Pete Bloom
Gary Boberg
Kevin Brennan
Tim Brewton
Christy Bricknell
Dan Brimm
Dorothy Brown
Gregory Brown
Dorothy Brownold
Bob Budesa
Stephanie Burns
Karen Burnson
Don Cameron
Lisa Carpenski

Sonya Daw
Tye de Pena
Cristina de Sobrino
Mike Deacon
Ray Deaconess
Robert DeCandido
Gordon Dicus
Joe DiDonato
Elizabeth Donahue
Kimo Dressendorfer
Cheryl Ducummon
Sean Duggan
John Edmisten
Jennifer Estep
Bob Fiero

Kevin Brennan

Canadian Recovery Program Hack Site Attendants and Field Personnel

Alberta

Jim Allen
Ursula Banasch
Julie Bauer
Ron Bjorge
Steve Brechtel
Andrew Burnett
Carmen Calihoo
Rob Corrigan
Gordon Court
Gary Erickson
Ken Froggat
John Dunlop
Coral Grove
Mike Grue
Shauna
   Gudmundson
Jody Joachim
Jason Kerr
Todd Lang
Darren Linn
Ann Lukey
Wayne Nelson
Ray Nickel
Pat Paul
Jim Potter
Petra Rowell
Brad Tomm
Bruce Treichel
Dragomir Vujnovic
Francine
   Wieliczko
Alan Wisely

Survey crew near Rankin Inlet, N.W.T.

Manitoba

George Archibald
Jean Bancroft
Bradley Barker
Gib Bell
Robert Berger
Elizabeth Blatz-
   Harvey
Andrew Bochenek
Francois Bouchart
Maureen Bouchart
Don Campbell
Greg Campbell
Daniel Chranowski
Barbara Christie
Mike Cobus
Craig Cooper
Victor Cotton
Ellen Cramm
Graham Crawshaw
Leah Deforest
Delta Winnipeg
   Hotel Staff
Ken De Smet
Andy Didiuk
Lynn Dooley
James Duncan
Patsy (Lane) Duncan
T.E. Eatons
   Company Staff
Patti Ewashko
James Feist
Bruce Fiske
Fort Osborne
   Complex Staff

Ken Gardner
Robert Garson
Nancy Gehlen
Greg Geniall
Megan Gillespie
Gimli High School
   Environmental
   Council
Joel Gosselin
Gord Graham
Ted Grewe
Jaynie Jackson
Kate Johnson
Duane Johnston
Robert E. Jones
Skip Keeley
Judy Kienas
Ed Klemm
William Koonz
Anita (Steeg)
   Kovacs
Barbara Haffner
David Hatch
Elizabeth Haug
Karl Himmer
George Holland
Pat Lennox

Rich Leonard
Sandi Levandoski
Tracy Maconachie
Manitoba
   Conservation
   Operations
   Branch Staff
Manitoba
   Conservation
   Regional Staff
Manitoba
   Conservation
   Wildlife &
   Ecosystem
   Protection
   Branch Staff
Manitoba
   Government
   Services
Janice Martin
Kristi Mays
Janis McCarthy
Glenda McGarty
Gordon McKee
Blair McMahon
Joe Mezibrowski
Ted Muir
Jacques Nadon
Dan Needles
Wayne Neily
Robert W. Nero
Ken Nolan
Jim & Helen Owen
Joanne Parsons
Ellen Patterson
Jeff Plouff
Radisson Hotel
   Winnipeg Staff
Sheri Ramsey
Brian Ratcliff
Orville Richard
Larry Riddell
Dave Roberts
John Romanec
Mark Segstro
Jason Shepherd
Merlin Shoesmith
Gerry Sliworsky
Ulrike (Schneider)
   Sliworsky
Dana Slusar
Dan Soprovich
Horst Spill
Richard Stardom
Doug Storey
Barbara Svenson
Anthony
   Szumigalski
Cheryl Talbot
Peter Taylor
Robert Taylor
Russ Tkachuk
United Grain
   Growers Staff
University of
   Manitoba Staff
Robert & Nancy
   Wheeldon
Barbara
   Wojnarewicz

New Brunswick

Charles Beaton
Yves Bosse
Denis Comeau
Dorice Caissie
C . Charlton
Brad Comeau
Francois Granger
Larry Harbidge
Brian Harvey
Shawn Hicks
Christina Langton
Greg Marks
Michel Martin
Laurence
   McGillivary
Micheal McQuarrie
George Mercer
Ken Myers
Allan Nicol
Derek Quann
Gordon Shepard
Sedgwick Sinclair
K. Stephenson
Michael Sullivan
Eugene Taylor
Rob Walker
Harold Weeks
Marie Eve Wen
Duane West
William Whitman
Stephen Woodley

Nova Scotia

Mike Boudreau
Al Foster
E. Hudgins
Peter MacDonald
Colin MacKinnon
Erich Muntz
Reg Newell
Cynthia Pekarik
Stephanie Peppard
Craig Smith
Colman Spence
William Whitman

Phil Trefry checks incubating Peregrine eggs.

Ontario

Ted Armstrong
Volodko Barkowski
Kevin Beange
Gary Belleau
Jeff Black
Shawn Bolton
Dan Brosemar
Kathy Brosemar
Wendy Brown
Matt Ceolin
Marie Claude
Ed Czerwinski

Heather Danielson
Michael Dube
Gar Evans
Iva Evans
Jim Evans
Kim Fewchuck
Erwin Goertz
Frank Goodall
Barb Graham
Ken Harman
Rosemary Hartley
Matthew Hebb
Scott Herriman
Jack Hotson
Gail Jackson
Jillian Johns
Meredith Johnson
Michelle Johnson
Kathy Jones
Scott Jones
Andrea Kinsley
Harold Kish
Bob Knudsen
Downey LeBar
Tim Lineham
Scott Longridge
Janis Luck
Ken McIlwrick
Maureen McIlwrick
Steve McRae
Dennis Monaghan
Ken Mosley
Natasha Miflin
Jim Miller
Brad Pine
Kelly Piper
Neil Ray
Warren Robertson
Rusty Rustenburg
Lisa Shaver
Diane Slye
Cam Snell
Steve Strand
Rob Swainson
Marlene Wandel
Kathy Wilkinson
Laura Wyper
Kelly Withers
David Workman
Jennifer Wyma

Québec

Gary Acheson
Agents de
   Conservation de
   la faune
John Baird
Louis Belzile
David Bird
François Bélanger
Guy Bergeron
Paul Bisaillon
Bruno Blais
Suzanne Blais
Daniel Bolduc
Chris Brown
Réjeanne Camiran
Centre éducatif les
   Palissades
Denis Comeau
Jean-Marc
   Coulombe
Charles Dauphiné
Bruce M. Di Labio
Marlène Dionne
Michel Drew
Peter Dunn
David Duval
Denis Faucher
Jean-Pierre Fillion
Fernand Fiset
Jim Foley
Pierre Gagnon
Robert Galbraith
Jean Giroux
Marie Giroux
Michel Giroux
Anne Harfenist
Serge Labonté
Pierre Laporte
Mario Laverdière
Pierre-Jules Lavigne
Fabienne Lavoie
Pierre Lavoie
Jean-Guy Lefebvre
Michel Lepage
Vincent Létourneau
Eva Mc Crossin
Raymond McNicoll
Doug McRae
Lucie Métras
Pierre Morency
Laura Muldoon
Réginald Ouellet
P. Peyron
Christian Pinard
Iola Price
Raymond
   Quenneville
Austin Reed
Ian Ritchie
Pierre St-Hilaire
Daniel St-Pierre
Steve Tinker
Peter Tucker
Jacqueline Vincent
Stephen Woodley

Saskatchewan

Doug Bush
Tom Donald
Dale Guthormsen
Barb Hanbidge
John Hanbidge
Betsy Haug
Ken Holliday
Lynn Oliphant
Hugh Saunders
W.J. Patrick
   Thompson
Bob Rafuse
Stacy Tessaro
Jon Triffo

Chapter 15

The Endangered Species Act, the U.S. Fish and Wildlife Service, and Peregrine Falcon Restoration

William Burnham and Tom J. Cade

The effort to restore the Peregrine Falcon was well underway before President Richard Nixon announced to the nation

on 8 February 1972 that current law did not provide the necessary tools to save vanishing species. He was referring to the Endangered Species Preservation Act of 1966 and the amended version passed in 1969. Congress responded, and on 28 December 1973 Nixon signed into law the present-day Endangered Species Act (ESA). In August 1999, with the delisting of the Peregrine Falcon and its removal from the "protection" of the ESA, Secretary of the Interior Bruce Babbitt credited the ESA as the primary reason for the successful restoration. How did the ESA and its implementing agency for wildlife and plants, the U.S. Fish and Wildlife Service (FWS), affect this, certainly the largest and probably the most successful species restoration program ever accomplished?

Protection by ESA

During the battle over the snail darter and the Tellico Dam project, the U.S. Supreme Court interpreted the intent of Congress and the President in passing the ESA to mean that "endangered species were to be afforded the highest of priorities...and that the plain intent of Congress in enacting this legislation was to halt and reverse the trend toward species extinction, whatever the cost." (*TVA v. Hill*, 437 U.S. 174, 184, 1978). Based on this interpretation, and considered broadly, anything or anyone that threatens a population or even an individual of a species listed as endangered is in violation of the law. The ESA, therefore, provides **protection** not only for the individual, population, or entire species or subspecies but also its habitat. Loss or degradation of habitat can perpetuate and even hasten the "trend toward species extinction."

Section 4 of the ESA allows FWS to designate "critical habitat" for endangered species. Environmental activists often try to use this provision to force legal protection of habitat per se rather than from concern to recover a particular species. The

◀ **Figure 15.1** Painting by George Lodge from the collection of Kent Carnie. Reproduction by kind permission of Copyright holder Tryon Gallery.

Figure 15.2 Bill Burnham ▶ accepts a congratulatory gift for The Peregrine Fund from Jamie Rappaport Clark, U.S. Fish and Wildlife Service director at the time of Peregrine delisting proposal announcement.

Spotted Owl controversy is an example of over-emphasizing habitat protection or preservation to benefit a listed species, in that case for a species only listed as threatened under the ESA after FWS had been forced by court action to list it. By protecting habitat in this way there is only disincentive for species recovery, because the legal protection of the habitat remains in effect only as long as the species is listed. As long as natural habitats and ecosystems cannot be protected for their own intrinsic value, most endangered species can be expected to remain listed indefinitely (Doremus and Pagel 2001).

Protection provided the Peregrine under the ESA added little, if any, additional conservation benefit for the species. The ESA had no influence on protecting the Peregrine from its primary threat and reason for decline, use of DDT, or in ending its use. Use of DDT was legally prohibited in Canada in 1969 and in the United States in 1972. Under the Migratory Bird Treaty amendments of 1972 the Peregrine was provided protection from human persecution; by that time, however, shooting, egg-collecting, or taking of individual falcons had no measurable effect on Peregrine populations. Designation of critical habitat for Peregrines was unnecessary as the Peregrine is amazingly adaptable and opportunistic, breeding and wintering in a variety of habitats, including cities. "Protection" under the ESA was unnecessary and provided no positive benefit for Peregrine restoration. In fact, it may have worked to the contrary because of the onerous permitting system imposed to do work with the species and the excessive involvement of law enforcement.

In all the restoration activities across the length and breadth of our nation, involving many diverse interests that came together for the common purpose of restoring the Peregrine Falcon, we never had a major conflict that could not be resolved by using common sense, goodwill, and reasonable approaches. The Peregrine never became involved in a formal jeopardy consultation, or any disruptive ESA-related conflicts that emerged in later years for other species. There were no lawyers, no court injunctions. Yes, there were problems, from high-level political decisions to the more mundane, such as highway construction and blasting near nests, timber cutting, bridge and building maintenance, rock climbing on nesting cliffs, waterfowl hunting around refuges where Peregrines nest, deliberate shooting of falcons at pigeon lofts, and even problems with Peregrines killing other endangered birds. But in all cases these real-world problems were solved at the local level in the field through informal consultations and agreements among the concerned parties.

Use of Nonindigenous Falcons for Restoration

The first big problem involving interpretation of the ESA and Peregrine recovery had to do with the definition of "species"—not the biological definition but the legal definition in the Act: "The term 'species' includes any subspecies . . . and any distinct population segment of any species of vertebrate fish or wildlife which interbreeds when mature." By this definition a subspecies or any "distinct population segment" of a species can be declared threatened or endangered independently of the species as a whole. In North America both the *tundrius* and *anatum* subspecies of Peregrine were listed as endangered, but the *pealei* subspecies was not, because its populations in the Pacific Northwest maritime regions were determined not to be threatened by pesticides or other factors, although locally on Langara Island, British Columbia, the population declined by more than 50%.

When reintroduction and translocation began to receive serious consideration as techniques for restoring endangered species, both biological and legal questions arose as to the suitability of various stocks for release in the range of an endangered species, subspecies, or population. Should only stocks of indigenous origin be used to reinforce depleted populations? In the case of reintroduction into a totally vacated range, how genetically similar to the original animals should the reintroduced ones be? Would it be legal to use federal funds for endangered species to release animals from a nonendangered source population into the range of an endangered species?

The last question was first raised by a former chief of the U.S. Forest Service (USFS) in regard to a proposed release of nonendangered Canadian wolves into the range of endangered wolves in the Upper Great Lakes region of the United States (he was hoping to avoid involvement in wolf releases). We soon realized we would face the same kinds of questions in regard to recovery of Peregrines in the eastern United States. By the late 1960s only a single known pair of Peregrines remained (in southern Quebec) in the former range east of the Rocky Mountains and south of the boreal forests, and no eastern *anatum* Peregrines remained in captivity. Thus, any Peregrines released back into that region would have to come from non-native stocks regardless of their subspecific designation.

Following a preliminary consideration of this problem by representatives of the International Association of Fish and Game Commissioners (as it was then known), National Audubon Society (NAS), and The Peregrine Fund at the North American Wildlife Conference in Washington, D.C., in 1969, Roland Clement of NAS convened a meeting in Greenwich, Connecticut, in February 1974 to address these issues more formally in an attempt to reach agreement on some ground rules for eastern Peregrine recovery. By that time the first experimental hacking of captive-bred Pere-

grines was being planned for that spring at New Paltz, New York, under Heinz Meng's supervision.

Attending the meeting were representatives from FWS, other governmental agencies, and conservation organizations, several prominent raptor biologists, and two biologists from the Massachusetts Audubon Society, William Drury and Ian Nisbet, who played an important role in formulating a biological rationale for the plan finally adopted. One possibility was to use stock as genetically similar as possible to the former eastern "Rock Peregrines"—presumably from still extant populations of the *anatum* subspecies; another was to use the closest ecological counterparts from the temperate regions of Europe. Unfortunately, by the early 1970s all those populations of Peregrines were highly endangered, and

▲ **Figure 15.3** Dignitaries abounded at the press conference announcing the release of Peregrines in New York City in 1981. Included in the photo are Mayor Ed Koch, Secretary of the Interior James Watt, President of World Wildlife Fund Russell Train, and others.

▲ **Figure 15.4** An hours-old chick rests next to its soon-to-hatch sibling.

263

... *natural selection would have an array of genotypes from which to pick those individuals best adapted to the current conditions of the eastern environment.*

obtaining permits for a sufficient number of breeding pairs would not be possible. In the end, the group recommended that the eastern recovery program be based on introduction of the most promising, ecologically preadapted stock available regardless of geographic origin (Clement 1974). Furthermore, Drury (1974) and Nisbet emphasized that the best strategy would be to maximize the genetic variability of stock to be introduced by cross-mating individuals from different geographic origins, so that natural selection would have an array of genotypes from which to pick those individuals best adapted to the current conditions of the eastern environment.

This idea became the cornerstone of our eastern breeding and release program, and we eventually ended up with a mixture of falcons derived from individuals of seven subspecies, from western North America (*anatum*), boreal Canada and Alaska (northern *anatum*), arctic Alaska (*tundrius*), Aleutian and Queen Charlotte Islands (*pealei*), Scotland (*peregrinus*), Spain (*brookei*), Chile (*cassini*), and Australia (*macropus*). The gene pool of the current reintroduced population has alleles from all of these sources.

This strategy was adopted by the then recently appointed Eastern Peregrine Falcon Recovery Team (Rene Bollengier, Jr., leader) and forwarded as a recommendation to the Office of Endangered Species in Washington, D.C. Largely as a result of some discussions with then Assistant Secretary of the Interior Nathaniel Reed, FWS approved the recovery team's recommendation and in a 1976 memorandum stated that the goal for eastern Peregrine recovery was the restoration of an adaptable breeding population. In achieving that goal FWS would rely on the team to select those subspecies that would best contribute to its success, and FWS would support the team's decisions. The memorandum further stated that FWS considered the use of nonendangered, nonindigenous subspecies to be essential for Peregrine restoration in the East and, therefore, the ESA classification of the subspecies chosen would have no bearing on the use of endangered species funds to support the recovery effort.

Complications soon arose. In 1977 President Carter issued an executive order on exotic organisms, restricting federal agencies from introducing foreign organisms into "natural ecosystems" of the United States and encouraging states, local governments, and private citizens to abide by the same restriction. This order had been secretly promoted by a group of organizations that had failed in their attempt to do the same thing by regulation in a forum open to public comment. The

Peregrine Fund received a telegram on 30 June 1977 from the Regional Director of FWS in Boston directing us to stop the further release of exotic subspecies of Peregrines in the eastern United States. About the same time, FWS also issued a memorandum stating that endangered species funds could not be used to support activities involving nonendangered or nonindigenous species unless they were being considered for listing as threatened or endangered, thereby eliminating federal support for the release of *pealei* stock in the East.

If these directives had remained in effect, the number of Peregrines available for release in the East would have been greatly reduced, as by that time many of the falcons were mixtures of two or more subspecies. The eastern Peregrine recovery team entered into a series of negotiations with the head of the Office of Endangered Species, Keith Schreiner, a hard-headed but, in the end, fair-minded person who got caught in a maelstrom of opposing views. More than 20 scientists and professional ornithologists, including the doyen of biosystematics, Professor Ernst Mayr, wrote letters supporting the continuation of the release of non-native and exotic strains of Peregrines in the eastern United States. The issue was featured prominently in the news section of *Science*: "Bird Lovers and Bureaucrats at Loggerheads over Peregrine Falcon" (Wade 1978). Following a memorable meeting in Annapolis, Maryland, with Keith Schreiner, Howard Larsen, the regional director of FWS in Boston, and the recovery team, FWS issued a "Policy Statement on the Propagation and Release of an Eastern Peregrine Falcon Population."

Prepared in 1978 and still in effect, this hard-won policy has three parts:

Part 1—North American Peregrines may be used for the propagation and establishment of an eastern Peregrine Falcon population. This program may be supported with endangered species funds.

Part 2—The Endangered Species Program will, however, support and may fund the propagation and release of Peregrine Falcons from other geographic regions only for specific research purposes. These research projects are subject to approval by FWS director on a case by case basis.

Part 3—This policy is applicable only to Peregrine Falcons in the East and is not intended to be applied to any other species, now or in the future.

The first part made it possible to release *pealei* in addition to *tundrius* and *anatum*. The second part provided a way to justify the continued release of exotic Peregrines in accordance with the

National Audubon Society

NEW YORK, NY 10022 (212) 832-3200 CABLE: NATAUDUBON

International Association
of
Fish and Wildlife Agencies

I.A.F.W.A.

(ORGANIZED JULY 20, 1902)

Mr. Ren...

National Wildlife Federation

1412 16TH ST., N.W., WASHINGTON, D.C. 20036

Mr. Keith M. Sch...
Associate Direct...
Species Progr...
U. S. Fish and W...
Washington, D. C. ...

Dear Mr ...

I am
Feder.
a part
we are

In part

THE UNIVERSITY OF ROCHESTER
DEPARTMENT OF BIOLOGY
ROCHESTER, NEW YORK 14627

SMITHSONIAN INSTITUTION
Washington, D.C. 20560
r° S A.

13 January 1978

The Wilson Ornithological Society

FOUNDED DECEMBER 3, 1888

The Wilson Bulletin

OFFICIAL ORGAN

DOUGLAS A. JAMES, PRESIDENT
DEPARTMENT OF ZOOLOGY
UNIVERSITY OF ARKANSAS
FAYETTEVILLE, ARKANSAS 72701

GEORGE A. HALL, FIRST VICE-PRESIDENT
DEPARTMENT OF CHEMISTRY
WEST VIRGINIA UNIVERSITY
MORGANTOWN, WEST VIRGINIA 2...

ABBOT S. GAUNT, SECOND VICE-PRES
DEPARTMENT OF ZOOLOGY
OHIO STATE UNIVERSITY
COLUMBUS, OHIO 43210

JEROME A ...

1319 EIGHTEENTH STREET, N.W.   WASHINGTON, D.C. 20036

PHONE: 202 466 2160   CABLE: PANDAFUND   TELEX: 64505

WORLD
WILDLIFE
FUND-U.S.

Mr. Keith ...
Endangered
U. S. Fish
Washington,

Dear Mr. Sc...

I have
Cade titled
Peregrines f...
United State...
vation Commit...
formal action
opinion on th...

I certai...
establishment
States. He st...
ductive for me
do, however, e...
ter. I must a...
though differe...
program. I al...
program, which

24 January 1978

Mr. Keith Schreiner
Associate Director Federal Assistance
Fish and Wildlife Service
Department of the Interior
C Street NW
Washington, DC 20240

Dear Keith:

Dr. Cade has asked for my comments on the use of
non-indigenous races of the Peregrine in the Eastern
Peregrine Falcon Recovery Plan.

Surely the point is that a peregrine, even if of a
race different from that originally inhabiting the eastern
United States is better than no peregrines at all. Further,
although all should applaud concern about the introduction
of exotics, it really becomes valid at levels of taxonomic
distinction of species or greater.

World Wildlife Fund firmly endorses Dr. Cade's approach.

With all best wishes,

Sincerely yours,

Thomas E. Lovejoy, Ph.D.
Program Director

TEL:sm
cc: Dr. Thomas Cade

cc: T. J. Cade ✓
    E. G. Bolen

100% RECYCLED PAPER

◀ **Figure 15.5** Numerous letters of support were written after a 1977 executive order threatened to place severe limits on Peregrine releases in the eastern United States. *(See excerpts, right.)*

"...National Audubon will do all in its power to see that this program is carried forward with dispatch and not abandoned or side-tracked for legal technicalities of doubtful relevance."

Richard L. Plunkett
Staff Ecologist
National Audubon Society

"Surely the point is that a peregrine, even if of a race different from that originally inhabiting the eastern United States is better than no peregrines at all."

Thomas E. Lovejoy
Program Director
World Wildlife Fund-U.S.

"We feel that Dr. Cade's positions are very well taken and agree with his assessment that the time for decision is past and that it would be unfortunate and arbitrary for the U. S. Fish and Wildlife Service to reverse itself now."

Thomas L. Kimball
Executive Vice President
National Wildlife Federation

"The President's Executive Order 11987, was clearly not designed to speed the extinction of such a marvelous bird .... It would be very ironic to have the survival of the peregrine falcon threatened by a too literal interpretation of a law written to perpetrate it."

S. Dillon Ripley
Secretary
Smithsonian Institution

"My concern about this matter is profound, particularly as I see a danger of archaic thinking impeding progress in a very important program."

Robert K. Selander
Professor and Chairman
Biology Department
The University of Rochester

▲ **Figure 15.6** Bill Heinrich and Forest Service biologist Bruce Smith place Peregrines at a hack site in the Targhee National Forest.

President's order on exotic organisms, because the order also states that the introduction of exotics may be permitted if the Secretary of the Interior finds that such introduction will not have adverse effects on natural ecosystems (James 1988).

This policy, which developed haltingly over a span of four years, stands as one of the more unusual administrative decisions made in connection with the ESA, and it made possible the tremendous effort from 1975 to 1991 to release more than 1,200 young Peregrines in the eastern United States and the consequent establishment of a viable, self-sustaining breeding population (Barclay and Cade 1983; see Chapter 5). By extension it also provided the opportunity for a comparable program in the Midwest and around the Great Lakes region because that region was part of the Eastern Peregrine Falcon Recovery Plan (see Chapter 10).

Law Enforcement

The FWS's Division of Law Enforcement, the NAS, and certain others made much of the need for protection of Peregrines and their eyries. Law Enforcement seemed obsessed with this issue during Clark Bavin's tenure as its chief. A fiscal year (FY) 1975 annual report for Law Enforcement listed one of its major accomplishments under the migratory bird program as development of a master file "on all known parties interested in raptors." Mr. Bavin had notified Tom Cade that he kept an active file on him and all of his associates.

The FY 1976 report said, "Illegal nest scooping and live-trapping of raptors for falconry occurs [sic] throughout the United States.... Many such violators will resort to any means or devices necessary to steal eggs or nestlings.... The endangered Peregrine Falcon has become one of the most valuable gifts that anyone can offer a falconer in the Middle East. Some Americans find it very lucrative to smuggle the birds out of the country to wealthy Middle East monarchs who have paid up to $25,000 for the birds." Law Enforcement had not provided any tangible evidence as a basis for these allegations.

Law Enforcement undercover agents were identified attending scientific meetings incognito to seek incriminating evidence by listening in on innocent hallway conversations and to the reports given in the proceedings, as a means to snoop out possible cases to investigate. Beyond investigation, Law Enforcement also had authority for issuing permits and promulgating new regulations.

In 1974, at the direction of Assistant Secretary of the Interior Nathaniel Reed, there was a major shift in attitude and enlargement in Law Enforcement. The division was reorganized into semiautonomous districts with "strike force capability in responding to the District's investigative and law enforcement needs" (Annual Report—FY 1975, FWS). A 1974 Law Enforcement news release boasted of newly recruited agents who were ex-CIA, ex-FBI, and ex-Secret Service agents, who had come into FWS fresh from their Watergate experiences. One agent who visited us to band falcons at our Fort Collins, Colorado, facility was a former big-city homicide detective and had absolutely no wildlife or biology background, which turned out was the case for most new agents, who had to be sent to a six-week school to learn the difference between a duck and a hawk. These were individuals who knew little or nothing about fish and wildlife, or about the habits of hunters and fishermen, scientists, and other "users" of animal resources.

The modus operandi shifted Law Enforcement personnel from being "conservation officers" and protectors of wildlife to "special agents" equivalent in role to the FBI. The Law Enforcement headquarters was totally separated from other FWS personnel and placed behind locked doors and impenetrable glass, which even FWS directors had trouble entering. Security exceeded even that provided for the Secretary of the Interior. With this change, anyone with an interest in wildlife became suspect, including FWS biologists. This new breed was ill-suited to pursue and apprehend

The National Audubon Society and Peregrine Restoration

Roland C. Clement

I spent boyhood summers on a lake where Ospreys dominated the scene in the 1920s.

L. A. Fuertes's wonderful watercolors of the birds of prey, and his early *National Geographic* article on falcony, were also part of my growing-up process.

I was apprenticed to Maurice Broun as a bird-bander before he became famous as Hawk Mountain's first warden/naturalist. While studying wildlife management at the University of Massachusetts, I met Joseph A. Hagar when he was studying Peregrines in western Massachusetts, and at Cornell in 1950 I studied in the shadow of Tom Cade and Heinz Meng. And during World War II, I had been a weatherman at Indian House Lake, northern Labrador, where I enjoyed a southward migration of over 40 Gyrfalcons in the autumn of 1944, a lemming year.

It is no wonder, then, that when I became headquarters biologist for the National Audubon Society in 1960, raptor conservation was a focus of mine. The Society had published John B. May's *The Hawks of North America* in 1934. I knew Joseph Hickey, and John W. Aldrich, the National Museum's ornithologist, introduced me to Alva Nye, Jr., who was very active in the North American Falconers Association.

I was thus aware of the Peregrine's problems almost from the beginning. It was I who "blew the whistle" on the taking of passage Peregrines on the Atlantic Coast in 1968, simply by asking the fish and game directors of the coastal states to declare a moratorium on taking until we could better assess the bird's status. It amazed me that they all agreed to do so, and I soon felt the heat. This imposed responsibilities, so I organized a small conference within the annual National Wildlife Conference, held in Washington, D.C., in the spring of 1969. We listened to one another and established a working relationship to combine our best efforts on behalf of Peregrine recovery.

But our colleagues in the U.S. Fish and Wildlife Service felt it would be difficult to "sell" a recovery program based on captive propagation with "foreign" birds of uncertain genetic make-up, since there were so few eastern birds left. Therefore, at a luncheon that included several of the 1965 Madison conference principals, held at an American Ornithologists' Union meeting on Cape Cod in 1973, we organized a "second Peregrine conference" to

...Nature would do the selecting if we produced the experimental population.

Brian Walton

address these concerns. This was held in Greenwich, Connecticut, in 1974. Two of my Audubon colleagues, William H. Drury, Jr., and Ian C. T. Nisbet, of Massachusetts, broke the logjam by convincing everyone that Nature would do the selecting if we produced the experimental population. I like to think this consensus enabled the creation of the recovery team program.

Ironically, despite this progress I encountered negativity at Audubon headquarters. Two editors and the executive vice president simply decided that the emergency called for a ban on falcony. I was Vice President for Science, but that was discounted. *AUDUBON* magazine and *American Birds* published antifalconry pieces, and our local chapters were supplied with antifalconry arguments, but not my cooperative views. This impasse lasted nearly four years, until Audubon's board of directors concluded that the Society would not oppose such uses as falcony if scientific population assessments seemed to warrant it and state programs exercised reasonable control. The Boise celebrations were a homecoming for me.

Roland C. Clement *is a former Vice President of the National Audubon Society and an early proponent for cooperation between falconers and other conservationists at a time when others only wanted to fight.*

poachers and other offenders of wildlife laws by the customary methods of direct observation, pursuit, and interdictions in the field when a suspect committed a violation. Instead, they resorted to undercover operations and elaborate scams.

For all intents and purposes, Clark Bavin liaised directly with the Assistant Secretary of the Interior, circumventing the director of FWS. His interactions with the assistant secretaries did not always develop as probably he hoped. While this chapter was being written, Jim Ruos, former FWS raptor specialist, provided the following story.

"I don't recall the date, but it was in the mid-70s. Nat Reed, Assistant Secretary of the Interior, called my boss directly at Migratory Bird Management for me to meet with him immediately. As no subject was given, I figured that I was in a heap of trouble or, quite unlikely, to brief Reed on some important emerging raptor issue.

On arrival at Reed's office, I was surprised that this was to be a three-some meeting… Reed, Clark Bavin, and myself. Bavin and I sat waiting in silence while Reed completed an unrelated 20-minute phone call. At that point, I knew for sure that Bavin was going to lodge a protest of my criticism about LE operations.

When Reed finished his phone call, he addressed Bavin directly in the eye and said, "Goddamn it Clark, get off the back of The Peregrine Fund." The 30-second meeting ended with no response or further comment. Obviously, my attendance was to serve only as a witness!

That made my day, but surely must have pissed off Bavin."

This event may have helped galvanize Clark Bavin's attitude for the future.

Clark Bavin was to FWS Law Enforcement what J. Edgar Hoover was to the FBI in approach and other similarities. Mr. Bavin also seemed to want everyone, and particularly those making decisions about his division's funding, to believe protection of the Peregrine was paramount and that falconers were the Peregrine's primary threat. The ESA was being seen as the new cash cow. Included in his definition of "falconers" were certainly many authors of this book, The Peregrine Fund and its directors, and evidently many, if not most, of its cooperators.

The problems continued. In July 1975, Special Agent in Charge Harry Stiles visited our Fort Collins, Colorado, facility unannounced. Mr. Stiles was accompanied by his wife. Bill Burnham, director of the facility, was in Greenland at the time, and Bill Wood, Pat Burnham's brother, was feeding the quail and chickens. Pat was not on site at the time of the visit. Without introducing himself, Mr. Stiles asked to see the falcons. When Bill Wood replied that he had been given strict instructions from Bill Burnham not to take anyone into the falcon barns, Mr. Stiles showed him his FWS identification and demanded to see the falcons. While touring the facilities, he asked Bill Wood leading questions about the origins of specific falcons. An emergency message was sent to Bill Burnham in Greenland, but as no more was heard from Mr. Stiles, Bill did not return prematurely from his research. This and other incidents were documented by Frank Bond in a 22 September 1977 letter to Clark Bavin.

In a December 1977 meeting between Tom Cade, Secretary of the Interior Cecil Andrus, and Assistant Secretary Robert Herbst, Tom complained about Law Enforcement's treatment of raptor biologists, falconers in general, and The Peregrine Fund in particular. As part of a follow-up letter to the meeting, Tom detailed "examples of the generally negative, suspicious, and unhelpful attitude of most agents" and drew attention again to Bond's September letter. No noticeable improvement occurred. Almost 10 years later Tom Cade provided new examples in letters to William Horn, then Assistant Secretary for Fish and Wildlife and Parks, and FWS Director Frank Dunkle and wrote, "We have experienced continual problems with agents and officials of FWS Division of Law Enforcement. My staff and I have been kept under surveillance and investigation by FWS agents more or less continually for more than ten years, even though in all that time they have never served any warrant or brought any specific charges against any member of The Peregrine Fund. During this time agents have often engaged in activities which to us are patently improper, abusive, unauthorized, harmful to our reputation in the professional community, and sometimes illegal…. It is like having an Army with no civilian control at the top. A number of fundamental changes need to be made to bring the Division back into harmony with the resource management and conservation philosophy of the main, substantive divisions and offices of FWS. For one, law enforcement officials should not have the responsibility for drafting regulations; for another, they should not be the ones who approve and issue permits."

…restrictions on the movement of raptors inhibited ready exchange among breeders, thereby reducing their ability to breed raptors.

Raptor Exemption

Despite Law Enforcement and FWS opposition, legislative relief was provided to benefit Peregrine Falcon restoration through the ESA Amendments of 1978. The "raptor exemption" excluded from the prohibitions of the ESA raptors "legally held in captivity or in a controlled environment on November 10, 1978" and any progeny. "Congress intended that the raptor amendment facilitate the exchange of captive-bred raptors through the elimination of certain ESA permit requirements that were criticized before Congress by representatives of raptor breeders. These representatives argued that restrictions on the movement of raptors inhibited ready exchange among breeders, thereby reducing their ability to breed raptors. They also argued that certain ESA restrictions prevented the exercise of falconry with endangered raptors, thus reducing the incentive to breed them" (48 FR 1362, 1983).

The amendment was necessary because, as Senator John Tunney wrote to John Culver, Chairman, Subcommittee on Resource Protection, United States Senate, on 21 April 1978, "It has come to my attention that an amendment I sponsored has been misinterpreted by our Department of the Interior. I refer to the exemption placed in the Endangered Species Act of 1973 regarding species held in captivity or in a controlled environment as of the date of the enactment." He went on to suggest a clarifying amendment be passed into law. His suggestion was consistent with those of others, including The Peregrine Fund's. Leading our efforts to amend the ESA was Frank Bond, then Vice President of The Peregrine Fund. In his 19 July 1977 testimony to the Senate Committee on the Environment and Public Works, he identified most of the problems mentioned in this chapter and proposed solutions that were ignored or rejected by the Department of the Interior and FWS. Although others of us, and the list is long, including the North American Falconers Association (NAFA), participated in and supported this profound legislative accomplishment, Frank Bond led the charge, and the achievement was primarily to his credit.

Clifton Witt wrote about the ESA amendments of 1978 in the December 1978/January 1979 issue of the American Federation of Aviculturists' publication, *The A.F.A. Watchbird:* "Exempting captive Raptors and their progeny is the real `blockbuster' however. It is an example of how a small group of dedicated aviculturists, namely the Falconers, accomplished what no other animal-interest group has been able to do. The amount and qual-

Figure 15.7 Tom Cade and Secretary of the Interior Cecil Andrus in Washington, D. C. at release of Peregrine Falcons on the roof of the Interior Building, 1979.

File photo

Courtesy of the Department of the Interior

ity of work and perseverance that was required of them in this lobbying effort is impressive. They deserve our admiration, commendation, and sincere thanks."

What resulted because of the "raptor exemption"? Nothing officially for almost five years, as FWS seemed to do its obstinate best. In a 17 July 1978 letter by Tom Cade to then Interior Secretary Cecil Andrus, Tom wrote, "I personally supported this amendment because our program to establish captive produced falcons in the wild depends to a very important degree upon the help we can receive from skilled falconers to hold and to handle birds for us . . . . Removing captive produced raptors from the prohibitions of the ESA has not yet resulted in making the permit procedures to involve these citizens in our program any easier

Figure 15.8 Secretary of the Interior Manuel Lujan, Jr. and Frank Bond (right), 1989.

than before.... Scientists, breeders, and falconers have waited patiently for nine months to see a notice in the Federal Register modifying these limitations on the use of endangered and threatened raptors. None has appeared." Assistant Secretary Robert Herbst responded to Cade, blaming the conflicting regulations implementing the Migratory Bird Treaty Act for the delay and stating, "while the regulatory process may not be as expeditious as some might like, it is designed to be as thorough as possible." The "thoroughness" was reconfirmed to Senator Malcolm Wallop by Secretary Andrus in a 29 October 1979 letter saying, "This draft is currently being reviewed by the various affected offices within the Fish and Wildlife Service, and should be ready for publication in the Federal Register in the very near future." A problem with bureaucracies is that responsibility is diffused, and a petitioner can never find anyone to blame. It is never anyone's fault. The Congressionally mandated relief was finally and officially implemented on 8 July 1983 in the form of revised falconry regulations (50 CFR 17.7), promulgated under the Migratory Bird Treaty Act. Permits were to be issued by the Division of Law Enforcement through the Special Agents-in-Charge in each FWS region. (For further information see Kennedy 1987.)

Captive-breeding Regulations

Further new regulations affecting Peregrine restoration were proposed by FWS in January 1983 and created a firestorm of controversy even within the falconry community as they proposed allowing sale of captive-bred raptors to qualified individuals. This proposal followed an effective lobbying effort by Bob Berry and the North American Raptor Breeders Association (NARBA). NARBA believed that allowing sale of captive-produced raptors would make more Peregrines available for the restoration program and reduce pressure on wild raptor populations (note: removal of raptors from the wild for falconry in North America has never been shown to have affected populations). The proposal followed a September 1982 Environmental Assessment (author Jim Ruos) by FWS stating there would be no negative resulting effect. With the encouragement of the Deputy Assistant Secretary for Fish and Wildlife and Parks, J. Craig Potter, the "raptor propagation regulations" went into effect on 8 July 1983 (amended 15 March 1984) in the same date as the "raptor exemption." Even before, however, because of the promise from the "raptor exemption," the number of propagated Peregrines

and other raptors had begun to increase rapidly. The new 1983 regulations allowing individuals breeding raptors to recoup expenses and if possible make a profit from their labors further spurred captive-propagation efforts. For Peregrine propagation, an important financial benefit for breeders came from sale of young for release to the wild. Virtually all of the Peregrines released in the Midwest restoration effort were purchased from breeders (see Chapter 10). The belief of proponents of the 1978 amendment and 1983 propagation regulations that providing incentives (falcons and dollars) for private-sector involvement would benefit the Peregrine restoration program was proven correct.

The payment to propagators per Peregrine for release to the wild averaged $1,200 but was never more than $2,000. Prices paid to propagators by falconers for Peregrines for falconry ranged from $500 to $3,500 but have gone down since the Peregrine was delisted. For falconry, females are more valuable than males because they can capture larger quarry. Certain propagators who are believed to produce Peregrines of exceptional ability are paid the top prices. Most female Peregrines, however, are now sold to falconers for $1,000 or less, and propagators have difficulty even finding good homes for males. Never were the alleged and exaggerated prices professed and publicized by FWS Law Enforcement and others paid for Peregrines.

Factual information from FWS was difficult to obtain, a constant problem during the Peregrine restoration program. During much of Clark Bavin's reign as chief, Law Enforcement promoted a running expose of unverifiable information on numbers of Peregrines illegally taken from the wild, international sales and black markets, and other sensational statements in support of their actions.

Operation Falcon

In 1981, to prove its case, FWS Law Enforcement began what would become known as Operation Falcon, one of numerous "sting" operations carried out during Clark Bavin's tenure as chief. They hired a falconer who had previous difficulties with the law, John Jeffrey McPartlin of Great Falls, Montana, as their "confidential informant." Through Mr. McPartlin, FWS went into the national and international trading business taking Peregrines, Gyrfalcons, and Prairie Falcons from the wild to be offered for sale, an action that was authorized by regulation under the Migratory Bird Treaty Act and only by special authorization under the ESA. One sting operation, in which an FWS agent removed eyass Pere-grines from a nest in Utah and presented them to a falconer, was clearly a violation of the ESA, but when confronted by this fact Clark Bavin and Don Carr of the Justice Department refused to file charges against the agent. On 26 June 1984 Clark Bavin announced to a Congressional budget hearing that in justification for his request for money in FY85 a major enforcement action would be announced in four or five days. On 29 June 1984, as Bavin promised, many falconers and raptor breeders across the nation were awak-ened by agents knocking at their doors demand-ing to see records, their birds, and as Will Shor, former editor of NAFA's *Hawk Chalk,* details in his 29 July 1984 report, "in some cases, every-thing in their houses." Shor said, "most were questioned about their own activities and those of other falconers. Virtually all were required to respond to a prepared interrogatory about The Peregrine Fund."

The FWS's press release boasted of the breaking of a multimillion dollar international black-mar-ket trade in hawks and falcons. Nothing could have been farther from the truth. Virtually simul-taneously, the NAS's Director of Wildlife, Amos Eno, issued a press release calling on FWS and Congress to act promptly to appropriate $2 mil-lion for the FWS to fund 20 additional law enforcement agents to crack down on this illegal traffic. Eno went on to say that "today's revela-tions indicate that prominent falconers are cal-lously contributing to the destruction of raptors in their pursuit of profit and personal aggrandize-ment." Close communication obviously existed between Eno and Bavin as they knew each other well when Eno was Nathaniel Reed's assistant at the Department of the Interior.

In a 29 June 1984 "memorandum" (the same day as the press release) attached to the NAS press release on Operation Falcon from Amos Eno to G. Ray Arnett, Assistant Secretary of the Interior, Mr. Eno wrote, "Goddamn it, we told you this is exactly what would happen. I strongly urge you to take the lead in cleaning up the current regula-tions and not to entertain any more of Roger Thacher's [sic] [president of NAFA] proposals for down-listing or taking from the wild. The poten-tial for abuse is simply too immense and too prevalent." Mr. Arnett responded in a handwritten note on the same memo back to Mr. Eno, "As seems to be the M.O. with you Audubon folks, you come off the wall w/o the benefits of full knowledge. That seems to keep putting us at odds unnecessarily. It may be good for fund raising,

Amos, but does darn little for building coopera-tion! Your release is way off the mark."

One apparent goal of Operation Falcon was to damage The Peregrine Fund. Agents read prepared questionnaires with slanderous allegations about The Peregrine Fund to those they interrogated. On the day of the sting, Fran Hamerstrom, well-known raptor biologist, telephoned Jim Weaver to warn him about the questions she had been required to answer about The Peregrine Fund. Having sat through one interrogation, University of Minnesota scientist Harrison Tordoff wrote Tom Cade, "It was a bizarre event. Since the inves-tigation is clearly aimed at discrediting The Pere-grine Fund, it is clear that ill will for the Fund exists somewhere." In another interrogation, agents told the suspect that Tom Cade and his associates were already in jail and that he might as well tell what he knew to make it easier on himself. In another instance agents report-edly said that The Pere-grine Fund has gotten too big for its britches, and it's time to cut it down to size, and that the people of The Pere-grine Fund have gotten greedy, and now they are going to pay for it. Mr. McPartlin reportedly had been telling people that he was out to get The Peregrine Fund. It was no wonder, as both Jim Weaver and Bill Burnham had reported him to Law Enforcement for ques-tionable activities; they had traced a falcon trans-mitter that had been attached to a Peregrine that disappeared prematurely from a release site back to him. The transmitter had a manufacturer's internal serial number, which was read during repair and reported to The Peregrine Fund.

In a 15 January 1981 letter three years before the sting, Jeff McPartlin wrote Bill Burnham, "When I read the Cornell newsletter and see pic-tures of captive-bred Peregrine Falcons released to the wild and then returning to breed on their own in the wild, I realize that the countless man hours and care devoted by the Cornell team has pro-duced an awesomely wonderful event in nature.

▲ **Figure 15.9** Peregrine chick.

As just one guy who loves raptors and falconry, I offer my thanks." In the letter he also offered a Peregrine Falcon. Burnham responded in a 3 February 1981 letter rejecting the offer and wrote, "Jeff, to be quite honest, your past activities bother me somewhat. Some of the activities you were involved in a number of years ago you are still paying for in Colorado as well as in Wyoming." McPartlin immediately wrote back (6 February 1981), "It is true my past has been a very difficult experience to live down . . . . Yes, I have traded birds in the past. Yes, I have been associated in activities contrary to what would be considered ethical . . . . I must honestly attribute many of my past mistakes to youthful lack of consideration and maturity. . . . However, years can temper one and bring some degree of wisdom where there was none, or if it existed, was not applied. Like all young falconers at the time, I wanted to be a 'big shot,' a 'somebody.' Those feelings have long gone by the wayside. All I want to do is what makes my bird happy afield." Obviously he wanted much more. In his last letter to Burnham, dated 18 March 1981, he ended it by writing, "Please believe that I want to be of assistance, and I expect nothing for any assistance I might provide."

Tom Cade summed up the Law Enforcement attack on The Peregrine Fund in a 21 September 1984 letter to Interior Secretary William Clark. "This 'investigation' is absolutely without substantive justification or 'probable cause,' as witnessed by the fact that it has been impossible for law enforcement officials to obtain search and seizure warrants or arrest warrants against any member of The Peregrine Fund, Inc. It has been a witch hunt from start to finish. The law enforcement people working under the direct supervision of Agent Rick D. Leach have been all too eager to rely on rumors, their paid, undercover informer with his equally untruthful cronies in the falcon-trafficking underworld, as the basis for a nation-wide, official interrogation best calculated to defame and malign The Peregrine Fund, Inc."

After Tom Cade shared this same information and similar comments with NAS President Russell W. Peterson, Mr. Peterson responded as follows: ". . . let me make it clear to you, Tom, that in light of my information you and The Peregrine Fund and many of your collaborators deserve the commendation and respect of the conservation community for the major contribution you have made to not only bringing the Peregrine Falcon back from the abyss but for advancing the knowledge necessary to save other endangered species. I believe in your honesty and dedication and in the sincerity of your resolve to see that those who are guilty of the illegal taking and marketing of birds of prey are severely punished."

The Peregrine Fund was not the only innocent involved with the Peregrine to be affected. There were many others. Especially notable were Washington, D.C., FWS biologist Jim Ruos and Canadian Wildlife Service (CWS) research scientist Richard Fyfe. Both men ended their careers prematurely and had their lives altered forever because of the event. Years later, Richard Fyfe was eventually awarded the Order of Canada for his role as leader of the Canadian Peregrine recovery program from 1970 to 1986, but it was far too late. Also innocent of any wrongdoing, David Mossop, then Senior Wildlife Management Biologist for the Yukon, was arrested, jailed, and falsely charged with criminal conspiracy, and only after great professional embarrassment and personal injury were all charges dropped (McKay 1989).

In the end, FWS was forced to return confiscated birds to their owners; charges were dropped against several individuals; and there were several cases in which FWS failed to get convictions because its evidence was baseless. There later followed what amounted to an oversight hearing before Congressman (now Senator) John Breaux's subcommittee, at which Tom Cade and others testified. The FWS and Department of the Interior were hauled on the carpet for their actions. Law Enforcement's sting operations left a bad taste in the mouths of many people, including Congressmen and Interior officials.

FWS Law Enforcement was finally brought under control by budgetary restrictions imposed by the U.S. Congress. American falconry emerged politically stronger than it had been before Operation Falcon, but it will be a long time before American falconry overcomes the stigma left in the minds of the uninformed public who remain unaware of the real circumstances surrounding Operation Falcon. Many falconers who experienced it, however, are still suspicious of FWS and what or who may lurk around the corner.

Permitting

Although many of the actions by Law Enforcement might at best be considered harassment or poor judgement, their authority to issue permits was a constant obstacle to Peregrine restoration. This authority provided it considerable control, forcing biologists regularly to reach above Law Enforcement for relief. In a 22 December 1977 letter to Department of the Interior Assistant Secretary Robert Herbst, Tom Cade explained that he was still waiting reissuance of his Special Purpose Permit for The Peregrine Fund. His former permit allowed for keeping no more than four raptors in captivity without written exception from FWS's director. He then held 150 falcons as part of the Peregrine restoration program! Earlier the same year in a report by Bill Burnham to Tom Cade, board members, and donors, Bill complained of needing eight different permits and other permissions to propagate and release Peregrines to the wild the previous spring/summer and of the resulting time and effort required to seek the permits.

Thomas L. Striegler, later FWS Chief of Law Enforcement, first proposed moving migratory bird permit issuance out of Law Enforcement to Migratory Birds to then Chief Clark Bavin in the 1980s. The Division of Law Enforcement historically had all permitting prior to 1972, but that began to shift somewhat in the 1970s and 1980s with the implementation of new laws. Mr. Bavin was not sympathetic to relinquishing any authority from the Division of Law Enforcement. Following Bavin's death in 1990, John Doggett, the new FWS Chief who was also a lawyer, saw value in shifting the authority, and Striegler and Doggett succeeded in transferring all permitting to the Migratory Bird Management Office (MBMO). Tom Striegler had concluded many years earlier that decisions regarding the issuance of permits were to be based on biological criteria and not on law enforcement concerns. Since the Division of Law Enforcement had been underfunded for its permitting responsibility, he felt that perhaps Fish and Wildlife authorities might provide greater funding to the MBMO when they recognized permitting as a biological function.

Just acquiring an Endangered Species permit is a long, laborious process requiring the application be published in the Federal Register for public comment. To obtain an ESA permit to work with Peregrines in the wild regularly required over six months and sometimes over a year, even for a renewal. A separate Special Purpose permit was required for captive propagation, another FWS permit for banding of falcons, and further permits to handle injured Peregrines and retrieve carcasses of dead ones. To scare off an eagle attempting to kill a released Peregrine was yet another permit that had to be renewed and reported on quarterly. Then there were the National Environmental Policy Act (NEPA) requirements to be met prior to a release, separately permissions from federal agencies or private individuals on whose land the release was to

occur, and finally the permits and permissions from individual states. Added to these, when we wished to exchange genetic stocks of Peregrines for breeding with the CWS facility at Wainwright, Alberta, there were requirements and permits under the Convention on International Trade in Endangered Species (CITES). These requirements were all prior to passage of the 1992 Wild Bird Conservation Act, which, if it had existed then, would have added yet another level of complication for any international movement of birds. Permitting has become more cumbersome with passage of additional laws and regulations.

Since the 1970s, and despite meetings about permit problems with virtually every Interior Secretary and most Assistant Secretaries and FWS directors, there has been no meaningful relief. Even former Vice President Al Gore's National Performance Review staff was involved and responded that "after discussing the matter with . . . , I quickly became convinced this subject is so complex that rather than speak in generalities, your goals might be best served by developing an overall concept for what it is you want and a road map of those impediments, including regulation, which preclude you from doing it." At our request language was included in the proposed Endangered Species Conservation and Management Act of 1995 legislation to unify, simplify, and streamline the permitting process. Congress did not pass the bill.

With the threat of Congressional action, a greater interest in improving the permitting system seemed to exist in FWS. At the request of Bill Burnham, Jamie Clark, FWS Director and a former Peregrine hack site attendant (see sidebar, Hack Site Attendant Experiences, Chapter 14), organized a 16 April 1998 meeting of her top staff to discuss permitting problems. At the meeting she promised an improved permitting system within six months; no regular improvements occurred during her entire tenure or the Clinton era. What did occur, however, was a positive change in attitude of the Office of Management Authority permitting staff. Beyond Ms. Clark, we must credit Marshall Jones and Ken Stansell for that change. The FWS seemed finally to recognize that its permitting process and enforcement were seriously impeding conservation of species and scientific research. Following these meetings and promises, however, and with the next permit application we made to a new permit clerk, we regressed a decade. It was as if nothing that had transpired before was known by him or mattered.

▲ **Figure 15.10** Senator Larry Craig.

▲ **Figure 15.11** Congressman Norm Dicks.

▲ **Figure 15.12** Secretary of the Interior Donald Hodel.

▲ "Peregrine Day," sponsored by Boise Cascade Corporation, was held at the nation's capitol to recognize the release of the 2,000th Peregrine to the wild in the United States, and involved many dignitaries, 3 June 1987. (File photos)

In March 2001, in meetings between The Peregrine Fund and Secretary of the Interior Gale Norton and FWS, FWS again committed to correct permit problems. Months later in a follow-up phone call, FWS explained that the new director had other priorities. We then met with the new FWS director, Steve Williams, in June 2002 about permitting problems and the need to complete the monitoring plan for the Peregrine. Ken Stansell returned to the World Center for Birds of Prey in October 2002 with two Washington permitting persons, and two other FWS permitting staff came from Regions 1 and 2 to meet with us. Their desire to find solutions was sincere and appreciated. We hope the current administration and FWS staff will finally carry through.

Recovery Teams and Plans

Beyond providing protection, the ESA is supposed to promote recovery of viable populations of "threatened and endangered" species. After "listing" of a species, to promote recovery FWS appoints recovery teams that are charged with developing recovery plans, which, after review, are approved for potential implementation.

Because of the Peregrine's continentwide distribution and great popularity, former FWS Director Lynn Greenwalt established four recovery teams in 1974 to develop four regional recovery plans for the Peregrine Falcon. Teams were established for Alaska, the Pacific Coast states and Nevada, the Rocky Mountains and Southwest, and the eastern United States. Fifty-two people, both government and private sector, participated on these teams. The four recovery teams met together a single time in 1976 but otherwise worked independently. The initial recovery plans were officially approved for the Rocky Mountains/Southwest in 1977, for the eastern United States in 1979, and

for the Pacific Coast and Alaska in 1982. These plans totalled 486 pages. The Canadians separately developed their own plan in 1988 (see Chapter 17).

Usually recovery plans are detailed, complex documents, sometimes taking years to write and costing tens of thousands of dollars or more to develop. They are static documents, based on historical and current information and knowledge, which are supposed to guide species recovery actions, potentially for decades. Most plans, however, are outdated before even working their way through what is usually a lengthy review and approval process. Many also have detailed, unrealistic budgets which are never funded. Although well intended, these rigid plans can be counterproductive to recovery actions and even delisting of species as new information and needs develop.

The Peregrine recovery plans were no exception. Updating plans can be a lengthy process and almost as complicated as their original development. For example, to write an "addendum" to the two plans for the western states, FWS selected five representatives for the region (Jim Enderson as leader, Al Harmata, Grainger Hunt, Lloyd Kiff, and Clayton White). They held meetings in nine states to accept input and produced a document which an FWS employee later revised and distributed, representing her views as that of the team's members. The effort took three years, and the addendum was never approved. By contrast, the Eastern plan was rather quickly updated by interaction between the Region 5 FWS endangered species coordinator and members of the recovery team.

A far better procedure for developing recovery plans, as originally envisioned by Earl Baysinger, an official of the FWS Office of Endangered Species, would be to have three to five people, mostly experts on the topic, create a brief recovery

▲ **Figure 15.13** John Fery (left), Chairman of the Board and CEO of Boise Cascade, and Senator Robert Byrd.

▲ **Figure 15.14** Jim Weaver (right) shows Senator Robert Kasten a young Peregrine.

▲ **Figure 15.15** Congressman John Dingell and Tom Cade.

strategy, just a few pages long, providing a realistic, straightforward recovery goal, description of the species and problem causing its decline, and in general terms suggesting recovery actions. From this strategy, a "working group" could be formed to develop and implement the actual recovery actions if they are required.

Peregrine Falcon Delisting Process

The first Peregrine population to be delisted was the *tundrius* race (north of the tree line) in Alaska and Canada. The population there had never been as severely reduced as in the south (Cade et al. 1988) (see Chapter 11). Following a five-year review instituted in 1978, FWS downlisted the *tundrius* race to threatened in 1984 (49 FR 10520, March 20, 1984). In 1991 FWS notified the public it was reviewing the status of *tundrius* again (56 FR 26969, June 12, 1991), and a proposal to delist the Arctic Peregrines was published in the Federal Register in 1993 (58 FR 50796, October 5, 1994). The process took about three-and-a-half years to complete by FWS biologists Skip Ambrose and Ted Swem. These biologists should be congratulated for an expertly prepared final delisting document.

The delisting of the *anatum* population (from tree line south into the United States; "American Peregrine Falcon") was much more lengthy and complex. In Tom Cade's 1985 letter to Rollin Sparrowe, Chief of Migratory Bird Management for FWS, he suggested FWS begin the down-listing process from endangered to threatened for the American Peregrine Falcon because it would take at least five years to accomplish. The suggestion, passed on to the Office of Endangered Species, fell on deaf ears. After considerable pressure was applied on FWS by Bill Burnham, Tom Cade, and others, the first step was taken 10 years later. On 30 June 1995 FWS announced it was *considering*

proposing the delisting of the Peregrine (60 FR 34406). There was considerable debate and discussion following this biological bellwether announcement and notice in the Federal Register. The response was largely positive, but not everyone wanted the species even down-listed, let alone delisted, despite the fact that it no longer met the criteria for the endangered or threatened classification in the ESA. Complicating the delisting process were budgetary constraints, changed priorities, and political posturing between the Democratic Administration and the Republican Congress. Also, according to FWS, environmentalists threatened to sue if any dollars were used for delisting species before all the candidate species were listed. FWS biologist Robert Mesta, also responsible for the California Condor program, was charged by FWS Regional Director Mike Spear to accomplish the delisting process. The International Association of Fish and Wildlife Agencies offered its assistance, as did others (Cade 1998).

More than three years later FWS published the actual proposal for delisting the American Peregrine Falcon (63 FR 165:45446-45463, August 26, 1998). FWS Director Jamie Rappaport Clark traveled to The Peregrine Fund's World Center for Birds of Prey to announce the proposal.

By law FWS had only 12 months to act on the delisting proposal. Following the delisting announcement, The Peregrine Fund invited The Raptor Center and the Santa Cruz Predatory Bird Research Group to join it in holding a celebration for all who participated in the restoration program. The celebration would begin on 20 August 1999 at the World Center for Birds of Prey in Boise, Idaho. There is no doubt in our minds that without the fixed date of this celebration, the Peregrine Falcon would not have been delisted within the 12 months, or possibly another year beyond. Ms. Clark, Mr. Spear, and Mr. Mesta have our sincere thanks for that achievement. During the 20 August 1999 press conference at the World Center, Secretary Babbitt announced the delisting of the Peregrine and the notice was published in the Federal Register five days later (64 FR 164:46542-46558, August 25, 1999). The time required from publication of first notice to last was almost four years and three months. Beginning to end, the process was much longer.

Still incomplete, however, is the legally mandated five-year monitoring period after delisting. The proposed monitoring plan (66 FR 147, July 31, 2001), however, extends for 15 years, but even if approved, funding for implementation is questionable. If we look to the example of the *tundrius* Peregrine, no monitoring plan was implemented. For the *tundrius* and the *anatum* race alike, one thorough survey at the end of the five years would be sufficient. Because several biologists have continued to monitor their populations since delisting and Peregrine numbers continue to increase, those data could probably be considered sufficient and representative for regional populations of the species.

Some people worried during the delisting process, and do even now, that without being listed under the ESA the Peregrine Falcon would be unprotected. As explained, "protection" provided under the ESA had nothing to do with the Peregrine's recovery, eliminating the cause of its decline, or threats to recovery.

The Peregrine is still protected by the Migratory Bird Treaty Act, Lacey Act, and state wildlife laws. These protections transfer management of the species back to the states, and simultaneously allow for a "take" of Peregrines for falconry purposes. Peregrines to be taken from the wild are a fixed maximum number of nestlings and, we hope in the future, immature (hatch-year) migrant falcons. The first nestling *anatum* Peregrine Falcons were removed from the wild in 2001. Permits were available from state wildlife agencies for falconers to take 12 Peregrines in Utah and eight in Arizona, but only three and five nestlings, respectively, were actually removed from the wild for falconry. Five of the permits available in Arizona were not even applied for. This first year of Peregrine take should have helped put to rest fears of overharvest. Instead, Defenders of Wildlife and others sued FWS to stop the harvest of Peregrines. This lawsuit and argument against harvest are not based on biology or science but on emotion and political agendas. It is unfortunate that the energy and resources being expended in litigation cannot be redirected to some actions of value to endangered species and wildlife conservation.

The falconers deserve this opportunity to have access to wild-hatched Peregrines again because it was the falconers who donated their falcons, knowledge, and even funding to begin the Peregrine restoration program (see Chapter 16). We were able to develop a captive-breeding population by borrowing their Peregrines. We depended on their knowledge of eyrie locations, management of captive falcons, and even how to release them to the wild.

Peregrine restoration will not be complete and the recovery come full circle until nestling and immature migrant Peregrines are annually removed from the wild for falconry.

Conclusion

Returning to the questions at the beginning of this chapter, how was the recovery of the Peregrine Falcon affected by the ESA and FWS? The relationship between those restoring the Peregrine Falcon and FWS could probably best be described as one of love and hate. Since FWS was the primary federal agency responsible for endangered wildlife, including the Peregrine Falcon, and was mandated and funded by Congress for endangered species recovery, there was no choice but for the private sector, state wildlife agencies, and other federal agencies to work with it. Although FWS was many times viewed as an obstacle and its Law Enforcement as an antagonist to recovery actions, some FWS biologists were valued colleagues in the restoration program, and many of their names appear in this book, including authors of two chapters. The strong mistrust of "falconers" and jealousy of The Peregrine Fund by some in FWS in the 1970s and 1980s, although disruptive, probably helped galvanize the attitudes of those working on the restoration to accept nothing less than complete success—viable wild populations and delisting. The record does not support any statement suggesting that the recovery of the Peregrine occurred because of substantive actions by FWS. The endeavor was largely a private sector–led enterprise with state wildlife and even other federal agencies (Bureau of Land Management, US Forest Service, and National Park Service) having a larger role. Although we may have felt differently throughout much of the restoration program, in retrospect we cannot confirm that the recovery occurred despite FWS as an agency, but certainly despite its Division of Law Enforcement.

The falconers deserve this opportunity to have access to wild-hatched Peregrines again...

What about the ESA? Did the Peregrine recover primarily because of the ESA, as Secretary Babbitt proclaimed? We have explained that protection by the ESA for the Peregrine provided no measurable benefit to recovery of the species and was a regular, if not constant, obstacle because of its emphasis on law enforcement and permitting. Since the Peregrine is such a cosmopolitan species, there was not even a designation of critical habitat for it, except in a few small areas.

The ESA did, however, provide a platform for cooperation and a vehicle for funding. The provisions embedded within the ESA for cooperative actions to preserve and recover species are critical. Little can be accomplished without cooperation. The ESA speaks to cooperation between the federal government and the states. It would be a better law if it included conservation and research organizations, universities, and private landowners as cooperators. We believe the ultimate success or failure for conservation of all species, such as the Peregrine, cannot be dictated or accomplished by government alone. Private-sector involvement, commitment, cooperation, and leadership are crucial.

Although it is hard to prove, we believe the almost universal cooperation witnessed on behalf of the Peregrine would have occurred without the ESA, but probably not at the same high level. The Peregrine's proponents took advantage of the increased interest in endangered species flowing from the ESA to promote the restoration. The Peregrine's charismatic appeal and plight captivated people's imaginations, and they did not wish to see the species lost. Therefore, they gave their support, including financial contributions. The ESA fostered cooperation and was a source for funding, especially through the Section 6 provisions to the states. Without the ESA, dollars for endangered species actions in FWS and appropriations for other agencies would have no doubt existed but would have been less. In short, restoration of the Peregrine would have occurred without the ESA of 1973, but probably not as quickly or at the same high level and scope.

We were fortunate the Peregrine restoration was largely complete before the Spotted Owl controversy and more recent conflicts related to endangered species. The ESA is the strongest environmental law in the United States, and without a measure of common sense, or when used primarily for the advantage of an organization, agency, or political cause, its application can be counterproductive to the very purpose of its creation—restoration of viable populations of endangered species. Sometimes misuse of the ESA was attempted in the name of the Peregrine, but fortunately and gratefully, FWS and most of those involved in the restoration program opposed such attempts, so that issues were resolved on their face value. After what has transpired with other listed or proposed species using the ESA threat to stop development projects and private use of public lands and natural resources, we doubt that restoration of the Peregrine Falcon could be accomplished today. The level of private-sector trust and cooperation necessary for success may no longer exist. Some of that blame must fall on the agencies that promulgate and implement the overly restrictive ESA regulations and some on outside organizations and individuals who have misused the Act to further agendas Congress never intended. Today to restore populations of California Condors and Aplomado Falcons we resort to using an "experimental nonessential" designation and "safe harbor" permit, respectively. These tools in essence diminish, if not remove, most legal impositions of the ESA, so that the species can be recovered. In essence the birds are legally reclassified under the ESA so they can be biologically recovered.

Too often the ESA is improperly used as a "bully" tool to deal with almost every change that even relates indirectly to the environment. The nation should support the ESA for the reasons it was enacted. It is a moral and spiritual imperative to save imperiled species.

▲ Figure 15.16–15.17 The delisting celebration featured remarks by current Idaho Governor Dirk Kempthorne (left) and former Idaho Governor Phil Batt. Support from state officials has been crucial.

Biographical information for Tom Cade can be found at the end of Chapter 5 and for Bill Burnham at the end of Chapter 8.

Chapter 16

Falconers, Essential Leaders of the Peregrine's Recovery

Frank M. Bond

*F*alconry had its origins many centuries ago, first as a utilitarian means of taking wild animals for sustenance,

but it later became an art to witness the spectacle of an extraordinary flight. From films and literature, the vast majority of the citizens of Europe and North America often associate falconry with knights riding out of the Middle Ages with Peregrines on their fists. Those images are subsumed into the modern practice of the art by working men and women who aspire to witness that natural struggle between a predator and its prey. Without specific allusion, in *Meditations on Hunting* José Ortega y Gasset, the Spanish novelist, historian, and philosopher, captured the essence of falconry in his insightful analysis of man's primordial instinct to hunt.

Modern falconers, like their ancestors, regard the Peregrine as the classical bird of falconry. More than any other species, it represents perfection because of its inherent characteristics. Its beauty and aloofness make it charismatic, but its speed and power in pursuit of its prey inspire awe.

The Peregrine can be quite docile, manageable, and tractable, lending itself to a close relationship with man. Few people, other than falconers, have been thrilled by a Peregrine in full stoop from 2,000 ft at speeds reaching 200 mph as it seeks to intercept a duck or grouse at the end of its arcing trajectory. For those few, that vision is the measure of the falcon's beauty.

Falconers recall their first encounter with a Peregrine. With that initial impression, their lives change forever. Generations of falconers through centuries of time assumed that a rightful place of the Peregrine taken from a cliff or trapped on passage was on the hand of man. It was not until the second half of the 20th Century that falconers, because of their experience and passion, were summoned to become the essential leaders of a movement to save a species in peril.

As the reality of a dwindling population of Peregrines in North America and Europe became clearer in the 1960s, particularly after Derek Ratcliffe's startling discovery of the relationship between DDT and eggshell thinning (see Chapter 2), the grim reality of a potential demise of the Peregrine began to settle in with many American and Canadian falconers. Professor Joseph Hickey's 1965 conference on the status of the

◀ Figure 16.1 *Partners in the Field* ©Anthony R. Croswell. Reproduction rights courtesy Frank Bond.

▲ **Figure 16.2** The bell helps the falconer keep track of the falcon in the air and on the ground.

Peregrine joined falconers and other biologists to confirm that Peregrines were in an inexorable decline. In the eastern United States, falconers' favorite "Rock" Peregrine eyries gradually became silent forever. In the West, the eyries were not completely abandoned, but it was a struggle to locate an occasional successful pair. Throughout North America and Europe, voices of doom predicted the extirpation of the species on the two continents. For falconers, even local extirpation meant that one of the classic birds of the sport would not be available to satisfy their passion.

It now seems incredible, but many early environmentalists, including some in the prominent national organizations, essentially declared that Americans should "let the Peregrine go" as testimony to the stupidity of the use of DDT and other pesticides in agriculture. Others underscored that pessimism with their certain knowledge that Peregrines could never be bred in captivity in meaningful numbers for a recovery

program. The obvious rhetorical question then became, would it not be a double indictment of humanity if we brought the Peregrine to the brink of extinction and then failed even to attempt a recovery? Since extinction was not an option, some members of the North American falconry community responded to the challenge.

The inherent demand for specialization and self-interest underlies the principle of evolution. The Peregrine genetically and, to some degree, the passion of falconers embody the power of that principle. From the earliest recognition of the plight of the Peregrine, a few falconers, later assisted by hundreds, became the leadership and the backbone of the Peregrine recovery effort. Their "self-interest" in saving the Peregrine evolved into the legendary success story of conservation biology in North America in the 20th Century.

In the 1950s, a series of disconnected events and forces coalesced to create the beginning of an ultimately coordinated recovery effort. The North American Falconers Association (NAFA) formed in November 1961 at Harold M. (Hal) Webster's house (Valkenswaard) south of Denver, Colorado. Approximately 45 falconers from many states attended the founding meeting. Some of these original NAFA founders, such as Jim Enderson, Don Hunter, Tom Smylie, Jack Stoddard, Clee Sealing, and Butch Olendorff, in various ways played a role in the Peregrine's recovery.

In the 1960s, few states protected raptors under law. Even into the early 1970s, Congress unsuccessfully tried to pass separate legislation to protect raptors. Not until the United States agreed to the addition of raptors to the lists of birds protected by the various migratory bird treaties with Great Britain (on behalf of Canada), the former USSR, Japan, and Mexico, were birds of prey federally protected. Slowly through the 1970s the states extended protection with the leadership and support of the falconry community. Protection at federal and state levels initiated raptor management. Even though falconers and biologists understood the Peregrine crisis, the U.S. Fish and Wildlife Service (FWS) did not have the authority to undertake any management for conservation or falconry purposes without the authority of federal law. Finally, the broad authority of the Migratory Bird Treaty Act gave FWS power to promulgate falconry regulations and to institute some early government-sponsored research and management programs. Falconers such as Stan Marcus, Roger Thacker, Al Nye, Walter Spofford, and Tom Cade provided important testimony before Congressional hearings to bring about this desired result in 1971.

The year 1973 turned out to be a pivotal one for the Peregrine. President Richard M. Nixon took office at a difficult time for the nation. With his appointment of William Ruckelshaus as the first administrator of the Environmental Protection Agency, by executive order Nixon banned DDT from manufacture and use in the United States. This singular event changed the course of Peregrine recovery, so that in time, all of the efforts carried out for the recovery were not made futile by a continued use of the persistent pesticides. Even under tremendous pressure, Nixon and Ruckelshaus did not bend. It was a remarkable time for change in attitudes about the environment. Although Nixon continues to be vilified for Watergate, many people forget that in the first two years of his administration he supported and signed the Endangered Species Act (ESA), Clean Water Act, Clean Air Act, and National Environmental Policy Act. Also, his administration's officials represented the United States at the formation of the Convention on International Trade in Endangered Species of Wild Fauna and Flora. Nathaniel Reed, then Assistant Secretary of the Interior for Fish and Wildlife and Parks, did not hesitate to assist in the Peregrine recovery strategy and simultaneously to be directly involved with the promulgation of the first falconry regulations. Although the rigid federal interpretation of the ESA has been a roadblock to the recovery of some species in recent years, important funding by Congress under the auspices of the ESA helped Peregrine recovery significantly.

In the early 1970s the needed elements for a successful Peregrine recovery effort became clearer. First, coordination of regional recovery programs on a geographical basis needed to consider the differing requirements of disjunct Peregrine populations. The ESA requires that recovery plans be prepared to set forth the recovery strategy and the goals for success. Fortunately, FWS did not seek to declare critical habitat under the ESA for the Peregrine. Whether by calculated decision or simple omission, the Peregrine did not generate conflict over land use practices among private, federal, and state landowners because of critical habitat.

Second, despite the pessimism of some critics, captive propagation became essential to produce Peregrines for release in areas where local populations dwindled or were totally extirpated. By this time there remained few successful active nests where Peregrines could be taken for propagation purposes, so falconers' birds necessarily made up much of the initial stock of breeding programs.

Third, there was a great need for field teams to coordinate and monitor the birds to be released. Initially falconers did all of the releases and most of the monitoring. Later, hundreds of volunteers from all walks of life supported them as hack site attendants.

Early Captive Propagation

Because of the uncertainty of the future source for the "long wing" falcons, a few falconers began contemplating captive propagation of various species as an alternative to the capture of birds from the wild. Previously, captive breeding simply was unknown, and most early falconers subscribed to the belief that the successful rearing of young in captivity was virtually impossible, except in circumstances of pure luck. Historically, falconry books passingly referenced captive propagation, but no written record of any successes with Peregrines exists before the 20th Century. Yet by the middle of the century, at least a few attempts at propagation succeeded, and there may have been others in remote parts of the world which went unrecorded.

The well-known German falconer Renz Waller began falconry before World War I and continued his pursuit of the sport throughout his life. He published a short account of successful propagation of Peregrines during World War II in his falconry book *Der Wilde Falk ist Mein Gesell*. His effort succeeded under unusually extreme circumstances, because of the ravages of war. Before World War II he made an unsuccessful attempt to breed Goshawks. Another falconer had his female Peregrine, Rittersporn, and a tiercel, Blitz. By 1941, Blitz died and Rittersporn returned to

▲ **Figure 16.3** Renz Waller, 1938.
Figure 16.4 The first captive-bred Peregrine. ▶

...would it not be a double indictment of humanity if we brought the Peregrine to the brink of extinction and then failed even to attempt a recovery?

Courtesy Archives of American Falconry

Richard Meng

Figure 16.5 Larry Schramm holding Alex the Great and wearing "armor"—slicker and rain hat—for protection while in the tiercel's pen. ▶

Figure 16.6 Heinz Meng and his first Peregrine, October 1941. ▶

Carl Jones

Frank Bond

▲ **Figure 16.7** Tom Cade holding a Mauritius Kestrel chick.

▲ **Figure 16.8** (Right) Jim Weaver with his falcon Lukey and dogs Spot and Babe on a winter day in the Jemez Mountains, New Mexico.

Waller where he paired her with a lame-winged haggard tiercel found under a power-line tower. From this pair he produced a falcon in 1942, lost early after fledging to an accident, and another in 1943, which he trained and flew through the year until she was lost in 1944 in a tame hack after she had molted. The success at such a time of deprivation is fantastic. Renz Waller had to feed his pair cat and dog with some pigeons and a few sparrows. In 1944 while he was away for a day, he returned to find his home and studio in Dusseldorf burned to the ground from an American air raid. His falcons miraculously survived in their garden mews.

Larry Schramm of Portland, Oregon, had been associated with falconry for several decades, but he also had a fascination with propagating exotic game birds. He took an interest in breeding Peale's Peregrines in 1963. He had a pair of eyasses from a British Columbia falconer, George Galicz, that finally produced a pair of young birds in 1968, one of which survived to maturity. Larry used a methodical approach by pairing tame eyasses for natural breeding.

The next early success came from Heinz Meng, a New York State University at New Paltz professor, who produced the now famous Prince Philip in 1971 (see sidebar, Breeding Peregrines and Releasing Their Young to the Wild, Chapter 5). This tiercel Peregrine later became a significant semen donor at The Peregrine Fund's facility at Cornell. Heinz Meng had been flying Peregrines and other species for years, so his knowledge of falconry practices coupled with his biology background provided him a base of knowledge to begin the process of achieving predictable results.

The Peregrine Fund

By the end of the 1960s, several falconers in the United States and Canada began their own "backyard" projects with a pair or two to see if some systematic success might be possible. Tom Cade, however, had an historic vision of an entire program to restore the Peregrine to its wild haunts across the continent. "Backyard" projects would be unpredictable. There had to be sufficient pairs to produce Peregrines on a scale inconceivable to most people (see Chapter 5).

Tom Cade's years as a falconer in his college and graduate school days in Alaska and California naturally influenced him to turn to falconers for support. His founding of The Peregrine Fund at Cornell University is well known. He began his search for a manager of the Sapsucker Woods facility with Bob Berry. At his home near Philadelphia, Bob already had success breeding

Goshawks, and he was attempting to breed Peregrines. Bob was not in a position to take the job, as a large family insurance business required his time and attention (see Chapter 3). When Tom Cade turned to Jim Weaver, he found a well-known falconer who at the time farmed in Illinois. Jim agreed to move into the famous Cornell "Peregrine Palace" in 1971 to manage the odd assortment of species available then (see sidebar, Dream Job of a Lifetime, Chapter 5).

In 1975, The Peregrine Fund became a formal nonprofit organization separate from Cornell University. For the founding board of directors, Tom Cade invited falconers Jim Weaver, Bob Berry, Frank Bond, and, in 1982, Bill Burnham as members.

Jim Weaver led the raptor propagation efforts in the eastern United States. His legendary skills as a falconer gave him insight into behavioral issues of breeding and release that fostered incredible success. In 1973, Jim produced the first young Peregrines for The Peregrine Fund. Through many of those years that he managed the Cornell facility, he served as a member of the board of directors of NAFA and then as president in the mid-1980s.

Bob Berry had been a falconer from childhood. He is a consummate falconer whose skills and determination as a breeder, particularly with the Gyrfalcon, have led the Peregrine restoration effort through some significant periods of difficulty. He will be forever known as the "Godfather" of radio telemetry for raptors. The famous RB 4 receiver is named for Robert Berry. From that early development with William Cochran of radio telemetry dedicated to falconry, the modern version of that technology is now applied to all wildlife species research. Bob founded and serves as president of the North American Raptor Breed-

ers' Association (see Chapter 3).

Bill Burnham was a Colorado falconer doing field research on Peregrines and Gyrfalcons in Greenland when Jim Weaver recruited him to join The Peregrine Fund. He managed the western propagation facilities in Fort Collins and led the early western field restoration. Through the 1980s to the present, he has overseen every aspect of the consolidation of The Peregrine Fund in Boise, the California Condor and Aplomado Falcon recovery efforts, and the international programs. His guidance of The Peregrine Fund converted its focus eventually from a single-species restoration program to one of the most significant raptor conservation organizations in the world (see Chapter 8).

Frank Bond, a New Mexico falconer and early Peregrine propagator, began as a founding board member. In the 1970s, FWS director Lynn Greenwalt appointed Frank to serve on the original Rocky Mountain/Southwest Peregrine Falcon Recovery Team. He continues to serve The Peregrine Fund as general counsel and assists with international and Washington legislative and regulatory matters. He has led a great deal of effort by NAFA to secure appropriate falconry regulations, and he has participated in all of the proceedings that amended the ESA, including the so-called raptor exemption in 1978, which made Peregrines

▲ Figure 16.9 (Top left) Bob Berry accomplished some of the original research on breeding Goshawks in captivity and was the first to inseminate a raptor artificially using birds sexually imprinted on humans.

▲ Figure 16.10 (Top right) Bill Burnham.

▲ Figure 16.11 Frank Bond, 1978, with captive-produced Peregrines about to be fostered to a pair of wild falcons in New Mexico.

▲ Figures 16.12–16.15 (Clockwise from top left) Bill Heinrich with Slate, an immature male Gyrfalcon; Cal Sandfort feeding Peregrine chicks; Brian Walton with a Harris's Hawk; and Pete Jenny and nestling Aplomado Falcon.

more easily available for propagation and falconry purposes.

Bill Burnham hired a young Colorado falconer, Bill Heinrich, as the second employee at the Fort Collins facility. Eventually Bill Heinrich led the field teams for all western Peregrine releases outside California. Over the years he managed approximately 1,500 hack site attendants, coordinated the field releases state by state, and served as liaison with federal and state authorities (see Chapter 8).

Dan Konkel joined The Peregrine Fund in the mid-1970s. He began as an assistant in food production to finally become an integral part of the Peregrine production team for the birds released in the western states (see sidebar, Mother Giant: Cross-fostering Peregrines into a Prairie Falcon Eyrie, Chapter 8).

With the expansion of the Fort Collins facilities, Bill Burnham added another Colorado falconer, Cal Sandfort, to the team. Cal led a small group of dedicated propagators to produce the vast majority of the Peregrines released in the West. He made great contributions to the formula used for the delicate process of egg incubation and hatching. He achieved remarkable success by

hatching and raising about 2,000 Peregrines (see sidebar, The Magnitude: What It Takes to Raise and Release a Peregrine, Chapter 8).

J. Peter Jenny began his falconry career in Pennsylvania, where he also served as a hack site attendant working with Bob Berry. After he moved to Wyoming, he joined The Peregrine Fund full time and managed the Latin American program. He then became a vice president and now leads the Aplomado Falcon restoration project (see Chapter 14).

Brian Mutch joined The Peregrine Fund full-time after he graduated from the University of Montana. Even before, he supervised hack site attendants. In that role he coordinated significant releases of young Peregrines throughout the West. With recovery complete, he continues as one of the principal members of the Aplomado Falcon and California Condor recovery efforts (see sidebar, Devil's Garden, Chapter 8).

In the 1980s Brian Walton merged his Santa Cruz Predatory Bird Research Group with The Peregrine Fund for a period of time. Brian Walton played a significant role in the California falconry community from his youth. Through the decades, he has led the field research, captive propagation, hack site releases, and postrelease monitoring in

Falcons, Falconry, and The Peregrine Fund

J. Lindsay Oaks, Jr.

▲ Lindsay Oaks.

Falcons, falconry, falconers, and my association with The Peregrine Fund have been an integral part of my life and have ultimately had a major impact on many aspects of my personal and professional life. Falcons and falconry became an all-consuming part of my life by the age of 12—virtually all of my free time was devoted in some way to the sport, and most of my friends (and heroes) were falconers. Obtaining my falconry license was the greatest event in my life at the time. Seeing a Peregrine Falcon in the wild, as happened one winter day in Denver, was another. As I think was true for most falconers in the early 1970s, the Peregrine to me represented perfection, the ultimate falconry bird, and also a symbol of the havoc that man had created with our natural world. The fact that these falcons had become extinct in some of their range, and endangered in other parts of their range with some question as to whether they could be saved, meant that I might never again see these birds in the wild, nor would I ever be able to have the privilege of using a Peregrine in falconry.

By 1977, while still in high school, I had found a way to become involved with the Peregrine Falcon and attempts at its recovery. At this time, The Peregrine Fund offered me a summer job raising quail and chickens to feed the falcons at the facility in Fort Collins, Colorado.

To me The Peregrine Fund was an exciting place with an exciting mission, and any opportunity to contribute to the cause (and just to be able to see all those Peregrines!) was exciting beyond words. Although the job was never advertised as anything other than a lot of hard and dirty work, there was nothing I would rather do. And work I did, for four summers while starting my undergraduate years in college, three summers raising food, and one summer attending a hack site in southern Colorado.

Although I did not realize it at the time, even this less-than-glamorous job was beginning to affect my career choices. Although I had always had an interest in the sciences, the exposure to highly dedicated people using science to solve a major problem was a powerful influence in focusing my interest in the basic sciences and a career in veterinary medicine. Once I began the veterinary medicine program, I was no longer able to work for The Peregrine Fund or practice falconry because of time constraints. However, the hiatus was broken immediately upon finishing veterinary school when I got my first job as a veterinarian at the Dubai Falcon Hospital in the United Arab Emirates. This assignment was arranged through a friend and colleague, Dave Remple, another falconer whom I met through The Peregrine Fund. Three years in the Emirates gave me not only an unprecedented amount of clinical experience with falcons (where else in the world can one have a busy two-man practice that does nothing but falcons?) but also a unique perspective on falcons and falconry in other parts of the world. It also gave me a further appreciation for the importance of conservation of Peregrines and other birds of prey, as it became clear what could happen when there was no conservation ethic. At the Falcon Hospital I also got my first introduction to biomedical research, which along with a long-standing interest in microbiology and infectious diseases, eventually drew me back to academia.

In due course I completed a residency in infectious diseases and a Ph.D. in virology at Washington State University. By this time, my primary professional interests and research were no longer devoted to birds but to the diseases of horses and humans. Nevertheless, my love of falcons and interest in their diseases still remained, and The Peregrine Fund gave me opportunities to contribute again—this time as a consultant when infectious disease problems or concerns arose. Most recently, this has involved traveling to other countries to investigate disease outbreaks in birds of prey. Of course, by now many things had changed. The Peregrine Falcon was well on the way to recovery. The Peregrine Fund had moved to Boise, Idaho, and was now operating the World Center for Birds of Prey with programs involving other birds. I was somewhat older and had a lot more credentials. And thankfully, I no longer shoveled quail manure. In this last regard, I have to give Bill Burnham, who has watched my transition over the years, a lot of credit for entrusting significant decisions regarding disease to the quail boy.

I have thought back many times to that day some 25 years ago when I was so thrilled at being able to go work at The Peregrine Fund. Many of my life's greatest adventures have been tied directly or indirectly to my association with The Peregrine Fund. Many of my closest friends were also made directly or indirectly because of my association with The Peregrine Fund and the places it took me. Had I said "no" on that particular day, I think my life would have been very different and considerably less interesting!

Lindsay Oaks, D.V.M., Ph.D., *is with the Department of Veterinary Microbiology and Pathology at Washington State University. Presently he is investigating the cause of vulture deaths in Pakistan and other potential infectious diseases of raptors.*

Archives of American Falconry

S. Kent Carnie

Today the Archives' library contains the most extensive collection of English-language falconry works in the world.

In the early 1980s American falconers became alarmed at the paucity of documentation of the beginnings of their sport. Although North American falconry history literally goes back to the conquistadores and pilgrim fathers, the sport first attracted popular attention, particularly in the United States, in the 1930s. With the deaths of those around whom the sport centered during that decade, unique, historically priceless collections of letters and photographs rapidly disappeared for want of any effort to collect them and any central repository in which to preserve them.

Officials of the national falconers organization, the North American Falconers Association (NAFA), shared that concern but recognized that they lacked a physical facility in which the results of any collection efforts might be housed. Similarly, as an organization actively seeking falconry legislation, NAFA was not eligible for the tax-deductible status all agreed was needed to compensate donors of the valuable literature and art so closely associated with the sport's history.

The Peregrine Fund, uniquely, offered those very prerequisites. Of equal importance, the founders of The Peregrine Fund all were ardent, "hard-core" falconers. All recognized the need to save the falconry heritage just as they were dedicated to saving populations of the sport's flagship species, the Peregrine.

In 1985 the Board of Directors of The Peregrine Fund established the Archives of American Falconry as an integral, financially self-sustaining program within the organization. Collection efforts to save the sport's heritage began the following year. Donated materials were housed in The Peregrine Fund's administration building at its World Center for Birds of Prey in Boise, Idaho, moving from room to room as collections expanded. By 1990, however, the extent of archival collections was such that a separate, dedicated facility was required. The Peregrine Fund founding member Bob Berry solicited funding support from the falconry community, and the James N. Rice Memorial Wing was built, named in honor of Bob's late mentor.

Although legal ownership of donated historical materials remains with The Peregrine Fund as required by federal tax provisions, the board of directors of the organization has formally recognized that, in the larger sense, it conducts these historical preservation efforts on behalf of the American falconry community as a whole. As such, it has guaranteed the integrity of all the materials and funding donated to the Archives.

With the construction of the Rice Wing, the Archives undertook efforts to develop an endowment fund to provide interest income to finance its daily operations. It also initiated a program of oral history collection and now publishes historic falconry materials under its Heritage Publication Series, funded by a separate publications fund. By 2001 the Archives had published two volumes, the first of which went out of print within 18 months.

Today the Archives' library contains the most extensive collection of English-language falconry works in the world. It maintains cabinets of letters, diaries, and notes of pioneer American falconers as well as one-of-a-kind translations and original manuscripts. The Archives possesses all the publications of national American falconry organizations and those of many state and provincial groups. Its collections of art are extensive but were limited until recently by storage and display space. Its

Jim Skidmore

S. Kent Carnie's *formal association with The Peregrine Fund began when he served on its board of directors from 1977 to 1983. He earned an honors degree in zoology from the University of California and has conducted graduate studies at Princeton University, the University of Tehran, and the Instituto Allende. A graduate of the U.S. Army's Foreign Area Specialist Training Program, he enjoyed a 20-year military career, mostly in Iran and in the Pentagon, dealing with affairs Iranian, retiring as a Lieutenant Colonel. With a lifelong involvement in falconry at the practicing level, he has also held a variety of appointed and elected positions in the North American Falconers Association. Having proposed creation of the Archives of American Falconry as an integral part of The Peregrine Fund, he has served that unique institution as founding curator since 1986, a position he enjoys today.*

Courtesy Archives of American Falconry

▲ "Doc" (Robert) Stabler with Lady Mary and Mirza (Peregrines) and Bonnie (Goshawk). His personal library essentially began the Archives collection and attracted many others.

California. The restoration of the Peregrine Falcon in California is synonymous with the name of Brian Walton (see Chapter 9).

Willard Heck first volunteered in 1974 for The Peregrine Fund, helping construct the initial falcon barn at the Fort Collins, Colorado, facility. In September of the following year he joined the organization as an employee and began assisting Jim Weaver with falcon propagation. He assumed responsibility for egg incubation and rearing of young falcons at the Cornell University facility in 1979. During the Peregrine nonbreeding season, he traveled below the equator to Mauritius to hatch and rear kestrels, becoming a key team member in restoration of the Mauritius Kestrel. When the Cornell operation was closed he moved to Boise, Idaho, and the World Center for Birds of Prey where he continued his responsibility for propagation of Peregrines for release in the East. Willard retired from The Peregrine Fund in 1994 and once again joined Jim Weaver, but this time at Jim's ranch in New Mexico where Willard raises Teita Falcons and is involved in a large variety of other projects, including serving as the Executive Secretary of the Grasslans Charitable Foundation (see sidebar, Adapt, Adjust, and Improvise, Chapter 5).

Also at Cornell, Jim Weaver invited a Connecticut falconer, Victor Hardaswick, to work on captive

Jim Weaver

▲ **Figure 16.16** Willard Heck and Goshawk, Danby.

Figure 16.17 Victor Hardaswick. ▶

Photo provided by Victor Hardaswick

collections of falconry furniture, both historic and contemporary, contain examples of the work of many of the world's finest falcony-craftsmen. An extensive collection of photographs ranges from early glass lantern-slides to the latest video and DVD productions.

The extent and success of these collection efforts reflect the generosity of the falconry community. Similarly, they have served to attract further donations, extending the scope of the Archives' collections to a worldwide perspective. Inevitably, the Archives out-

grew its original Rice Wing facility. In 2002 contributions from Bob Berry and others in the falconry community enabled the Archives to construct a "new" Rice Wing, including expanded storage and display facilities, in a million-dollar, 10,000-sq-ft building which it shares with The Peregrine Fund's technical library and scientific collections. In it, the Archives now enjoys a facility truly appropriate to its dedication to the collection and preservation of the evidence of our falconry heritage for the long-term future.

Figure 16.18 (Left) Steve Sherrod.

Figure 16.19 (Right) Morley Nelson at a NAFA meet, November 1974.

▲ Figure 16.20 Stan Temple with friends DC and Lizzy.

propagation at the Cornell falcon facility. He assisted Willard with propagation. Victor is now a major private breeder of Goshawks and falcons in South Dakota.

Steve Sherrod also contributed to the restoration program in the East. His initial involvement was as a Cornell graduate student researching Peregrines and then becoming a staff member and the eastern Peregrine release coordinator for The Peregrine Fund. After leaving the organization he was importantly involved in Bald Eagle restoration in the southeastern states and recently assumed a leadership role with the North American Grouse Partnership.

Another falconer biologist who contributed importantly to Peregrine restoration in the East was Stanley Temple (see sidebar, Lightning at Carroll Island, Chapter 5). Stan began the hands-on work with Mauritius Kestrels following his graduate research and was the eastern release coordinator for one season for The Peregrine Fund before replacing Joe Hickey upon Joe's retirement from the University of Wisconsin.

When Bill Burnham was confronted with moving all of The Peregrine Fund's facilities in Fort Collins to a new location, Morlan (Morley) Nelson, clearly one of America's best-known early falconers, made the initial contacts in the Boise community to investigate how the organization might be received. As a falconer and film maker, Morley provided Bill access to Boise community leaders and government officials to help make the transition from Colorado to Idaho possible. Morley has served as a board member for years.

When The Peregrine Fund constructed its first administration building in the early 1980s, S. Kent Carnie proposed the formation of a repository for falconry memorabilia, papers, and artifacts. Until his retirement, Kent was a U.S. Army intelligence officer (see sidebar, Archives of American Falconry, this chapter). Nevertheless, from his early youth through college at the University of California at Berkeley, where he studied with the celebrated zoologist Starker Leopold (a son of Aldo Leopold), he pursued falconry in a single-minded way.

Kent understood the history of American falconry and falconers' contributions to the conservation and welfare of birds of prey. With Kent as Archivist and the aid of NAFA and of many individual falconers, Bob Berry raised the money to build the James N. Rice (see Chapter 3) wing in the new administration building to house the Archives of American Falconry. Kent has amassed a collection greater than any other in the world representing a testimonial to the seamless connec-

Provided by Richard Fyfe

Photo provided by Pat Redig

▲ **Figure 16.21** (Left) Richard Fyfe.

▲ **Figure 16.22** (Right) Pat Redig, founder of The Raptor Center.

tion between Peregrine restoration and falconry (see sidebar, Archives of American Falconry, this chapter).

At its core, The Peregrine Fund joined falconers from across the United States for their knowledge of Peregrines to provide the basis of a successful conclusion. Later, other nonfalconers joined the organization to provide important contributions to the restoration.

Other Organizations and Falconers

Early in the 1970s, FWS sought to undertake its own captive propagation effort at its research facility in Patuxent, Maryland. The motive was noble but the means inadequate. The FWS attempted to propagate birds using the northern latitude, passage tundra Peregrines in improperly designed facilities. It did not invite falconers to assist, and without falconers leading the program, other falconers were not prepared to donate their eyass Peregrines. Most falconers realized that the Patuxent project had little chance of success, so they loaned their birds to The Peregrine Fund. The Patuxent project did not succeed.

The Canadian Wildlife Service (CWS) did not make the same mistake. Under the guidance of another falconer, Richard Fyfe, CWS established a project at Wainright, Alberta (see Chapter 6). Even though Richard Fyfe was a federal employee, he surrounded himself with a few falconers to build a successful team. Together, under extreme winter weather conditions at that northern latitude, they produced significant numbers of *anatum* Peregrines for their successful release efforts in southern Canada.

Through the upper Midwestern part of the United States, Peregrines nested along the Mississippi River. Although the eastern effort was intended to encompass some of this region, the restoration did not really begin until Patrick

Lucy Widener

◀ **Figure 16.23** Pete Widener propagates some of the most highly sought-after Peregrines for falconry.

Redig founded The Raptor Center (see Chapter 10). Pat's early falconry career led him to become one of the leading raptor veterinarians in the world. Instead of constructing a large, separate propagation facility, the upper Midwest recovery effort relied on the production of birds by falconers from their relatively small "backyard" projects. Since there were fewer birds needed, for releases Pat took the less expensive alternative of acquiring donated birds or purchasing birds at reasonable prices. His cooperating falconers assisted in the full range of the restoration efforts in the central United States (see sidebar, Midwest Peregrines: Propagators and Leaders, Chapter 10).

On his ranch near Sheridan, Wyoming, Pete Widener produced Peregrine fledglings dedicated to the upper Midwest recovery efforts for years. At the same time, he served as a long-time member of the board of directors of The Peregrine Fund and was a strong voice for the contributions made by falconers to the Peregrine restoration.

Figure 16.24 (Left) Jim Enderson was the first to propagate low latitude *anatum* Peregrines.

Figure 16.25 (Right) Les Boyd ▶ demonstrates a method of voluntary semen collection he pioneered that was an important breakthrough for captive propagation.

▲ **Figure 16.26** Dan O'Brien constructs a Peregrine release site.

Figure 16.27 Ralph ▶ Rogers, 1984.

In Colorado, James Enderson, a professor of biology at The Colorado College since 1962 and a lifelong falconer, dedicated his personal enthusiasm and career to the Peregrine. He began his early breeding efforts in the late 1960s and had initial success in the early 1970s. Not only was he the principal investigator of Peregrines in Colorado, but he also chaired the second Rocky Mountain/Southwest Peregrine Falcon Recovery Team. For years he too has been a member of The Peregrine Fund's board of directors. Because of his field studies and research, Jim Enderson is recognized as one of the world's experts on the Peregrine (see Chapter 4).

Early propagation efforts met significant obstacles because breeders relied on naturally breeding birds which proved extraordinarily difficult to pair.

Some breeders had limited initial success at "stripping" semen from males for early trials with artificial insemination (AI). However, stripping the male with the subsequent insemination of the female was extremely disturbing to a pair, when there was some hope the pair might also reproduce naturally. Les Boyd, one of the best known falconers in America, perfected voluntary semen donation. Following early examples of using human-imprinted raptors for AI (Hamerstrom 1970, Berry 1972, Temple 1972, Grier 1973), he coaxed imprinted male falcons to copulate voluntarily on a specially designed hat which he wore into the chamber (Boyd et al. 1977). Of course, it was an amusing image, but his semen-collection process, particularly for insemination of noncopulating females, was perhaps the single most important breakthrough in Peregrine propagation. Using his methods, The Peregrine Fund and other propagators were able to assemble a small team of imprinted males to provide the semen for fertilization of thousands of eggs.

In terms of efforts in the field, many other falconers have contributed importantly through the years. Ralph Rogers, a former president and long-time board member of NAFA, participated in Peregrine surveys in his home state of Montana and in Greenland. More recently he has dedicated research time to the status of Peregrines in Argentina. Through the years Ralph has bred Peregrines and coordinated some of the releases in Montana.

Similarly, Dan O'Brien, a South Dakota writer, novelist (all of his books weave in his lifelong passion for falconry as a theme), and bison rancher, worked under Bill Heinrich's direction at The Peregrine Fund to coordinate Peregrine releases throughout the West. At home on his South Dakota ranch, he continues to pursue tradi-

◀ **Figure 16.28** Tom Smylie.

◀ **Figure 16.29** Don Hunter (1922–2002), founder of The Raptor Research Foundation.

tional falconry hacking, which may refine new techniques for better management of future raptor release efforts.

Tom Smylie undertook the most significant early work to rediscover the historical New Mexico Peregrine eyries and to locate several previously unknown pairs (see sidebar, A Dream Come True, Chapter 14). He first became smitten by falconry when as a football player for the University of New Mexico in a game with the Air Force Academy, he saw their cadge of falcons. He did not join his teammates in the locker room at half time but stayed on the field to see the Air Force cadets fly their falcons. Tom Smylie put together two pairs of Peregrines in the late 1960s and, together with Frank Bond, did some of the early work in "hacking back" several young Prairie Falcons produced by Jim Weaver at The Peregrine Fund in the early 1970s. Later Tom became Assistant Regional Director of Public Affairs for FWS, and in that capacity assisted in smoothing over some rough spots in the recovery program. During his FWS years he trapped and banded tundra Peregrines on the Dry Tortugas off the coast of Florida, and in retirement he managed several hack sites in the Rocky Mountains.

From South Dakota, cattle rancher and lawyer Don Hunter loaned several birds to the eastern program (see Chapter 1). Don, originally from Pennsylvania, became a falconer in the association with some of the early best-known American falconers from that region. By the mid and late 1960s, Don had hosted two of the early NAFA field meets near his ranch in Centerville. He had attempted some early breeding, and through those years he traveled to Washington, D.C., frequently as president of the National Cattlemen's Association. During one of his many Washington trips he

spoke with a Secretary of Agriculture about the perils of DDT to Peregrines and other species. Following Joe Hickey's conference in 1965, Don proposed the development of a raptor organization dedicated to basic scientific research. With the assistance of others, he organized The Raptor Research Foundation, now a scientific organization with membership throughout the world.

Another falconer who began early in life, William Mattox focused on the Peregrine and continued throughout the restoration. Bill first searched for and monitored eastern Duck Hawks at eyries in New Hampshire and Vermont. After traveling to Greenland in 1951 to collect Gyrfalcons and Peregrines for falconry, he began the long-term Greenland Peregrine Falcon Survey in 1972 (see Chapter 12).

In 1964 and 1965, Frank Bond was a student at the University of Madrid. He spent that year

▲ **Figure 16.30** Bill Mattox, November 1955.

Frank Bond

Bill Heinrich

▲ **Figure 16.31** Félix Rodríguez de la Fuente (center) with Spanish falconers.

▲ **Figure 16.32** (Right) Ed Freienmuth assisted with Peregrine releases in western Colorado, and his wife, Charlotte, fed and looked after countless people involved in the Peregrine restoration effort.

hawking with the renowned Spanish falconer Félix Rodríguez de la Fuente. The *brookei* subspecies of Peregrine from the Iberian Peninsula somewhat avoided the perils of DDT by its isolation south of the Pyrenees Mountains. Tom Cade believed these Spanish Peregrines might be suitable for release in the eastern United States.

In 1972, Tom and Frank traveled to Spain after arranging through Félix Rodríguez de la Fuente to take two pairs of eyasses. Félix started his career as a dentist early, but by 1972 he abandoned dentistry for television, producing and hosting a Spanish national television weekly natural history program. Until his death in 1980 while filming the Iditarod dog sled race in Alaska, Félix collaborated with The Peregrine Fund. Arguably, he was one of the greatest falconers of the 20th Century.

In central Spain, Tom and Frank collected two pairs with the help of Félix's assistant, falconer Jesús Brizuela. To export the birds, they met with Spain's equivalent of the minister of natural resources for final permit approval.

The western program needed a more specialized plan as the early Rocky Mountain/Southwestern Peregrine Falcon Recovery Plan required all the birds to be of the *anatum* subspecies. Besides some of the birds removed from the wild by double-clutching eggs, falconers provided the significant core *anatum* breeding stock.

When Bill Burnham undertook the management of the Fort Collins facility, he brought with him a pair of *anatum* Peregrine Falcons from Colorado. Jim Enderson then provided several more pairs of *anatum* Peregrines.

From New Mexico, Tom Smylie achieved limited breeding success with two pairs of *anatum* fal-

cons from the Jemez Mountains. One pair had laid fertile eggs, but none of the eggs hatched live chicks. At The Peregrine Fund, under somewhat different conditions, they became part of the important, early successfully breeding pairs.

Similarly, Frank Bond added another pair of *anatum* falcons, also from the Jemez Mountains. This pair, which had originally been taken by Tom Smylie, produced several young, but not in the significant numbers they did later in Fort Collins and Boise.

Two imprinted tiercel semen donors established themselves as the most significant birds for the western recovery effort. Jim Enderson, in Colorado Springs, bred the first, named BC. Remarkably he produced approximately 350 young for the release. Clay Bird, another imprinted tiercel, was the first *anatum* Peregrine Frank Bond hatched in New Mexico. In his astounding propagation career spanning almost two decades, Clay Bird fathered approximately 550 young for release (see Chapter 19).

In 1971, a group of falconers founded the North American Peregrine Foundation in Colorado. Its purposes were to encourage and conduct research techniques to breed endangered species; to create a captive population of raptors for education, scientific, and recreational purposes; and to receive and disburse funds for those objectives. The original officers were Stanley Marcus, president (at the time also president of NAFA), Steven Hannon (a Colorado lawyer) vice president, and Edward Freienmuth, treasurer (also the NAFA treasurer). Later they were joined by well-known falconers Roger Thacker (a longtime NAFA president) and John Campbell of Alberta. The organization received substantial contributions from the falconry community. The Peregrine Fund was the principal beneficiary of its donated funds.

The North American Peregrine Foundation also supported a Prairie Falcon breeding project at Ed Freienmuth's home, with the hope of expanding to Peregrine Falcons for purposes of release to augment wild populations. It created a falconry establishment operated by California falconer Bob Martin near Clarksville in eastern Colorado for a few years. Here the foundation provided falconers an opportunity to hunt their birds on pheasants and, for those falconers who had Peregrines, encouraged them to donate their Peregrines to captive-breeding facilities. The foundation essentially ceased its operation when Ed Freienmuth died in 1993.

Government Partners

The conservation assistance provided by Tom Smylie in FWS and by Richard Fyfe in CWS, previously noted, acknowledges the important roles some falconers played in their positions as government employees. Because of the nature of a continent-wide restoration effort and the complex web of laws guiding endangered species recovery, many government employees aided tremendously in the Peregrine's success. Most of them were not falconers, but some key figures had been lifelong falconers.

James L. Ruos was the first raptor biologist employed by FWS in its Office of Migratory Birds. He quietly persuaded FWS senior leadership to adopt the promising private conservation components of the early recovery effort, even when it required FWS to abandon its own propagation efforts at Patuxent. At the same time, Jim undertook his own "backyard" Peregrine propagation effort with birds that he had flown for years (see Chapter 15).

The Colorado Division of Wildlife hired Gerald (Jerry) Craig as the first full-time raptor biologist on the staff of any western state wildlife agency. Being a falconer through school motivated Jerry to pursue a wildlife career. He was instrumental in providing the Colorado Division of Wildlife's facility in Fort Collins to The Peregrine Fund for its first western breeding barns. He served as team leader of the first Rocky Mountain/Southwest Peregrine Falcon Recovery Team as well as a member of the second team (see Chapter 17).

Finally, two other state government officials, also falconers, oversaw with federal officials the difficult endangered species delisting process and the development of falconry harvest protocols for eyass *anatum* Peregrines. First, Bruce Taubert, as Assistant Director of the Arizona Department of

▲ Figures 16.33–16.36 (Clockwise, left to right) James L. Ruos; Jerry Craig; Brian Millsap; Bruce Taubert.

▲ Figure 16.37 "The Haxton Hawking Club" convened each fall during the early 1970s to hawk pheasants in the farm country near Clarksville in northeastern Colorado. Back row: Tom Cade, Jim Ince, Grainger Hunt, and Tom Smylie; front row: Ralph Rogers, Frank Bond, and Jim Weaver.

If some people still associate falconers and Peregrines with the Middle Ages, perhaps the modern falconer/ conservationist will replace that image.

Bill Mattox

▲ **Figure 16.38** Immature Peregrine.

Game and Fish, secured the support of the International Association of Fish and Wildlife Agencies to nominate the *anatum* subspecies for delisting. He partially drafted some of the harvest plan.

Brian Millsap, a falconer biologist and senior manager for the Florida Department of Game and Fresh Water Fisheries, joined Bruce Taubert in the delisting process. Brian provided much of the biological background materials for the Peregrine harvest by falconers. Through this period he served as president of NAFA, and just as he completed his NAFA term of office, became president of The Raptor Research Foundation, then accepted a position with FWS to direct the Office of Migratory Birds, once again completing the circle of falconry and conservation.

Conclusion

Perhaps by the early 1980s, the Peregrine restoration team realized there would be success in this great international effort. By 1985, at the second conference in Sacramento, California, on the status of the Peregrine, field researchers presented quite a different picture for the bird from the bleak picture of the 1965 Madison conference (Cade et al. 1988). Although several falconers summarized their own research and observations, the majority of the presenters were nonfalconers. The proceedings painted a picture of hope and inevitable success. The Peregrine's charisma had clearly attracted a far larger group of people. Today, all across North America, people gathering in cities, suburban locations, and remote haunts to witness the Peregrine's

rites of spring bear witness to the hard work of falconers and many others.

As posterity contemplates the astounding success of the Peregrine's recovery, the vision and courage to achieve it will largely be attributed rightly to Tom Cade and his initial team of falconers. In August 1999, The Peregrine Fund organized a grand celebration in Boise for the delisting of the Peregrine. The conference activities there included a recount by many speakers of the component parts of the restoration effort. When Frank Bond made his presentation on the contributions of falconers, he asked all those falconers on the stage and in the crowd to stand in recognition. Approximately two-thirds of the presenters and the audience of nearly one thousand stood. An audible gasp erupted from those still seated as everyone became aware of the falconers' dedication to the restoration. The celebration

doubled as a grand reunion of falconers spanning four decades of disciplined work.

The Peregrine conservation story mixes people, money, difficult decisions, and the triumph of optimism for recovery over the pessimism of extinction. If some people still associate falconers and Peregrines with the Middle Ages, perhaps the modern falconer/conservationist will replace that image. Future falconers who are assured the pleasure of flying Peregrines must revere the falconers of the last four decades of the 20th Century, as they made it possible for a new generation of falconers to pursue their passion. The individual contributions of the falconers mentioned, and those hundreds across America, Canada, and throughout the world who were not included in this account, are honored for this extraordinary success.

▲ **Figure 16.39** Enjoying the scenery and morning sun before the afternoon hunting, eastern Idaho.

Frank Bond *is a lawyer practicing natural resources law in New Mexico. Formerly he served in the New Mexico House of Representatives and as Chairman of the New Mexico Commission on Higher Education. As a fourth-generation New Mexican he grew up on family ranches, and he continues to own and operate his own ranches. As an undergraduate at The Colorado College in the mid-1960s he became enchanted with falconry after he met Robert M. "Doc" Stabler, a professor of zoology and one of the best-known early American falconers. Frank had the good fortune of hawking with Félix Rodríguez de la Fuente in Spain for a year when he was a student at the University of Madrid. He was invited by Tom Cade to be one of the founders of The Peregrine Fund, where he continues to serve on the Board of Directors and as general counsel. In the 1970s he became one of the early falconers to breed Prairie and Peregrine Falcons. He is the general counsel of the North American Falconers Association and Vice President for the Americas of the International Association for Falconry and Conservation of Birds of Prey. He continues to practice falconry, flying Gyrfalcons and Peregrine Falcons.*

Chapter 17

Peregrine Restoration from a State Biologist's Perspective

Robert Oakleaf and Gerald R. Craig

S*tate wildlife agencies had an important role in Peregrine Falcon restoration* although the level of involvement varied greatly among states, ranging from authorizing the activities of others to releasing falcons and monitoring results themselves. This chapter documents the recovery actions in Colorado and Wyoming, two states where state wildlife biologists had active and important roles in the recovery program.

Wyoming

Robert Oakleaf

Literally thousands of people and hundreds of agencies and organizations were involved in restoring Peregrine Falcons. State biologists were in a unique position. Most of us were close enough to observe the progress and feel the fascination and excitement of the story unfolding, but we had the option of determining our own comfort level as to the extent we would participate. Restoration of the Peregrine Falcon is an amazing success story. A predator was released across the nation as a fully classified endangered species with widespread public support and relatively little controversy. Currently, endangered species are reintroduced following federal rules attaching the "nonessential experimental" label and usually amid extreme controversy.

What made it work? Could anything like it happen again? These questions have haunted many of us since we began to observe population increases and eventually participate in the August 1999 delisting celebration. Other chapters detail many specific ingredients of this success story. I attempt to articulate factors that were important to a successful recovery effort from my perspective while working as a state nongame biologist in Nevada (1973–1977) and Wyoming (since 1977).

Priority

State wildlife programs, especially in the West, are infamous for being underfunded and understaffed. Prioritizing species and actions to receive attention is a constant challenge. From a

◀ **Figure 17.1** *Eye to Eye* ©Terry Isaac. By arrangement with the artist and Mill Pond Press.
For information on art prints by Terry Isaac, please call Mill Pond Press, Inc. at (800) 237-2233.

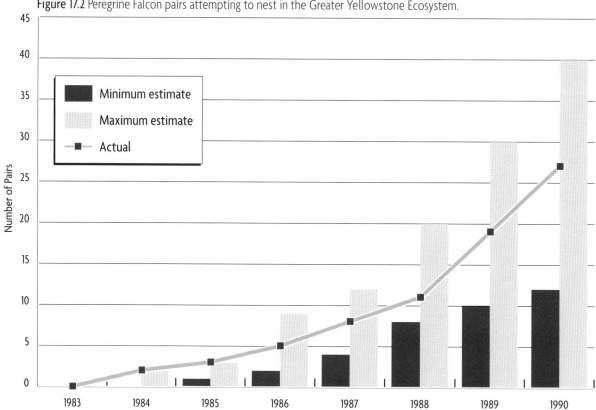

Figure 17.2 Peregrine Falcon pairs attempting to nest in the Greater Yellowstone Ecosystem.

national perspective, Peregrines had to be considered a high priority because of documented declines and less than adequate production of a few remaining pairs (Fyfe et al. 1976). Although the species was not in danger of becoming extinct worldwide, long-term persistence in the United States certainly appeared questionable. Species are now listed without empirical data and entirely on the basis of anecdotal information about population declines and without reference to viability of existing population numbers or even a realistic attempt to anchor a temporal perspective as to which decade (or even century) should influence baseline management objectives.

What was the potential for a state to contribute significantly to the restoration effort? The answer was obvious for many states with significant numbers of historical eyries. Nevada and Wyoming, however, happened to be two states with few breeding records (Bond 1946). In both states, I encountered criticism that Peregrines never existed in significant numbers and therefore should not receive massive amounts of attention. Was lack of data due to an environment not suitable for significant numbers of breeding Peregrines? Or was it due to other factors? Records of Peregrine eyries typically come from early biological surveys, egg collectors, falconers, and university studies. These sources were relatively uncommon in both Nevada and

Wyoming before population crashes and presented the likelihood that few historical records indicated a lack of effective searches. The potential for habitat to contribute significantly to Peregrine restoration efforts appeared limited in Nevada and varied significantly from historical habitat I learned about while visiting vacant eyries with Carl Thelander and Brian Walton in California and Oregon habitat identified by Dan Fenske. Peregrine habitat identified in Utah (Porter and White 1973) with extensive wetlands and proximate cliff areas is present in Nevada but extremely limited. I was left with the impression that significant portions of state wildlife efforts should not go to Peregrines in Nevada. Brian Walton, however, would convincingly argue that anywhere reintroductions successfully added young benefitted the national effort.

In Wyoming, I searched unpublished records and visited people who were willing to share information about nesting locations that were not previously common knowledge (e.g., Yvon Chouinard, Warren Higby, Frank Craighead, and others), indicating at least 18 locations where Peregrines previously nested. Even Bill Burnham knew of a location in Wyoming where recently fledged young indicated nesting. The record is in a location where he almost died of thirst and exhaustion in an unsuccessful attempt to find Peregrines but later became a favorite fishing destination for himself, his father, and many of us

298

who heard his story and later documented reoccupancy by Peregrines.

Extensive surveys for nesting Peregrines were conducted in Wyoming from 1978 through 1980. Although only one pair of Peregrines was found (2 km into Montana), they failed and the site eventually became vacant. Habitat, however, appeared to compare favorably with historical sites known in adjacent states. Wyoming had a dearth of historical breeding records, but the habitat appeared to be a continuum with historical breeding habitats in adjacent states. Late in 1979, I could picture over 100 specific areas where Peregrines should breed in Wyoming.

Potential for Programs to be Effective

Additional considerations were important for a species or project to become high priority with state programs. The primary causal factor of Peregrine population declines was identified and mitigating federal legislation enacted (Enderson et al. 1995). Reintroduction was an obvious and logical next step. Most state wildlife agencies evolved with release and stocking programs of game species, and most states were ready to embrace Peregrine reintroduction. Some biologists, however, doubted the environmental contamination that occurred over decades would suddenly disappear following restrictive regulations. Early in the Peregrine reintroduction effort, I was often confronted with the question "What good will it do to release Peregrines if contaminants are still present in the environment?" This question was especially relevant to more northern states such as Wyoming, where Peregrines are likely to migrate to Mexico, a country that still uses a wide variety of pesticides (Henny et al. 1982). The best way to answer this question was to attempt reintroduction and include a good monitoring program.

Attributes of the Species and Public Interest

The Peregrine Falcon is a well-known charismatic species. Cade (1982) eloquently describes the species' attraction to devotees through the centuries. Even before restoration efforts were initiated, there was a wealth of information and interest from a broad spectrum of the public. The Peregrine is a very adaptable species. If effective programs to restore Peregrine populations could not be developed, what chance would there be for many recently listed species about which little is known, and which receive little public interest and are thought to be severely restricted to specific environmental conditions?

Most biologists were not immune to the charisma of Peregrines and, once exposed, seemed willing

to devote significant portions of their time to restoration efforts. I did, however, note that some administrators of state wildlife programs were concerned that their newly fledged nongame programs in the late 1970s would become falcon programs and their biologists would become raptor specialists. Most state biologists needed to resist the temptation of working primarily on one species and at least give the impression they were addressing some of the many other species and issues needing attention.

Adequate Funding and Planning

I was always impressed with the amounts and wide variety of funding sources for Peregrine projects. It was not that money was unlimited and easy to obtain. Everyone had to work at it. The Peregrine Fund developed its successful fund-raising for captive breeding. Reintroduction in Wyoming was initiated with a grant from the Rocky Mountain Conservation Fund of the Safari Club and matching funds from the Wyoming Game and Fish Department. Northwest Wyoming, near Jackson, was selected to initiate restoration efforts, primarily because of a continuum of historical and potential breeding habitat that extended into Idaho and Montana. In addition, this area, commonly referred to as the Greater Yellowstone Ecosystem (GYE), and the habitat were managed by eight different government agencies with over 20 different administrative divisions, a situation that translated into over 20 different budgets or potential funding sources.

It was necessary, however, to continue selling the program. I worked with Bill Heinrich of The Peregrine Fund and state biologists Wayne

▲ **Figure 17.3** Inventories in Wyoming (1978–1980) identified over 100 cliffs that appeared to be excellent Peregrine habitat but lacked historical records of breeding pairs.

Dale Mutch

▲ **Figure 17.4** Participants of the 1989 annual Peregrine reintroduction adaptive management meeting included Doyle Brown, Bob Oakleaf, Barb Franklin, Bill Heinrich, Brian Mutch, Jim Willmarth, and Ed Levine.

Figure 17.5 Bill Heinrich ▶ checking for potential hack ledges in Death Canyon overlooking Phelps Lake in Grand Teton National Park.

John Weaver

Melquist and Dennis Flath of Idaho and Montana, respectively. Recognizing that it would take a large number of Peregrines to reestablish a viable nesting population, we developed objectives and plans for reintroduction efforts that were geographically concentrated but spread over a large potential funding base. As is the case with many new projects, cooperative funding was easiest to obtain the first few years while the project was new and receiving a considerable amount of attention. Government funding is typically tied to specific geographic areas and usually takes at least two years to obtain. Specific expenditures in new

areas for expanding populations had to be planned and articulated. In 1984 we used a stochastic model (Grier 1980) and input data to predict possible population trends in Wyoming, if cooperative efforts were being successful. Our hope was to provide individuals who were seeking funding with a tool for evaluating progress and the amount of effort left to achieve objectives.

There were at least two unknowns that made it difficult to predict population growth. Few nesting pairs of Peregrines remained in California by the mid-1970s (Fyfe et al. 1976). Yet the female at Morro Rock quickly recruited a replacement when the tiercel was injured and brought into captivity. Apparently a nonbreeding segment of the population was maintained, even during extreme population declines to near extinction, with presumably vast amounts of vacant habitat remaining. Would this nonbreeding segment have to be established first before breeding pairs became established and populations began recovery? Hunt (1988) later articulated the concept of nonbreeding, or "floating," segments of Peregrine populations. Also confounding the modeling effort was the unknown potential for released Peregrines to be recruited to breeding populations farther south, especially in states such as Arizona and southern Utah. With these and other unknowns, the modeling effort was simply a way of depicting our best guess as to what could be expected.

In 1988 the Wyoming program was left in a lurch with elimination of significant amounts of funding. I like to think the modeling helped. It gave us another talking point for selling the program. By 1985 we knew we had established two pairs by successfully hacking an average of 52 falcons per pair. By 1988 a new pair was being established for every 21 falcons that were successfully hacked. Using estimates shown in Figure 17.2, we could show that a new pair would be added to the growing Peregrine population with every eight to 10 falcons successfully reintroduced. These biological data could be converted to something bureaucrats could understand (i.e., money). In 1985 we were averaging $117,000 of expenditures for hacking to establish one pair, $47,000 per pair in 1988, and a predicted $18,000 per pair by 1990. It made no sense to quit reintroduction efforts in 1988. But it was important from a state perspective to have a target date when available funding could be redirected toward other pressing needs. When is enough, enough? The most creditable time to answer this question is before you can be accused of being personally biased for continued work on one high-profile species, regardless of whether the work is needed.

Attributes of Personnel and Program

Important ingredients for successful restoration were the professional commitments by The Peregrine Fund personnel and cooperators. In fewer than 10 years, captive breeding evolved from a program whose potential was completely unknown to a program that produced birds for a national reintroduction effort. The Peregrine Fund worked through hacking in eastern states and struggled and experimented with fostering and cross-fostering in the West. Reintroduction techniques and systems were developed and appeared successful. In other words, reintroduction of Peregrine Falcons was likely to be effective.

Working with The Peregrine Fund was a treat for state biologists. The Fund was goal oriented and extremely committed. Its personnel who worked in Wyoming included Bill Heinrich, Brian Mutch, Jim Willmarth, Ed Levine, and Dan O'Brien, to name a few of the reintroduction specialists, and over 170 hack site attendants. Truly a significant part of the formula for success can be attributed to those individuals involved and the commitment to a common goal. Many of them seemed to have recklessly abandoned all aspects of a personal life and all chances for a career in anything permanent. After all, they were working hard at a goal that would leave them without a job.

Hack site attendants were absolutely essential to success of Peregrine restoration efforts. Different sites demanded different abilities. All attendants, however, had to accept one demand I know many of us could not—stay in one spot for two months of the summer. Attendants received little individual recognition from media coverage of restoration progress. I did notice, however, that personnel supervising and assisting with logistics paid special attention to emphasizing how important and valuable attendants were to the program. Every year, I was amazed at Bill Heinrich's ability to hire and field a large number of attendants and consistently select individuals who, by the end of the eight-week hack, would have proved to be so capable of accomplishing the challenge. State biologists who frequently hire and field temporary employees are well aware of the difficulties associated with such endeavors.

▲ **Figure 17.6** Dale Mutch scrutinizes the first eyrie he located in Wyoming, following fledging.

Brian Mutch

I was consistently impressed with special attributes of the approach to reintroduction. State biologists tend to focus on wildlife populations. Although the goals were oriented toward the population levels, each individual falcon received extraordinary care and attention from The Peregrine Fund personnel. The welfare of individual falcons always had priority over how much was accomplished in a given day or week or even the comfort level of an employee.

Of special interest was the knowledge of the species exhibited by Heinrich and other reintroduction specialists. Most were falconers, and no doubt being experienced in falconry and the management of falcons from captivity to hunting situations greatly contributed to success. They all seemed to have a deep understanding of what was important to a Peregrine from a husbandry standpoint and which instincts needed to be addressed and which did not. I frequently heard discussions as to which was more important to recovery—falconers and falconry or science and wildlife biology. It seemed like a meaningless debate. What was noticeable and important for success was that most of The Peregrine Fund personnel had the special combination of being falconers and wildlife biologists either by training or were strongly influenced by basic principles of the profession and capable of working with people. It was the people with that rare combination of characteristics who deserve much of the credit for the Peregrine success story.

Flexibility and Adaptive Management of Programs

Bill Heinrich was constantly evaluating the reintroduction approach to streamline it and make it easier. Evaluations of and modifications to the program were significantly enhanced by annual adaptive management meetings (Figure 17.4). In 1980, hack sites were managed with the idea that it was important to provide Peregrines with live or freshly killed quail. Maintaining a supply of live quail near reintroduction areas and keeping them at camps and out of reach of grizzly bears proved extremely challenging. The realization that Peregrines did as well with frozen quail may seem like a minor finding, but the change to

Many of them seemed to have recklessly abandoned all aspects of a personal life and all chances for a career in anything permanent.

▲ **Figure 17.7** Bill Heinrich and Bob Oakleaf, along with hack site attendants Jennifer and Tom Grant, place young Peregrines into a hack box. This was one of the first Wyoming release sites, established at Webb Canyon in Grand Teton National Park in the early 1980s.

maintaining freezers and frozen quail was almost of revolutionary proportions by eliminating a major logistical problem. Eliminating live quail did have its drawbacks, however. Gone with the quail were the stories told to tourists encountered on Grand Teton National Park trails about what we were doing carrying cages full of live quail. Also gone were rumored social events in Jackson that were garnished with pilfered quail and quail eggs.

Bill Heinrich and I started selecting hack sites in the Teton Mountains, looking for large cliffs and sites that resembled Peregrine nesting habitat (Figure 17.5). The logistics of working Teton sites were challenging. As we became older and wiser, it became obvious there were advantages to hack sites on smaller rocks. The important point was that smaller rocks near enough to breeding habitat would continue to capitalize on the falcon's instinct of returning to the general area of a natal site. Aside from the obvious advantages of easier logistics, smaller cliffs could be located away from other avian predators. We soon learned that ground predators or disruptive behavior of bears could be controlled with an electric fence. Fledged young seemed to have an easier time locating and returning to smaller cliffs during the first few days following release. In addition, we did not need to worry about returning falcons attempting to nest and forcing us to locate a new site before it was time to move to a new area. As the program progressed, smaller cliffs were favored, and we would more frequently hear the classic Bill Heinrich comment "Since when did we start putting hack sites on boulders?"

I knew almost nothing about what was needed for a release site when reintroduction was initiated in Wyoming. Later, I found the whole process

of locating and building a hack site intriguing and assisted as often as I could. There were always speculation and wagers as to how birds would do at a site. Everyone involved had a favorite hack site. Some sites were located after weeks of searching for a location with desirable characteristics. Others were located during Peregrine surveys, years in advance of when we could use them.

Three of these cliffs were monitored for years before releases and stand out in my mind. It was a mystery to me why they were not frequently used by other nesting raptors. The Peregrine Fund successfully hacked 53 Peregrines at these sites until returning pairs were established. All three sites still have Peregrines that typically nest in the hack box and had fledged 32 young through 1999. Apparently, these are the only cliff sites in western states where Peregrines have nested in hack boxes instead of selecting natural ledges (W. Heinrich pers. comm.). Also a mystery to me was the origin of hack site names (i.e., Death Canyon, Suicide, Diamond Cutter, or Dead Indian).

One step that received little variation was the transportation of supplies and construction of a hack box. It was typically done with assistance of a helicopter, usually one that was on a contract as standby for firefighting, meaning it was free. Installing hack boxes almost seemed mundane and somewhat mechanical. I was involved with some installations, however, that varied and were somewhat revealing of personalities of some colleagues. Installation of some sites varied by being packed in on our backs; one was packed in with horses, and one site was constructed mostly after sunset during somewhat inclement weather. I learned:

1. When some people think they might be having a heart attack, they just disappear until it is over;
2. There are surefire ways of preventing marmots from becoming addicted to the glue in plywood;
3. Bill Heinrich must have developed a deep personal bias against horses at an early age;
4. Dale Mutch and Brian Mutch always pay attention to taking care of the sandwiches, assuring they are packed in a dependable manner; And
5. Some people can find entertainment anywhere, anytime, and under any conditions.

The Peregrine Fund's flexibility also extended to human aspects of the project and clearly added to the success. I watched as the Fund dealt with many different types of personalities and governmental quirks, regulations, and policy. In Wyoming, Peregrines were hacked in a national wildlife refuge, two national parks, a national monument, three national forests (including eight different ranger districts), four Bureau of Land Management (BLM) Resource Areas, and three private ranches. Each site had its own administrative sensitivities, which were successfully addressed by The Peregrine Fund. In addition, associated with these areas were many land uses that could be perceived as conflicting with Peregrines. There was a deep commitment, however, to fit the restoration effort into existing land use patterns. The reintroduction of Peregrines as an endangered species was treated with respect and an obligation to avoid conflict wherever possible. Conflict could be and was avoided by temporarily not using a hack site, relocating a site, or releasing more birds at a site with minimum conflict.

Monitoring Results

Monitoring and evaluating progress are essential components of any successful program. Results in Wyoming were similar to those in other states, though they may have varied temporally somewhat. Intensive surveys from 1978 through 1980 documented that a breeding population of Peregrines no longer occurred. Peregrine reintroduction efforts were initiated in Wyoming during 1980. Although we had coordinated objectives with Montana and Idaho, specific Wyoming objectives were to (1) release a minimum of 15 falcons annually, (2) establish 10 nesting pairs by 1991, and (3) establish 30 pairs by 1996. All of these objectives were attained. Over 325 (mean = 20/yr) Peregrines were hacked in Wyoming (1980–1995). The nesting population increased at an average of approximately 35% annually. Eleven pairs attempted to nest in 1989, and by 1994, 30 pairs had fledged over 50 young in Wyoming. The population has continued to increase geometrically. Currently, we are locating a much smaller percentage of newly established pairs because of the increasing logistical problems associated with population expansion and a decrease in funding and personnel available for nesting surveys. Since the 1984 nesting season, however, we have confirmed breeding pairs at over 51 locations in Wyoming.

The above summary sounds simple. In 1979, however, it still seemed like an overwhelming challenge to go from hacking four juvenile Peregrines to establishing a breeding population that would have a high probability of persistence and specifically occupy habitats of Wyoming. In 1983, it was especially worrisome. I could not find a pair of Peregrines to save me. If there was a flaw to the approach of starting in the best and most extensive habitat, it was that early results of Peregrine nesting could be missed. Was I wasting everyone's time and money trying to establish a breeding population of Peregrines in Wyoming? Maybe Wyoming was a biological hiatus. Maybe Wyoming-released Peregrines were part of the expanding populations being documented in Arizona and southern Utah.

Wyoming was committed to a monitoring program. If the reintroduction program was to succeed, we needed to document results and progress. I also needed data to address questions such as "Are you sure there were no Peregrines before reintroduction?" and "Are you sure they were not coming back on their own anyway?"

Finally, I located a breeding pair in 1984 in Yellowstone National Park at a site that had been studied by Jay Sumner from 1966 through 1973. The last year of occupancy was 1969. The male was from a hack site 80 km west and the female from a hack site 100 km south. Habitat that I considered to be among the best in Wyoming was the first to be reoccupied. Even more fascinating was the fact that the nest site had been vacant for 10 years with no adults to influence a behavioral tradition or pass along a mystical genetic programming for selecting specific nesting ledges. Yet these captive-produced falcons selected the exact ledges used by previous occupants.

Inventory efforts were greatly enhanced when I was able to employ Dale Mutch in 1989 to focus almost entirely on surveys for the next five breeding seasons. I almost ruined Mutch as he located a new pair of Peregrines at literally the first cliff on his 1989 work schedule (Figure 17.6). Fortunately, he was able to make an attitude adjustment necessary for persevering through many cliffs with negative results, while consistently locating new pairs. In addition to

John Weaver

▲ **Figure 17.8** Bill Heinrich checks out the "gestalt" of a ledge in the Tetons that later became the Death Canyon hack site.

303

Terry McEneaney

Figure 17.9 One of the first young (wild) Peregrines to fledge from a reintroduced pair in Wyoming.

. . . it would behoove biologists to take the important factors of the Peregrine success story. . . and apply them to specific projects.

the previously mentioned Peregrine Fund personnel, many people assisted with Peregrine surveys. Especially helpful were Bob Hollister, Ed Levine, Dan Stevenson, and Tom Laurion. Terry McEneaney moved to Yellowstone National Park in 1987 and is still collecting valuable information on production and locations of new pairs in Yellowstone.

The effectiveness of this monitoring effort continues to amaze me and is a credit to individuals conducting surveys. Nesting Peregrines were documented at 29 locations by 1993. Eighteen (62%) were located within two years of first being occupied (based on age of known adults and/or dates cliffs were last surveyed with negative results). As the Peregrine population has expanded, it has become more difficult to keep up with progress. Excellent baseline data, however, allow us further evaluations documenting the population increase. Forty-one (80%) of the known nest sites in 1999 (n = 51) were surveyed prior to recent occupancy by Peregrines. Of these 41 sites, 25 (61%) were previously occupied by Prairie Falcons, 12 (30%) were previously vacant (excluding Red-tailed

Hawks and ravens), and three were previously occupied by Golden Eagles.

Monitoring results clearly document that Peregrines were extirpated from Wyoming. Certainly, reintroduction efforts can be credited for the recovering population.

Application of Peregrine Restoration Model to Other Programs

Many state biologists jump (or get pushed) into endangered species recovery programs. Some of us will look to the Peregrine story to see whether factors contributing to success are possible for other species and future programs. All of these factors will not be there for any given species. I am convinced, however, that it would behoove biologists to take the important factors of the Peregrine success story (whether they use the few I discussed or identify additional ones), translate them into a generic form, and apply them to specific projects. The magical combination of cards will probably never be dealt again. But to paraphrase Steve Baptiste, you need to know what has been dealt and try and get the good ones that are left.

Courtesy Bob Oakleaf

Bob Oakleaf *grew up in and graduated from high school in Fort Collins, Colorado, and obtained a B.Sc. in wildlife biology from Colorado State University in 1969 and an M.Sc. in wildlife management from the University of Nevada, Reno in 1972 while studying Sage Grouse. After two years in the Army, he returned to Nevada as a nongame biologist for the state from 1974 through 1977. In 1977 Bob accepted a position with the Wyoming Game and Fish Department, where he still serves as Nongame Coordinator supervising Wyoming's Nongame Program. In addition to Peregrines, Bob has worked on Goshawks, Bald Eagles, Ferruginous Hawks, black-footed ferrets, swift fox, lynx, and other nongame species.*

Peregrine Restoration in the Greater Yellowstone Ecosystem

William Heinrich and Robert Oakleaf

In the spring of 1980 we met for the first time—Bob Oakleaf, nongame biologist for the Wyoming Game and Fish Department, and Bill Heinrich, raptor biologist for The Peregrine Fund. Each of us had spent many years working with raptors, and we had a passion for the outdoors, which included camping, hunting, fishing, and occasionally hiking. Having that, and just a few other things, in common, we seemed to make a pretty good team for what lay ahead. The Peregrine Fund's western headquarters had been in existence for five years, and Bill had two years of Peregrine hacking experience from sites in Colorado, New Mexico, and Utah. With Bob's encouragement, the Wyoming Game and Fish Department was ready to come on board and support Peregrine releases in the state. Bob was familiar with the Tetons and the areas we would be attempting to work in, all of which gave us just enough ammunition to be dangerous. In the spring of 1980 we entered Grand Teton National Park through the Moran Bay entrance with the goal of setting up and releasing Peregrines from hack sites in the Tetons. After several fixed wing flights and weeks of hiking, often from sunup to sundown, we ended up selecting Death Canyon, Moran Bay, and Webb Canyon. At the time they seemed to have the only cliffs in the Tetons that were not occupied by Golden Eagles or Prairie Falcons. Later, we were fortunate in finding some of the hardiest hack site attendants ever hired to work some of the most difficult release sites ever selected. The success of the initial releases in 1980 set off a chain of events that would eventually make it possible to repopulate the Peregrine Falcon throughout the entire region. In 1981 Montana joined the program, followed by Idaho in 1982. By 1995 over 1,098 Peregrines had been released in the three states, with the majority of releases occurring in the Greater Yellowstone Ecosystem (GYE). In 1980 the

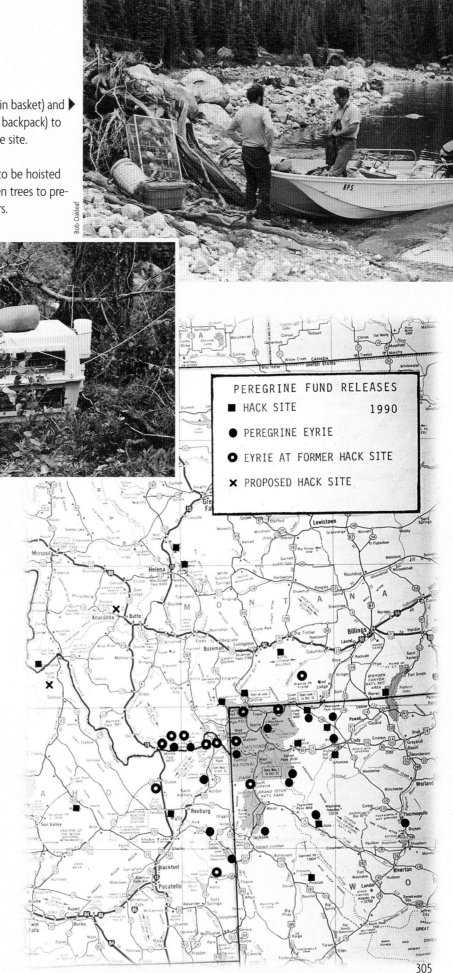

▶ Unloading falcons (in basket) and their food (cage on backpack) to be carried to release site.

Bob Oakleaf

▼ Falcon food ready to be hoisted into the air between trees to prevent access by bears.

Bob Oakleaf

PEREGRINE FUND RELEASES

■ HACK SITE   1990

● PEREGRINE EYRIE

◉ EYRIE AT FORMER HACK SITE

✕ PROPOSED HACK SITE

Peregrine Falcon had completely vanished from the GYE. Today its population has been restored, and the numbers surpass known historical levels.

The remarkable recovery of the Peregrine Falcon in this region, spearheaded by The Peregrine Fund, is the result of an aggressive program involving the cooperation of state wildlife agencies in Wyoming, Montana, and Idaho and the National Park Service, the U.S. Forest Service, the Bureau of Land Management, and the U.S. Fish and Wildlife Service (FWS).

Peregrines had suffered a severe decline in the West, and by the late 1970s surveys indicated that this stunning bird of prey had completely disappeared from Wyoming, Montana, and Idaho. The GYE was selected as a release area because it contained excellent habitat for the falcon and because over 30 breeding pairs of Peregrines had nested in this region prior to their disappearance. Also, since the area crossed several state boundaries and contained an abundance of public lands, an additional bonus was the excellent opportunity for biologists from many agencies to work together.

Eleven young Peregrines were released at three different sites in Grand Teton National Park in 1980. The following year, a release site was established in Montana, and the year after that, one in Idaho. Reintroduction continued, and in 1984 two different pairs of Peregrines returned to

the area to breed. Bob found the one that had reoccupied a former Peregrine eyrie in Yellowstone National Park which had been vacant for 15 years. These birds had been raised in captivity, yet they had nested in the same eyrie in the cliff that their ancestors had chosen years earlier. Another pair was discovered by FWS biologist Terry McEneaney, and it occupied a cliff above Montana's Centennial Valley.

About half of the young annually produced by most birds of prey die within the first year of life, and the Peregrine is no exception. Despite the expected losses, the reestablished Peregrine population continued to grow as more and more birds were released. In 1991, 29 nesting pairs were located. Between 1980 and 1991, a total of 500 captive-raised young had been released in the GYE, and 140 young had fledged from the established pairs.

Peregrines were banded prior to hacking so that released falcons could be identified separate from wild-produced young. Observations of banded adults at eyries provided interesting information. For example, in Wyoming, all of

the nesting pairs during the 1980s were banded, confirming the population entirely originated from hacked birds and recruitment from wild pairs was not occurring. During the first half of the 1990s, the ratio of haggards that originated from natural eyries and those of captive origin equaled the ratio of young fledged in the wild to young fledged at hack sites suggesting that we were documenting most of the natural production of the recovering nesting population. Monitoring data and observations of banded adults clearly document that Peregrines were extirpated from Wyoming and similar results extended into adjacent areas of Montana and Idaho. Certainly, reintroduction efforts can be credited for the recovering population. As the nesting population and natural production increased, more wild young were fledging than being released in the hacking program. As expected, by 1995-1996 only 30% (n=28) of nesting adults with observed band status were of captive-raised origin.

Documenting band numbers and identifying individual falcons were extremely

Reintroduction efforts can be credited for the restored population.

interesting but time-consuming, and they resulted in small sample sizes despite a considerable amount of effort. Band recovery data, however, helped guide the release program. For example, band numbers were read on 11 adults (three males and eight females) at Wyoming eyries. Distances between release sites and falcons' eventual nesting locations ranged from 0 to 75 km for males and from 18 to 260 km for females, with medians of 37 and 121 km, respectively. Similar dispersal distances were noted at Idaho and Montana sites. As Peregrine restoration progressed and new hack sites were located, these dispersal distances were considered. Interestingly, these dispersal distances are roughly similar to dispersal reported for Peregrine populations recovering without benefit of reintroduction (Mearns and Newton 1984, Ambrose and Riddle 1988).

Band observations also provide information on wintering areas. Peregrines released in Wyoming have been recorded wintering in Sinaloa, Mexico, and farther south (Burnham et al. 1988).

The number of Peregrine pairs now present represents a vast increase over the 32 pairs known to have nested in the region historically. Population growth should continue as long as suitable habitat and a clean environment exist. The upper limit of breeding pairs the GYE could hold is unknown.

Bill Heinrich *coordinated the Peregrine release effort throughout much of the western United States and continues in a similar role for The Peregrine Fund's restoration projects for the Aplomado Falcon and California Condor. See biographical information in Chapter 8.*

Bob Oakleaf *supervises the Wyoming Game and Fish Department's Nongame Program. See the biographical information in this chapter.*

Colorado

Gerald R. Craig

As I look back, I know most people cannot appreciate the sense of urgency, frustration, and even despair of the early Peregrine situation. Today, captive propagation is an everyday tool. In the late 1960s and early 1970s, however, even the National Audubon Society strongly questioned the effort and urged that the birds remain in the wild to suffer a more noble demise. Everything published or discussed painted a bleak picture of a severely declining population. We fully anticipated that the *anatum* subspecies of the West would become extinct as had recently occurred in the East. The only real hope was a captive flock that would be a reservoir from which to draw if the pesticide threat diminished sometime in the future.

Colorado has been fairly proactive about raptors since implementation of a falconry licensing program in 1963. Involvement with Peregrine Falcon management was inevitable when the Colorado Division of Wildlife (CDOW; then the Division of Game, Fish and Parks) appointed the nation's first raptor biologist. I was lucky to land the job. My interest in falconry, membership in The Raptor Research Foundation, boyhood friendship with Bob Stabler and Jim Enderson, and later association with Butch Olendorff in college probably assured that Colorado would be active with Peregrines. Among my first duties (aside from settling on the official definition and spelling of the word raptor) was to examine the status of the state's nesting Peregrine population and recommend protection if necessary. Jim Enderson had intermittently surveyed nesting Peregrines in the Rocky Mountain region, so it was logical to form a partnership and intensify the Colorado inventories. It was also fortuitous that Jim had initiated the first tentative steps to breed the *anatum* Peregrines he held for falconry. It was evident that captive propagation had to be a critical component of the recovery effort, and it would have been redundant for the state to develop its own programs.

Colorado chose to help support Enderson's project and that of The Peregrine Fund and concentrated on monitoring and managing the wild pairs. Jim and I were lucky to enlist the help of Dan Berger at the outset, and he participated in our monitoring and management efforts throughout the 1970s and most of the 1980s. Results from the 1973 breeding season were sobering. Half (11

Courtesy of Jerry Craig

of 22) of the historical sites had pairs, and only one produced young. Poor productivity and thin eggshells in Colorado Peregrines paralleled the situation in the East, and the species was placed on the state's endangered list.

Continued poor wild productivity and loss of nesting pairs caused us to intervene in the egg-breakage cycle. We removed two eggs from a set of four wild eggs, kept them warm in a pair of gloves placed in the sun on the dashboard of Dan's Cadillac, and hurried to Enderson's facilities for incubation. The day after they hatched, we took them home, only to discover the remaining eggs were broken and the pair had abandoned their eyrie. The orphans were successfully introduced into a wild brood elsewhere, confirming that we could hatch some of the eggs if taken before they broke under the incubating adults. Young could also be fostered back into the wild. In 1974, Jim and I visited

▲ **Figure 17.10** Jerry Craig making a potentially dangerous but typical ascent from a Peregrine eyrie.

307

Geoff Tshbine

Figure 17.11 Bill Burnham (left) and Jerry Craig (right) place captive-produced Peregrine chicks in a basket for transport to the eyrie.

▼ **Figure 17.12** Jerry Craig and Dan Berger place thin-shelled wild Peregrine eggs into a portable incubator for transport to The Peregrine Fund.

Steve Petersburg

another site and replaced their eggs with those "borrowed" from an unwilling Prairie Falcon. One of the eggs was infertile; the other was severely dented and did not hatch. We then contacted Jim Weaver of The Peregrine Fund, and he agreed to fly from New York to Colorado with two Peregrine nestlings they had produced. When we returned, we found two healthy Prairie Falcon chicks which we replaced with the Fund's Peregrines. This manipulation ended successfully with two fledglings chasing their foster parents up and down the canyon. Unfortunately, the success was too late. Peregrines disappeared from the canyon for 14 years.

Colorado cooperated with The Peregrine Fund by providing wild Prairie Falcon eggs for work on artificial incubation, and the foster effort sparked a new partnership. As Enderson, Weaver, and I

returned from the canyon, we began contemplating a western facility where eggs could be removed from the wild, hatched in captivity, and returned to wild pairs to be reared. Jim Weaver went back to Ithaca to talk with Tom Cade, and I convinced Wayne Sandfort and Bob Tully to provide a site. Bill Burnham, a Colorado falconer/propagator from Canon City, was appointed manager, and construction of the first breeding chambers was soon underway. Upon completion, falcons were moved from Ithaca, and the following spring Enderson transferred all of his breeding Peregrines which were a major part of the Fund's *anatum* stock.

The wild Peregrines continued to deteriorate. In 1980 we wondered if the end was near. Although we occasionally located previously undocumented wild pairs, they too experienced attrition, and overall occupancy declined. Only four pairs produced eggs out of 12 occupied sites in 1979. By 1982 all of the Front Range sites were vacant, and statewide only 11 eyries were in use.

Our manipulation efforts were in full swing at this time. All previously occupied cliffs were visited annually to document the presence of adults, and when they laid eggs, we rappelled in and exchanged their eggs with plastic replicas. I experimented with various replicas and finally worked out a pattern that my coworkers felt was better than the real thing—they didn't break! Eyries were visited within a week to 10 days after clutch completion, and real eggs were replaced with replicas. We often used helicopters to get to the top of remote cliffs, and rappels frequently exceeded

400 ft. The ascents back up the rope were arduous. Dan and I usually took turns on these rappels, mostly because whoever took the eggs the first time did not relish repeating the descent with young birds. Many of these descents were life threatening, and now we marvel that nobody was seriously hurt. If that had occurred, it probably would have been the end of the program. Time was critical when handling eggs, and after several clutches had been collected, all-night drives to Fort Collins often ensued.

After the Fund relocated its western program to Boise in 1984, our all-night driving escapades ceased, and Enderson flew the eggs to Idaho. We estimated that the total cost of getting each wild egg to the incubator was probably $1,200 counting observer time, personnel, vehicles, and aircraft. Eggs from 108 breeding pairs were manipulated between 1976 and 1990. In all, 357 wild eggs were brought to the Fund for artificial incubation, and 226 young were hatched and returned to wild pairs. We replaced the eggs of most pairs (67) with plastic replicas. We sometimes used no replica eggs, inducing second clutches (recycling). The Peregrine Fund had developed this strategy for their captive birds. By taking first clutches within 10 days of laying, we caused wild pairs to produce second clutches on 41 occasions, yielding an additional 116 eggs that would not have been produced in the wild. While we were manipulating wild pairs, The Peregrine Fund produced 290 additional young which were placed with wild pairs or hacked at vacant wild sites. Between 1978 and 1990, 63 hack sites received 278 young for release. Approximately 80% of the young successfully fledged by hacking and fostering, comparing favorably with the wild fledge rate.

The population began to expand from the low of 1982, and by 1990 we stopped fostering and hacking. The state's recovery goal of 31 breeding pairs was achieved in that year, but eggshell-thickness improvement lagged until 1997. Peregrines were removed from the Colorado list of threatened and endangered species. By 2000, the population was robust. The recovery goal is nearly tripled, and lower-class cliff nest sites are being occupied. Eggshell thinning still occurs among some clutches, but productivity is good. During the recovery period, and even now, we could only speculate on basic critical population factors such as mortality and movement patterns. Colorado now has three decades of biological information, including one of the most extensive benchmark collections of wild eggs. The population is also sufficiently large for us to begin to obtain basic but critical population parameters (habitat requirements, mortality, movements, etc.) that were not available during the recovery phase.

Passage of the Endangered Species Act (ESA) of 1973 came at a fortuitous time for Peregrines in Colorado. As I recall, we were the second state to qualify for Section 6 funding under the Act, permitting us to expand our investigations of wild Peregrines and provide financial support to The Peregrine Fund's Western Project. In 1974, CDOW and U.S. Fish and Wildlife Service (FWS) hosted a preliminary meeting of western states to explore the potential for a Peregrine recovery team for the

▲ **Figure 17.13** A Peregrine eyrie and former release site near Wolf Creek Pass, Colorado.

Figures 17.14 and 17.15 Many ▶ state wildlife biologists made important contributions to the Peregrine's recovery, to include David Anderson (right), Washington Department of Wildlife, and Al Heggen (below), Utah DWR. See Chapters 5, 8, 9, and 10 for names of others.

Bill Henrich

Bill Henrich

western U.S. The Rocky Mountain/Southwestern Peregrine Falcon Recovery Team was appointed by FWS the following year, and I agreed to chair a team comprising representatives from the three states (Colorado, New Mexico, and Utah), the U.S. Forest Service (USFS), BLM, National Audubon Society, National Park Service (NPS), and The Colorado College. We met almost bimonthly for two years, and thanks to the patience and dedication of Frank Bond, Jim Enderson, Al Heggen, Gene Knoder, Joel Kussman, Morley Nelson, Dee Porter, and Dale Wills, a final plan was approved and published in two years. It was the second recovery plan published by FWS under the ESA.

Unfortunately, FWS never applied the plan or required states to follow its guidelines. Although Texas, New Mexico, Wyoming, and later Arizona did a creditable job monitoring their wild stocks, basic inventories were not standardized, were sometimes inadequate, and as a result were not comparable. The tendency of most agencies was to pick high-visibility projects such as hacking and ignore monitoring to document population changes. Hacking and fostering were not proven recovery techniques, but I believed fostering was likely to succeed quickly because wild falcons reared young. Although effort by states was not federally coordinated, The Peregrine Fund provided direction through distribution of their cap-

Colorado Peregrine Observer

(Years individuals served as Team Leaders are marked in bold)

Alderman, Keith 94
Alston, Joe 78
Antonucci, Kimberly 93
Armstrong, Joni 89
Bachoroski, Michelle 89
Banski, Brad 78
Basili, Dominick 88
Bauer, Elizabeth 80, 81
Beane, Ron 84, 85, 86, 87, 88, 89, 90
Beauvais, Gary 92
Berg, Barry 91
Berger, Dan 78, 79, 80, 81, 82, 83, 84, 85, 86, 87, 88, 89
Berman, Mike 78, 79, 80, 81, 82
Berner, Louis 87, 88
Bertram, Mark 85
Blom, Arthur 93
Bohanon, Tom 78, 79
Bouton, Jeff 89, 90
Bowden, Elizabeth 82, 83, 84
Braker, Beth 78
Braun, Paul 87
Brazie, Rob 86, 87, 88, 89
Brennan, Kevin 86
Brown, Mary 94, 95
Bunn, Richard 89
Busby, Bill 78, 79
Carlson, Beth (Irene) 89
Carlson, Deanne 78
Cavallaro, Robert 94
Clemens, Robert 96, 97, **98**
Coleman, Shari 95
Cottrell, Marcy 78
Crowley, Larry 88
Darnall, Nathan 94, 95, 96
DelPiccolo, Renzo 86, 87
Doney, Gregg 94, 95, 96, 97, 98
Durland, Dan 91, 92
Elder, Mark 80
Enote, James 79, 80, 81
Ferreira, Tammy 90, 91, 92, 93, 94
Fiala, Frank 78, 79
Fowler, Timms 83, 84
Garrett, Lisa 94, 95, 96, 97, 98
Gordon, Spencer 89
Grebence, Brandon 79, 80, 81, 82, 83, 84, 85
Hansen, John 88
Hardrick, Brenda 90
Hastings, Bruce 89
Heasley, Jeff 91, 92, 93
Hiebert, Jeffrey 93
Henry, Ann 87, 88
Hines, Jane 92, 93, 94
Hubenthal, Grace 96
Kearns, Jeff 91, 92, 93
Keiss, Bob 91
King, John 84
Kim, Dan 91, 92
Kralovec, Mary 89, 90
Krampetz, Fred 89
Langley, Richard 93
Lanzone, Mike 00

Larrabee, Jon 95, 96
Leska, Susie 95, 96
Lockwood, Michelle 98, 99, 00
Lucas, Jeff 95
Maumenee, Niels 96
Maurer, Mike 87, 88
Marchowsky, Kori 93
Mason, Joanne 87, 88
Maynard, Larry 90, 91, 92, 93, **94, 95**
McCain, Emile 98
McDaniel, R. S. 89
McKinley, James 78, 79
McWhorter, Marta 79, 80, 8
Meese, Bob 78, 79, 80, 81, 82, 83
Meyers, Terry 96, 97, **98, 99, 00**
Miller, Trent 89, 90
Miller, Trish 00
Moore, Lee 93
Mullen, Nancy 87, 88, 89
Munsell, Steve 82
Murphy, Craig 89, 90, 91, 92
Palmer, Dave 85
Patz, Jon 79, 80
Pendleton, Brian 78, 79, 80
Peper, Chris 95, 96, 97, **99, 0**
Pleune, Ryan 98
Potter, Ann 78
Powell, Scott 92
Pratt, Dick 86, 87
Reese, Kimberly 88
Riegel, Jeff 92
Robert, Mark 83, 88, 89, 90, **92, 93**
Roe, Laurie 79
Rosendale, Gail 82
Rucks, Jeff 79, 81, 82
Ryan, John 89
Schoonmaker, Peter 83
Schultz, Chris 86, 87, 88, 89, 9
Selters, Julie 88
Silverman, Francie 78
Sisk, Tom 84, 85, 86
Staughton, Marsha 91, 92
Stiehl, Mike 78
Stolzenburg, Herb 82
Stover, Stephanie 89
Tennis, Brett 99, 00
Teresa, Sherry 79
Tessari, Joe 89
Timchak, Joe 83
Trahan, Nicole 99
Tucker, Staci 94, 95
Turner, Matt 96
Vana, Sandy 83
Voltura, Mary Beth 89
Wight, Sara 98
Wightman, Catherine 93, 94, 95, **96, 97, 98**
Williams, Richard 80
Wood, Rachel 78
Woodruff, Kent 78

Provided by Jim Enderson

tive-produced young. In retrospect, hacking was an important source of stock to replenish the wild. By recycling, fostering, and augmenting wild pairs in Colorado, we reduced competition for the captive-bred young from the Fund.

That recovery plan did guide Colorado's recovery program. The program was really a cooperative effort among the federal land management agencies. The NPS, USFS, and BLM funded hack sites and provided funds for inventories. Early on, the majority of our remaining wild pairs were in parks and monuments, and officials readily permitted us to manipulate their pairs. Steve Petersburg at Dinosaur National Monument encouraged us to recycle the pairs nesting there to supplement the supply of captive-bred young in 1988–1990.

The Peregrine recovery decades were uncertain, and sometimes depressing and frightening, but events were sometimes fortuitous and likely will never be repeated. I shake my head when I compare the obstacles facing biologists attempting to recover endangered species today. Under the present conditions, I doubt we could recover the Peregrine. Biologists today have more sophisticated tools, but I wonder how much the program would have been delayed, for example, if DNA testing of fostered young was required to assure genetic integrity. Would we have had to prove fostering and hacking before involving Peregrines? How many environmental assessments, population viability analyses, and hearings would need to be sanctioned? Would satellite transmitters be required on each released falcon? Biologists now face many more philosophical hurdles. In the 1970s environmentalism was a new and strong political will supporting the ESA and recovery efforts. We were lucky dealing with a charismatic species of common appeal to people with diverse interests. Now the pendulum has swung the other way, and politically induced barriers are many.

Although we are basking in the glow of a remarkable achievement, we must remain vigilant. Peregrines demonstrated intolerance to environmental contamination. I fear people are doomed to repeat their mistakes. New changes are inevitable, and old problems may return. As I write this, efforts are underway to resurrect DDT. FWS is understaffed, underfunded, and has failed to lead throughout the recovery process. After delisting, it is imperative to maintain a scientifically credible national monitoring program to give early warning if problems reoccur. As human population expansion increases pressure on our natural resources, it is important to remain vigilant and to have recovery systems on standby to rescue our raptor populations.

Although we are basking in the glow of a remarkable achievement, we must remain vigilant.

Jerry Craig was born in California in 1947, and his family eventually settled in Colorado Springs, Colorado, where he met falconer Robert Stabler—an event that changed his life. Jerry became hooked on falconry and raptors in general. After receiving a bachelor's degree in wildlife biology at Colorado State University, he pursued a Masters of Science degree there. He was later hired as the first raptor biologist for the Colorado Division of Wildlife. In that position Jerry was instrumental in developing and implementing Colorado's raptor research and conservation program and falconry regulations. With Jim Enderson, and later Dan Berger, Jerry also developed the restoration program for the Peregrine Falcon in Colorado and was selected to lead the nine-member Rocky Mountain/Southwestern Peregrine Falcon Recovery Team. It was with Jerry's leadership that The Peregrine Fund located the program for Peregrine restoration in Colorado. He also developed a program for monitoring the state's expanding Bald Eagle population and guided raptor rehabilitation efforts in Colorado and at Colorado State University. Jerry was recognized for his many accomplishments, receiving a host of awards during his long and productive career. During this time, he and his wife, Sally, have also raised three daughters and now have four grandchildren.

STEVE ALLER
—1983—

Chapter 18

The Federal Role
in Peregrine Falcon Recovery

Paul R. Nickerson

*T*he recovery of the Peregrine Falcon and the evolution of the U.S. Fish and Wildlife Service (FWS) into an agency interested in more than waterfowl numbers

and setting annual duck and goose hunting seasons began about the same time. The seminal event that set the stage for falcon restoration was the Madison conference in 1965, when it became apparent that most of the Peregrine legacy in the Lower 48 was gone and that Alaska was following a similar pattern. In 1966, the first of three Endangered Species Acts (ESAs) was passed, requiring FWS to look well beyond its traditional constituencies, broaden its oversight into the well-being of most animal and eventually plant communities, and seek species expertise to improve the lot of creatures which, until then, had not been within its purview. Ironically, it was two raptors, the Peregrine Falcon and Bald Eagle, that led the way.

In the mid-1960s, the National Audubon Society kept track of the eagle numbers, and private falconers were chronicling the Peregrine's drastic

decline. FWS researchers were instrumental in documenting the causes of widespread reproductive failure in these and other raptors, but management was left to others, or else did not exist. Passage of the ESA of 1973, coupled with the personal commitment of several biologists within FWS and other federal agencies, shifted the paradigm significantly. Work by FWS biologists to reduce raptor electrocutions, bolster sagging eagle and Osprey populations, and coordinate nationwide eagle surveys reflected a change in agency attitude that grew stronger with time.

The Peregrine, however, posed a challenge that was unique. Once the Peregrine Falcon in North America was listed as an endangered species under the ESA, responsibility for restoring it was vested with FWS, but FWS had no idea how to proceed with that task. Fortunately, there were people who did, so the first step toward reversing the species' slide was to identify those with the capabilities and commitment to begin the effort, convene them quickly, and develop a recovery plan.

Recovery planning is the process that identifies the tasks, costs, responsible entities, and a timetable for bringing an endangered or threatened species to the point where it can be removed from the list. The plan also establishes the biological criteria or benchmarks FWS uses to determine

◀ **Figure 18.1** Peregrine Falcon painting by Steve Aller. Reproduction rights courtesy of The Peregrine Fund.

when delisting or reclassification to threatened species may be appropriate.

FWS appointed four recovery teams to develop these plans for the Peregrine Falcon: Eastern, Rocky Mountain/Southwest, Pacific Coast, and Arctic. Team leaders were either from FWS or state agencies. I can say from personal experience with the eastern team that no one I met during the entire recovery period was more committed to a cause than Rene Bollengier, the first leader of the Eastern Peregrine Recovery Team. Rene worked for FWS, but his commitment did not stem from agency affiliation nearly as much as it did from devotion to the species. We were faced with a real challenge in the East, because our breeding birds were gone—extirpated. Although Rene's tenure ended in the mid-1980s, he still cared enough to attend the public hearing FWS held in Concord, New Hampshire, in 1998, when delisting was imminent, because he was concerned that five years was not a long enough post-delisting monitoring period. As a result of this concern, expressed by Rene and others, FWS has increased the post-delisting monitoring period to 13 years. Did I mention that Rene had undergone heart surgery a few weeks before the hearing?

Now the federal role in Peregrine recovery is becoming a bit clearer. Step one, of course, was putting the species on the list to acknowledge formally its biological plight. Next came overseeing and processing recovery plans. Finally, the toughest task was plan implementation, because all the great ideas have to be paid for, coordinated, and reported on. Because of the species' wide distribution, and because some populations were gone and some remained, recovery strategies were somewhat different. In the East, we were involved in a restoration rather than a recovery, because we had nothing left. In the West, remnant pairs still existed, so basic strategies were different, particularly with respect to stock origins. In Alaska, enough pairs remained that captive breeding and releases were not needed. Debate on which subspecies should be released in various parts of the country raged for several years, and ultimately FWS issued a policy statement that released birds had to come from North American stock, except

that non–North American birds could be released for research purposes at certain sites in the East with case-by-case approval of the FWS directors. So policy development was another emerging federal role in the management of endangered species. But I am getting ahead of the story.

The eastern recovery strategy was twofold: (1) develop a technique to raise large numbers of birds in captivity and (2) find an effective way to release them to the wild. The assumption was that enough of the released birds would survive,

Courtesy Rene Bollengier

▲ **Figure 18.2** Rene Bollengier.

mature, and return to nest. The expertise to raise significant numbers of birds in captivity existed with The Peregrine Fund, but funds to carry this out on a grand scale were lacking. Another role of the federal government in restoring endangered species is to pay for it, or at least part of it. Many federal agencies contributed hundreds of thousands of dollars, perhaps millions to the recovery effort. The U.S. Forest Service (USFS), National Park Service (NPS), Bureau of Land Management, and the Department of Defense (DOD), in addition to FWS, were major supporters of Peregrine recovery. Through its grants program to states, FWS also provided funds for Peregrine work by the various states throughout the country.

The first Eastern Recovery Plan was completed in 1979, with updates done in 1987 and 1991. The initial objective was establishment of 175 to 200 breeding pairs in the East; roughly half the number that existed pre-DDT. Plan updates called for the pairs to be distributed over five recovery regions to ensure the recovery was occurring range wide, and they established modest goals of 20 pair minimums in each of the five recovery regions to consider down-listing the eastern Peregrine to threatened status.

During the early releases, which occurred in just a few states, logistical arrangements were not particularly complex, but with time and success, keeping track of everything and everybody involved became more difficult. The FWS assumed a greater coordination role as the effort increased, and as the states assumed more and more responsibility for release activities within their own borders. The FWS organized and conducted coordination

Finally, the toughest task was plan implementation, because all the great ideas have to be paid for, coordinated, and reported on.

meetings with various partners and oversaw transition as new phases of recovery were called for. Major milestones included shifting the effort to northern New England to escape the Great Horned Owl threat in the early 1980s and intensifying the southern release efforts in the mid-1980s. FWS biologists were particularly instrumental in strengthening the effort in Virginia, West Virginia, North Carolina, Tennessee, and South Carolina, and hundreds of birds were released there from the mid-1980s to the early 1990s.

Early releases were conducted from hack towers in marshes in Maryland and New Jersey. Some of these were on national wildlife refuges, others on state land. Often FWS had to secure permits for the towers' construction, and sometimes we paid for them as well. Recovery milestones were many, but the first productive nesting on a tower in a New Jersey marsh in 1980 convinced me we would succeed. Birds raised in captivity could be released to the wild with reasonable expectation that some of them would survive and return to nest. That was a great day. There were many more to follow.

Although FWS was responsible for overseeing the recovery of the Peregrine, other federal agencies played a critical role in assuring its success. The USFS was active from the beginning in providing release and hack site logistical support, site protection, and funding. In the East, falcons were released on national forests in Maine, New Hampshire, Vermont, West Virginia, Virginia, and North Carolina. Their descendants are now nesting at wild cliff sites in many of these states. The DOD was also a major player in the eastern recovery effort (see Chapter 5). It contributed significant amounts of funding, and its personnel were involved in extensive banding activities along the East Coast and extending as far away as Greenland and Alaska. These banding activities, along with those of provincial and FWS biologists in Canada and Alaska, documented the existence of a steadily improving population. Collectively, the results of all of this work led FWS gradually to remove the Arctic Peregrine Falcon from the list of endangered species; first by reclassifying it as threatened in 1984, and then by delisting it altogether in 1994. The subspecies is thriving today.

The NPS also provided hack sites and logistical support. Its task was made tougher in that popular trails at Acadia National Park in Maine had to be rerouted while the hack site was active. Later on, when birds returned and nested in the park, similar restrictions were necessary. Although there was some public concern expressed about the temporary closures, the falcons were given the protection they needed.

In 1981, the first wild pair to use a historical mountain habitat nested successfully in New Hampshire, fledging two young. As more and more pairs became established throughout the 1980s, the release effort was scaled back, and the focus shifted to monitoring and nest protection.

Although there was some disturbance and vandalism, most returning pairs were successful or, if not, were disrupted by natural occurrences (weather, raccoons), not humans. State agency personnel did most of the monitoring, though The Peregrine Fund staff still assisted any nest-site manipulation and did much of the early banding. That, too, was eventually assumed by FWS and the states. Addled eggs collected were analyzed by FWS to determine presence and levels of the same contaminants that eliminated the Peregrine from the East in the first place. That will continue even though the falcon has been delisted.

The ESA works well when the mission takes center stage, as it did in this case. Recovery has been achieved.

Courtesy Paul Nickerson

Paul Nickerson, *originally from Bourne, Massachusetts, joined the U.S. Fish and Wildlife Service in 1970 following a two-and-a-half year tour with the U.S. Army. He has a B.Sc. in wildlife management from the University of Maine and an M.Sc. in forestry from the University of New Hampshire. His first assignment in Washington was assessing the impacts of pesticides on fish and wildlife and assisting in the coordination of the National Pesticide Monitoring Program. He went on to serve as a member of a national task force designed to reduce raptor electrocutions on power lines, and he coordinated the first nationwide Bald Eagle surveys in 1973–1974. The interest in eagles ultimately led to his involvement with endangered species and to his current position as the Endangered Species Chief for Region 5, where he has served since 1975. Clearly, one of the most satisfying aspects of his work in the Northeast was watching Peregrines go from extirpated to recovered in two decades.*

"Virgonigra"

D.M.HENRY

Chapter 19

Memorable Peregrine Falcons

William Burnham, James H. Enderson, William Heinrich, Harrison B. Tordoff,

Frank M. Bond, Tom Smylie, and Tom J. Cade

*A*s this book and the many references in its Literature Cited reveal, much has been written about the Peregrine Falcon, both popular and scientific.

The Peregrine has captured human imagination and emotion since the beginning of our written history, and no doubt long before. As Roger Tory Peterson (1948) wrote: "Man has emerged from the shadows of antiquity with a Peregrine on his wrist. Its dispassionate brown eyes, more than those of any other bird, have been witness to the struggle for civilization, from the squalid tents on the steppes of Asia thousands of years ago to the marble halls of European kings in the seventeenth century."

A gift from nature is experiencing a Peregrine at its eyrie or seeing its form flash across the sky. "There is no more exciting sound in all nature than the angry raucous rasp of a Peregrine challenging all who enter its domain, nor more magnificent sight than its dark silhouette emblazoned on a cloud, the unmistakable hallmark of nature's perfection" (Treleaven 1977). "That cloud-biting

anchor shape, that crossbow flinging through the air . . . " (Baker 1967). "The Peregrine Falcon is one of the noblest and surely one of the most romantic birds in the world—beautiful, bold, fearless, so swift in flight that it is master of the air and falls upon its prey like a thunderbolt from the sky" (Murphy 1963). "Speaking generally, the Peregrine may be regarded as the most perfect type of combined strength, speed, and destructive power in birds. The proportions are such as could not be altered with any advantage . . . " (Michell 1900).

Before the Peregrine restoration program, to see a Peregrine usually meant traveling to some distant place and a remote cliff. Few people ever had the opportunity to enjoy this experience for themselves and had to be satisfied with an author's words or photographs. "A falcon crag is one of those very special places on the face of the earth where we human beings have the opportunity to become peculiarly attuned to the oneness of living things and the environment . . . remove the falcon from the scene and the whole landscape becomes diminished by more than the absence of the bird. The natural integrity—the rightness—of that particular place is somehow distorted, and the cliff is never the same again. We say it is a `dead eyrie,' and the difference is the same as the difference between a living falcon stooping for

◀ Figure 19.1 *Virgonigra* by D. M. Henry. Reproduction rights courtesy Frank Bond.

▲ **Figure 19.2** Peregrine in flight.

prey and her poisoned corpse lying prostrate on the rocks below the cliff" (Cade and White 1976b).

Today, we can see the Peregrine not only in these distant and remote locations but also out our office windows in tall city buildings, while driving or walking across city bridges, or even while looking up on a stroll through parks or along busy city streets. "I remember in my childhood seeing or rather recognizing my first Peregrine as he glided through immeasurable space among the clouds, and never in all my life can I recall having witnessed anything in wild Nature which left an impression so indelible and so full of romance as that small black cross against the sky" (Batten 1923).

It is no wonder that falconers hunger for Peregrines and were determined to do their utmost to ensure the species would survive and flourish. Falconry is only an active form of birdwatching. Rather than waiting for something to happen, the falconer tries daily to create situations to see the Peregrine fly as it naturally does in the wild. The pinnacle of the sport is achieved when the falcon performs near its potential and as witnessed in nature. This is not a matter of training. You do not train a Peregrine to fly. You may train it to come back after being released or to wait-on high over your head in anticipation of a potential quarry to be flushed, but the flying is a different matter. The Peregrine's spectacular flying ability is woven into the helical strands of DNA and honed by natural selection. The falconer must just find

ways to allow the potential to develop within each Peregrine he or she repeatedly releases to the sky. If the falconer is lucky, a year of effort may produce that one truly unbelievable flight that will be remembered for a lifetime.

Hack site attendants responsible for release to the wild and feeding of captive-bred falcons, and biologists working with wild Peregrines, are other groups of people who regularly witnessed the awesome ability, and at times tenacity, of Peregrines. Seeing a young falcon go from its first unsteady flight with feathers not yet fully developed to a mastery of the sky in a few short weeks is unforgettable. So is having an infuriated, screaming adult Peregrine rocket by your head (or worse, strike your head) as you dangle from a rope at its eyrie. Memories such as these last forever, and each of us who has thrilled at these experiences also has memories of those exceptional Peregrines that are held above all others.

The memorable Peregrines did not all live in the wild. Some spent most or even all of their lives indoors. As the authors of this book contributed to the restoration of the species, so did these falcons by producing semen, eggs, and young, or by serving as foster parents. Their existence and stories, although not as spectacular as those of wild Peregrines, were even more important to what was accomplished. This chapter recounts some of the memorable Peregrines, captive and wild, as a tribute to their contributions and abilities, which were essential to the Peregrine Falcon restoration story.

Old Lady and Ratinsky

William Burnham

It was 1970. The Peregrine was gone from the eastern United States and almost so in the West. I had searched for two springs to find Peregrine eyries with young. My intention was to take two eyasses for captive breeding. Their progeny would then be used for falconry and maybe even be released to the wild, but then such a notion was only speculation. Finally, I found a breeding pair. With my father to help, we climbed from the streambed to an area on the cliff where I knew the Peregrines had been incubating. As I neared the location, calling to the Peregrine so as not to startle her as she sat on her eggs or young, she launched her unsuccessful defense of two downy white young only recently hatched. After a short climb, then a rappel, I was sitting in the eyrie in confusion and guilt wondering whether I should really be there and what to do. Falconers never ever "scoop the eyrie"—take all the young. Do I take one or both, come back when the young are older, or just forget the whole damn thing? If I take them and they die or do not breed, I will have become part of the problem and contributed to the Peregrine's predicted extinction. What if they are the same sex and I can never find mates? These and dozens of other questions and doubts raced through my mind.

The Peregrines turned out to be of opposite sex and were hand-raised together, as they would remain for the rest of their long lives. I cautiously exercised both falcons in falconry, flying them only at the lure and not at quarry, then placed them in a breeding chamber. Old Lady laid her first clutch at three years of age and copulated with Ratinsky the first time in the spring of 1975. They had arrived with Pat and me at The Peregrine Fund's new facility in Fort Collins, Colorado, several months earlier. Theirs were the first and only young Peregrines (two tiercels) raised at the facility in 1975. During their life they produced a total of 22 young. Only the first two were kept for captive breeding, with the others released to the wild. From one of the first two males, two more young were retained and propagated, as was one of their young. From the original pair and their retained progeny and their mates, a combined total of 184 young Peregrines were released to the wild. Old Lady's and Ratinsky's genes are now spread across the continent, as some of the young were even released in eastern states. I never did keep and fly one of their young for falconry, as the need was too great for the restoration program, and just possibly because the guilt remained about a courageous pair of wild Peregrines on a spring day in Colorado. It can sometimes be difficult to separate emotion from logic, or people from their falcons.

◀ **Figure 19.3** Old Lady in immature plumage, 1971.

▼ **Figure 19.4** Ratinsky, 1973.

◀ **Figure 19.5** Lil in juvenile plumage, 1962.

▲ **Figure 19.6** Lil, caught on the Laramie Plains in August 1962, was one of a few wild-caught Peregrines to eventually breed in captivity. Here she incubates infertile eggs in 1968.

Famous Peregrine Falcons in Population Restoration

James H. Enderson

Lil - I caught Lil on 17 August 1962 on the plains two miles west of the Laramie, Wyoming, airport, the first of hundreds of Peregrines I would catch over the years. She was in the company of an immature Prairie Falcon and could not have been out of the eyrie more than a few weeks. Her juvenile plumage was very dark (Figure 19.5). In 1963–1964 she became fairly effective at catching ducks, with coaching by Bob Dandrea and Ken Riddle. Bob noticed that she became mildly carsick when hooded, explaining her initial lack of interest in ducks. The first time we took her hawking unhooded, she caught a Gadwall. In the spring of 1965 she shared a small A-frame loft with Shane, my three-year-old Peale's Falcon. No eggs were laid, but in 1968 she laid one set in a larger loft (Figure 19.6), all the more unusual because she was not taken as a nestling but was wild-caught, albeit at a young age. Ordinarily, such falcons rarely lay eggs. In 1970 I loaned her

Jim Enderson

Jim Enderson

Jim Enderson

▲ **Figure 19.7** Steve Martin used Little Bird for educational programs long after she could no longer lay eggs. Fiercely defensive in the breeding loft, she was docile before audiences.

▲ **Figure 19.8** Blu at the age of seven weeks, bathing by standing on a lawn sprinkler, 1969.

Figure 19.9 Spock at ▶ the age of four weeks in 1969 was kept in the company of Blu.

to Heinz Meng, but she did not lay. Back in Colorado, paired with Blu, she laid two sets in 1971. The second set was extended to 13 eggs, all infertile. In 1972, they attempted copulation, but none of nine eggs were fertile. In 1973–1975, she produced three (one died), four, and four young, respectively, with Blu without artificial insemination (AI). She continued to reproduce from 1976 onward at The Peregrine Fund. In 1982, at age 20, she came home from Fort Collins because she no longer laid. She seemed calm and steady as usual but died suddenly a few days later. Morgan Berthrong did a complete necropsy. She suffered mild arthritis but died from massive bacterial invasion through the gut wall.

The Colorado Division of Wildlife had her mounted, and she remains on display, with an obituary, at the regional office in Colorado Springs. Her significance relates to the opportunistic way she was to figure into Peregrine recovery. Her young were among the first breeding stock available, enabling early expansion of fostering and hacking programs by 1978.

Little Bird - Little Bird was taken as a three-week-old nestling from southwestern Colorado in May 1967 for the purpose of captive breeding. From the start she was blocked (perched) near other Peregrines, and she paired with Spock from 1971 onward. They did not copulate, but by AI they produced the first temperate-zone Peregrine in captivity on 21 May 1973.

Dayle, my wife, fed the youngster, Alpha. She used a puppet resembling an adult we fashioned from balsa wood and thick black and white felt. The idea was to avoid imprinting on humans. Little Bird showed we could expect to boost production

greatly by AI. She produced one young in 1973 and 1974 and two in 1975.

She was a richly marked Peregrine and never seemed settled in captivity. But in 1981, age 14 years, I gave her to Steve Martin, who used her in educational programs (Figure 19.7). He said she became very gentle and was easy with crowds. Somehow I find that incredible. The bird pounded me too many times protecting her young. Once, when I changed her bath through a low door to the loft, she hit my hand so hard it throbbed for hours. Little Bird died 17 October 1986, age 18 years, of leukemia in Escondido, California.

Blu and Spock - Both of these males were taken from nests in the north-central Rocky Mountains in 1969 for the purpose of completing two pairs for breeding tests. This came at a time when it was clear the regional population was in deep decline. Accessible nests with young were difficult to find. Worse, I faced the ethical question of robbing eyries when the population was so gravely small. Only now, in light of the outcome we are celebrating, do I feel good about taking into captivity these two birds when reproduction in the wild was a mere trickle. They were seldom separated as they matured (Figures 19.8 and 19.9), and in their first fall they made the car trip to Cornell where I spent a year on sabbatical leave. In fact, four Peregrines and two Prairie Falcons made the trip. As they developed, they were often around people, and both Blu and Spock were relaxed in captivity. In 1973 both were initially used as semen donors, but when Blu began copulating with Lil, he was spared that indignity. Spock and Little Bird did not copulate, but there was no sign of aggression. In the end Blu and Spock, through their initial 13 offspring,

Baltimore Peregrines

John Barber

I met Tom Cade at a Raptor Research meeting early on in the life of The Peregrine Fund. Tom spoke with passion about returning Peregrines to breed in eastern North America. His vision was difficult to grasp—sightings of migrating Peregrines were pinnacles of excitement for most birders.

Several years later, I began working in the tallest building in downtown Baltimore where a female Peregrine, Scarlett, was nesting by herself on the 33rd-floor ledge. The Peregrine Fund had hacked her on a marsh tower on the eastern shore of Maryland, but she disappeared, only to appear later on the "cliffs" of buildings in Baltimore. I watched Scarlett for five years while she laid infertile eggs each spring and raised fostered eyasses provided by The Peregrine Fund. All our attempts at releasing a mate for her failed, and she eventually found herself a mate to help hatch the first urban Peregrines in the eastern United States in decades. I had an intimate view of her daily life, with her nest box on a ledge inches outside an office window. I collected the infertile eggs, identified prey remains, and took care of other raptors that unwittingly migrated through her territory and often paid for their temerity with deep gashes in their backs from Scarlett's attacks. No two days were ever the same with the Baltimore Peregrines.

The earliest indication in Baltimore of success in the Peregrine restoration program first emerged in the mid-1980s when every lost Peregrine was replaced rapidly by birds from the growing "floating" population. The great sadness of finding a Peregrine dead from strychnine, sickness, or collision was replaced with joy at seeing another bird soaring around the buildings. So many of the early efforts were focused on introducing individual birds to individual territories prior to the emergence of a floating population that could provide new mates for single nesting birds.

I was also continually amazed by the variety of prey that the Baltimore Peregrines brought to their young. We had public-relations problems when a television crew filming the nest box photographed several homing pigeon bands lying in the box. While I thought Northern Saw-whet Owls were absent from downtown Baltimore, the Peregrines occasionally caught and cached them on the building, including several in one day. I recorded over 50 bird species and one bat that the Peregrines caught around the Baltimore territory. The Peregrines were opportunistic hunters, catching resident bird species most of the year, but also many migrant species during the peaks of spring and fall migration.

After almost 20 years as "caretaker" for the Baltimore falcons, I can relate that each falcon had its own personality in its hunting strategies, favorite prey species, and behavior around the nest box and young. But the excitement of seeing a Peregrine soaring over the city "cliffs," chasing a Mallard or Northern Flicker, or feeding young, has never faded.

Scarlett's "cliff," the former USF&G building in Baltimore. Below (inset), Scarlett feeds her young.

J. Barclay

File photo

John Barber *served as caretaker for the Baltimore Peregrine Falcons while working for the U.S. Fidelity and Guaranty, headquartered in the building where the falcons nested. Prior to working in Baltimore, John worked in the Division of Birds at the Smithsonian Institution and studied Common Black-Hawks in Arizona. He is a licensed bird-bander, now living in Cleveland, Ohio, and works across Cleveland's Public Square from another downtown Peregrine nest site. He earned a B.A. from Earlham College in biology and political science and an M.B.A. from Loyola College of Maryland. He has published numerous articles on urban Peregrine Falcons.*

Courtesy Peg Barber ©1983

John Barber at the nest ledge of an office building.

Figure 19.10 "BC" was an imprinted male taken as a tiny chick from central Colorado in 1971. He became the first voluntary semen donor at The Peregrine Fund in Fort Collins.

were significant in rearing the founders of the vast population we now enjoy.

BC (Beer Can) - This two-day-old nestling taken from central Colorado in 1971 was the last Peregrine I took from an eyrie. It was to be paired with one of two unmated Peregrines on loan, depending on its sex. Peregrines were soon to be protected in Colorado, and nationally, and the window for acquiring nestlings from the wild would be closed for 30 years. BC was hand-reared to assure tameness, but this inadvertently created a bird aggressive to other Peregrines. He grew up "thinking people were falcons" (Figure 19.10). Could it be that the last bird taken in Colorado would prove to be worthless? In 1972 Stan Temple and I learned how to strip semen from a wild male Prairie Falcon, and BC was literally pressed into service. He was the father of three of the four young produced by Little Bird. BC went off to The Peregrine Fund with the rest of the lot in 1975. There, Bill Heinrich found a way to make BC much more effective by training him to copulate on his hat. Instant high-quality semen was now available several times a day, and the semen went everywhere. Eventually, other donors came on line, but BC was the first donor in the restoration project, and his genetic legacy was spread across the land by the scores of birds he sired. In 1984, still donating semen, BC made the journey to Boise with the rest of the breeders in a U.S. Forest Service aircraft. Within a few years he assumed a new role, that of greeting visitors to the World Center for Birds of Prey. On a visit in 1988, I walked up to his loft where dozens of people passed daily. I gave my "ee-chup" call he had first known 17 years before. He paused, bowed, and then gave a frenzy of "ee-chups." I must believe he still knew me.

BC Becomes a Voluntary Semen Donor

William Heinrich

I will never forget Les Boyd's visit to Fort Collins, Colorado, in the spring of 1978. Several years earlier Les had perfected a method of teaching imprinted male falcons to copulate on an old Army surplus flight hat. The hat was modified by the addition of a closed-cell foam rubber tube wrapped around the circumference and attached with a smooth bead of clear silicone rubber. When worn, the hat gave the appearance of a man wearing a large black donut on his head.

Prior to Les's visit, Bill Burnham and I had been catching BC in a large net in order to force him to the ground where we could grab him and remove him from his breeding chamber into the hallway where Bill would forcibly collect the semen. This was done while I held BC down on a specially designed foam pad. Not only was this traumatic to the falcon, but also to Bill and me. We liked BC, and we knew he liked us as well, because he was imprinted on humans.

After spending hours talking to Les on the phone, I was able to convince Bill that we should temporarily quit using BC as a semen donor until we could give Les's technique a try. Bill was agreeable, but only if training BC to copulate on the hat took a minimal amount of time. We could not afford to miss fertilizing any eggs if we were unsuccessful in stripping semen from other males in the program, and BC was always a sure bet.

Les traveled to Fort Collins from Pullman, Washington, and began teaching me the proper technique of how to train BC to copulate on the hat. First he had me don the hat, then take a 12-ft ladder into BC's chamber and lean it against the nesting ledge while he hid in the upstairs hallway and observed me through one-way glass. In my pocket was a dead Coturnix Quail which I was to use to lure BC over to the ledge so we could initiate the appropriate food transfer that was necessary for the next step. The transfer went well as BC flew over, landed, took the quail in his beak, and then flew over to another ledge where he stashed it.

From the hallway I could hear Les's persistent coaching. "Now make eye contact with him and begin the `ee-chip' courtship vocalization. Okay, turn around with your back to him, bend over while continuing to vocalize, but be careful to keep your head level so he will have the proper copulation angle." The 10 minutes or so I had been on the ladder now suddenly began to feel like hours while I waited for BC to come and land on my head. After repeating the eye contact-turn around-and bend over procedure about 10 more times, I was beginning to lose my patience.

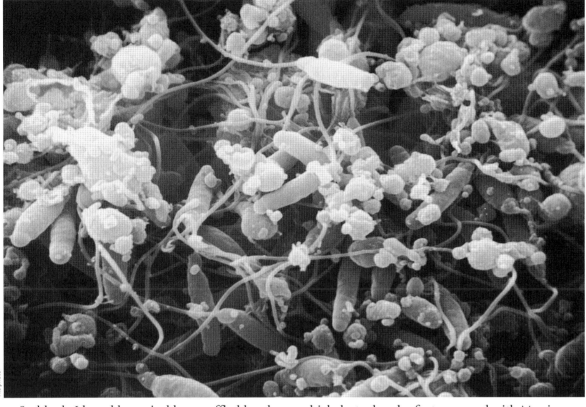

File photo

Figure 19.11 Peregrine semen viewed at 3600X magnification. The elongated structures with tails are the sperm.

I was now certainly convinced that Les was insane and that I was the victim of one of the sickest jokes that had ever been played on a human being.

Suddenly I heard hysterical but muffled laughter coming from the hallway. I was now certainly convinced that Les was insane and that I was the victim of one of the sickest jokes that had ever been played on a human being. I immediately came down the ladder, removed it from the chamber, and met Les still laughing in the hallway.

To make a long story short, Les finally convinced me that it was not a joke and that if I had waited just a little longer BC would have copulated on the hat. Les left Boise, and I continued to work with BC three times a day. Finally, two days later BC successfully copulated on the hat. We had our first voluntary semen donor!

Special Midwestern Peregrines

Harrison B. Tordoff

Meg - Some individual Peregrines stand out from the crowd. In St. Paul, Minnesota, a huge female named Meg 12R, produced by Jack and Connie Oar in 1986, has nested every year beginning in 1988 in a box on the North Central Life building. She has had six mates and has fledged 39 young over the years, more than any other Midwest female, and she is still going strong as this is written (summer 2000). Meg is half *pealei,* half *peregrinus,* and true to her ancestry, she does not migrate. She was hacked in Minneapolis and may have never ventured as far as 20 miles in her on-going 14-year career.

Sota - Meg's current mate, Sota 8/*E, was fledged wild at the Mayo Clinic in Rochester, Minnesota, in 1994. He was intact when banded as a

chick, but when he first appeared with Meg in 1998, he was missing the inside and middle toes on both feet, leaving only the hind toe and outside toe on each foot. Forceps, instead of grappling hooks. His feet are healed with no blemishes, and his soft parts are bright orange, indicative of good health. Despite his missing toes, Sota has helped Meg fledge three broods of three young each. How did he lose his toes? We do not know. Perhaps he chose a bad site for roosting on an especially cold winter night and froze his toes.

Sibella - In Milwaukee, female Sibella 20V has reigned over the downtown area for 12 years. She was hacked from a cliff on remote Isle Royale in Lake Superior in 1988 and moved immediately to the big city. She has had only two mates, the first for two years and Bill 74T for the past 10 years. She has fledged 37 of her own young plus two that were fostered.

Atlanta - Female Atlanta L/*C was fledged wild in 1996 at a power plant in Green Bay, Wisconsin. In December that year, she was found in Yellow Springs, Ohio, with an open fracture of the right metacarpal. After 10 days in a local rehabilitation facility, she spent four months at The Raptor Center, University of Minnesota, was flown on a creance for two months, then released in late April 1997 at Racine, Wisconsin. She visited a nest site in 1998 in Michigan City, Indiana, then nested that same year in a box on a smokestack at Pleasant Prairie in southeastern Wisconsin. In February 1999 she moved to a smokestack nest box in Oak

▲ **Figure 19.12** McArthur was captive-produced and hacked at Fort Sheridan, Illinois, in 1988. He nested at Milwaukee's Firstar Center from 1988–1990 and fathered seven young; two with Madonna in 1988 and five with Sibella.

Figures 19.13 Sibella ▶ with four young in her nest box at Milwaukee's 41-story First Wisconsin Center.

Creek, Milwaukee, where she killed the resident three-year-old female and nested for the next two seasons. This bird is determined to succeed!

Jingles - The oldest living male Peregrine in the Midwest, as far as we know, is Jingles, hacked in Chicago in 1986. For nine years he was paired in Chicago with the oldest female, Harriet, hacked in Minneapolis in 1985. Harriet was injured in a fight in 1998 and spent eight months at The Raptor Center. She was released in Minneapolis in August 1998 and was unreported until found with a severe case of trichomoniasis in St. Paul on 9 May 2000. She is still in treatment at this writing. Pat Redig speculates that her aging immune system may have become incapable of coping with this ubiquitous disease.

Clay Bird aka Frank

Frank M. Bond

Clay Bird was a male *anatum* bred in captivity in Santa Fe, New Mexico, in 1978. He was the first Peregrine Falcon bred in captivity in New Mexico. His parents were New Mexico *anatum* Peregrines from the Jemez Mountains west of Santa Fe.

Through the 1960s, Tom Smylie was the first falconer to make a serious effort to relocate some of the known historical Peregrine eyries in New Mexico. Tom also located other eyries not previously known. By the late 1960s Tom had taken two pairs of Peregrines for captive propagation.

In 1971, I approached Bill Huey, then Assistant Director (and later Director) of the New Mexico Department of Game and Fish, to seek permission to take a pair of Peregrines for captive propagation. Bill Huey was an innovator in conservation biology as he led the effort to attempt to create an alternative flock of endangered Whooping Cranes to migrate between Gray's Lake, Idaho, and Bosque del Apache, New Mexico.

Without hesitation, Bill Huey issued letters of permission for the pair of Peregrines that Tom Smylie took in 1971 (male) and 1972 (female) from the southern Jemez Mountains for me. Ironically, when Bill Huey later became director of the department, he appointed a biologist absolutely opposed to the Peregrine reintroduction who thwarted every effort to implement a hands-on recovery in the state. New Mexico did, however, indirectly become the beneficiary of the Peregrines released in southern Colorado and Utah to augment its small remnant population. Before the releases, however, and with permission, Bill Burnham, Bill Heinrich, and I manipulated the eggs of an eyrie near Las Vegas, New Mexico, to assist that pair and to broaden the genetic base of the captive birds at The Peregrine Fund.

Clay Bird's parents were not flown so they did not come into breeding condition early. The female was laying eggs, but she was not copulating successfully with her mate. In 1978, with the help of Bill Heinrich, we artificially inseminated her with semen stripped from her mate and also from a California *anatum* at The Peregrine Fund. At that time, I was serving in the New Mexico House of Representatives, so the coordination of the inseminations was difficult because Bill Heinrich was driving from Fort Collins to Santa Fe every third day for the early morning inseminations.

The first egg hatched in May 1978. During this period Clay Buchanan, Director of the New Mexico Legislative Counsel Service, visited to see the new bird. Clay and I had become close friends during my service in the New Mexico House. As the head of the administrative body that ran the New Mexico Legislature, Clay was a legendary figure of "insider" power in the state. This first *anatum* male was named for Clay, because he took great interest in the Peregrine recovery effort and the technical aspects to achieve it. Later he witnessed Clay Bird take the first teal duck served him in early September.

Scarlett, 1977-1984

The Baltimore Sun

Tom Maechtle

We were the only city with an insurance company that employed a staff ornithologist.

Don't weep for Scarlett. The breed survives. She came to our city unwanted, unsought, uninvited. In time she was cherished, even loved, not only for the fame she brought to Baltimore and to The Peregrine Fund which had nurtured her and to the cause of endangered nature, but for the thrills she provided to all who beheld her. Scarlett perished 10 or 15 years too early, from causes yet to be analyzed fully. But we never had a right to possess her here. And the vital work she did lives on.

Raptors give no mercy. They want no tears.

Slowly, painstakingly, the Peregrine Falcons return to the skies of eastern North America from which DDT and a hundred other man-made perils drove them... Each year, it seems there are more specimens in our midst of the speed-diving hunter the falconers prized.

Thank Scarlett.

Seventeen* eyasses she raised from adopted eggs, perhaps half of them still out there, somewhere, flying, killing, staking territory, mating, and four of her own, this year, after several failures. So Scarlett's genes, as well as her nurturing, live on, reclaiming the Eastern skies.

A thousand pigeons breathe easier today.

Was the city sky a jungle? Scarlett made it so. The great sight, downtown, of the predator swooping on the pigeon, whirling above the traffic, returning to her nest on the 33rd floor ledge of the U.S.F.&G. Building, is no more. Other tourist sights will have to lure people to the harbor on their own, now. As a tourism promoter, Scarlett helped them long enough.

We were the only city with an insurance company that employed a staff ornithologist. But there will be new distinctions, as unplanned as Scarlett.

Scarlett was a mother; Scarlett was a killer. She was nobody's pet. She lived wild and died wild. Scarlett is no more. But someday, somewhere, someone will look out from a most unlikely man-made cliff, from the top of a brick forest, and see the merciless eyes, the short and wicked beak, the speed of the dive, the kill of mid-air.

Misplace no sentiment. Scarlett's posterity lives. Rejoice in that.

*Editor's Note: It was 18 eyasses.

Reprinted by permission of *The Baltimore Sun*, September 8, 1984.

Figures 19.14 Cal Sandfort ▶ collects semen from Clay Bird (aka Frank), an imprinted Peregrine trained to copulate on a specially constructed hat from which semen will be collected.

Clay Bird/ Frank became the father of an estimated 500 to 550 birds released as part of the recovery effort.

In late spring 1978, Congress amended the Endangered Species Act (ESA) with the so-called "raptor exemption." As Clay Bird became a fledgling, I called U.S. Fish and Wildlife Service raptor biologist James L. Ruos to notify him that I would fly Clay Bird as a falconry bird under the new exemption. Jim, in a quick response, told me that I could not, because the federal falconry regulations would not be modified for a while to permit the use of captive-bred Peregrines. I responded that since the law was clear, I was going to fly Clay Bird. Jim called me back several days later to say that "they" (FWS officials) had a meeting and that I could go ahead and fly the young Peregrine, but he implored, "Don't spread the word." Clay Bird then became the historic first captive-bred *anatum* to be flown in falconry just a few weeks following the ESA amendment. He also was the first captive-bred *anatum* flown at a North American Falconers Association meeting later that year at Thanksgiving. In his first two years, he became a really successful game hawk.

In about 1979, I sent my adult pair of New Mexico *anatum* Peregrines to The Peregrine Fund at Fort Collins. In 1980, Clay Bird joined several other imprint *anatum* tiercels at The Peregrine Fund, which included Jim Enderson's famous tiercel, BC. The team of imprints became the backbone of the

semen-donor colony. At The Peregrine Fund, Clay Bird was always known as Frank.

Cal Sandfort managed the Peregrine propagation effort for The Peregrine Fund. From his notes and recollection, Clay Bird/Frank became the father of an estimated 500 to 550 birds released as part of the recovery effort. His production, coupled with the approximately 350 birds from BC, really dominated the *anatums* released in the United States, on a percentage basis. Considering that a very successful wild male may produce 20 to 25 young birds in a total productive lifetime, Clay Bird and BC are the two most dominant male contributors to the gene pool in North America.

By 1997, Cal Sandfort concluded that Clay Bird's useful life as a semen donor had come to an end. His production dwindled at the same time that the Peregrine propagation efforts decreased. That spring I was in Boise for a meeting at The Peregrine Fund, so on a Wednesday I took Clay Bird back home to New Mexico. The following Sunday The Peregrine Fund's imprint barn burned down from the spontaneous combustion of some oily rags. All of the imprints perished, along with Cal Sandfort's priceless notes on the production of each imprint. Clay Bird lived another 18 months, dying peacefully from natural causes in Santa Fe where he was hatched 21 years earlier. Measured by his legacy, his long life was charmed.

Porgy and Bess

Tom Smylie

My inspiration to breed Peregrines began in 1967 as a result of comments made by the well-known English falconer Ronald Stevens. I had begun corresponding with Ronald over the years after being introduced to him by my close friend Bob McCallum, who was a personal friend of Ronald and had visited him at his estate in Ireland. Ronald had brought to my attention that nesting Peregrines were fast disappearing from age-old eyries in the British Isles.

He was exceptionally knowledgeable of those eyries since during World War II he was assigned by the government to eradicate Peregrines along the coasts of Britain. It seems the Peregrines were responsible for capturing large numbers of pigeons, some of which carried important messages about downed pilots in the English Channel. It was not a job he cherished, but it did make him very familiar with Peregrine populations. By the end of the war, Peregrines in many parts of Great Britain were destroyed.

By 1955, however, their recovery had become virtually complete only to begin a downward slide from environmental contamination. Ronald, in noting these changes, suggested I might want to consider doing what he had begun by setting up pairs for breeding. At that time I was not thinking of having breeders to perpetuate the species but to have Peregrines to use in falconry.

With Ronald planting the seed in 1968, I began to design and build breeding chambers at my home in the mountains. With no guidance to go by, I decided to make three chambers 8 ft high, 16 ft wide, and 24 ft long, open only at the top, with a snow-fencing roof for air and light. At one corner of each chamber I placed a 50-gal wooden barrel on its side to duplicate the nesting cavities I found in the wild. I then went to several eyries in the mountains of New Mexico and took two 10-day-old downy eyasses. I used an old mounted Peregrine to feed them so they would not imprint on humans. When they were three-and-a-half weeks old, I placed them in the chamber and fed them through a hole with the mounted Peregrine so they would not see me. I named them Porgy and Bess, and they later became a cornerstone of breeding pairs for The Peregrine Fund. They did well in the chambers I had constructed and were undisturbed since they could only see up, and not nearby human activities.

In the spring of 1970 I noted the falcon spending a great deal of time in the barrel. In checking, to my amazement there was a clutch of four eggs. Now what do I do? I called my friend and highly regarded raptor biologist, Jim Enderson of The Colorado College, to tell him of my plight. In a few days he came down from Colorado Springs to candle the eggs. Three eggs were infertile, and one had an embryo, which failed to hatch.

In 1971 Frank Bond of Santa Fe, New Mexico, with whom I had often flown falcons, brought Tom Cade to my home for a meeting. Tom explained what he wanted to do at Cornell in hopes of saving the Peregrine from extinction and asked if I would make my pairs available to The Peregrine Fund for breeding. Tom's quiet but strong sincerity, enthusiasm, and commitment for this yet to be proven undertaking convinced me to make the birds available. Later Jim Weaver arrived and took these now invaluable birds, Porgy and Bess, plus another pair I had taken in 1969, back to Ithaca. Another pair, which I had given to Frank Bond, proved to be valuable breeders and ultimately wound up in The Peregrine Fund's project as well.

When one looks back on one's life, one can see several cornerstones. Undoubtedly, my taking and then giving my Peregrines to The Peregrine Fund was one of those cornerstones. Porgy and Bess, under the highly skillful tutelage of Tom Cade, Jim Weaver, and others at the Fund, produced 19 young over nine years. In 1996, at the age of 18, Porgy had to be put down because of severe cataracts. After Bess was no longer productive as a breeder, I had her given to Steve Martin, the exceptional bird trainer and educator. She played an integral part in Steve's shows for several years. She was a living example of the plight and recovery of the Peregrine Falcon, because people cared.

My greatest disappointment was that none of the progeny from the New Mexico Peregrines were ever released in New Mexico because of bureaucratic obstinacy at the head of the state's Endangered Species Program. However, the birds have recovered in New Mexico, due in part to recruitment from releases in nearby states. The eyries where I took Porgy and Bess over 30 years ago are now active.

In 1968 I was criticized by other falconers for "putting birds in cages" instead of flying them. Others said they would never breed in captivity. I am glad I did not listen to the naysayers and followed my instincts. I strongly feel that my giving the falcons to The Peregrine Fund was one of the most significant acts of my life. I have always been proud to be associated with The Peregrine Fund and to play a role in the recovery of this magnificent bird, for I believe the skies would be empty without them.

▲ **Figure 19.15** Bess with a wild eyass in the breeding chamber Tom Smylie constructed at his home in New Mexico.

Figure 19.16 The Sun Life falcon in Montreal with eggs in her nest box, circa 1940.

Figure 19.17 Scarlett with ▶ two of her chicks, circa 1979.

Famous Eastern Peregrines

Tom J. Cade

Historically there is no doubt that the Sun Life falcon, which lived for 17 years on the insurance company building in Montreal and in retrospect revealed reproductive indications in the early 1950s of pesticide problems, was the most famous Peregrine of the prerecovery period. She was identifiable by a distinctive twist of feathers in her upper breast. Her story has been chronicled in an article by G. Harper Hall (1970) entitled "The Story of the Sun Life Falcons."

Scarlett - Later, several of our released falcons became well known as they established eyries and initiated recovery of the Peregrine on the East Coast. The first and most remembered was Scarlett, a female hacked from the old gunnery tower on Carroll Island, Edgewood Arsenal, Maryland, by Lisa Klein and Julie Lee in 1977. Her parents were Grainger Hunt's old California tiercel, Sergeant Pepper, and Vinnie Cassone's Argentine Female (actually from Chile). Scarlett quickly became the darling of the news media and the citizens of Baltimore, and she probably did more than any other bird to draw public attention to the plight of the Peregrine.

Scarlett was first reported perching and roosting on ledges of the U.S. Fidelity and Guaranty (USF&G) home office building (now belonging to Legg Mason, Inc.) near the inner harbor district of downtown Baltimore in January 1978. She remained headquartered there year-round for her entire life, until her untimely death from a massive throat infection of the fungus *Candida* sp., which probably caused starvation from an inability to swallow food, in the late summer of 1984. The *Baltimore Sun* published a moving tribute to her (see sidebar, Scarlett, 1977-1984, this chapter).

During Scarlett's career she was carefully watched and cared for by several company employees who became Peregrine enthusiasts, notably Pricilla Dieter, who later wrote a children's book about Scarlett under the name Pricilla Jenkins, and John Barber, who published papers on her feeding habits and other behavior (see sidebar, Baltimore Peregrines, this chapter). One season Tom Maechtle, working for The Peregrine Fund, obtained an unparalleled series of photographs of Scarlett at her nest, and another year the artist Karen Allaben-Confer produced a fine collection of black-and-white sketches of Scarlett and her young.

Scarlett soon established a preference for a south-facing window ledge on the 33rd-floor, looking out over Baltimore's inner harbor. In the spring of 1979, when she began displaying and vocalizing to her reflection in the bronzed glass window panes, which functioned as one-way mirrors, we convinced the company to allow us to place two nest trays at the corners of the ledge. Being somewhat concerned about the decor of their recently constructed building, the managers decided that the nest trays should be built of the same pink Spanish granite as the outside walls of the building.

Scarlett immediately accepted these plush quarters and began making nestscrapes, and it appeared likely that she would soon lay eggs. We tried to provide her with two mates from captivity, but neither stayed around to bond with her. The first was an old passage-trapped tundra Peregrine named Blue Meanie, which we held for a few days in a cage atop an adjacent building. On his release, Scarlett flew out to join him and the two flew together around and behind the USF&G building. That was the last time we saw him. A few weeks later he was found dead in Ontario headed toward James Bay—true to his origins, he had flown almost due north for 450 miles! We were on a learning curve.

After the second male also left, Scarlett laid a set of three infertile eggs. Later we replaced her eggs with some downy young Peregrines, which she readily accepted and successfully fledged.

As no males showed up to pair with Scarlett, over the next four breeding seasons we continued our attempts to provide her with mates we released from captivity. In 1980 a captive-produced male named Rhett bonded with Scarlett and remained with her through the season. Unfortunately Scarlett's eggs were again infertile, but the pair raised fostered young together. In November Rhett was poisoned by strychnine from a pigeon he caught around the grain elevators in Baltimore harbor. Again in 1983 another tiercel, named Ashley, bonded with Scarlett, courted and fed her, and mated, but by that time it was late in the season, and he apparently no longer had viable sperm to fertilize her eggs. We provided them with fostered young, which both Ashley and Scarlett fed and fledged.

The love affairs of Scarlett the falcon were beginning to turn out as dismally as those of her namesake, Scarlett O'Hara in *Gone with the Wind*, for Ashley was shot and wounded after the breeding season. He recuperated in captivity and was rereleased only to be killed soon after in an apparent traffic collision on the Francis Scott Key Bridge, although in retrospect it could have been in a fight with another Peregrine.

Surprisingly, the next breeding season Ashley was replaced by a new, unbanded tiercel. Not having a band meant he came from an eyrie we did not know existed, because up to that time all young from known nests had been banded. We soon found a "new" pair on the Francis Scott Key Bridge, and examination of sites there suggested that breeding could have been occurring for several years, although this bridge is a notoriously poor nesting location. In keeping with the tradition of naming these Baltimore falcons from characters in Margaret Mitchell's famous novel, this male was dubbed Beauregard. At last Scarlett had the right mate, and she produced and hatched four fertile eggs. The four young were strongly on the wing at the time of her death.

Scarlett established a tradition of nesting at what has proved to be a prime location. Beauregard stayed on, capturing a new mate within days of Scarlett's death, and in the intervening 15 years through 2000 he had four partners. He disappeared after the breeding season of 2000 and was himself replaced by a new tiercel. In the 22 years since Scarlett laid her first set of eggs, the production of young at 100 Light Street has been 18 fostered and fledged and more than 50 fledged by natural reproduction.

Red-Red - Several of the Peregrines nesting in New York City have become well known, especially from the detailed account of their lives in Saul Frank's (1994) remarkable little book *City Peregrines: A Ten Year Saga of New York City Falcons.* One female in particular, Red-Red, stands out in my mind because she was a big, broad-chested, dark-headed bird that—although a subspecies hybrid in ancestry—looked exactly like many of the Duck Hawks that used to nest in Vermont and New Hampshire. She was named Red-Red for Cornell University's colors. She came from a release site in northern New England and settled on the New York Hospital/Cornell University Medical Center along the East River in 1988 and produced her first two young that spring. Several of the hospital staff, particularly John Aronian and Barry Freed, became great devotees of Red-Red and her mates and acted as their guardians for state authorities and later in cooperation with Chris Nadareski of the City of New York Department of Environmental Protection. Chris has supervised the management of New York's falcon population since the early 1990s (see sidebar, Peregrine Falcons and How They Have Changed the Skies of New York, Chapter 5). During Red-Red's breeding career of 13 years, she fledged more than 40 young before failing to appear at the nest in the spring of 2001. As in Scarlett's case, her tradition of breeding at the New York Hospital site continues through a successor.

The love affairs of Scarlett the falcon were beginning to turn out as dismally as those of her namesake, Scarlett O'Hara...

Figure 19.18 Tom Cade ▶
and Percy.

J. Sherwood Chalmers

Perseus (Percy), a Falcon for All Seasons -

"All that thy seasons bring,
Oh Nature, is fruit for me."
Marcus Aurelius

In 1979 The Peregrine Fund initiated an experiment to trap back a dozen hacked Peregrines and have them trained and flown by falconers for two years, eventually to be released as adult pairs or as mates for single birds on territory. Perseus, named after the son of Danaë and Zeus of Greek legend, was one of those birds. Hatched in an incubator from an egg of Colorado origin, he was hacked for 17 days at Owl's Head, New Hampshire, before coming into my hands.

He proved to be one of the best falcons I ever flew. Calm and steady from the beginning, he hooded without a flinch and flew to the lure on the second day of training. Although required to wear a transmitter as a condition of being flown free for the experimental project, he never strayed far away and mostly waited on directly over me at 300 to 500 ft. He loved my pointing vizsla, and the two worked as a great team.

With a hunting weight of 520 to 540 g, Percy was not a large tiercel, but he was fast and maneuverable and became adept at catching small quarry the size of Mourning Doves, both by waiting on and by ringing up. His favorite prey were the abundant yellow-bellies in the open hay fields and meadows around my country home near Dryden,

New York. Vishi, my vizsla, relished pointing them, and with Percy waiting on above, she often got her nose within a foot or so of the frozen bird. It was then only a matter of flushing at the right moment. Vishi learned to follow the flight and repoint after the put-in, and Percy learned to follow the dog as she worked over the field.

One morning, hunting together, they managed to catch five quarry in less than two hours. It was the finest day's hawking I ever experienced. I will never forget watching Vishi go into a point as she was jumping over a ditch: she turned 180 degrees in midair and landed pointing a bird in the ditch.

In January 1981 I took Percy west to hunt Lesser Prairie-Chickens in eastern New Mexico with Jim Weaver, Kent Carnie, and Bob Martin. I was not sure he would go for quarry of that size, although he was perfectly able to take feral pigeons. The first time I flushed a small group of chickens under him, he stooped immediately and feathered a bird. He tailed it off out of sight, and when he did not return, I assumed he had caught it.

I turned on the telemetry to check his direction and got no signal. That troubled me a bit, and I quickly drove in the direction he had disappeared. About a mile away I came upon a small fire burning around the base of an electric utility pole, which was charred at the top, its ground wire melted away at the upper end.

Looking around, I found Percy on the ground, unable to fly but standing erect. Most of his tail

Gone but Not Forgotten

Jack Kaskey, Press of Atlantic City

Atlantic City's celebrity Peregrine was hatched by parents released from the hack tower at Sedge Island 25 miles to the north.

Atlantic City - New Jersey's oldest Peregrine Falcon, a feisty female that brought a touch of the wilderness to the manmade skyscape of Atlantic City, is dead. The 16-year-old Peregrine was a kind of celebrity, nesting every year since 1985 atop the Atlantic City Hilton Casino Resort on a 23rd floor ledge outside the penthouse suites. The nest where she ultimately raised 25 chicks was visible from the butlers' kitchen, winning her friends among the hotel staff and making her a media symbol of Peregrines' recovery from pesticide contamination that wiped out the birds east of the Mississippi. "She was a good old bird," said Nancy Ross, a former penthouse-level maid who now runs the Hilton's VIP desk. "Gone but not forgotten."

The falcon was a constant at a casino that changed its name every few years, from the Golden Nugget to Bally's Grand to The Grand, and finally to the Hilton. The Hilton named a gourmet restaurant "Peregrines" in her honor.

She died four months ago, her beak bloodied after apparently crashing into the adjacent Ocean Club condominium, said Kathleen Clark, principal biologist with the state's Non-game Species Program.

Although she's gone, her penthouse nest remains active. In recent weeks, her partner has taken up with a new female on the 23rd floor, but the new bird may be too young to breed this year. "Life goes on," Clark said. "Hopefully, we will see a continuation of that nesting."

Peregrines are the world's fastest birds, capable of traveling 200 mph diving for prey. Clark figures the Hilton Peregrine was diving for pigeons perched on the garage wall when she missed her mark. Clark, who heads the state's Peregrine program, rushed the wounded bird to a rehabilitation center in Basking Ridge, but the falcon didn't make it through the night. "It was really pretty shocking for me personally," she said.

The Hilton Peregrine was the oldest of the 34 birds that have established 17 nests statewide, she said. The biologist came to know the bird quite well through the years, although the bird did her best to keep the biologist at bay. Clark ventured onto the 23rd floor ledge every spring to put leg bands on the newly hatched chicks, so they could be identified later. Often, Clark had to return to the ledge to fetch an unhatched egg or to examine a sickly chick. The falcon did not appreciate these intrusions. She defended her chicks fiercely, dive-bombing biologists and news photographers with her powerful talons. "She put good deep scratches on their heads," Clark said. "She drew blood on my assistant."

The bird's ferocity increased with age. "There was no question, she dominated her cliff, even though it was a building," Clark said. "I certainly had a lot of respect for her."

It wasn't until the bird died that she revealed a mystery that long puzzled those who knew her: where was she from? Biologists previously had read enough of her leg band to determine she was hatched in 1985, but they couldn't get close enough to read the final digit, the one that ultimately revealed her birthplace. It turns out she was hatched on Barnegat Bay's Sedge Island Wildlife Management Area, just 25 miles north of Atlantic City. That means she was one of the first New Jersey Peregrine chicks born in the wild after the eggshell-weakening pesticide DDT was banned. Biologists hand-raised her parents on Barnegat Bay as part of a successful effort to restore Peregrines using captive-bred birds.

She was also the only New Jersey-hatched Peregrine biologists know of that remained in the state as an adult. Most New Jersey-born Peregrines take up residence to the south. "She never left New Jersey—a lifelong Atlantic City resident," Clark said. You could say the feisty old bird was a Jersey girl. "She was," Clark agreed, "through and through."

(Reproduced from the *Press of Atlantic City*, New Jersey, 20 February 2002)

The falcon was a constant at a casino that changed its name every few years, from the Golden Nugget to Bally's Grand to The Grand, and finally to the Hilton.

▲ **Figure 19.19** Red Baron.

and all of his outer primaries had been burned off, and his left leg and foot, which carried the transmitter, were badly burned. Many of the feathers on his belly were singed. The antenna of the transmitter, which must have made contact with a hot wire while he was perched on the ground wire, had been burned off, and the guts of the transmitter were fried; the bell on his right leg had two holes blown through one side and out the other. Apparently most of the current had passed through the transmitter and bell into the ground wire, thus saving Percy from death by electrocution.

It took Percy almost a year to heal. His feathers molted out in fine shape with no damage to any of the follicles, but his left foot had only limited movement and turned inward, so that he had to stand on the outside of that foot without being able to grasp a perch. Nevertheless, he began flying again and was soon up to his previous aerial performance, but although he could still catch quarry—even pigeons—he was never again as effective as he once had been.

In March 1982, despite Percy's somewhat incapacitated condition, we decided to try to pair him with Scarlett, who after four years in Baltimore was still without a mate. Percy did not like our idea at all and took off to the suburbs, where he was trapped back and returned to Cornell.

I continued to fly him some that spring, but in the fall we decided to try him as a captive breeder, since he was a Rocky Mountain *anatum* and from a genetic line not represented by our other breeders. He turned out to be an excellent mate for several females. Because his injured foot turned inward with the toes folded together in exactly the posture a tiercel uses to place his feet on the back of a female when copulating, he had no difficulty in mounting and mating, and he fathered numerous progeny both at Cornell and later at the World Center in Boise.

In 1991 we transferred Percy to Bill Satterfield's breeding project in Texas, where he remained until the fall of 1994, after which he was sent to Vic Hardaswick in South Dakota. Under Vic's care, Percy fathered five more offspring with two females, all the young being released in the Midwest. But his old, injured foot caused him much discomfort in the cold Dakota winters, so Vic finally sent him to Tim Kimmel in Kansas, where he died just before Christmas Eve 1998 at the age of nearly 20 years—a long career of noble service. Perseus was his name, and he had the indomitable spirit of Ulysses flowing in his veins.

The Red Baron—a Fit Falcon -

"...if we resort to captive breeding of condors, we are not saving the bird; we are only saving the genes and feathers....A condor raised in captivity is different from a wild condor in ways we may never learn how to measure. But we will know the difference in our hearts."
From *YØDELER*, a publication of the San Francisco Bay Chapter of The Sierra Club, June 1979.

When The Peregrine Fund began releasing captive-produced Peregrines in 1974, critics voiced reservations about how well such birds would be able to survive and reproduce in the wild. Some thought that because we were releasing non-indigenous falcons in the eastern United States, they would be maladapted to critical environmental factors such as photoperiod or other seasonal biotic events in the eastern states. Others worried that the process of rearing falcons in captivity and their partial domestication would render them physically and behaviorally inferior to truly wild falcons and therefore incapable of survival and reproduction in the real world.

The best criterion for judging the individual fitness of a falcon for survival is how well it performs as a hunter, since this is the main function for which natural selection has molded the bird's morphology and behavior. All those features that are distinctively "falcon" are adaptations related to predation.

A tiercel that took up residence in the New Jersey salt marshes in 1976 was one of the first to reassure us about the quality of our released Peregrines. We called him Red Baron because he was such a spectacular hunter, downing his prey high in the air after a series of aerobatics between pursuer and pursued reminiscent of World War I fighter-plane combat. He was an especially favorable subject for observation because he hunted over open coastal marshes and a majority of his attacks began from a perched position on a utility pole after high-flying migrant passerines, mostly Blue Jays, and shorebirds. Also, he brought his prey back to the pole from which he started, so the entire performance from beginning to end could be witnessed. In 1978 Marty Gilroy and Tom Allen recorded 81 of the Baron's hunts, and 73% resulted in captures. In 1979 he reached his maximum stride, catching 95 birds in 102 hunts, for a 93% success rate. He had one amazing run of 68 consecutive hunts in 44 days without missing. To my knowledge no other wild Peregrine has matched this record.

In 1979 I spent a day with Marty Gilroy at Manahawkin to observe the Red Baron hunt and reported the following: "I have watched the Red Baron fly from a utility pole to the limits of my vision in 7-power binoculars, at which point I estimate he was about 3,000 ft high, and more than a mile off. He would then make two or three quick stoops at a bird I could not even see, set his wings in a glide, and come right back down to the same pole with a small sandpiper or a passerine in his feet. He does not go for every bird that passes over. He waits on his perch pole, scanning the sky with his telescopic eyes until he spots the one bird in perhaps 20 or 30 that he somehow knows he can catch and goes for it."

"When I watch this magnificent tiercel hunt, I am reminded of another time and place, 5,000 miles away on the Yukon River where I have seen the wild relatives of this very falcon make similar hunts after winnowing snipe high over the boreal forest. What has been said of the California Condor may have meaning in some poetical sense; but for these falcons, I tell you truly, I cannot see a difference with my eyes, nor do I feel a difference in my heart, which pounds against my chest with the same vicarious excitement when the Red Baron stoops over the New Jersey salt marshes, as it did in 1951 when I first saw this high flying style of hunting performed by the wilderness inhabiting peregrines of Alaska." (Adapted from *The Peregrine Fund Newsletter* No.7, 1979 and *The Falcons of the World* [1982].)

We called him Red Baron because he was such a spectacular hunter, downing his prey high in the air after a series of aerobatics between pursuer and pursued reminiscent of World War I fighter-plane combat.

Biographical information for Bill Burnham can be found at the end of Chapter 8, for James Enderson at the end of Chapter 4, for William Heinrich in his sidebar in Chapter 8, for Harrison Tordoff at the end of Chapter 10, for Frank Bond at the end of Chapter 16, for Tom Smylie in his sidebar in Chapter 14, and for Tom J. Cade at the end of Chapter 5.

Chapter 20

The Contribution of Peregrine Research and Restoration to a Better Understanding of Peregrines and Other Raptors

Ian Newton

Nesting at low density, mostly in remote terrain and in difficult sites, the Peregrine is by no means easy to study.

At the time of the organochlorine crisis in the 1960s, the species was poorly known, despite the pioneering studies of Hickey (1942), Cade (1960), Ratcliffe (1962), and others. From then on, however, further studies rapidly got underway, and through international effort, our understanding of Peregrine biology gradually improved. This chapter summarizes some of the main findings from this research, points to some gaps and deficiencies, and examines how, in my view, they fit within the wider context of bird population ecology. I omit the findings on pesticide impacts, because they are discussed elsewhere in this volume by Derek Ratcliffe and others.

Densities

In many areas where they were studied pre-DDT, Peregrines showed remarkable stability in breeding density and distribution from year to year, with pairs occupying the same nesting territories over long periods (though often with more than one nest site). Year-to-year fluctuations in densities were usually within about 15% of the mean long-term average, which is a remarkable degree of stability compared with many other birds. However, the fluctuations meant that not all potential territories were used every year. Over a period of years, some territories were occupied more often than expected by chance at the population levels observed, whereas other territories were occupied in fewer years (Ratcliffe 1962, Hagar 1969, Court et al. 1988, Mearns and Newton 1988). Such variations in occupancy, evident over a period of years, were associated with variations in nest success, with nesting attempts in the

Figure 20.2 Pacific coast ▶
Peregrine launching in flight
to defend her eyrie.

Brian Walton

most frequently used territories (with large nest-ing cliffs) being most often successful (Hagar 1969, Mearns and Newton 1988). Since such patterns lasted longer than the expected lifetimes of individual Peregrines, it seemed that the territories (cliffs) themselves varied in quality (and attractiveness), with the better ones being more consistently occupied. Further evidence for this proposition was that in many areas where the pesticide-induced decline and recovery were monitored, nest-cliffs were often reoccupied in reverse order to their abandonment, with the last to lose their birds being first to regain them (e.g., Kleinstäuber and Kirmse 1988).

Where potential nest sites were available in excess, regional variations in mean densities seemed broadly related to food supply. In Britain, mean nest-spacing varied from 2.6 to 10.3 km in different regions, according to land productivity and associated prey supply (though prey were not measured directly) (Ratcliffe 1969, 1993). The highest densities were on coastal cliffs with large seabird colonies, as is commonly found in other parts of the range (e.g., Beebe 1960 for Queen Charlotte Islands, White 1975 for Aleutian Islands). The breeding populations of most regions remained stable as far back as records go, but a one-fifth decline in pair numbers occurred in the Western Highlands of Scotland between 1890 and 1950, which Ratcliffe (1969) attributed to a long-term decline in prey caused by extractive land management. He thus argued for a relationship between density and food supply both on a geographical parallel and on a long-term change in

density, associated with long-term change in food.

Since then, more evidence has emerged for a link between Peregrine breeding densities and food supply. After organochlorine pesticides were withdrawn from use, the depleted Peregrine population of Britain began to recover, in some areas reaching densities greater than recorded at any time previously, a change attributed by Ratcliffe (1993) to a known increase in the availability of homing pigeons, the main prey. Furthermore, a decline of Peregrine numbers on Langara Island off British Columbia, from 21 to 23 pairs in 1952–1958 to 5 to 7 pairs in 1968–1989, followed a marked decline in the alcid that formed the prey for that population (Nelson 1990). There is thus considerable circumstantial evidence that where nest sites are not limiting, the breeding densities of Peregrines in many areas are linked to food supply.

Nevertheless, I know of no studies in which the densities of prey have been actually measured in different regions and related to Peregrine densities, and in some regions Peregrines seem unexpectedly scarce relative to apparent prey supply. They are absent altogether from some areas with abundant prey species, including the Faeroe Islands north of Britain, Iceland, and various islands north of the Aleutian chain. Moreover, all the studies mentioned above refer to resident Peregrine populations, and the situation may differ in some migratory populations, in which numbers may be limited in wintering areas. So far, relationships between densities of predator and prey have been much better documented in other raptor and owl species than in the Peregrine (Newton 1979, 1998).

Nest Sites

In some regions with abundant prey, Peregrines are clearly limited by shortage of nest sites. In Britain, for example, as over much of the range, they are more or less restricted to cliffs for nesting and are almost absent from two-thirds of the country devoid of cliffs, nesting only in quarries or occasionally on tall buildings (cliff substitutes). In other mountainous regions their nesting densities from area to area correlate with the densities of cliffs (e.g., Dónazar et al. 1989, Gainzarain et al. 2000). In some fairly restricted parts of the range, however, they use other types of sites. On flat parts of the Eurasian tundra (but not on the North American tundra), ground nests are frequent, being placed on small mounds, and in the Baltic region ground nests are also found on islets in bogs in the forest zone. These are all areas where the human population is low. In some more restricted regions, notably in Australia, some islands off western Canada, central Europe, and (in the past) the Mississippi Valley, Peregrines use trees, either cavities or the old stick nests of other birds, such as eagles.

The use of these alternative sites enables Peregrines to breed in some areas devoid of cliffs and otherwise unavailable to them. Presumably the habit of tree nesting arose independently in each of these widely separated areas and persisted by tradition. In middle Europe, tree- and cliff-nesting populations were almost contiguous (Mebs 1969), and in the Baltic region cliff, tree, and ground nests were interspersed (Thomasson 1947). As is now known from ringing (banding), birds using different kinds of sites freely interbreed, and individuals raised in one type of site will nest in another, so the habit of tree or ground nesting is not genetically controlled. It remains a mystery why the use of noncliff nest sites is so localized when, by nesting in trees (say), Peregrines could spread over huge areas otherwise unavailable to them.

Regional variation and cultural transmission of nest-site preferences are therefore more than behavioral curiosities: they are important in limiting abundance and distribution. Although studies on Peregrines have brought this issue to the fore, examples are available of the same phenomenon from other raptors and other birds (Newton 1979, 1998).

Peregrines have long used old buildings for nesting, either isolated or in small towns, especially in Europe, but until recently they nested in relatively few modern cities, despite abundant tall buildings with potential nest sites and pigeons as prey. Historically, the cities involved showed a curiously scattered distribution on all the main continents (Newton 1979), implying that the habit arose independently each time. On most such buildings, nesting persisted for no longer than a few years, but human interference may often have stopped it.

This situation has changed in parts of North America since young Peregrines have been raised and released on buildings (Cade and Bird 1990). Many such young, identified from their rings (bands), returned to nest in cities, and some attracted mates raised on rural cliff sites. In 1993 some 88 Peregrine pairs were located in 61 cities across North America, and not only in cities where releases were made (Cade et al. 1996). At the time they comprised about 34% of 95 known nests in the East and 58% of 43 known nests in the Midwest.

Numbers of city-nesters have increased greatly since then. By 2000, no fewer than 14 pairs nested in the confines of New York City, giving the largest number recorded in a single city, and perhaps the greatest nesting density recorded anywhere in inland North America. Considering the previous scarcity of records from North America, the releases from buildings may well have contributed to the recent spread of city nesting there, which again implies some cultural transmission of nest-site preferences. Even though some city-nesting birds had been raised in natural sites, they may have been influenced in their settling locations by birds already there. Nevertheless, the city environment has itself changed in the Peregrine's favor in the last 50 years, with more tall buildings, more specially provided nest sites, more pigeons as prey, and more tolerant human attitudes.

In some regions, cities provide nest sites where Peregrines would otherwise be unable to breed. Similarly, the deliberate placement of nest boxes on cliffs lacking natural ledges, on smokestacks, and on other tall structures rapidly led to their occupation by Peregrines, where none were present before (Septon et al. 1996), again pointing to the role of nest sites in limiting breeding distributions and densities.

Several large raptors eat Peregrines and take precedence in occupation of nesting cliffs. They could thus deter Peregrines from nesting at particular cliffs and hence restrict breeding to only a proportion of the potential sites available. Such predators include the Golden Eagle, plus the Eagle Owl in Eurasia and the Great Horned Owl in North America (for specific examples of predation or take-over of nest sites, see Mebs 1969, Lindberg 1988, Redig and Tordoff 1988). Several authors have commented on the tendency of Peregrines to avoid nesting near Golden Eagles (Dónazur et al. 1989, Poole and Bromley 1988, Ratcliffe 1993). In northern Spain, cliffs occupied by nesting Peregrines were significantly farther than were unoccupied cliffs from both nesting Golden Eagles and nesting Eagle Owls (Gainzarain et al. 2000). It seems that in this area, where cliffs were limiting, Peregrines were still avoiding (or being removed by) both these predators. Eagle Owls tended to prefer cliffs near valley bottoms, where their prey were most available, a factor that may encourage Peregrines to select the cliffs on higher ground. The extent to which Great Horned Owls are responsible for the relatively low occupancy of potential nest cliffs by Peregrines in parts of the eastern United States is an open question.

▲ Figure 20.3
Scarlett, a long-time Baltimore resident.

. . .the city environment has itself changed in the Peregrine's favor in the last 50 years . . .

Table 20.1 Annual survival of Peregrines as calculated from general ring recoveries.

Region of ringing (number of recoveries) N[1]	Minimum % killed by man	Oldest bird (year of death)	First year		Later years		Source
			% survival	Mean expectation of further life[1]	% survival	Mean expectation of further life[1]	
Sweden (223)	48	17	41	1.2	68	2.6	Lindberg 1977
Finland (48)	78	16	29	0.9	81	4.8	Mebs 1971
Germany (125)	43	14	44	1.3	72	3.1	Mebs 1971
United States (65)	45	14	30	0.9	75	3.5	Enderson 1969
SE Australia (46)	21	?	45	1.3	94	16.2	Olsen and Olsen 1988
Britain (50)	?	16	70	2.8	81	4.8	Mead 1993

[1] N = total number of recoveries.

[2] Calculated by the formula 2-(1-S)/2(1-S), where S is the annual survival as a fraction of unity.

Table 20.2 Minimal annual survival calculated for territorial adult Peregrines in different areas.

Region of ringing (years)	Males				Females				Both Sexes				Mean further life (years)[2]	Source
	Number in year A[1]	Number in later year			Number in year A[1]	Number in later year			Number in year A[1]	Number in later year				
		on same territory	on different territory	overall (%)		on same territory	on different territory	overall (%)		on same territory	on different territory	overall (%)		
South Scotland (1976–82)[4]	8	6	0	-	75	61	7	68(91)	83	77	7	74(89)	8.6	Mearns and Newton 1984
Alaska (1981–85)[4,5]	-	-	-	-	40	29	2	31(77)	-	-	-	-	3.8	Ambrose and Riddle 1988
NW Territories (1981–87)[5]	40	34	0	34(85)	70	52	5	57(81)	110	86	5	91(83)	5.4	Court et al. 1989
British Columbia (1968–89)[3]	47	35	0	35(74)	57	36	0	36(63)	104	71	0	71(68)	2.6	Nelson 1988, 1990
Colorado (1981–85)[3,4,5]	23	19	1	20(87)	34	26	2	28(82)	57	45	3	48(84)	5.8	Enderson and Craig 1988
Midwest U.S. (1987–95)[4,5]	115	-	-	91(79)	136	?	?	126(93)	251	-	4	217(86)	6.6	Tordoff and Redig 1997
Greenland (1972–85)[5]	-	-	-	-	24	18	2	20(83)	-	-	-	-	5.4	Mattox and Seegar 1988
Tasmania (1980–88)	17	15	0	15(88)	40	33	0	33(82)	57	48	0	48(84)	5.8	Mooney and Brothers 1993

[1] In this table, a territory is included more than once if its occupant was caught in more than two successive years, the unit of comparison being one territory-year.

[2] These figures give estimates of mean expectation of further life as 2-(1-S)/2(1-S) where S is the annual survival as a fraction of unity.

[3] Individuals identified from photographs (mainly of head pattern) rather than from ring numbers.

[4] Increasing population.

[5] Migratory population.

Population Regulation

Although food and nest-site availability may be the ultimate (extrinsic) factors that limit Peregrine breeding densities, the proximate (intrinsic) factor is territorial behavior, through which the birds somehow adjust their spacing to correspond with the resources available. To the human observer, this is most apparent in vigorous defense of the nest site by the resident pair against intruding Peregrines, but defense behavior must presumably extend well beyond the nest site, for otherwise sites between established pairs could be occupied by other pairs. The role of territorial behavior is further shown by the speed with which adults that die at nesting sites are replaced by other individuals, which then proceed to nest (examples in Newton 1979, Mooney and Brothers 1993, Ratcliffe 1993). This confirms the existence of a nonterritorial "floating" component in the population which contains mature adults. Essentially the same mechanism of territorial exclusion has been shown to operate in many other birds by experiments in which individuals deliberately removed from nesting territories were quickly replaced, in some species by known nonbreeders (Newton 1992).

This system of territorial limitation of breeding density also suggested how the total numbers of Peregrines (breeders and nonbreeders) might be regulated (Hunt 1988, Newton 1988). This is an intriguing question, for while breeders are confined to areas with nest sites, floaters could also live in the more extensive areas that lack nest sites but hold sufficient prey. The living space for floaters thus seems unlimited. Because the input to the floating sector is inevitably limited by the numbers and productivity of breeders, however, the input of young to the floating sector must also be limited. Hence, the total numbers of floaters could be set where annual additions to this sector (from reproduction and exit from the breeding sector) match the annual subtractions (from mortality and entry to the breeding sector). Hunt (1998) called this number "Moffat's equilibrium," after the Irish ornithologist who first suggested this system for passerines, and showed that for various combinations of reproductive and survival rates, floaters could outnumber breeders. Thus, if the reproductive and survival rates found for an increasing population in south Scotland also prevailed in a stable one, and no environmental factor was limiting, then the nonbreeding sector would stabilize at a minimum of three birds per breeding pair (Newton 1988). The numbers of floaters, because they depend largely on reproduction, may vary from year to year much more than the numbers of breeders, but they provide a constant source of new recruits to replace adults lost from nesting territories, and thus maintain the stability of the territorial population. While we yet have no way of testing this model directly, several observations are consistent with it, not least the rapid replacement of lost breeders and the existence among the replacement birds of individuals in adult plumage.

Regulation of total numbers around an equilibrium implies that one or more demographic parameters must vary in a density-dependent manner. Because only territorial birds can raise young, the mean per-capita production by the total population must decline as the numbers of floaters (and hence the total population) increase. Hence, per-capita reproductive output could vary inversely with the size of total population but not necessarily with the size of the breeding population. Also, if adult mortality varies little from year to year, then a roughly constant number of new breeders is recruited each year, regardless of the number of potential recruits available. Recruitment to the breeding population must then also vary inversely with the sizes of the floating and total populations. If adult birds had precedence over first-year birds in recruitment, we would also expect to see density-dependent variation in the age of first breeding, which with a fixed breeding sector would get later with increase in the size of

the floating and total populations. In agreement with this expectation, first-year recruits are observed mostly in depleted or increasing populations (with vacancies available) but not in populations thought to be close to capacity level (see later).

To my knowledge, no evidence has emerged for density dependence in adult mortality, but considering the fights that occur at nest cliffs (leading occasionally to death; Tordoff and Redig 1997), the incidence of such mortality may well vary with the numbers of competing floaters available (for evidence of density-dependent mortality and breeding failure caused by floaters in the Golden Eagle, see Haller 1996).

Survival

The earliest estimates of annual survival rates in Peregrine populations (first four regions in Table 20.1) were all based on records from a time when Peregrines were more heavily shot than today, and when populations were depleted or declining. At that time the chemical composition and design of rings were in some countries not as good as now, so some birds may have lost their rings through wear. Moreover, such records may also have suffered from a more general problem that young birds are more likely to die through human-related causes than older ones, and hence have a greater probability of their deaths being reported. All these various factors are likely to have biased the survival estimates on the low side, compared with what would be expected in a stable population equipped with lasting rings. The other two estimates in Table 20.1 were higher, being based mainly on more recent data from stable or increasing populations, but again sample sizes were small.

Systematic trapping of adults at nest sites did not begin until the 1970s, initially by Mearns and Newton (1984) in south Scotland and later by others in North America, Greenland, and Australia, so that along with photographic studies aimed at individual identification, we now have estimates of minimal survival rates from eight different regions (Table 20.2). The figures are minimal because, in most of the areas concerned, a small proportion of individuals changed their territories from year to year. This means that some additional individuals might have left the areas altogether, in which case they would not have

▲ **Figure 20.4** Close-up of Peregrine rings (bands).

▲ **Figure 20.5** Peregrine with prey.

expectation of further life is 8.6 years, and 12% of second-year birds would reach 20 years old. In contrast, with a constant 68% survival, the mean expectation of further life is only 2.6 years and less than 0.1% of birds would reach 20 years. After a certain age, however, survival must decline, or theoretical lifespans become unrealistic. The oldest bird in Table 1 died in its 17th year, and the oldest known wild Peregrine, a female recognized by plumage features that nested on the Sun Life building in Montreal, lived to be more than 18 years (Hall 1970), whereas a few falconry birds have lived to be more than 20 years.

Estimates of prebreeding survival (until year two) have been made indirectly from other demographic parameters, assuming a closed population, at 44% for an increasing population in south Scotland, and at 22% for a stable population (Newton and Mearns 1988).

Whatever may be said about the accuracy of these various estimates, they are all within the range expected for a bird of this size and life history. They contrast with lower estimates obtained in earlier years from general ring recoveries. However, we still lack reliable direct estimates for survival through the first year or up to the first breeding attempt, and for adult floaters, all of which would be useful in population modeling.

Age of First Breeding

Birds in first-year plumage were recorded as present at nesting cliffs in three increasing populations but not in two stable ones. In south Scotland, Mearns and Newton (1984) recorded one male (0.5% of the total) in first-year plumage, compared with 19 females (5% of the total). All the birds were paired, so in no case was lack of breeding due to lack of mate, yet only seven females laid eggs. In the Midwestern United States, Tordoff and Redig (1997) did not in their paper distinguish the sexes but recorded 20 (11%) of 174 territory holders seen in 1987–1992 as yearlings, compared with 13 (5%) of 264 territory holders in 1993–1995 ($\chi^2 = 6.50$, P < 0.05), when the population was larger (for similar findings elsewhere, see Cugnasse 1984 for the French Massif Central and Monneret 1988 for the French Jura). These scanty records therefore fit the findings from other raptors that young birds are more likely to be found among the breeders in depleted or increasing populations than in saturated populations close to capacity level, and that young females are more often found than young males.

Details of age of first breeding are available from at least five populations (Table 20.3). They suggest that most Peregrines start to breed at age

been retrapped and instead counted as dead. Males showed greater site fidelity than females (in fact no convincing territory changes by successful males were recorded), but males also proved harder to catch, so in most areas they provided smaller samples than females. Of the populations studied, three were resident and five were migratory, and three were stable and five were increasing (i.e., recovering from past organochlorine impacts) (Table 20.2).

In these eight regions, overall annual survival estimates (both sexes combined) varied between 68 and 89%. The lowest estimate, 68%, from British Columbia, was so far below the range of other estimates that it warrants comment. It was based on a small population (5–7 pairs) from a single small island (Nelson 1988, 1990). No territory changes were detected on the island, but any changes that involved movement off the island would have been missed. If females had moved in the same proportion as recorded in most other studies, this would have raised the estimate of female survival from the recorded 63 to 74%, and the overall survival estimate from 68 to 74%, still lower than for Peregrines in other areas. In all studies, the survival estimates varied from year to year, but in none was this variation significant statistically. Despite the greater chance of breeding females being lost by emigration, one study recorded a significantly lower survival among breeding males than among breeding females (79 vs. 93%, P = 0.0034; Tordoff and Redig 1997).

The implications of the survival estimates on longevity and breeding life are substantial. Thus on a constant 89% survival of breeders, the mean

Table 20.3 Numbers of Peregrines trapped at nesting sites and found to be breeding for the first time at different ages.

Region	Number of males aged (years)						Mean Age	Number of females aged (years)						Mean Age	Source
	1	2	3	4	5	6		1	2	3	4	5	6		
S. Scotland	-	4	1	1	-	-	2.5	2	13	1	-	-	-	2.0	Mearns and Newton 1984
Alaska	-	-	-	-	-	-	2.6[1]	-	-	-	-	-	-	2.8[1]	Ambrose and Riddle 1988
NW Territories	-	1	-	-	-	1	4.0	-	-	1	-	-	-	3.0	Court et al. 1988
Midwest U.S.	6	28	10	8	3	3	3.7	12	28	9	1	-	-	1.9	Tordoff and Redig 1997
Tasmania	-	-	2	-	-	-	2.0	-	3	1	1	-	-	2.6	Mooney and Brothers 1993

[1] Numbers of males 5 and females 20.

Table 20.4 Breeding success of Peregrines in south Scotland in relation to (a) height of nest cliff and (b) features of nest site (Mearns and Newton 1988).

(a) Height of nest cliff (m)	Less than 10	11–20	21–40	More than 40
Number of pairs	74	145	89	89
Number that laid	52	126	72	78
Number (%) that produced young	22(42)	70(56)	42(58)	55(71)
Number of failures due to known human nest robbery	7	17	4	2

Significance of variation in clutch success between categories: including known human robberies, $\chi^2 = 13.15$, $P < 0.005$; excluding known human robberies, $\chi^2 = 17.04$, $P < 0.001$.

On regression analysis of number of young raised per attempt (y) against cliff height (x) measured in 10-m units: $y = 0.74 + 0.12x$, $r = 0.167$, $n = 397$, $P < 0.001$.
Excluding known human nest robberies: $y = 0.86 + 0.12x$, $r = 0.159$, $n = 362$, $P < 0.01$.

(b) Nest site	(1) Open	(2) Sheltered on one side	(3) Sheltered on two sides	(4) Overhung	(5) Well overhung	(6) In hole or other recess
Number of clutches	47	55	42	86	55	19
Number (%) that produced young	24(51)	27(49)	22(52)	52(60)	38(69)	15(79)
Number of failures due to known human robbery	4	10	5	7	5	2

Significance of variance in clutch success between categories 1-2, 3-4, and 5-6: including known human robberies, $\chi^2_2 = 8.38$, $P < 0.025$; excluding known human robberies, $\chi^2_2 = 8.00$, $P < 0.025$.

On regression analysis of numbers of young raised per attempt (y) against ledge shelter (x) in six categories: $y = 1.03 + 0.14x$, $r = 0.153$, $n = 305$, $P < 0.01$.
Excluding known human robberies: $y = 1.19 + 0.14x$, $r = 0.155$, $N=272$, $P<0.02$.

Table 20.5 Sex ratios among nestling Peregrines in different areas.

Region	Number of broods	Number of males	Number of females	Ratio females/ males	Source
S. Scotland	133	148	167	1.13	Newton and Mearns 1988
N. England	218	285	289	1.01	G. Horne in Ratcliffe 1993
NW Territories	42	56	52	0.93	Court et al. 1988
Greenland	527	774	792	1.02	Restani and Mattox 2000
Canberra, Australia	?	495	545	1.10	Olsen and Cockburn 1991
Victoria, Australia	?	359	417	1.16	Emison 1988
Tasmania,	?	121	134	1.11	Mooney and Brothers 1993
Overall	-	2238	2398	1.07	-

▲ **Figure 20.6** Releasing a migratory Peregrine after banding on Matagorda Island, Texas, 1973.

two and three years, but others not until age six. However, the possibility of bias in these figures is great. In a short study, many birds ringed as chicks may not have entered the breeding population by the time the study ended (thus reducing the mean recorded age at first breeding), whereas among the older age groups the suspicion always remains that birds may have nested elsewhere at an earlier age and passed unnoticed. However, despite females more often changing territories, the recorded mean age of first breeding was lower in females than in males. This fits the observation that in captive birds, most females start at age two and most males at age three. Many wild Peregrines may of course have been physiologically capable of breeding at a much younger age than they were able to obtain a nesting territory and attempt breeding for the first time.

Reproduction

Since Peregrines normally lay only three or four eggs per clutch and raise no more than one brood per year, their maximum reproductive rates are limited to three or four young per territorial pair per year. Any reduction below this level reflects the frequency of total and partial nest failure. Measurements of overall productivity from populations unaffected by organochlorine pesticides are mostly in the range 1.5 to 2.5 young per territorial pair per year. Heavy rain during the incubation and early nestling periods can greatly depress nest success, either by reducing hunting success or by soaking and flooding exposed nest sites (Mearns and Newton 1988, Olsen and Olsen 1989, Emison et al. 1993). In arctic areas, produc-

tivity in some years is reduced by snowstorms, which sometimes occur during the laying and incubation periods (e.g., Court et al. 1988). Variations in prey abundance may also affect productivity, as shown, for example, by the influence of lemming numbers on Peregrines at Rankin Inlet, Northwest Territories (Court et al. 1988), and of El Niño–induced prey shortages on those nesting on the Olympic coast of Washington State (Wilson et al. 2000).

Whatever the effects of weather and food supplies, mean productivity of the same population can vary up to fivefold between years, much greater than the variation that occurs in breeding density. The main sources of variation are in the proportions of territorial pairs that produce eggs and in the proportion of laying pairs that produce young. Clutch and brood sizes vary relatively little from year to year. Beyond the fact that first-time breeders (especially first-year birds) are less likely to produce young than older, more experienced birds, no studies have dealt with age-related variation in fecundity. In some other bird species, young produced early in the season are more likely to recruit to the local breeding population than later young. At least one study produced evidence for such a relationship in the Peregrine, but the trend was only marginally significant (p = 0.07; Restani and Mattox 2000).

The preference of Peregrines, mentioned above, for the tallest cliffs available might be expected to have some basis in nest success. In south Scotland, Peregrine nest success was clearly related to the height of the nesting cliff, with only 42% of clutches on the lowest cliffs producing young, rising to 71% on the highest (Table 20.4). Nonbreeding was also more frequent on the lowest cliffs (30%) than on the highest (12%), and clutch and brood sizes tended to be smaller on the lowest cliffs but not significantly so. Moreover, when the actual nest sites were classed according to the degree of shelter they conferred, the proportion of clutches that produced young increased from 51% in the most exposed sites to 79% in the most protected (Table 20.4). This finding was not unexpected, considering the effect of rain on nest success.

At least seven studies have reported the sex ratio of nestling Peregrines (usually at the time of ringing) (Table 20.5). All but one showed a slight surplus of females, but in none of the individual studies, or in the overall sample, was the inequality in ratio statistically significant (overall, $\chi^2 = 2.7$, P > 0.05). This equality fits with the findings on other raptors (Newton 1979, Olsen and Cockburn 1991), which contain some of the few bird species in which nestling sex ratios can easily be recorded. In the Scottish Peregrine study, the sex ratio was examined at the egg stage retrospectively for broods in which all eggs gave rise to large young, and was again close to unity. The figures from all these studies are not necessarily free of error, and if, as Emison (1988) suggested, males in some single-sex broods might have been wrongly classed as females, this could have brought the true ratio closer to parity. Males also leave the nest at an earlier age than females, so some males may have been inadvertently missed at ringing.

Migration

The enormous and widescale efforts put into banding Peregrines in North America over the past 30 years, coupled with the trapping efforts at migration sites such as Assateague Island on the East Coast (Maryland-Virginia) and Padre Island on the Gulf Coast (Texas), have greatly increased the numbers of recoveries available for analysis of migration and wintering areas. In addition, many Peregrines have been radio-tagged and tracked on migration from satellite receivers, providing details of the routes and stopping places of individuals (e.g., Fuller et al. 1998).

This new information has helped confirm earlier findings, based on more scanty information, namely that although they may concentrate at favorable coastal localities, Peregrines are in general broad-front migrants, which readily cross large stretches of open sea; and that migrants from North American and Greenland breeding areas winter mainly in Central and South America (most southerly ring recovery about 38°S).

To some extent leap-frog migration occurs, in that birds that breed farthest north tend to winter farthest south (compare the ring recoveries given by Burnham et al. 1988 and Enderson and Craig 1988 for mid-latitude breeding populations with those of Ambrose and Riddle 1988 and Restani and Mattox 2000 for high-latitude ones). In addition, although Peregrines breeding in tundra and boreal regions are wholly migratory, those from more southern latitudes are partial migrants, and some adults remain in cities over winter (Septon 2000). Some longitudinal segregation of migration routes is also apparent, but perhaps less than expected. Thus, birds from extreme western Alaskan populations are retrapped on fall migration mainly on the West Coast (California) and also on the Gulf Coast and to a much smaller extent on the East Coast whereas birds from the extreme eastern (Greenland) population are retrapped mainly on the East Coast and to a

smaller extent on the Gulf Coast (Anderson et al. 1988, Yates et al. 1988). As the latter site receives migrants from the whole of the north, from Alaska to Greenland, there must be considerable spread in the directions and routes taken by birds from specific breeding areas (and even by siblings from the same nest; see Ambrose and Riddle 1988, Yates et al. 1988). With Alaskan birds turning up on both West and East Coasts, implied departure directions lie between south-southeast and east-southeast, an overall arc of about 45 degrees. From the viewpoint of the migration site, Assateague Island receives birds in a 90 degree arc from west Alaska to west Greenland, and the Gulf Coast on a 100 degree arc from the same areas (calculated from data in Yates et al. 1988). Many individuals have been trapped at the same migration site in different falls, but very few at different sites, implying that after they have made one journey, most stick to the same flyway each fall (Ward et al. 1988). Some birds, traveling the East Coast southward, may travel north through the Gulf Coast route, on a path resembling the loop migration of many shorebirds and others. Further evidence for a loop migration is the scarcity of records at Assateague Island in spring (in contrast to Padre Island).

Since many species of birds show marked sex and age differences in migration and wintering areas, it is surprising that so little attention has been paid to this aspect in Peregrines. However, among birds ringed on breeding areas in Greenland and recovered in winter, Restani and Mattox (2000) noted that males migrate farther from the breeding areas than do females (the reverse of natal dispersal differences; see later). Of birds ringed at nest sites in Greenland in June–July, and recovered in November–April, males had moved on average some $10,692 \pm 384$ km and females $5,661 \pm 233$ km. All the 12 males were in South America, whereas all but one of the 33 females were in Central America or the Caribbean. region.

In partially migrant populations, juveniles may leave the breeding areas in greater proportion than adults (see Anderson et al. 1988 for *F. p. pealei*). No differences in the timing of fall passage between adult and juveniles were noted at Assateague Island (Ward et al. 1988), but at Padre Island in fall, males arrived significantly earlier than females, on average, and adults before juveniles (Hunt et al. 1975). At both sites, juveniles were present in greater proportion than

▼ Figure 20.7 Peregrine in flight.

To judge from their flight speeds, Peregrines could travel the daily mean distances within a few hours.

▲ **Figure 20.8** Young Peregrines at hack site moments after the barred front was removed.

example, a longer migration of males than of females has been recorded from ring recoveries of Eurasian Sparrowhawks and Snowy Owls (Belopolski 1971, Kerlinger and Lein 1986), while earlier autumn departures of adults than of juveniles have been noted in several species of European raptors (including Peregrines) in regions where the whole population is migratory (Kjellén 1992).

Natal Dispersal

Long-term studies involving the ringing of nestlings, together with the trapping and ringing of adults, have provided information on natal dispersal: the distances that individuals move between their natal site and subsequent breeding site. Again, birds that move outside the local study area are less likely to be trapped than those that settle within, so the distances are unlikely to be representative. Birds that move outside one area may of course be caught by a different researcher in another area, but the fact remains that long-distance moves are less likely to be recorded. Such bias could also reduce any differences in distances that might occur between sexes or cohorts.

For Peregrines, information is available not only from birds fledged naturally but also from young released from hack sites. We have no reason to think the two groups might differ in dispersal behavior, as both are responding to conditions at the time, and in one relevant analysis involving large samples, no significant difference emerged between the dispersal distances of naturally fledged and hacked birds (Tordoff and Redig 1997).

Using data from both types of young, certain conclusions can be drawn: (1) apart from the release sites used initially, only rarely did birds nest at the site where they were raised or released (usually such sites would be occupied already); (2) most recorded natal-dispersal distances were less than 100 km, but some were much longer, the record for a wild-bred male (in Alaska) being 370 km (Ambrose and Riddle 1988), for a wild-bred female (in Greenland) 690 km (Restani and Mattox 2000), and for hacked birds 1,520 km for a male and 1,760 km for a female (both in the Midwestern United States; Tordoff and Redig 1997); (3) no directional preferences were apparent in any population, except for those imposed by local topography and nest-site availability; and (4) a greater proportion of females than of males moved long distances, so both median and mean recorded distances were greater for

expected from their likely proportion in the population, partly because from some breeding areas they migrate in greater proportion than adults, but possibly also because they stay longer at stopping sites than adults. A significantly earlier fall passage in adult than in juvenile Peregrines was also recorded at Cedar Grove, Wisconsin (Mueller et al. 2000), and at Falsterbo in Sweden (Kjellén 1992).

In their study of radio-marked birds, Fuller et al. (1998) obtained 22 complete and 12 incomplete southward migration tracks from northern populations and seven complete and 11 incomplete northward migration tracks. The average southward migration covered 8,624 km, at an average rate of 172 km per day, giving about 50 days for the full journey. For the northward migration, the equivalent average figures were 8,247 km, 198 km per day, and about 42 days. In these analyses, age and sex groups were not separated, nor was the consistency of individual routes between fall and spring discussed.

Three adult Peregrines radio-tagged at nest sites on the Kola Peninsula of northern Russia wintered in southwest Europe, in the Netherlands, France, and Spain, respectively. Their migrations covered about 3,760 km, 4,120 km, and 5,110 km, respectively, and took at least 17, 14, and 26 days, at mean rates of 221, 294, and 197 km per day (Henny et al. 2000). These birds were all adults, which made faster progress, on average, than the North American birds, which included many juveniles and longer journeys. To judge from their flight speeds, Peregrines could travel the daily mean distances within a few hours. As expected, the longer journeys took more days.

Most of these general features are shared by some other raptors and by some other birds. For

Table 20.6 Natal dispersal distances of Peregrines, as measured by the linear distances (km) between natal site and subsequent breeding site.

Region	Males				Females				Source
	N	Median	Mean	Range	N	Median	Mean	Range	
S Scotland	24	20	?	5–75	15	68	?	3–185	Mearns and Newton 1984
Alaska	6	?	69 ± 74(SD)	4–206	20	?	121 ± 87(SD)	2–370	Ambrose and Riddle 1988
Canada[1]	22	?	51.8 ± 101.8(SD)	0–300	13	?	263.1 ± 292.4(SD)	0–72	Holroyd and Banasch 1990
NW Territories	6	6.6	?	6–14	1	20.5	?	?	Court et al. 1989
Western States	4	?	68	30–90	5	?	279	(100–512)	Burnham et al. 1988
Midwest U.S.[2]	73	?	174	0–1520	67	?	354	0–1760	Tordoff and Redig 1997
Greenland	2	?	28.1 ± 4.4(SE)	?	6	?	27.1 ± 4.4(SE)	?	Restani and Mattox 2000
Tasmania	2	?	20	?	?	?	78.1	?	Mooney and Brothers 1993

[1] Released (hacked) birds only, records from the whole of Canada.
[2] Partly wild birds and partly released (hacked) birds, but no significant difference between the groups.

Table 20.7 Proportion of ringed males and females trapped as breeders in particular study areas where they were known to have been hatched.

Region	Males		Females		Difference (χ^2)	Source
	Number trapped	Number hatched locally (%)	Number trapped	Number hatched locally (%)		
S. Scotland	23	14(61%)	64	14(22%)	10.1, P < 0.01	Mearns and Newton 1984
Alaska	23	5(22%)	83	20(24%)	0.06, N.S.	Ambrose and Riddle 1988
NW Territories	25	6(24%)	38	1(3%)	7.0, P < 0.05	Court et al. 1989
Greenland	?	35	?	7	18.8, P < 0.001[1]	Restani and Mattox 2000

[1] In this case, the χ^2 value was obtained by testing the observed ratio against the numbers of each sex ringed (banded) as nestlings, but in the others, the value was obtained by comparing the numbers of local and nonlocal young among birds of each sex that were trapped.

females than for males (Table 20.6).

Further evidence for shorter dispersal by males than by females stems from the finding that in three out of four study areas, a greater proportion of the breeding males than of the breeding females that were trapped had been hatched in the study area itself (Table 20.7). This held despite the approximately equal sex ratio among fledglings in these areas (Table 20.5), and the roughly similar survival rates (in most areas) of males and females. Hence, the most plausible explanation of the results in Table 20.7 is that more females than males moved outside the study areas to breed. In Greenland, Restani and Mattox (2000) found no sex difference in the moves recorded within the study area (Table 20.6) but a big difference in the proportions of locally raised males and females that nested within the region (Table 20.7).

Substantial differences in recorded dispersal differences were apparent between regions (Table 20.6). These differences are consistent with two explanations: (a) that they are artifacts of variation in size of study areas, with longer moves recorded from the bigger areas, or (b) that the differences are genuine, perhaps affected by variation

in the distances between nest sites (or territories) among areas, with longer moves in areas where territories are more widely spaced. Tordoff and Redig (1997) attributed the longer moves recorded in the Midwestern United States to the relatively long distances between potential nest sites in that area (both cliffs and cities). Examination of distances in terms of "territories crossed" rather than kilometers may help resolve this question. It is also possible that in the early stages of recovery, when densities were much lower than normal, many birds had to disperse farther than usual to find a mate.

The sex bias in dispersal, with males moving shorter distances than females, fits the pattern shown by other raptors, and by many other birds. But the fact that Peregrines nest at such low densities, and disperse over relatively long distances, means that longer distances are more likely to be underecorded than in most other birds.

Breeding Dispersal

The majority of breeding Peregrines (all retrapped males and most retrapped females) occupied the same territories year after year.

▲ **Figure 20.9** Ian Newton (lower left) and his classmates in 1963 with Ian's supervisor, David Lack (middle row, center). Other ornithological notables in the photograph are Peter Evans (shorebirds, back row, third from left); Chris Perrins (songbirds, middle row, second from left), who succeeded David Lack as Director of Oxford's Edward Grey Institute; and Mike Harris (seabirds, middle row, far right).

My own supervisor, David Lack, advised against working on raptors . . . but on this point I ignored his advice.

When females changed territories, they invariably paired with a new male (where checked). This implies that the high mate fidelity shown by most pairs could itself have been an incidental consequence of high territory fidelity. The females that changed territories in the various areas provided an opportunity to measure breeding dispersal, the distances between the nesting territories used in successive years. In studies that gave full details, the distances were 3, 8, 10, 10, 29, 32, and 33 km in south Scotland; 1.3, 3.5, 4.0, 4.6, and 5.3 km at Rankin Inlet, Northwest Territories; and 5 and 226 km in Alaska. These distances are again likely to be influenced by nest spacing in the areas concerned and also to be biased toward shorter moves that occur within study areas; the single long move in Alaska was to a different area. Many of the moves recorded were to an adjacent territory. In general, despite the likely biases, breeding-dispersal distances seem much shorter than natal-dispersal distances.

At least two studies provided indications that territory changes by females were much more likely to occur after a breeding failure than after a success, but with small samples, in neither study was this tendency statistically significant (Mearns and Newton 1984, Court et al. 1989). It would, however, be consistent with findings in some other raptors (James et al. 1989, Newton 1991) and some other birds.

Taken together, the findings on dispersal suggest that in their occupation of nesting territories, most

Peregrines make the longest shifts in their prebreeding years (natal to first breeding site) and thereafter retain the same territory or make relatively short-distance territory changes in the same general area.

Discussion

Although much has been learned in the past 30 years about the demography and movements of Peregrines, substantial gaps remain, and some aspects still rest on an inadequate factual basis. Priorities for future studies include:

(1) factors influencing breeding density, especially the role of food supply and predators (involving actual assessments of food supply and predator distribution);

(2) numbers, distribution, behavior, and survival of floaters (involving radio-tagging of many individuals, as in the study of Northern Goshawks by Kenward et al. 1999);

(3) age composition of the breeding population and age-related trends in survival and reproductive rates (involving large-scale marking and retrapping/resighting of nesting adults);

(4) natal- and breeding-dispersal distances, to acquire a more representative series of distances (involving radio-tagging of many individuals and careful collation and analysis of existing records over large areas);

(5) factors influencing natal- and breeding-dispersal distances, such as level of occupancy and spacing of nest sites (involving collation of data from several areas and analysis at different stages of population recovery);

(6) age and sex differences in migration and wintering areas (involving further analyses of existing data);

(7) behavior, spacing, and threats on wintering areas (involving trapping and radio-tracking of individuals in particular areas).

As may be seen, some of these aspects could be explored by more detailed analyses of existing data, and others by prolonging present studies, but others will require a fresh approach, such as more extensive use of radio-tagging. In the studies of natal dispersal, records from hacked birds could be used along with those of wild-bred ones.

In the recent surge of interest in raptors, some aspects have become better known in Peregrines than in any other species, notably global distribution and abundance, regional trends in numbers and breeding success, diet, and pesticide impacts. This is largely a consequence of the widescale interest in the species and the hundreds of people involved over the years in survey work (much of it summarized in Cade et al. 1988). Other aspects, particularly on demography and population limitation, have progressed less rapidly in Peregrines than in some other species, notably the Eurasian Sparrowhawk (Newton 1986, Zollinger and Müskens 1994), Eurasian Kestrel (Dijkstra 1988, Village 1990, Korpimäki and Norrdahl 1991, Korpimäki and Wiehn 1998), and Merlin (James et al. 1989, Warkentin et al. 1991). These smaller species, operating on smaller spatial and temporal scales, nest at higher densities in more accessible sites and disperse over smaller distances than Peregrines, and thus more readily provide the large samples needed for statistical analyses.

Concluding Remarks

Research on the Peregrine, stimulated by the pesticide-induced decline, has done more than add to our knowledge of Peregrines themselves. It resulted in a surge of interest in all raptors, a group previously largely neglected by biologists, culminating in regular conferences, increasing publication in the scientific literature, and even a journal devoted specifically to research on birds of prey. Increased attention to raptors might have occurred anyway, but the funding made available because of the organochlorine problem enabled this interest to flourish, with work in many remote areas.

Previously, raptors had been largely ignored by research biologists because, nesting at low densities and in difficult places, a lot of effort was needed for little return of data. Samples were nearly always small and statistically frustrating. My own supervisor, David Lack, advised against working on raptors for this very reason, but on this point I ignored his advice.

For many years, the organochlorine problem provided a common focus for raptor research, and the continuing decline in Peregrine numbers gave a sense of urgency and common purpose. It fostered a level of collaboration and camaraderie at that time seldom seen in ecological research, involving enthusiasts in many parts of the world and from many walks of life.

Another major impact was in conservation. Apart from the hard-won fight with the agrochemical industry, the Peregrine effort showed that a difficult bird could be bred in captivity on a large scale, and that such captive-bred birds could be released to the wild to establish self-sustaining populations. Against some opposition from within the conservation movement, it helped to make the "hands-on" approach to management acceptable. Captive breeding and reintroduction have since come to play more important and appropriate roles in conservation management, with efforts turning increasingly to the depleted populations of other birds and animals.

Kurt Burnham

Ian Newton *began his ornithological career by studying the ecology and feeding behavior of finches, based at the University of Oxford. He then moved to work for the Natural Environment Research Council in Britain, studying waterfowl and then birds of prey. For more than 25 years, he conducted a population study of the European Sparrowhawk in south Scotland. He has authored about 250 papers in the scientific literature and five books, including* Population Ecology of Raptors *(1979),* Population Limitation in Birds *(1998), and* The Speciation and Biogeography of Birds *(2003). He has received several prestigious awards and was elected Fellow of the Royal Society in 1993.*

In 1998 Ian was awarded the Order of the British Empire (OBE) by the Queen for his contribution to the science of ornithology.

Chapter 21

Conclusions

William Burnham and Tom J. Cade

*T*his book documents the restoration program for the Peregrine Falcon in North America at all levels of endeavor, but it does more.

It is also a tribute to the many men and women who so steadfastly devoted their energies to the idea that we human beings can put right what we have done wrong.

Although the Peregrine is atop the food web, nesting at low densities and having widely dispersed populations limit its potential role to function as a keystone species in its environment. Even losing the Peregrine completely would not likely have resulted in an unraveling of ecological systems, although our natural world would certainly be poorer for its loss. More important to the restoration program than the biological role of the Peregrine in nature was its place in the hearts and minds of thousands of people. The Peregrine was and remains a major "flagship species" of the conservation movement, and during the years of organochlorine pesticide use it became an important barometer of environmental contamination, as well as a major icon around which the public cry for a stop to the use of persistent pesticides focused.

This book summarizes 35 years of work involving numerous organizations and more than a thousand individuals. What is the significance of all this effort and money spent to restore a bird to its former distribution and abundance? Foremost, the Peregrine is back in most of its old haunts, as well as in some new and unusual places, and people again have the good fortune to observe the Peregrine in action, to marvel at its superlative skills as a flyer, whether in courtship displays around its eyrie or in pursuit of prey. For Peregrine devotees, that is no small thing.

As explained earlier, the beginning of Peregrine restoration preceded the current Endangered Species Act (ESA), recovery teams and plans, and many other government-instituted solutions for saving species. It did happen at a time of increasing public awareness and interest in the environment, societal changes that no doubt assisted the restoration. Saving species and wild places became increasingly important in North America. The concept of biodiversity had not yet been formalized, and no professional society existed exclusively for the promotion of biological conservation.

◀ Figure 21.1 Painting by John Schmitt. Reproduction courtesy of The Peregrine Fund. Image used for 1999 Peregrine Celebration.

As the largest, most visible, and ultimately most successful program to restore an endangered species, Peregrine recovery in North America played a role in the environmental trends of the 1970s and 1980s that ultimately led to a new emphasis in conservation called conservation biology, the melding of pure science with applied conservation. This new discipline or philosophical approach to the conservation of living things had multiple origins that converged into the formation of the Society for Conservation Biology in 1986 and in the publication of a major and highly respected scientific journal. As pronounced by one of its founders, Michael Soulé (1987), "The society is a response by professionals, mostly

Figure 21.2 Estimated Peregrine Falcon breeding range before 1970. ▶

Figure 21.3 Known Peregrine Falcon breeding range 1970 to 1975. ▶

biological and social scientists, managers and administrators, to the biological diversity crisis that will reach a crescendo in the first half of the twenty-first century."

Among the major scientific contributions to this movement, one would probably start with publication of *The Theory of Island Biogeography* by MacArthur and Wilson (1967) and also include Paul Ehrlich's powerful expositions on species extinctions and environmental degradation in relation to the human population explosion, E. O. Wilson's various writings about biodiversity and biophilia, Norman Myers's warnings about the rapid loss of the world's tropical forests, the discussions of population geneticists such as Otto Frankel and Michael Soulé about the loss of genetic diversity in small, depleted, or isolated populations, and the development of population viability theory by Michael Soulé and others.

Another pervading theme, originating mainly from zoological gardens and their societies, and especially championed by William Conway of the New York Zoological Society, emphasized the role of captive breeding in zoos as a way to maintain ex situ populations of endangered species, with the eventual goal of reestablishing propagules from these captive storehouses back into nature. These practical aims were strongly linked to population genetics theory and to Soulé's theory of minimum viable populations. They became institutionalized through the World Conservation Union (IUCN) Species Survival Commission, which established a Captive Breeding Specialist Group (now Conservation Breeding Group) under the strong and committed leadership of Ulysses S. Seal, recently deceased, and a Re-introduction Specialist Group, originally headed by Mark R. Stanley Price of Arabian oryx fame.

The Peregrine Fund participated in both specialist groups, and it also provided input into three meetings that influenced the establishment of conservation biology as a recognized discipline. The first was the Symposium on Management Techniques for Preserving Endangered Birds organized by Stan Temple (1978) at the University of Wisconsin and held 17–20 August 1977, in which various hands-on methods of dealing with threatened birds were first highlighted (Stan later served as one of the early presidents of the Society for Conservation Biology). Another was the symposium and workshop Application of Genetics to the Management of Wild Plant and Animal Populations held in Washington, D.C., 9–13 August 1982 and sponsored by the U.S. Man and the Biosphere Program (see Cade 1983). The third was the National Forum on BioDiversity held in Washington, D.C., on 21–24 September 1986 under the auspices of the National Academy of Sciences and the Smithsonian Institution (see Cade 1988b).

Captive breeding (conservation breeding) and reintroduction have been continually under discussion in conservation biology circles from the beginning, as an examination of the journals *Biological Conservation* and *Conservation Biology* reveals. Critics have often questioned the technical effectiveness of captive breeding and reintroduction as methods for species restoration, as well as the ethical desirability of such hands-on methods compared with more holistic approaches such as habitat preservation and ecosystem management. Nevertheless, captive breeding and reintroduction have proved effective in restoring several rare or threatened raptor and other species populations to vacated range, and their importance will no doubt increase as more and more species become threatened by habitat degradation, fragmentation, and loss. As Cade and Temple (1995) and Cade (2000) emphasized, these hands-on, species-specific methods lie at one end of a spectrum of actions needed to conserve biodiversity, with ecosystem management at the other end. They are neither better nor worse than other methods of conservation; they are simply applied for different purposes. The more holistic actions focused on ecosystems and habitats are essential for maintaining biological diversity, preventing additional species from becoming vulnerable to extinction, and providing ecological scope for the recovery of endangered species; but once a species becomes threatened, it usually requires special attention to its particular needs for restoration.

Although species restoration efforts (most notably for the American bison and several species of waterfowl) had occurred in prior decades in association with the emerging discipline of wildlife management, saving the Peregrine was the primary one that broke new ground and provided other conservationists with the optimism and encouragement for similar efforts with other species. Obvious examples in North America involved captive breeding and reintroduction and restoration efforts for the Southern Bald Eagle, California Condor, Northern Aplomado Falcon, and black-footed ferret. Possibly the greatest success story of all has been the restoration of the Mauritius Kestrel (Jones et al. 1995). Reduced to only two surviving pairs in the wild, the Mauritius

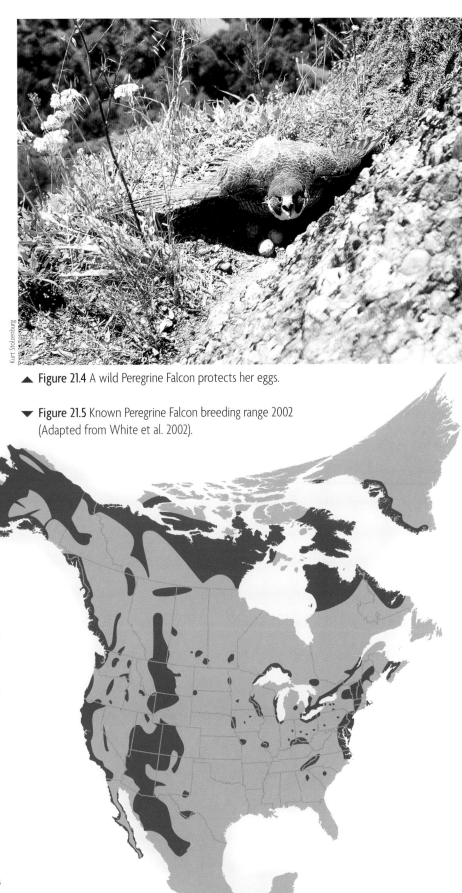

Kurt Stolzenburg

▲ **Figure 21.4** A wild Peregrine Falcon protects her eggs.

▼ **Figure 21.5** Known Peregrine Falcon breeding range 2002 (Adapted from White et al. 2002).

351

File photo

Erin Gott

Christie Van Cleve

▲ Figure 21.6–21.9

Techniques developed for restoring Peregrines have greatly influenced the restoration of other raptors. Top: the first release of Bald Eagles by hacking, in New York, 1976, by The Peregrine Fund and NYS Department of Environmental Conservation. These birds paired and had a successful nest four years later. Left, Aplomado Falcon; above right, California Condor; below, Mauritius Kestrel.

Willard Heck

Kestrel population has increased through careful management employing the techniques developed for the Peregrine. Today there are about 800 kestrels in the wild in Mauritius and no indication that population growth is complete (Boroughs 2001). Projects for the Peregrine, Bearded Vulture, Griffon, White-tailed Sea Eagle, Red Kite, and other species were also initiated and continue in Europe. By the late 1990s, worldwide there were more than 50 projects involving some 25 species of diurnal birds of prey based on the Peregrine model (Cade 2000) and at least 75% of them had achieved some success in establishing viable populations in nature.

The Peregrine restoration program was also a training ground for hundreds of young conservationists, and whether they later pursued a career in biology or not, the experience of being part of the program enriched their lives. We have been told so time and time again by many of those who worked at hack sites and otherwise participated in the Peregrine effort. Many did go on to pursue professional careers in biology, and some have distinguished themselves as scientists, government department and agency heads, and conservation leaders. Others chose different professions but carry with them the special sense one gains from being part of a winning team that made an important difference.

Before Peregrine restoration, the term hacking was associated only with falconry and even in that field was largely unknown and untried in modern times. Peregrine restoration took the term to a new level of meaning—hack sites, hack site attendants, hack boxes, hack towers, hack manuals—became widely understood in the new vocabulary of reintroduction technology. Likewise, few biologists knew what fostering or cross-fostering meant. Terminology associated with captive breeding of falcons was also developed or popularized and used for other species and projects, behavioral imprint and double-clutching being examples. The sight of a falcon copulating on a hat became well enough known that a cartoon appeared in *The New Yorker* on the subject.

These terms were reflections of the new technology and information on species management and restoration that developed with Peregrine recovery. The information and results spread far and wide, including coverage in journals such as *Science* and *BioScience* (e.g., see Appendix A, Bibliography of Eastern and Midwestern Peregrine Reintroductions, 1971–2000). Peregrine restoration even became subject matter for general biology and wildlife science textbooks. The technology and resulting literature for captive breeding of Pere-

North American Peregrine Falcon Victory Celebration

William Burnham

On 20 and 21 August 1999 a series of events and activities occurred which will never be forgotten by those who participated and which made everyone involved feel better for having been there. It was the delisting of the Peregrine Falcon as an endangered species and the North American Peregrine Falcon Victory Celebration. Participants called the Celebration a "Peregrine Woodstock" and a "once in a lifetime happening." No single phrase, even paragraph, however, can capture that almost magical time, which lasted for two days.

Over 1,000 people gathered in Boise, Idaho, to be together and share the accomplishment in which they all took part—restoration of the Peregrine Falcon. They came from throughout North America and even abroad. The diversity of participants mirrored the recovery effort, as did their friendship and cooperation. The celebration was initiated by The Peregrine Fund and hosted by it, The Raptor Center, and the Santa Cruz Predatory Bird Research Group. Events included the delisting announcement by Secretary of the Interior Bruce Babbitt, a "Get Re-Acquainted Social" at the Boise Zoo followed by the "Peregrine Extravaganza" at the Velma Morrison Center, Boise State University. The following day began with "Looking Back, Considering the Accomplishment, and Summing Up Results" where speakers summarized 35 years of work involving numerous organizations and thousands of individuals. In the afternoon there was an open house at the World Center for Birds of Prey. The grand finale was the "Peregrine Party," an Idaho-style party hosted by The Peregrine Fund's Idaho Board members at Boise's historic Old Idaho Penitentiary and adjoining Idaho Botanical Gardens. In the warm summer evening, with the music of Pinto Bennett's western band, Peregrine enthusiasts gathered for the final time. They reminisced, speaking about experiences, falcons, and friends not present who played a part in this accomplishment. As the sun was replaced with red dusk and then night stars, conversations eventually faded to good-byes. People realized that never would this group gather again to save the Peregrine, nor savor the victory of its restoration. A two-pound bird with pointed wings, dark eyes, and a piercing cry united a small army, spanning nations and decades. Although the army may disappear, we need to ensure that this accomplishment, like the Peregrine, does not. This achievement illustrates what can be done when people care enough and work together to make a difference.

For biographical information on William Burnham see Chapter 8.

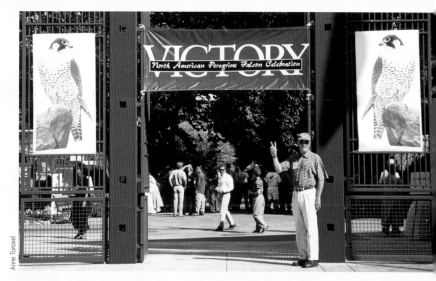

Top: Jim Enderson makes the vicotry sign at the entrance to Zoo Boise, kick-off site for the Peregrine celebration.

Middle: Peregrine Falcon delisting press conference, 9:30 a.m. on 20 August 1999. Speakers included, from left to right, Secretary of the Interior Bruce Babbitt, Tom Cade, Senator Mike Crapo, and Derek Ratcliffe. Bill Burnham served as master of ceremonies.

Below: The Peregrine Extravaganza, the grand finale curtain call of the celebration's first evening.

Russell Thorstrom

On behalf of The Peregrine Fund and all participants in the Peregrine restoration effort, Bill Burnham (left) accepts an award presented by Roy Disney from The Walt Disney Company. The award depicts Jiminy Cricket releasing Varda the Peregrine Falcon to the wild.

We pass on to our children and their children and generations to come, the wild restless beauty of a Peregrine's flight...

Tom Cade's Remarks:

Bill Burnham asked me to say a few words about why we are here tonight. During the past 35 years many of you in this audience and hundreds of others in the United States, Canada, and Europe have been engaged in a great, collaborative effort to restore the Peregrine Falcon to its rightful place in nature. That goal has been reached in North America, and it is indeed a time to celebrate, but also to reflect on the significance of what we have done.

On an occasion such as this one, when we come together to celebrate a human achievement of extraordinary dimension, I think of the words by Alfred Lord Tennyson, in his poem *Ulysses,* perhaps the most inspired words ever written about man's indomitable will to press on and not give up in the face of adversity. The poem is a dramatic monologue by an aging Ulysses, who has grown restless after his return home to Ithaca. He addresses his mariners, whom he has assembled to the ship for a last great voyage into uncharted waters. "I cannot rest from travel," he tells them, because "all experience is an arch where through gleams that untraveled world, whose margin fades forever and forever when I move....'Tis not too late to seek a newer world. Push off, and sitting well in order smite the sounding furrows; for my purpose holds to sail beyond the sunset, and the baths of all the western stars, until I die...To follow knowledge like a sinking star beyond the utmost bound of human thought." He ends by appealing to his mariners' pride: "...you and I are old," he

Bill Burnham's Remarks As Master of Ceremony:

We are here to celebrate the restoration of the Peregrine Falcon. All of you have played a part. Your part may have been as a donor, hack site attendant, propagator, field biologist, administrator, or another important role. Or you may be a family member who, through your support, made it possible for another person to participate.

This is a victory party for us and the Peregrine. Why has this recovery occurred? It is happening because you and thousands of other people wanted it to. You cared enough to make a difference, take a stand, make a contribution. We set aside our differences and agreed—the Peregrine Falcon would not disappear and it would again take its rightful place as an integral part of our natural world. The Peregrine is back by popular demand.

This evening we declare this victory for Joe Hickey, Rachel Carson, Jerry Herrick, Bill Wrigley, Ed and Charlotte Freienmuth, Walter Spofford, Jim Rice, Al Nye, Butch Olendorff, and our other friends and cooperators who are with us in spirit; for those who participated in and supported the effort and are present in person here or elsewhere; for the North American taxpayer whose hard-won dollars were combined with private donations to fund the actions. And we declare victory particularly for the future generations of humans who will become the stewards of our natural world, which now again includes the Peregrine Falcon. We pass on to our children and their children and generations to come, the wild restless beauty of a Peregrine's flight, its defiant cry as it defends its eyrie and young, and the embodiment of freedom the falcon represents. Within the Peregrine's dark eyes we see mankind's reflection, and in this instance we can feel pride.

says, but "Old age hath yet his honour and his toil.... Though much is taken, much abides; and though We are not now that strength that in old days moved earth and heaven, that which we are, we are: one equal temper of heroic hearts, made weak by time and fate, but strong in will to strive, to seek, to find, and not to yield."

My dear friends and colleagues, you and I have fought the good fight for the Peregrine, and we have won a great victory. We do not have to fall on our swords, for no one can deny that restoration of the Peregrine on two continents represents the largest and most sustained effort ever mounted to save an endangered species. What we have accomplished together is truly phenomenal, and I believe that recovery of the Peregrine will be recorded in the annals of conservation as a major event of the 20th century. But, as we all know, conservation is a continual series of challenges—the fight for conservation never ends—and so I exhort you, as Ulysses exhorted his mariners of old, not to rest in port, "to rust unburnished"; rather "to shine in use." Bend to your oars, "smite the sounding furrows," and press on to meet new challenges, for they surely await, and will always be waiting, for those who strive to keep the earth fit for life in all its many splendored forms.

grines have also disseminated throughout and greatly influenced the avicultural world. Manufacturers of incubators and brooders improved their equipment and made new items, such as portable incubators, based on improvements made by and the needs of falcon propagators. New businesses sprang up, examples being not only commercial propagation of raptors for restoration and falconry nationally and internationally but also the production of quail and chickens bred specifically to feed captive birds of prey.

In Chapter 20 Ian Newton documents contributions to the understanding and knowledge of the Peregrine made during the restoration program. Although many questions still remain to be answered, the Peregrine Falcon is now certainly one of the most studied and best-known birds of prey in the world, as well as one of the most popular.

When the Peregrine Falcon restoration began, there were many people and even organizations who had accepted the predicted, and believed to be inevitable, loss of species such as the Peregrine, Mauritius Kestrel, and California Condor. If it was possible to lose the multitude of Passenger Pigeons that once existed in North America, then the loss of remnant populations of these other species seemed certain. Gloom and doom dominated publications and presentations about endangered species. Comments were common about wasting money on lost causes and letting species die in dignity. Many believed it was impossible to breed the Peregrine predictably in captivity, let alone release and reestablish viable wild populations successfully with artificially produced birds. But each small success in Peregrine restoration led to the next, and this progress, combined with the public appeal of such a charismatic species, helped change attitudes. Optimism grew, and with it the courage of others to follow suit with other species. The successes in Peregrine Falcon restoration had an immeasurable influence on public and even government attitudes about endangered species. If hope for saving endangered species was not born in Peregrine restoration, it was certainly substantially nourished there.

As Chapter 15 explains, success was achieved despite many obstacles, some imposed by people and organizations who should have been solid allies. Much has been written about the role of falconers and the influence and benefit of falconry techniques to Peregrine restoration. There is no doubt that falconry and many falconers contributed importantly to the restoration effort, and a few falconers were key players in recovery actions. Not all falconers were supportive of the restoration program, however, and a few were

If hope for saving endangered species was not born in Peregrine restoration, it was certainly substantially nourished there.

outspoken critics, passing the effort off as a plot by scientists to support themselves. History and results seem to have settled such questions, and they need no further comment here.

In the early years of the program, falconers and a smaller group of biologists and other raptor enthusiasts comprised the Peregrine's principal constituency. At that time, the species had only recently become

protected and was still routinely shot. Over the years the Peregrine's popularity increased with the visibility of the restoration effort. City-released and nesting Peregrines probably had a great deal to do with that. People value the Peregrine because of its beauty in nature and inspiration and for other individual personal reasons. Even for many who may never see a Peregrine themselves, just knowing such a bird exists is important.

Every author in this book has an opinion as to why Peregrine restoration succeeded. Some have expressed their views in what they have written. The most obvious and probably unanimous reason was banning the use of DDT. The resulting much lower levels of DDT and its metabolites in the Peregrine's prey and in turn in the falcons themselves made the recovery possible. If the level of DDT use practiced in the 1950s and 1960s had continued, the Peregrine restoration effort would have certainly failed. Release of nearly 7,000 Peregrines is the second reason for the successful recovery of the species. Beyond these two reasons, some level of disagreement may exist. Falconers may believe recovery could not have happened without their contributions of knowledge, dedication, falcons, and money, and they are probably correct.

There were also many people who were not falconers who had critical roles. Private organizations, and in particular The Peregrine Fund, certainly played key roles. The Peregrine Fund did not recover the Peregrine Falcon, but it was certainly a driving force and coordinating body contributing to the ultimate success and delisting of the species. Two other organizations of special note are the Santa Cruz Predatory Bird Research Group, for recovery action in California and the Pacific Coast, and The Raptor Center at the University of Minnesota for restoration action in the Midwestern states. Governments also had their roles. The Canadian Wildlife Service was certainly instrumental in what was accomplished in

MUSEUM OF COMPARATIVE ZOOLOGY

The Agassiz Museum

HARVARD UNIVERSITY · CAMBRIDGE, MASSACHUSETTS 02138 · TEL. 617 495-2466

8 April 1991

Mr. Tom J. Cade
The Peregrine Fund, Inc.
5666 West Flying Hawk Lane
Boise, Idaho 83709

Dear Tom,

it has been a source of great satisfaction to me over the years to be able to give some support to your peregrine work. As a close friend of Dick Herbert and Joe Hickey I have been on countless peregrine excursions and was as distressed as anyone when the peregrines were disappearing.

When you started to develop your plans I was quite convinced that they were utopian and would not come to anything. When, owing to your incredible hard work and vision, you nevertheless succeeded, I felt quite guilty and have "attoned for my sins" by supporting your work.

When it comes to conservation, of course, we have the peculiar situation in this country that technical questions are decided by lawyers. This is as true for conservation as it is for the settling of malpractice suits in medicine. As a European by upbringing and idea-molding, I have never been able to understand how we can give lawyers such powers over matters of which they understand little or nothing. Naturally I was delighted to help Steve O'Brien, particularly in the treatment of subspecies, and made indeed the final version much stronger than it had been in the first draft.

With best wishes,

yours,

Ernst Mayr

Ernst Mayr

EM:wb

▲ **Figure 21.10** A 1991 letter from Ernst Mayr, the renowned taxonomist and ornithologist. Mayr writes "When, owing to your incredible hard work and vision, you nevertheless succeeded, I felt quite guilty and have 'attoned for my sins' by supporting your work."

Canada. In the United States, where the restoration effort was led more by the private sector than government, land management agencies and state wildlife agencies in particular still contributed importantly to the restoration effort at all levels. The army of hack site attendants, observers, and other field people were certainly critical, along with their families who agreed to their absence and supported them.

Then, of course, there were the essential private-sector financial and in-kind donors and contributors. Many times their support was not readily obvious and impossible to measure. The right words or recommendation at the correct moment to potential donors, government officials, and other necessary supporters made all the difference. These people expected no recognition or credit. They were satisfied just to help make the restoration effort succeed. We appreciate their support and partnership.

Although there were many such people (some we did not even know), one we wish to highlight is Richard Thorsell. Throughout his tenure in Washington, D.C., with the Edison Electric Institute (a lobbying group of the electrical industry), Dick continually assisted The Peregrine Fund. During his weekly meetings, meals, and parties with politicians and bureaucrats, he looked after both the electrical industry and the Peregrine and other raptors, which he loved. The fingerprints from his guiding hand appear in many places, including the experimental population amendment to the ESA (49 FR 33893, Aug. 27, 1984). He even talked the electrical industry into providing money and release sites at their facilities for Peregrines!

Finally, the support of the American public, including their tax dollars, was critical. The restoration of the Peregrine Falcon succeeded because all of these people and organizations cared enough to make a difference. People set aside their differences and decided they would not allow the Peregrine Falcon to be lost on their account and that it should continue to exist for the inspiration and enjoyment of future generations.

Is the Peregrine Falcon safe? The Peregrine occurs throughout much of the world and as a species has never been threatened with extinction, although particular subspecies and populations have been, and some still are. The Peregrine in North America is now as secure as most any other species of bird of prey and most other forms of wildlife. Its wide geographic distribution and range, adaptive ability to use a variety of habitats and nest sites from mountain cliffs to towers in marshes and urban environments, and the diversity of avian prey it uses all greatly reduce the chance of any single event, short of the magni-

File photo

Carol Berry

▲ Figure 21.11 The Peregrine Fund Board of Directors in 1977, a few hard core, never-say-die falconers. From left to right, Jim Enderson, Tom Cade, Bob Berry, Frank Bond, Kent Carnie, Jim Weaver, and Bill Burnham.

▲ Figure 21.12 The same group at the 1999 Peregrine celebration, from left to right, Jim Enderson, Tom Cade, Bob Berry, Kent Carnie, Bill Burnham, Frank Bond, and Jim Weaver.

▲ **Figure 21.13** Dick Thorsell with Golden Eagle in Morley Nelson's back yard. Standing next to him is Idaho Power Company Environmental Supervisor Allen Ansell. With Dick's encouragement, Morley Nelson and Idaho Power Company pioneered the prevention of raptor electrocution technology.

Figure 21.14 This wild ▶ female Peregrine, photographed by Al Hospers, was encountered by New Hampshire Audubon senior biologist Chris Martin on a banding expedition 3 June 2003. She has nested since 1997 at Cathedral Ledge.

tude and effect of DDT, placing the American and Arctic Peregrine Falcons in jeopardy again. Peregrine populations in North America (including Greenland) are robust and continue to increase.

It should be realized, however, that these populations will not continue to increase indefinitely and at some point will reach a level imposed by environmental limitations (see Chapter 20). This adjustment to carrying capacity may already be occurring in some areas as the influences of natural, density-dependent behaviors are being seen, as described by Bud Tordoff (Chapter 10) of Peregrines injuring and killing each other in competition for mates and territories. Within Peregrine populations in North America, overall survival and reproduction will eventually decrease as population density increases. These adjustments should not come as a surprise to biologists who monitor the population in future years.

Some people have asked if the problem with the Peregrine had occurred in the present day, could conservationists build and accomplish a successful recovery program now? We feel that it would be extremely difficult, if not impossible. Endangered species are too contentious to receive the widespread support needed for a cosmopolitan species like the Peregrine. Through provisions of the ESA, the species would immediately be used by certain environmental groups as a pawn to stop government and private sector activities with which they disagree and to promote agendas that are at best tangential to species recovery. We continually see this abusive use of the ESA with other endangered species with which we work and by people in both

the private sector and government. The honesty of arguing a case or cause on its substantive merits in contrast to the expediency of arguing on the basis of policy or political ideology seems to have become old-fashioned. Emphasizing this point, the U.S. Fish and Wildlife Service now annually spends tens of millions of dollars needed for endangered species recovery defending itself from litigation by groups working in the name of protecting the environment. None of these legal maneuvers bode well for restoration programs for species in jeopardy now or in the future.

Most of the authors of this book, having been at this endeavor for several decades, realize it is now increasingly up to younger biologists, falconers, and other conservationists to carry on. It is, or soon will be, their turn to become the stewards of wild things and wild places, including the Peregrine. It is easier to do nothing or criticize others who attempt action than to get involved personally, particularly when one is busy with life's many demands. But what if one does get involved? Can he or she as an individual have an impact, make a difference? The answer should be obvious from reading this book. The people mentioned in these chapters did make a difference, each in his or her own special way. The actions of caring, dedicated, energetic individuals and organizations who refused to be intimidated by challenge and opposition, or to give up from fear of failure, achieved meaningful and positive results.

Today there is greater need than ever to solve major environmental issues, such as the restoration of salmonid fishes in the Columbia-Snake River systems or the preservation of our remaining sagebrush-grasslands and associated wildlife such as the Greater Sage-Grouse. We hope that the spirit of balance and cooperation that developed among diverse interests in recovery of the Peregrine can be extended to solving these other problems.

The story of the Peregrine's recovery in North America and Europe provides hope and encouragement to the new generation of biologists and conservationists who may often feel overwhelmed by the complexity of the environmental problems created by the mass of humanity. Although much has been lost in nature, much abides; and we believe that a few thousand stout-hearted men and women working together with vision and purpose could rally the world to restore the global ecosystem to a more natural and balanced order of existence.

Biographical information for Bill Burnham can be found at the end of Chapter 8 and for Tom Cade at the end of Chapter 5.

A first or second generation female Peregrine, descended from released parents, stands guard at her eyrie in the forest of New Hampshire, scanning the sky for prey or enemy.

Unbanded, she is the perfect image of the free and wild falcon in her natural habitat, the ultimate goal of all our work. Perhaps her powerful eye can even see the distant ghosts of Coffin, Proctor, Hagar, Spofford, Herbert, Craighead, Hickey, Rice, Nye . . . hovering overhead.

Rest easy now, ye kindred spirits; we who follow kept the faith.

Appendices

Appendix A

Bibliography for Eastern and Midwestern Peregrine Reintroductions, 1971-2000
Compiled by H. B. Tordoff and T. J. Cade

Barber, J. 1989. Interspecific aggression in urban Peregrine Falcons. Maryland Birdlife 45:134-135.

Barber, J. 1989. (Abstract) The Peregrine Falcons of USF&G Corporation. Pages 35-37 *in* Perspectives in wildlife management: a how-to for corporate lands (J. Hausoul, Ed.). Wildlife Habitat Council, Silver Spring, MD.

Barber, J., and M. Barber. 1983. Prey of an urban Peregrine Falcon. Maryland Birdlife 39:108-110.

Barber, J. C. 1992. Unusual prey of urban Peregrine Falcons. Maryland Birdlife 48:74.

Barber, J. C. 1992. (Abstract) Who says your site is too small? Pages 11-13 *in* Birds, business, and biodiversity. Wildlife Habitat Council, Silver Spring, MD.

Barber, J. C. 1992. Urban Peregrine Falcons in Baltimore, Maryland. Pages 4-8 *in* AAZPA Regional Conference Proceedings. American Association of Zoological Parks and Aquariums, Wheeling, WV.

Barber, J. C., and M. M. Barber. 1988. Prey of an urban Peregrine Falcon-part II. Maryland Birdlife 44:37-39.

Barclay, J. H. 1988. Peregrine restoration in the eastern United States. Pages 549-558 *in* Peregrine Falcon Populations: Their Management and Recovery (T. J. Cade, J. H. Enderson, C. G. Thelander, and C. M. White, Eds.). The Peregrine Fund, Boise, ID.

Barclay, J. H. 1995. Patterns of dispersal and survival of eastern Peregrine Falcons derived from banding data. A report to the U.S. Fish and Wildlife Service. BioSystems Analysis, Santa Cruz, CA.

Barclay, J. H., and T. J. Cade. 1983. Restoration of the Peregrine Falcon in the eastern United States. Pages 3-40 *in* Bird Conservation. Vol. 1:3-40 (S. A. Temple, Ed.). International Council for Bird Preservation, University of Wisconsin Press, Madison.

Barclay, J. H., and T. J. Cade. 1984. The current status of Peregrine recovery in the eastern U.S. Transactions of the Northeastern Section Wildlife Society 41:85-91.

Brock, K. J. 1998. A Peregrine Falcon taking prey from a Merlin. Indiana Audubon Quarterly 76:117.

Burns, S. A., W. M. Jarman, T. J. Cade, L. F. Kiff, and B. J. Walton. 1994. Organochlorines and eggshell thinning in Peregrine Falcon *Falco peregrinus* eggs from the eastern United States, 1986-1988. Pages 709-716 *in* Raptor Conservation Today (B.-U. Meyburg and R. D. Chancellor, Eds.) World Working Group on Birds of Prey and Owls/Pica Press, Berlin/Robertsbridge, U.K.

Byre, V. J. 1990. A group of young Peregrine Falcons prey on migrating bats. Wilson Bulletin 102:728-730.

Cade, T. J. 1971. Survival of the Peregrine Falcon: protection or management. Raptor Research News 5(2):83-87.

Cade, T. J. 1974. Plans for managing the survival of Peregrine Falcons. Raptor Research Report 2:89-104.

Cade, T. J. 1980. The husbandry of falcons for return to the wild. International Zoo Yearbook 20:23-35.

Cade, T. J. 1982. Renaissance of the Peregrine Falcon. Living Bird Quarterly 2(1):6-9.

Cade, T. J. 1985. Peregrine recovery in the United States. Pages 331-342 *in* Conservation Studies on Raptors (I. Newton and R. D. Chancellor, Eds.). International Council for Bird Preservation Technical Bulletin no. 5.

Cade, T. J. 1986. Reintroduction as a method of conservation. Raptor Research Report 5:72-84.

Cade, T. J. 1988. Using science and technology to reestablish species lost in nature. Pages 279-288 *in* Biodiversity (E. O. Wilson and F. M. Peters, Eds.). National Academy of Sciences Press, Washington, D.C.

Cade, T. J. 1990. Peregrine Falcon recovery. Endangered Species Update 8(1):40-43.

Cade, T. J. 2000. Progress in translocation of diurnal raptors. Pages 343-372 *in* Raptors at Risk: 5th World Conference on Birds of Prey (R. D. Chancellor and B.-U. Meyburg, Eds.). World Working Group for Birds of Prey, Berlin/Hancock House, Blaine, WA.

Cade, T. J., and D. M. Bird. 1990. Peregrine Falcons, *Falco peregrinus*, nesting in an urban environment. Canadian Field-Naturalist 104(2):209-218.

Cade, T. J., and P. R. Dague. 1978. Peregrine Falcon recovery. Delaware Conservationist 22(2):22-24.

Cade, T. J., J. H. Enderson, L. F. Kiff, and C. M. White. 1997. Are there enough good data to justify de-listing the American Peregrine? Wildlife Society Bulletin 25(3):730-738.

Cade, T. J., J. H. Enderson, and J. Linthicum, Eds. 1996. Guide to Management of Peregrine Falcons at the Eyrie. The Peregrine Fund, Boise, ID.

Cade, T. J., and V. J. Hardaswick. 1985. Summary of Peregrine Falcon production and reintroduction by The Peregrine Fund in the United States, 1973-1984. Aviculture Magazine 91:79-92.

Cade, T. J., M. Martell, P. Redig, G. Septon, and H. Tordoff. 1996. Peregrine Falcons in urban North America. Pages 3-13 *in* Raptors in Human Landscapes (D. M. Bird, D. E. Varland, and J. J. Negro, Eds.). Academic Press, London.

Cade, T. J., P. T. Redig, and H. B. Tordoff. 1989. Peregrine Falcon restoration: expectation vs. reality. Loon 61(4):160-162.

Cade, T. J., and S. A. Temple. 1977. The Cornell University falcon programme. Pages 353-369 in World Conference on Birds of Prey, Vienna, 1975 (R. D. Chancellor, Ed.). International Council for Bird Preservation, Cambridge, U.K.

Cade, T. J., H. B. Tordoff, and J. H. Barclay. 2000. Re-introduction of Peregrines in the eastern United States: an evaluation. Re-introduction News 19:19-21.

Castrale, J., and A. R. Parker. 1999. Peregrine Falcon nesting and management in Indiana. Indiana Audubon Quarterly 77:65-74.

Clement, R. C, Ed. 1974. Peregrine Falcon recovery, proceedings of a conference on Peregrine Falcon recovery. Audubon Conservation Report no. 4.

Corser, J. D., M. Amaral, C. J. Martin, and C. C. Rimmer. 1999. Recovery of a cliff-nesting Peregrine Falcon, Falco peregrinus, population in northern New York and New England, 1984-1996. Canadian Field Naturalist 113:472-480.

DeMent, S. H., J. J. Chisolm, J. C. Barber, and J. D. Strandberg. 1986. Lead exposure in an "urban" Peregrine Falcon and its avian prey. Journal of Wildlife Diseases 22(2):238-244.

Enderson, J. H., W. Heinrich, L. Kiff, and C. M. White. 1995. Population changes in North American Peregrines. Transactions of the North American Wildlife and Natural Resources Conference. 60:142-161.

Evans, J. E., J. Coleman, and S. G. Galatowitsch. 1983. Minnesota's Peregrine Falcon reintroduction project: 1982 hack site report. Loon 55(1):3-8.

Faccio, S. D., and J. D. Corser. 1995. The reoccupancy of historic Peregrine Falcon nest sites in Vermont: their current status, and future prospects. Vermont Botanical and Bird Club Joint Bulletin no. 21.

Frank, S. 1994. City Peregrines: A Ten Year Saga of New York City Falcons. Hancock House, Blaine, WA.

Gilroy, M. J., and J. H. Barclay. 1988. DDE residues and eggshell characteristics of reestablished Peregrines in the eastern United States. Pages 403-411 in Peregrine Falcon Populations: Their Management and Recovery (T. J. Cade, J. H. Enderson, C. G. Thelander, and C. M. White, Eds.). The Peregrine Fund, Boise, ID.

Grier, J. W., and J. H. Barclay. 1988. Dynamics of founder populations established by reintroduction. Pages 689-700 in Peregrine Falcon Populations: Their Management and Recovery. (T. J. Cade, J. H. Enderson, C. G. Thelander, and C. M. White, Eds.). The Peregrine Fund, Boise, ID.

Hennen, M. 1996. Illinois Peregrines: back from the brink. Illinois Audubon 1996:14-16.

Kaufman, J., and H. Meng. 1992. Falcons Return. Second edition. KAV Books, Unionville, NY.

Kendall, J. C. 1989. Indiana's first Peregrine Falcon breeding record. Indiana Audubon Quarterly 67:203.

Loucks, B., and K. Kogut. 1985. The Peregrine returns. The New York State Conservationist/NYSDEC March-April:12-17.

Martin, C. J., and D. J. North. 1993. Peregrine Falcons incubate clutch of eggs for minimum of 73 days. Journal of Raptor Research 27:173.

Meng, H. 1974. Saving the Peregrine Falcon. The New York State Conservationist/NYSDEC June-July:22-24.

Meng, H. 1975. Reintroducing Peregrine Falcons to the wild. Journal of North American Falconers Association. Vol. 14:34-36.

Moen, S. M., and H. B. Tordoff. 1993. The genetic and demographic status of Peregrine Falcons in the upper Midwest. Report for U.S. Fish and Wildlife Service and Minnesota Department of Natural Resources Non-game Wildlife Program. Bell Museum of Natural History, University of Minnesota, St. Paul.

Nadareski, C. A., and B. A. Loucks. 1992. Watching the wanderer. The New York State Conservationist/NYSDEC September-October:34-43.

Redig, P. T., and H. B. Tordoff. 1988. Peregrine Falcon reintroduction in the upper Mississippi valley and western Great Lakes region. Pages 559-562 in Peregrine Falcon Populations: Their Management and Recovery. (T. J. Cade, J. H. Enderson, C. G. Thelander, and C. M. White, Eds.). The Peregrine Fund, Boise, ID.

Septon, G. A. 1989. A year of firsts and frustrations for Milwaukee's Peregrines. Passenger Pigeon 50(4):296-304.

Septon, G. A. 1991. Peregrine Falcon strikes Turkey Vulture. Passenger Pigeon 53(2):192.

Septon, G. A. 1993. Peregrines, people and the lakefront. Lore 43(1):14-16.

Septon, G. A. 1993. Potential for Peregrine Falcon habitat restoration along the Mississippi River. Restoration and Management Notes 11(2):177. University of Wisconsin Arboretum, Madison.

Septon, G. A. 1994. The best year yet! 12 Peregrines produced at three nest sites. The Wanderer 5(1):2.

Septon, G. A. 2000. Overwintering by urban-nesting Peregrine Falcons Falco peregrinus in midwestern North America. Pages 455-461 in Raptors at Risk: 5th World Conference on Birds of Prey (R. D. Chancellor and B.-U. Meyburg, Eds.). World Working Group for Birds of Prey, Berlin/Hancock House, Blaine, WA.

Septon, G. A., J. Bielefeldt, T. Ellestad, J. B. Marks, and R. N. Rosenfield. 1996. Peregrine Falcons, power plant nest structures and shoreline movements. Pages 145-153 in Raptors in Human Landscapes (D. M. Bird, D. E. Varland, and J. J. Negro, Eds.). Academic Press, London.

Septon, G. A., and J. B. Marks. 1996. Eggshell thickness and contaminant analysis of reintroduced, urban nesting Peregrine Falcons in Wisconsin. Pages 24-30 in Raptors in Human Landscapes (D. M. Bird, D. E. Varland, and J. J. Negro, Eds.). Academic Press, London.

Septon, G. A., J. Marks, and T. Ellestad. 1995. A preliminary assessment of urban Peregrine Falcon recovery in midwestern North America. Acta Ornithologica 30(1):65-69.

Sherrod, S. K. 1983. Behavior of Fledgling Peregrines. The Peregrine Fund, Ft. Collins, CO.

Sherrod, S. K., and T. J. Cade. 1978. Release of Peregrine Falcons by hacking. Pages 121-136 *in* Bird of Prey Management Techniques (T. A. Geer, Ed.). British Falconers' Club, Staffordshire, U.K.

Sherrod, S. K., W. R. Heinrich, W. A. Burnham, J. H. Barclay, and T. J. Cade. 1982. Hacking: A Method for Releasing Peregrine Falcons and Other Birds of Prey, 2nd edition. The Peregrine Fund, Ithaca, NY.

Sherrod, S. K., M. A. Jenkins, and T. J. Cade. 1990. Avian reintroductions as a management tool. Pages 150-157 *in* Proceedings of the Southeastern Raptor Management Symposium and Workshop (B. Giron Pendleton, M. N. LeFranc, and B.A. Milsap, Eds.). National Wildlife Federation, Washington, D.C.

Steidl, R. J., C. R. Griffin, L. J. Niles, and K. E. Clark. 1994. Reproductive success and eggshell thinning of a reestablished Peregrine Falcon population. Journal of Wildlife Management 55:294-299.

Temple, S. A. 1988. Future goals and needs for the management and conservation of the Peregrine Falcon. Pages 843-848 *in* Peregrine Falcon Populations: Their Management and Recovery (T. J. Cade, J. H. Enderson, C. G. Thelander, and C. M. White, Eds.). The Peregrine Fund, Boise, ID.

Temple, S. A., and T. J. Cade. 1988. Genetic issues associated with recovery efforts for three endangered raptors. Pages 17-29 in Proceedings of the International Symposium on Raptor Reintroduction, 1985 (D. K. Garcelon and G. W. Roemer, Eds.). Institute for Wildlife Studies, Arcata, CA.

Therres, G. D., S. Dawson, and J. C. Barber. 1993. Peregrine Falcon restoration in Maryland. Maryland Department of Natural Resources, Fish, Heritage and Wildlife Administration, Wildlife Technical Publication 93-1:1-24.

Tordoff, H. B. 1995. Return of the Peregrine. Hawk Mountain News 83:7-11.

Tordoff, H. B., J. S. Castrale, M. S. Martell, and P. T. Redig. 2000. Brood size and survival to breeding in midwestern Peregrine Falcons. Journal of Field Ornithology 71:691-693.

Tordoff, H. B., M. S. Martell, and P. T. Redig. 1998. Effect of fledge site on choice of nest site by midwestern Peregrine Falcons. Loon 70:127-129.

Tordoff, H. B., S. M. Moen, P. T. Redig, J. L. Longmire, and D. Foster. 1993. Peregrine paternity case. Loon 65(3):107-110.

Tordoff, H. B., and P. T. Redig. 1988. Dispersal, nest site selection, and age of first breeding in Peregrine Falcons released in the Upper Midwest, 1982-88. Loon 60(4):148-151.

Tordoff, H. B., and P. T. Redig. 1991. Peregrine Falcon nesting summary - midwest United States. Loon 63(3):191-193.

Tordoff, H. B., and P. T. Redig. 1997. Midwest Peregrine Falcon demography, 1982-1995. Journal of Raptor Research 31:339-346.

Tordoff, H. B., and P. T. Redig. 1998. Apparent siblicide in Peregrine Falcons. Journal of Raptor Research 32(2):184.

Tordoff, H. B., and P. T. Redig. 1999. Close inbreeding in Peregrine Falcons in midwestern United States. Journal of Raptor Research 33(4):326-328.

Tordoff, H. B., and P. T. Redig. 1999. Two fatal Peregrine Falcon territorial fights. Loon 71:182-186.

Tordoff, H. B., and P. T. Redig. 2001. Role of genetic background in success of reintroduced Peregrine Falcons. Conservation Biology 15:528-532.

Wendt, A., and G. A. Septon. 1991. Notes on a successful nesting by a pair of yearling Peregrine Falcons (*Falco peregrinus*). Journal of Raptor Research 25(1):21-22.

Wendt, A., and G. A. Septon. 1991. Egg shell thickness of Milwaukee Peregrine Falcons. Passenger Pigeon 53(2):191-192.

Wendt, A., G. A. Septon, and J. Moline. 1991. Juvenile urban-hacked Peregrine Falcons (*Falco peregrinus*) hunt at night. Journal of Raptor Research 25(3):94-95.

Appendix B

Scientific Names of Bird Species Mentioned in Text by Common Name

Common Name	Scientific Name
African Quelea	*Quelea quelea*
American Avocet	*Recurvirostra americana*
American Crow	*Corvus brachyrhynchos*
American Kestrel	*Falco sparverius*
Aplomado Falcon	*Falco femoralis*
Arctic Warbler	*Phylloscopus borealis*
Atwater's Prairie-Chicken	*Tympanuchus cupido attwateri*
Australian Zebra Finch	*Poephila guttata*
Bald Eagle	*Haliaeetus leucocephalus*
Band-tailed Pigeon	*Columba fasciata*
Barn Owl	*Tyto alba*
Barn Swallow	*Hirundo rustica*
Bearded Vulture, Lammergeyer	*Gypaetus barbatus*
Black-headed Grosbeak	*Pheucticus melanocephalus*
Blue Jay	*Cyanocitta cristata*
Brewer's Blackbird	*Euphagus cyanocephalus*
Broad-winged Hawk	*Buteo platypterus*
Brown Pelican	*Pelecanus occidentalis*
Brown-headed Cowbird	*Molothrus ater*
Burrowing Owl	*Athene cunicularia*
Cactus Wren	*Campylorhynchus brunneicapillus*
California Condor	*Gymnogyps californianus*
Canada Goose	*Branta canadensis*
Canyon Wren	*Catherpes mexicanus*
Carolina Parakeet	*Conuropsis carolinensis*
Cedar Waxwing	*Bombycilla cedrorum*
Cliff Swallow	*Petrochelidon pyrhonota*
Common Black-Hawk	*Buteogallus anthracinus*
Common Raven	*Corvus corax*
Cooper's Hawk	*Accipiter cooperii*
Coturnix Quail, Japanese Quail	*Coturnix coturnix*
Eagle Owl	*Bubo bubo*
Elf Owl	*Micrathene whitneyi*
Eurasian Kestrel	*Falco tinnunculus*
European Starling	*Sturnus vulgaris*
Evening Grosbeak	*Coccothraustes vespertinus*
Ferruginous Hawk	*Buteo regalis*
Forster's Tern	*Sterna forsteri*
Gadwall	*Anas strepera*
Golden Eagle	*Aquila chrysaetos*
Goshawk, Northern Goshawk	*Accipter gentilis*
Great Blue Heron	*Ardea herodias*
Great Crested Flycatcher	*Myiarchus crinitus*

Common Name	Scientific Name
Greater Sage-Grouse	*Centrocercus urophasianus*
Great Horned Owl	*Bubo virginianus*
Green-tailed Towee	*Pipilo chlorurus*
Griffon Vulture	*Gyps fulvus*
Gyrfalcon	*Falco rusticolus*
Harpy Eagle	*Harpia harpyja*
Harris's Hawk	*Parabuteo unicinctus*
Heath Hen	*Tympanuchus cupido cupido*
Herring Gull	*Larus argentatus*
Horned Lark	*Eremophila alpestris*
House Finch	*Carpodacus mexicanus*
House Sparrow	*Passer domesticus*
Ivory-billed Woodpecker	*Campephilus principalis*
Killdeer	*Charadrius vociferus*
Ladder-backed Woodpecker	*Picoides scalaris*
Lanner Falcon	*Falco biarmicus*
Lark Bunting	*Calamospiza melancorys*
Least Tern	*Sterna antillarum*
Lesser Goldfinch	*Carduelis psaltria*
Lesser Nighthawk	*Chordeiles acutipennis*
Lesser Prairie-Chicken	*Tympanuchus pallidicinctus*
Loggerhead Shrike	*Lanius ludovicianus*
Mallard	*Anas platyrhynchos*
Maroon-fronted Parrot, Thick-billed Parrot	*Rhynchopsitta pachyrhyncha terrisi*
Masked Bobwhite Quail	*Colinus virginianus ridgwayi*
Mauritius Kestrel	*Falco punctatus*
Merlin	*Falco columbarius*
Mourning Dove	*Zenaida macroura*
Northern Aplomado Falcon	*Falco femoralis septentrionalis*
Northern Flicker	*Colaptes auratus*
Northern Harrier	*Circus cyaneus*
Northern Mockingbird	*Mimus polyglottos*
Northern Saw-whet Owl	*Aegolius acadicus*
Northern Shrike	*Lanius excubitor*
Orange-breasted Falcon	*Falco deiroleucus*
Osprey	*Pandion haliaetus*
Passenger Pigeon	*Ectopistes migratorius*
Pigeon, Rock Dove, Homing Pigeon	*Columba livia*
Pine Siskin	*Carduelis pinus*
Piping Plover	*Charadrius melodus*
Prairie Falcon	*Falco mexicanus*
Pyrrhuloxia	*Cardinalis sinuatu*
Red Kite	*Milvus milvus*

Common Name	Scientific Name	Common Name	Scientific Name
Red-necked Phalarope	*Phalaropus lobatus*	Spotted Owl	*Strix occidentalis*
Red-shouldered Hawk	*Buteo lineatus*	Swainson's Hawk	*Buteo swainsoni*
Red-spotted Bluethroat	*Luscinia svecica*	Tawny Owl	*Strix aluco*
Red-tailed Hawk	*Buteo jamaicensis*	Turkey Vulture	*Cathartes aura*
Ring-billed Gull	*Larus delawarensis*	Wandering Albatross	*Diomedea exulans*
Ring-necked Pheasant,		Western Tanager	*Piranga ludoviciana*
Pheasant	*Phasianus colchicus*	White-tailed Sea Eagle,	
Rock Wren	*Salpinctes obsoletus*	White-tailed Eagle	*Haliaeetus albicilla*
Rough-legged Hawk	*Buteo lagopus*	White-throated Swift	*Aeronautes saxatalos*
Seychelles Kestrel	*Falco araea*	White-winged Dove	*Zenaida asiatica*
Sharp-shinned Hawk	*Accipiter striatus*	Whooping Crane	*Grus americana*
Sharp-tailed Grouse	*Tympanuchus phasianellus*	Wood Pigeon	*Columba palumbus*
Snowy Owl	*Nyctea scandiaca*	Yellow Wagtail	*Motacilla flava*
Snowy Plover	*Charadrius alexandrinus*		
Sora Rail, Sora	*Porzana carolina*		
Sparrowhawk, European Sparrowhawk, British Sparrowhawk, Eurasian Sparrowhawk	*Accipiter nisus*		

References:

Amadon, D., and J. Bull. 1988. Hawks and owls of the world: A distributional and taxonomic list. Vol. 3, No. 4. Western Foundation of Vertebrate Zoology, Camarillo, CA.

American Ornithologists' Union. 1998. Check-list of North American birds, 7th ed. American Ornithologists' Union, Washington, D.C.

Forshaw, J. M., and W. T. Cooper. 1973. Parrots of the world. Lansdowne Press, Melbourne, Australia.

Goodwin, D. 1970. Pigeons and doves of the world. Staples Printers Limited, London.

Howard, R., and A. Moore. 1980. A complete checklist of the birds of the world. Oxford University Press, Oxford, U.K.

Appendix C

Common Names of Peregrine Falcon *(Falco peregrinus)* Subspecies Referred to in the Text

Scientific Name	Common Names
F. p. anatum	Duck Hawk, American Peregrine Falcon, Rock Peregrine, Appalachian Peregrine, Great Footed Hawk
F. p. brookei	Spanish Peregrine, Mediterranean Peregrine
F. p. cassini	Cassin's Falcon, Austral Peregrine
F. p. macropus	Australian Peregrine
F. p. pealei	Peale's Falcon, Peale's Peregrine
F. p. peregrinus	British Peregrine, European Peregrine, Eurasian Peregrine
F. p. tundrius	Tundra Falcon, Tundra Peregrine, Arctic Peregrine, Beach Peregrine

Appendix D

List of Contributors
Addresses are in the United States Unless Otherwise Indicated

Joseph Alston
Superintendent
Grand Canyon National Park
P.O. Box 129
Grand Canyon, Arizona 86023

Robert E. (Skip) Ambrose
National Park Service
Natural Sounds Program
1201 Oakridge Drive, Suite 200
Fort Collins, Colorado 80525

Harry J. Armbruster
Wildlife Technician
Canadian Wildlife Service
Twin Atria Bldg., 4999-98 Avenue
Edmonton, Alberta, Canada T6B 2X3

D. Lee Aulman
Raptor Biologist
Santa Cruz Predatory Bird Research Group
Long Marine Lab
University of California, Santa Cruz
Santa Cruz, California 95060

Ursula Banasch
Biologist
Canadian Wildlife Service
Twin Atria Bldg., 4999-98 Avenue
Edmonton, Alberta, Canada T6B 2X3

John C. Barber
31700 Trillium Trail
Pepper Pike, Ohio 44124

Daniel D. Berger
Raptor Biologist
Co-founder, Cedar Grove Ornithological
  Station
1806 Grevelia Street
South Pasadena, California 91030

Robert Berry
Trustee, Wolf Creek Charitable Foundation
Rancher, Falcon Breeder, and Conservationist
Founding Board Member, The Peregrine Fund
1122 Soldier Creek Road
Wolf, Wyoming 82844

Frank M. Bond
Attorney at Law and Rancher
Founding Board Member, The Peregrine Fund
The Simons Firm, LLP
P.O. Box 5333
Santa Fe, New Mexico 87502-5333

Kurt K. Burnham
Projects Director, Greenland
The Peregrine Fund
5668 West Flying Hawk Lane
Boise, Idaho 83709

Patricia Burnham
Administrator
The Peregrine Fund
5668 West Flying Hawk Lane
Boise, Idaho 83709

William Burnham, Ph.D.
President and Founding Board Member
The Peregrine Fund
Director, World Center for Birds of Prey
The Peregrine Fund
5668 West Flying Hawk Lane
Boise, Idaho 83709

Renetta Cade
6484 Hollilynn Drive
Boise, Idaho 83709

Tom J. Cade, Ph.D.
Professor Emeritus of Ornithology,
  Cornell University
Professor Emeritus, Boise State University
Founder and Founding Chairman of the
  Board, The Peregrine Fund
The Peregrine Fund
5668 West Flying Hawk Lane
Boise, Idaho 83709

John A. Campbell
deceased

S. Kent Carnie
Curator
Archives of American Falconry
The Peregrine Fund
5668 West Flying Hawk Lane
Boise, Idaho 83709

Jamie Rappaport Clark
Former Director
U.S. Fish and Wildlife Service
504 Meade Drive, SW
Leesburg, Virginia 20175

Roland C. Clement
Vice President
National Audubon Society (retired)
1199 Whitney Avenue, Apt. 319
Hamden, Connecticut 06517

Gerald R. Craig
Raptor Biologist
Colorado Division of Wildlife (retired)
1409 S. Summitview Drive
Fort Collins, Colorado 80524

Phyllis R. Dague
Assistant to the Director
Laboratory of Ornithology
Cornell University
159 Sapsucker Woods Road
Ithaca, New York 14850

Roy E. Disney
Vice Chairman, Walt Disney Company
Chairman of the Board, Shamrock
  Holdings, Inc.
Chairman Emeritus and Board Member,
  The Peregrine Fund
The Walt Disney Company
500 South Buena Vista
Burbank, California 91521

Tery Drager
Administrator
Santa Cruz Predatory Bird Research Group
  (retired)
3533 South Highway 3
Etna, California 96027

James H. Enderson, Ph.D.
Professor Emeritus of Biology
The Colorado College
Board Member, The Peregrine Fund
The Colorado College
Colorado Springs, Colorado 80903

Ritt Enderson, DVM
East Valley Veterinary Hospital
1721 E. University Drive
Mesa, Arizona 85203

Thomas W. French, Ph.D.
Assistant Director
Massachusetts Division of Fisheries and
  Wildlife
Natural Heritage & Endangered Species
  Program
One Rabbit Hill Road
Westborough, Massachusetts 01581

Richard Fyfe
Research Scientist
Canadian Wildlife Service (retired)
Box 3263, Fort Saskatchewan
Alberta, Canada T8L 2T2

Willard Heck
Raptor Propagation Specialist (former),
  The Peregrine Fund
P. O. Box 23
Causey, New Mexico 88113-0023

William R. Heinrich
Species Restoration Coordinator
The Peregrine Fund
5668 West Flying Hawk Lane
Boise, Idaho 83709

Geoffrey L. Holroyd, Ph.D.
Research Scientist, Canadian Wildlife Service
Environment Canada
Chair, National Recovery Teams for Peregrine
  Falcons and Burrowing Owls
Adjunct Professor, University of Alberta
Canadian Wildlife Service
Room 210
4999 - 98 Avenue
Edmonton, Alberta, Canada T6B 2X3

Grainger Hunt, Ph.D.
Senior Scientist
The Peregrine Fund
552-205 James Drive
McArthur, California 96056

J. Peter Jenny
Vice President
The Peregrine Fund
Suite 210
1 East Alger
Sheridan, Wyoming 82801

Dan Konkel
Raptor Propagator (former),
  The Peregrine Fund
11 Beaver Drive
Sheridan, Wyoming 82801

Brian Latta
Raptor Biologist
Santa Cruz Predatory Bird Research Group
Long Marine Lab
University of California, Santa Cruz
Santa Cruz, California 95060

Ed Levine
Merlin Systems, Inc.
9125 Bienapfl Drive
Boise, Idaho 83709

Janet Linthicum
Raptor Biologist
Santa Cruz Predatory Bird Research Group
Long Marine Lab
University of California, Santa Cruz
Santa Cruz, California 95060

Tom Maechtle
Private Consultant
Raptor Biology
P. O. Box 207
Sheridan, Wyoming 82801

Mark S. Martell
Director of Bird Conservation
Audubon Minnesota
2357 Ventura Drive #106
St. Paul, Minnesota 55125

William G. Mattox, Ph.D.
President and Director
Conservation Research Foundation
8300 Gantz Avenue
Boise, Idaho 83709

Pete McLain
New Jersey Division of Fish and Wildlife
  (retired)
10 Cedar Drive
Toms River, New Jersey 08753

Heinz Meng, Ph.D.
Professor of Biology
State University of New York
Founder and Chairman of the Board
New Paltz Peregrine Falcon Foundation, Inc.
75 South Manheim Blvd.
New Paltz, New York 12561

Brian D. Mutch
Raptor Biologist
The Peregrine Fund
Suite 210
1 East Alger
Sheridan, Wyoming 82801

Christopher A. Nadareski
Research Scientist
New York City Department of
  Environmental Protection
465 Columbus Avenue, Suite 190
Valhalla, New York 10595

Ian Newton, D.Phil., D.Sc., OBE, FRS
Senior Scientist
Centre for Ecology and Hydrology
Chairperson, Program Committee,
  The Peregrine Fund Board of Directors
Monks Wood, Abbots Ripton
Huntingdon, Cambridgeshire PE28 2LS
United Kingdom

Paul R. Nickerson
U.S. Fish and Wildlife Service
7 Sparhawk Road
Londonderry, New Hampshire 03053

Robert Oakleaf
Non-game Coordinator
Wyoming Game and Fish Department
260 Buena Vista Drive
Lander, Wyoming 82520

J. Lindsay Oaks, Jr., D.V.M., Ph.D.
Department of Veterinary Microbiology
  and Pathology
Washington State University
Box 647040
Pullman, Washington 99164

David Peakall, Ph.D.
deceased

Brian Ratcliff
Coordinator, Project Peregrine
Thunder Bay Field Naturalists
Ontario Ministry of Natural Resources
307 Dog Lake Road
RR #12, Site 15-22
Thunder Bay, Ontario, Canada   P7B 5E3

Derek Ratcliffe, Ph.D.
Chief Scientist, Nature Conservancy Council
    of Great Britain (retired)
34 Thornton Close
Girton
Cambridge, England CB3 ONG

Patrick T. Redig, D.V.M., Ph.D.
Director, The Raptor Center
Professor
College of Veterinary Medicine
University of Minnesota
The Raptor Center
College of Veterinary Medicine
1920 Fitch Avenue
St. Paul, Minnesota 55108

Robert J. Ritchie
Senior Scientist and Co-founder, ABR, Inc.
Environmental Research and Services
ABR, Inc.
P.O. Box 80410
Fairbanks, Alaska 99708

Ruth Rudner
Writer
Former Hack Site Attendant,
    The Peregrine Fund
P. O. Box 2400
Corrales, New Mexico 87048

Gary G. Ruhser
Professional Engineer
Rusher Technical Service
Former Hack Site Attendant,
    The Peregrine Fund
N8947 Christopherson Road
Holmen, Wisconsin 54636

Jean C. Ruhser
Instructor of Ornithology Emeritus
University of Wisconsin-La Crosse
Former Hack Site Attendant,
    The Peregrine Fund
N8947 Christopherson Road
Holmen, Wisconsin 54636

Cal Sandfort
Raptor Propagation Specialist
The Peregrine Fund
5668 West Flying Hawk Lane
Boise, Idaho 83709

Machel Sandfort
The Peregrine Fund
5668 West Flying Hawk Lane
Boise, Idaho 83709

William S. Seegar, Ph.D.
U.S. Army Soldier
Biological and Chemical Command
Department of the Army
Chemical Research & Development Center
SMCCR-RSB
Research Directorate, Biotechnology Division
Aberdeen Proving Grounds, Maryland 21010

Greg Septon
Founder and Chairman
Wisconsin Peregrine Society
11100 West Ryan Road
Franklin, Wisconsin 53132

Tom Smylie
Assistant Regional Director
U.S. Fish and Wildlife Service (retired)
Albuquerque Biological Park
40 Peregrine Vista
Edgewood, New Mexico   87015

Stanley A. Temple, Ph.D.
Beers-Bascom Professor in Conservation
Department of Wildlife Ecology
Chairman, Conservation Biology and
    Sustainable Development Program
Gaylord Nelson Institute for Environmental
    Studies
University of Wisconsin
Madison, Wisconsin 53706

Harrison B. Tordoff, Ph.D.
Midwest Peregrine Restoration Effort
Professor Emeritus, Department of Ecology,
    Evolution, and Behavior
Bell Museum of Natural History
University of Minnesota
100 Ecology Bldg.
University of Minnesota
1987 Upper Buford Circle
St. Paul, Minnesota 55108

Brian James Walton
Coordinator
Santa Cruz Predatory Bird Research Group
Long Marine Lab
University of California, Santa Cruz
Santa Cruz, California 95060

Cheryl C. Walton
Santa Cruz Predatory Bird Research Group
Long Marine Lab
University of California, Santa Cruz
Santa Cruz, California 95060

F. Prescott Ward, V.M.D., Ph.D.
Midwest Research Institute
500 Orlando Blvd.
Indialantic, Florida 32903

James D. Weaver
President, Grasslans Charitable Foundation
Founding Board Member, The Peregrine Fund
Former Commissioner, New Mexico
    Department of Game and Fish
P.O. Box 23
Causey, New Mexico 88113-0023

Clayton M. White, Ph.D.
Professor of Zoology
Brigham Young University
Department of Integrative Biology
574 WIDB
Provo, Utah 84602

Charles F. Wurster
Professor Emeritus of Environmental Sciences
State University of New York at Stony Brook
Board of Trustees, Environmental Defense
15 Crane Neck Road
Setauket, New York 11733-1605

Mike Yates
Raptor Biologist, Raptor Research Center
Boise State University, Earthspan
2656 Wade Street
Minden, Nevada 89423

Literature Cited

Ambrose, R. E., and K. E. Riddle. 1988. Population dispersal, turnover, and migration of Alaska Peregrines. Pages 677-684 *in* Peregrine Falcon Populations: Their Management and Recovery (T. J. Cade, J. H. Enderson, C. G. Thelander, and C. M. White, Eds.). The Peregrine Fund, Boise, ID.

Ambrose, R. E., R. J. Ritche, C. M. White, P. F. Schempf, T. Swem, and R. Dittrick. 1988. Changes in status of Peregrine Falcon populations in Alaska. Pages 73-82 *in* Peregrine Falcon Populations: Their Management and Recovery (T. J. Cade, J. H. Enderson, C. G. Thelander, and C. M. White, Eds.). The Peregrine Fund, Boise, ID.

Anderson, C. M., D. G. Roseneau, B. J. Walton, and P. J. Bente. 1988. New evidence of a Peregrine migration on the west coast of North America. Pages 507-517 *in* Peregrine Falcon Populations: Their Management and Recovery (T. J. Cade, J. H. Enderson, C. G. Thelander, and C. M. White, Eds.). The Peregrine Fund, Boise, ID.

Ar, A., C. V. Panganelli, R. B. Reeves, D. C. Greene, and H. Rahn. 1974. The avian egg: water vapor conductance, shell thickness, and functional pore area. Condor 76:153-158.

Awender, E. 1979/1980. Modern falconry mourns a leader: Renz Waller 1895-1979. Journal of the North American Falconers Association. Vols. 18/19:60-61.

Baker, J. A. 1967. The Peregrine. Collins, London.

Banasch, U., J. P. Goossen, A. Einstein Riez, C. Casler, and R. Dominguez Barradas. 1992. Organochlorine contaminants in migrant and resident prey of Peregrine Falcons, *Falco peregrinus*, in Panama, Venezuela, and Mexico. Canadian Field-Naturalist 106:493-498.

Barclay, J. H., and T. J. Cade. 1983. Restoration of the Peregrine Falcon in the eastern United States. Bird Conservation 1:3-40.

Batten, M. 1923. Inland Birds. Hutchinson, London.

Beebe, F. L. 1960. The marine Peregrines of the northwest Pacific coast. Condor 62:145-189.

Beebe, F. L. 1964. The future of falconry. Pages 297-305 *in* North American Falconry and Hunting Hawks (F. L. Beebe and H. M. Webster, Jr., Eds.). North American Falconry and Hunting Hawks, Denver, CO.

Beebe, F. L. 1967. Experiments in the husbanding of the Peregrine. Raptor Research News 1:61-86.

Bell, D. A., D. P. Gregoire, and B. J. Walton. 1996. Bridge use by Peregrine Falcons in the San Francisco Bay area. Pages 15-24 *in* Raptors in Human Landscapes (D. M. Bird, D. E. Varland, and J. J. Negro, Eds.). Academic Press, London.

Bellrose, F., Jr. 1938. Duck Hawks nesting in western Tennessee. Wilson Bulletin 50:139.

Belopolski, L. O. 1971. Migration of Sparrowhawk on Courland Spit. Notatki Ornitologiczne 12:1-12.

Bent, A. C. 1938. Life histories of North American birds of prey. Part 2: Orders Falconiformes and Strigiformes. U.S. Natural History Museum Bulletin no. 170.

Berger, D. D., and H. C. Mueller. 1969. Nesting Peregrines in Wisconsin and adjacent areas. Pages 115-122 *in* Peregrine Falcon Populations: Their Biology and Decline (J. J. Hickey, Ed.). University of Wisconsin Press, Madison.

Berger, D. D., C. R . Sidebar, Jr., and K. E. Gamble.1969. The status of breeding Peregrines in the eastern United States. Pages 165-173 *in* Peregrine Falcon Populations: Their Biology and Decline (J. J. Hickey, Ed.). University of Wisconsin Press, Madison.

Berry, R. B. 1972. Reproduction by artificial insemination of captive American goshawks. Journal of Wildlife Management 36:1283-1288.

Berry, R. B., and F. P. Ward. 1975. Autumn migrations of Peregrine Falcons on Assateague Island, 1970-1972. Raptor Research Report 3:57-60.

Bond, R. M. 1946. The Peregrine population of western North America. Condor 48:101-116.

Boroughs, D. 2001. Mauritius Island. International Wildlife November/December:46-50.

Boyce, D. A., and C. M. White. 1979. Peregrine Falcon nesting habitat survey of the Mendocino, Six Rivers, Klamath, Shasta, and Trinity National Forests, 1979. U.S. Forest Service, San Francisco, CA.

Boyce, D. A., and C. M. White. 1980. Peregrine Falcon nesting habitat survey on the Freemont National Forest, 1980. U.S. Forest Service, San Francisco, CA.

Boyd, L. L. 1978. Artificial insemination of falcons. Symposium Zoological Society of London 43:73-80.

Boyd, L. L., N. S. Boyd, and F. C. Dobler. 1977. Reproduction of Prairie Falcons by artificial insemination. Journal of Wildlife Management 41:266-271.

Burger, J., and G. A. Fox. 2002. In memoriam: David B. Peakall, 1931-2001. Auk 119:812-814.

Burnett, J. A. 1999. A passion for wildlife: A history of the Canadian Wildlife Service, 1947- 1997. The Canadian Field-Naturalist 113(1):1-183.

Burnham, K. K. 2001. High Arctic Institute, Progress Report 2001. The Peregrine Fund, Boise, ID.

Burnham, W. A. 1983. Artificial incubation of falcon eggs. Journal of Wildlife Management 47:158-168.

Burnham, W. A. 1997. A Fascination with Falcons. Hancock House, Blaine, WA.

Burnham, W. A., and T. J. Cade. 1995. Raptor populations: the basis for their management. Transactions of the 60th North American Wildlife and Natural Resources Conference. 60:115-130.

Burnham, W. A., J. Craig, J. H. Enderson, and W. R. Heinrich. 1978. Artificial increase in reproduction of wild Peregrine Falcons. Journal of Wildlife Management 42:625-628.

Burnham, W. A., W. Heinrich, C. Sandfort, E. Levine, D. O'Brien, and D. Konkel. 1988. Recovery effort for the Peregrine Falcon in the Rocky Mountains. Pages 565-574 in Peregrine Falcon Populations: Their Management and Recovery (T. J. Cade, J. H. Enderson, C. G. Thelander, and C. M. White, Eds.). The Peregrine Fund, Boise, ID.

Burnham, W. A., and W. G. Mattox. 1984. Biology of the Peregrine and Gyrfalcon in Greenland. Meddelelser om Grønland. Bioscience 14:1-28.

Burnham, W. A., W. G. Mattox, M. A. Jenkins, D. M. Clement, J. T. Harris, and F. P. Ward. 1974. Falcon research in Greenland, 1973. Arctic 27:71-74.

Burnham, W., C. Sandfort, and J. R. Belthoff. 2003. Peregrine Falcon eggs: egg size, hatchling sex, and clutch sex ratios. Condor 105:327-335.

Burnett, J. A. 1999. A passion for wildlife: a history of the Canadian Wildlife Service, 1947-1997. Canadian Field-Naturalist 113:1-183.

Butler, A. W. 1878. The birds of Indiana, 22nd annual report, Indiana Department of Geology and Natural Resources, Indianapolis.

Cade, T. J. 1960. Ecology of the Peregrine and Gyrfalcon populations in Alaska. University of California Publication of Zoology 63:151-290.

Cade, T. J. 1970. The last wilderness. BioScience 20:591.

Cade, T. J. 1974a. Plans for managing the survival of the Peregrine Falcon. Raptor Research Report 2:89-104.

Cade, T. J. 1974b. The Peregrine Fund Newsletter no. 2.

Cade, T. J. 1982. The Falcons of the World. Cornell University Press. Ithaca, NY.

Cade, T. J. 1983. Hybridization and gene exchange among birds in relation to conservation. Pages 288-309 in Genetics and Conservation (C. M. Schonewald-Cox, S. M. Chambers, B. MacBryde, and W. L. Thomas, Eds.). Benjamin/Cummings Publishing, San Francisco, CA.

Cade, T. J. 1986. Propagating diurnal raptors in captivity: a review. International Zoo Yearbook 24/25:1-20.

Cade, T. J. 1988a. The breeding of Peregrines and other falcons in captivity: an historical summary. Pages 539-547 in Peregrine Falcon Populations: Their Management and Recovery (T. J. Cade, J. H. Enderson, C. G. Thelander, and C. M. White, Eds.). The Peregrine Fund, Boise, ID.

Cade, T. J. 1988b. Using science and technology to reestablish species lost in nature. Pages 279-288 in Biodiversity (E. O. Wilson and F. M. Peters, Eds.). National Academy of Sciences Press, Washington, D.C.

Cade. T. J. 1998. Delisting the Peregrine Falcon: management and mismanagement under the Endangered Species Act. Transactions of the 63rd North American Wildlife and Natural Resources Conference. 63:475-485.

Cade, T. J. 2000. Progress in translocation of diurnal raptors. Pages 342-372 in Raptors at Risk: 5th World Conference on Birds of Prey (R. D. Chancellor and B.-U. Meyburg, Eds.). World Working Group on Birds of Prey, Berlin/ Hancock House, Blaine, WA.

Cade, T. J., and D. M. Bird. 1990. Peregrine Falcons, Falco peregrinus, nesting in an urban environment. Canadian Field-Naturalist 104:209-218.

Cade, T. J., J. H. Enderson, and J. Linthicum, Eds. 1996. Guide to Management of Peregrine Falcons at the Eyrie. The Peregrine Fund, Boise, ID.

Cade, T. J., J. H. Enderson, C. G. Thelander, and C. M. White. 1988. Peregrine Falcon Populations: Their Management and Recovery. The Peregrine Fund, Boise, ID.

Cade, T. J., and R. W. Fyfe. 1970. The North American Peregrine survey, 1970. Canadian Field- Naturalist 84:231-245.

Cade, T. J., and R. W. Fyfe. 1978. What makes Peregrine Falcons breed in captivity? Pages 251-262 in Endangered Birds: Management Techniques for Preserving Threatened Species (S. A. Temple, Ed.). University of Wisconsin Press, Madison.

Cade, T. J., J. L. Lincer, C. M. White, D. G. Roseneau, and L. G. Swartz. 1971. DDE residues and eggshell changes in Alaska Falcons and Hawkbills. Science 172:955-957.

Cade, T. J., M. Martell, P. Redig, G. Septon, and H. Tordoff. 1996. Peregrine Falcons in urban North America. Pages 3-13 in Raptors in Human Landscapes (D. M. Bird, D. E. Varland, and J. J. Negro, Eds.). Academic Press, London.

Cade, T. J., P. T. Redig, and H. B. Tordoff. 1989. Peregrine Falcon restoration: expectation vs. reality. Loon 61:160-162.

Cade, T. J., and S. A. Temple. 1995. Management of threatened bird species: evaluation of the hands-on approach. Ibis 137 (Supplement):S161-172.

Cade, T. J., H. B. Tordoff, and J. H. Barclay. 2000. Re-introduction of Peregrines in the eastern United States: an evaluation. Re-introduction News 19:19-21.

Cade, T. J., and C. M. White. 1976a. Colville River watershed, Alaska. Pages 245-248 in The 1975 North American Peregrine Falcon survey (R. Fyfe, S. A. Temple, and T. J. Cade, Eds.). Canadian Field-Naturalist 90:228-273.

Cade, T. J., and C. M. White. 1976b. Alaska's falcons: the issue of survival. Living Wilderness 39(132): 35-47.

Cade, T. J., C. M. White, and J. R. Haugh. 1968. Peregrines and pesticides in Alaska. Condor 70:170-178.

Carson, R. 1962. Silent Spring. Houghton Mifflin, Boston.

Clement, R. C., Ed. 1974. Proceedings of a conference on Peregrine Falcon recovery. Audubon Conservation Report no. 4.

Cochran, W. W. 1985. Ocean migration of Peregrine Falcons: is the adult male pelagic? Pages 223-237 in Proceedings of Hawk Migration Conference IV (M. Harwood, Ed.). Hawk Migration Association of North America, Rochester, NY.

Corser, J. D., M. Amaral, C. J. Martin, and C. C. Rimmer. 1999. Recovery of a cliff-nesting Peregrine Falcon, Falco peregrinus, population in northern New York and New England, 1984-1996. Canadian Field-Naturalist 113:472-480.

Court, G. S., D. M. Bradley, C. C. Gates, and D. A. Boag. 1988. The population biology of Peregrine Falcons in the Keewater District of the Northwest Territories, Canada. Pages 729-739 in Peregrine Falcon Populations: Their Management and Recovery (T. J. Cade, J. H. Enderson, C. G. Thelander, and C. M. White, Eds.). The Peregrine Fund, Boise, ID.

Court, G. S., D. M. Bradley, C. C. Gates, and D. A. Boag. 1989. Turnover and recruitment in a tundra population of Peregrine Falcons *Falco peregrinus*. Ibis 131:487-496.

Craighead, F., and J. Craighead. 1939. Hawks in the Hand. Lyons and Burford, Publishers, New York.

Cramp, S., and P. J. Conder. 1961. The deaths of birds and mammals connected with toxic chemicals in the first half of 1960. Report no.1 of the BTO-RSPB Committee on Toxic Chemicals. Royal Society for the Protection of Birds, Sandy, Bedfordshire, U.K.

Cramp, S., P. J. Conder, and J. S. Ash. 1962. Deaths of birds and mammals from toxic chemicals, January-June 1961. Royal Society for the Protection of Birds, Sandy, Bedfordshire, U.K.

Cugnasse, J. M. 1984. Le Faucon Pèlerin *Falco peregrinus* dans le sud du Massif Central de 1974 á 1983. Alauda 52:161-176.

Dekker, D. 1984. Spring and fall migrations of Peregrine Falcons in central Alberta, 1979-1983, with comparisons to 1969-1978. Journal of Raptor Research 18:92-97.

Dekker, D. 1999. Bolt from the Blue. Hancock House, Blaine, WA.

Dijkstra, C. 1988. Reproductive tactics in the Kestrel *Falco tinnunculus*. doctoral thesis, University of Groningen, Groningen, Netherlands.

Donahue, A. P. 1985. Archives of American Falconry: Interview Series. Boise, ID.

Dónazar, J. A., O. Ceballos, and C. Fernández. 1989. Factors influencing the distribution and abundance of seven cliff-nesting raptors: a multivariate study. Pages 545-552 *in* Raptors in the Modern World (B.-U. Meyburg and R. D. Chancellor, Eds.). World Working Group on Birds of Prey, Eilat, Israel.

Drent, R. H. 1970. Functional aspects of incubation in the Herring Gull. Behaviour Supplement 17:1-132.

Drent, R. H. 1973. The natural history of incubation. Pages 262-311 *in* Breeding Biology of Birds (Farner, D. S., Ed.). Natural Academy of Sciences, Washington, D.C.

Drent, R.H. 1975. Incubation. Pages 332-420 *in* Avian Biology vol. V. (Farner, D. S. and J. R. King, Eds.). Academic Press, London, U.K.

Drury, W. H. 1974. Rare species. Biological Conservation 6:162-169.

Edge, C. N., and E. D. Lumley. 1940. Common hawks of North America. Emergency Conservation Committee publication no. 81.

Emison, W. B. 1988. Results from a banding study of Peregrine Falcon chicks in Victoria, 1972- 1997. Corella 22:87-91.

Emison, W. B., W. N. Bren, and C. M. White. 1993. Influence of weather on the breeding of the Peregrine Falcon *Falco peregrinus* near Melbourne. Pages 26-32 *in* Australian Raptor Studies (P. Olsen, V. G. Hurley, C. M. White, and D. J. Brimm, Eds.). Australian Raptor Association, Royal Australasian Ornithologists Union, Melbourne.

Enderson, J. H. 1969a. Peregrine and Prairie Falcon life tables based on band-recovery data. Pages 505-509 *in* Peregrine Falcon Populations: Their Management and Recovery (T. J. Cade, J. H. Enderson, C. G. Thelander, and C. M. White, Eds.). The Peregrine Fund, Boise, ID.

Enderson, J. H. 1969b. Population trends among Peregrine Falcons in the Rocky Mountain region. Pages 73-79 *in* Peregrine Falcon Populations: Their Biology and Decline (J. J. Hickey, Ed). University of Wisconsin Press, Madison.

Enderson, J. H., and G. R. Craig. 1988. Population turnover in Colorado Peregrines. Pages 685-688 *in* Peregrine Falcon Populations: Their Management and Recovery (T. J. Cade, J. H. Enderson, C. G. Thelander, and C. M. White, Eds.). The Peregrine Fund, Boise, ID.

Enderson, J. H., G. R. Craig, and W. A. Burnham. 1988. Status of Peregrines in the Rocky Mountains and Colorado Plateau. Pages 83-86 *in* Peregrine Falcon Populations: Their Management and Recovery (T. J. Cade, J. H. Enderson, C. G. Thelander, and C. M. White, Eds.). The Peregrine Fund, Boise, ID.

Enderson, J. H, G. R. Craig, W. A. Burnham, and D. D. Berger. 1982. Eggshell thinning and organochlorine residues in Rocky Mountain Peregrines, *Falco peregrinus*, and their prey. Canadian Field-Naturalist 96:255-264.

Enderson, J. H., C. Flatten, and J. P. Jenny. 1991. Peregrine Falcons and Merlins in Sinaloa. Journal of Raptor Research 25:123-126.

Enderson, J. H., W. Heinrich, L. Kiff, and C. M. White. 1995. Population changes in North American Peregrines. Transactions of the 60th North American Wildlife and Natural Resources Conference. 60:142-161.

Fimreite, N., R. W. Fyfe, and J. A. Keith. 1970. Mercury contamination of Canadian prairie seed-eaters and their avian predators. Canadian Field-Naturalist 84:269-276.

Fisher, C. H. 1901. Reminiscences of a Falconer. John C. Nimo, London.

Fox, N. 1995. Understanding the Bird of Prey. Hancock House, Blaine, WA.

Frank, S. 1994. City Peregrines: A Ten Year Saga of New York City Falcons. Hancock House, Blaine, WA.

Ford, E. 1993. Peregrine. Fourth Estate, London.

Franklin, K. 1999. Vertical flight. Journal of the North American Falconers Association 38:68- 72.

Fuller, M. R., W. S. Seegar, and P. W. Howey. 1995. The use of satellite systems for the study of bird migration. Israel Journal of Zoology 41:243-252.

Fuller, M. R., W. S. Seegar, and L. S. Schueck. 1998. Routes and travel rates of migrating Peregrine Falcons *Falco peregrinus* and Swainson's Hawks *Buteo swainsoni* in the western hemisphere. Journal of Avian Biology 29:433-440.

Fyfe, R. W. 1969a. The status of the Peregrine on Canada eastern coasts. Pages 175-176 *in* Peregrine Falcon Populations: Their Biology and Decline (J. J. Hickey, Ed.). University of Wisconsin Press, Madison.

Fyfe, R. W. 1969b. The Peregrine Falcon in northern Canada. Pages 110-114 *in* Peregrine Falcon Populations: Their Biology and Decline (J. J. Hickey, Ed.). University of Wisconsin Press, Madison.

Fyfe, R. W. 1976. The 1975 North American Peregrine Falcon survey. Canadian Field-Naturalist 90:228-273.

Fyfe, R. W. 1976. Status of Canadian raptor populations. Canadian Field-Naturalist 90:370-375.

Fyfe, R. W., H. Armbruster, U. Banasch, and L. Beaver. 1977. Fostering and cross-fostering of birds of prey. Pages 183-193 *in* Endangered Birds: Management Techniques for Preserving Threatened Species (S. Temple, Ed.). University of Wisconsin Press, Madison.

Fyfe, R. W., U. Banasch, V. Benavides, N. H. de Benavides, A. Luscombe, and J. Sanchez. 1990. Organochlorine residues in potential prey of Peregrine Falcons, *Falco peregrinus*, in Latin America. Canadian Field-Naturalist 104:285-292.

Fyfe, R. W., J. Campbell, B. Hayson, and K. Hodson. 1969. Regional population declines and organochlorine insecticides in Canadian Prairie Falcons. Canadian Field-Naturalist 83:191-200.

Fyfe, R. W., S. A. Temple, and T. J. Cade. 1976. The 1975 North American Peregrine Falcon survey. Canadian Field-Naturalist 90:225-273.

Gainzarain, J. A., R. Arambarri, and A. F. Rodríguez. 2000. Breeding density, habitat selection and reproductive rates of the Peregrine Falcon *Falco peregrinus* in Alava (northern Spain). Bird Study 47:225-231.

Ganier, A. F. 1932. Duck Hawks at Reelfoot heronry. Migrant 3:28-32.

Garrett, R. L., and D. J. Mitchell.1973. A study of Prairie Falcon populations in California. Administrative report no. 73-2, California Department of Fish and Game, Wildlife Management Branch, Sacramento, CA.

Geis, A. D., and E. L. Atwood. 1961. Proportion of recovered waterfowl bands reported. Journal of Wildlife Management 35:154-158.

Glutz, von Bloetzheim, U. K., K. Bauer, and E. Bezzzel. 1971. Handbuch der Vögel der Mitteleuropas. Vol. 4, Falconiformes. Academische Verlagsgesellschaft, Frankfurt.

Goss, N. S. 1891. History of the Birds of Kansas. Geo. W. Crane and Co., Topeka, KS.

Grier, J. W. 1973. Techniques and results of artificial insemination with golden eagles. Raptor Research 7:1-12.

Grier, J. W. 1980. Ecology: a simulation model for small populations of animals. Creative Computing 6:116-121.

Grinnell, J. 1932. Type localities of birds described from California. University of California Publication of Zoology 38:243-423.

Griscom, L., and M. S. Crosby. 1925. Birds of the Brownsville region-southern Texas. Auk 42:519-537.

Gunn, D. L. 1972. Dilemmas in conservation for applied biologists. Annals of Applied Biology 72:105-127.

Hagar, J. A. 1938. Duck Hawk. Pages 43-67 *in* Life Histories of North American Birds of Prey part 2 (A. C. Bent). U.S. National History Museum Bulletin no. 170.

Hagar, J. A. 1969. History of the Massachusetts Peregrine Falcon population, 1935-57. Pages 123-132 *in* Peregrine Falcon Populations: Their Biology and Decline (J. J. Hickey, Ed.). University of Wisconsin Press, Madison.

Hall, G. H. 1970. The story of the Sun Life falcons. Canadian Field-Naturalist 84:209-230.

Haller, H. 1996. Der Steinadler in Graubünden. Ornithogische Beobachter 9:1-167.

Hamerstrom, F. 1970. An eagle to the sky. Iowa State University Press, Ames, IA.

Harris, J. T. 1978. The Peregrine Falcon in Greenland—Observing an Endangered Species. University of Missouri Press, Columbia.

Hayes, G. E., and J. B. Buchanan. 2002. Washington state status report for the Peregrine Falcon. Washington Department of Fish and Wildlife, Olympia.

Heidenrich, M. 1997. Birds of prey, medicine and management. Blackwell Science Ltd., Oxford.

Henny, C. J., K. E. Riddle, and C. S. Hulse. 1988. Organochlorine pollutants in plasma of spring migrant Peregrine Falcons from coastal Texas, 1984. Pages 423-427 *in* Peregrine Falcon Populations: Their Management and Recovery (T. J. Cade, J. H. Enderson, C. G. Thelander, and C. M. White, Eds.). The Peregrine Fund, Boise, ID.

Henny, C. J., W. S. Seegar, and T. L. Maechtle. 1996. DDE decreases in plasma of spring migrant Peregrine Falcons, 1978-1994. Journal of Wildlife Management 60:342-349.

Henny, C. J., W. S. Seegar, M. A. Yates, T. L. Maechtle, S. A. Ganusevich, and M. R. Fuller. 2000. Contaminants and wintering areas of Peregrine Falcons, *Falco peregrinus*, from the Kola Peninsula, Russia. Pages 871-878 *in* Raptors at Risk: 5th World Conference on Birds of Prey (R. D. Chancellor and B.-U. Meyburg, Eds.). World Working Group on Birds of Prey, Berlin/Hancock House, Blaine, WA.

Henny, C. J., F. P. Ward, K. E. Riddle, and R. M. Prouty. 1982. Migratory Peregrine Falcons, *Falco peregrinus*, accumulate pesticides in Latin America during winter. Canadian Field-Naturalist 96:333-337.

Herbert R. A., and K. G. S. Herbert. 1969. The extirpation of the Hudson River Peregrine Falcon population. Pages 133-154 *in* Peregrine Falcon Populations: Their Biology and Decline (J. J. Hickey, Ed.). University of Wisconsin Press, Madison.

Herman, S. G. 1971. The Peregrine Falcon decline in California. American Birds 25:818-820.

Hickey, J. J. 1942. Eastern population of the Duck Hawk. Auk 59:176-204.

Hickey, J. J. 1969. Peregrine Falcon Populations: Their Biology and Decline. University of Wisconsin Press, Madison.

Hickey, J. J., and D. Anderson. 1968. Chlorinated hydrocarbons and eggshell changes in raptorial and fish-eating birds. Science 162:271-273.

Hickey, J. J., and D. W. Anderson. 1969. Life histories and population literature. Pages 3-42 *in* Peregrine Falcon Populations: Their Biology and Decline (J. J. Hickey, Ed.). University of Wisconsin Press, Madison.

Holroyd, G. L., and U. Banasch. 1990. The reintroduction of the Peregrine Falcon, *Falco peregrinus anatum*, into southern Canada. Canadian Field-Naturalist 104:203-208.

Houle, M. C. 1991. Wings for My Flight: The Peregrine Falcons of Chimney Rock. Addison-Wesley, Reading, MA.

Howey, P., D. R. Witlock, M. R. Fuller, W. S. Seegar, and F. P. Ward. 1984. A computerized biotelemetry and data logging system. Pages 442-446 *in* Proceedings of the 8th International Symposium on Biotelemetry (H. R. Kimmich and H. J. Klewe, Eds.). International Society on Biotelemetry, Nijmegen, Netherlands.

Hunt, W. G. 1966. Observation of Peregrines on the Texas coast. Master's Thesis, Sul Ross State University, Alpine, TX.

Hunt, W. G. 1988. The natural regulation of Peregrine Falcon populations. Pages 667-676 *in* Peregrine Falcon Populations: Their Management and Recovery (T. J. Cade, J. H. Enderson, C. G. Thelander, and C. M. White, Eds.). The Peregrine Fund, Boise, ID.

Hunt, W. G. 1998. Raptor floaters at Moffat's equilibrium. Oikos 82:191-197.

Hunt, W. G., R. R. Rogers, and D. J. Slowe. 1975. Migratory and foraging behaviour of Peregrine Falcons on the Texas coast. Canadian Field-Naturalist 89:111-123.

James, D. 1988. U.S. Fish and Wildlife Service policies for endangered and threatened raptors. Pages 61-73 *in* Proceedings of the International Symposium on Raptor Reintroduction, 1985 (D. K. Garcelon and G. W. Roemer, Eds.). Institute for Wildlife Studies, Arcata, CA.

James, P. C., I. G. Warkentin, and L. W. Oliphant. 1989. Turnover and dispersal in urban Merlins *Falco columbarius*. Ibis 131:426-429.

Jefferies, D. J., and I. Prestt. 1966. Post-mortems of Peregrines and Lanners with particular reference to organochlorine residues. British Birds 59:49-64.

Jenkins, P. B. 1996. Falcons Nest on Skyscrapers. HarperCollins Publishers, New York.

Jensen, S. 1966. Report on a new chemical hazard. New Scientist 32:612.

Jones, C. G., W. Heck, R. E. Lewis, Y. Mungroo, G. Slade, and T. Cade. 1995. The restoration of the Mauritius Kestrel, *Falco punctatus*, population. Ibis 137:173-180.

Jones, F. M. 1946. Duck Hawks of eastern Virginia. Auk 63:592.

Kaufman, J., and H. Meng. 1975. Falcons Return. William Morrow and Company, New York.

Kaufman, J., and H. Meng. 1992. Falcons Return second edition. KAV Books, Unionville, NY.

Kennedy, R. F., Jr., 1987. Falconry: legal ownership and sale of captive-bred raptors. Pace Environmental Law Review 4:349-399.

Kenward, R. E., V. Marcström, and M. Karlbom. 1999. Demographic estimates from radio-tagging: models of age-specific survival and breeding in the Goshawk. Journal of Animal Ecology 68:1020-1033.

Kerlinger, P., and M. R. Lein. 1986. Differences in winter range among age-sex classes of Snowy Owls *Nyctea scandiaca* in North America. Ornis Scandinavica 17:1-7.

Kessel, B., and T. J. Cade.1958. Birds of the Colville River northern Alaska. Biological Papers of the University of Alaska no. 2:1-83.

Kirven, M. N. 1982. Peregrine Falcon inventory and management recommendations for the Ukiah BLM district, 1982. Ukiah District Office, U. S. Bureau of Land Management, Ukiah, CA.

Kirven, M. N. 1983. Peregrine Falcon inventory and management recommendations for the Ukiah BLM district, 1983. Ukiah District Office, U.S. Bureau of Land Management, Ukiah, CA.

Kirven, M. N. 1984. Peregrine Falcon inventory and management recommendations for the Ukiah BLM district, 1984. Ukiah District Office, U.S. Bureau of Land Management, Ukiah, CA.

Kirven, M. N. 1985. Peregrine Falcon inventory and management recommendations for the Ukiah BLM district, 1985. Ukiah District Office, U.S. Bureau of Land Management, Ukiah, CA.

Kirven, M. N. 1986. Peregrine Falcon population monitoring and management in the Ukiah BLM district, 1986. Ukiah District Office, U.S. Bureau of Land Management, Ukiah, CA.

Kirven, M. N. 1987. Peregrine Falcon population monitoring and management in the Ukiah BLM district, 1987. Ukiah District Office, U.S. Bureau of Land Management, Ukiah, CA.

Kirven, M. N., and B. J. Walton. 1988. California Peregrine Falcon monitoring and management effort, 1988. Ukiah District Office, U.S. Bureau of Land Management, Ukiah, CA.

Kirven, M. N., and B. J. Walton. 1989. California Peregrine Falcon monitoring and management effort, 1989. Ukiah District Office, U.S. Bureau of Land Management, Ukiah, CA.

Kirven, M. N., and B. J. Walton. 1990. California Peregrine Falcon monitoring and management effort, 1990. Ukiah District Office, U.S. Bureau of Land Management, Ukiah, CA.

Kirven, M. N., and B. J. Walton. 1991. California Peregrine Falcon monitoring and management effort, 1991. Ukiah District Office, U.S. Bureau of Land Management, Ukiah, CA.

Kirven, M. N., and B. J. Walton. 1992. California Peregrine Falcon monitoring and management effort, 1992. Ukiah District Office, U.S. Bureau of Land Management, Ukiah, CA.

Kjellén, N. 1992. Differential timing of autumn migration between sex and age groups in raptors at Falsterbo, Sweden. Ornis Scandinavica 23:420-434.

Kleinstäuber, G. and W. Kirmse. 1988. Status of the Peregrine Falcon in East Germany, 1965-1985. Pages 179-189 *in* Peregrine Falcon Populations: Their Management and Recovery (T. J. Cade, J. H. Enderson, C. G. Thelander, and C. M. White, Eds.). The Peregrine Fund, Boise, ID.

Korpimäki, E., and K. Norrdahl. 1991. Numerical and functional responses of Kestrels, Short-eared Owls and Long-eared Owls to vole densities. Ecology 72:814-825.

Korpimäki, E., and J. Wiehn. 1998. Clutch size of Kestrels: seasonal decline and experimental evidence for food limitation under fluctuating food conditions. Oikos 83:259-272.

Lincer, J. L. 1975. DDE-induced eggshell thinning in the American Kestrel: a comparison of the field situation and laboratory results. Journal of Applied Ecology 12:781-793.

Lindberg, P. 1977. The Peregrine Falcon in Sweden. Pages 329-338 *in* Report of Proceedings World Conference on Birds of Prey, Vienna, 1975. (R. D. Chancellor, Ed.). International Council for Bird Preservation, Cambridge.

Lindberg, P. 1988. Reintroducing the Peregrine Falcon in Sweden. Pages 619-628 *in* Peregrine Falcon Populations: Their Management and Recovery (T. J. Cade, J. H. Enderson, C. G. Thelander, and C. M. White, Eds.). The Peregrine Fund, Boise, ID.

Liotta, P. H. 1989. Learning to Fly: A Season with the Peregrine Falcon. Algonquin Books, Chapel Hill, NC.

Lumley, E. D. 1937. Hawks. Emergency Conservation Committee, Conservation Series, Teaching Units. 61:1-11.

Maatsch, I., and U. Beyerbach. 1971. Über die Oinstrumentelle Samennubertragung bei einem Wanderfalken paar. Praktische Tierarzt 4:140.

MacArthur, R. H., and E. O. Wilson. 1967. The Theory of Island Biogeography. Princeton University Press, Princeton, NJ.

Mattox, W. G. 1975. Bird of prey research in West Greenland, 1974. Polar Record 17(109):387- 388.

Mattox, W. G., R. A. Graham, W. A. Burnham, D. M. Clement, and J. T. Harris. 1972. Peregrine Falcon survey, West Greenland, 1972. Arctic 25:308-311.

Mattox, W. G., W. R. Heinrich, J. Oar, S. J. Belardo, K. Riddle, and T. M. Smylie. 1980. West Greenland Peregrine Falcon survey, 1978. Arctic 33:199-202.

Mattox, W. G., and W. S. Seegar. 1988. The Greenland Peregrine Falcon Survey, 1972-1984, with emphasis on recent population status. Pages 27-36 in Peregrine Falcon Populations: Their Management and Recovery (T. J. Cade, J. H. Enderson, C. G. Thelander, and C. M. White, Eds.). The Peregrine Fund, Boise, ID.

McDonald, B. 1990. Archives of American Falconry: Interview Series. Boise, ID.

McGrady, M. J., T. L. Maechtle, J. J. Vargas, W. S. Seegar, C. Porras Pena. 2002. Movements of Peregrine Falcons Falco peregrinus wintering on the Gulf Coast of Mexico 1996-1998. Condor 104:39-48.

McKay, P. 1989. The Pilgrim and the Cowboy. McGraw-Hill, New York.

McNulty, F. 1972. Falcons of Morro Rock. The New Yorker December 23:67-74.

Mead, C. J. 1993. Peregrine ringing returns affecting Britain and Ireland. Pages 259-266 in The Peregrine Falcon, second edition (D. Ratcliffe). T & A D Poyser, London.

Mearns, R., and I. Newton. 1984. Turnover and dispersal in a Peregrine Falco peregrinus population. Ibis 126:347-355.

Mearns, R., and I. Newton. 1988. Factors affecting breeding success of Peregrines in south Scotland. Journal of Animal Ecology 57:903-916.

Mebs, T. 1969. Peregrine Falcon population trends in West Germany. Pages 193-208 in Peregrine Falcon Populations: Their Biology and Decline (J. J. Hickey, Ed.). University of Wisconsin Press, Madison.

Mebs, T. 1971. Todesursachen und Mortalitatsraten beim Wanderfalken (Falco peregrinus) nach den Wiederfunden deutscher und finnischer Ringvogel. Vˆgelwarte 26:98-105.

Mitchell, E. B. 1900. The Art and Practice of Hawking. Methuen, London.

Monk, J. G. 1979. Peregrine Falcon inventory, data evaluation and management recommendations, 1979. Ukiah District Office, U.S. Bureau of Land Management, Ukiah, CA.

Monk, J. G. 1980. Peregrine Falcon inventory, data evaluation and management recommendations, 1980. Ukiah District Office, U.S. Bureau of Land Management, Ukiah, CA.

Monk, J. G. 1981. Peregrine Falcon inventory, data evaluation and management recommendations, 1981. Ukiah District Office, U.S. Bureau of Land Management, Ukiah, CA.

Monk, J. G. 1982. Peregrine Falcon inventory, data evaluation and management recommendations, 1982. Ukiah District Office, U.S. Bureau of Land Management, Ukiah, CA.

Monk, J. G., and D. L. Harlow. 1984. California Peregrine Falcon reproductive outcome and management effort in 1982 and 1983. U.S. Department of the Interior, Fish and Wildlife Service, Endangered Species Office, Sacramento, CA.

Monk, J. G., M. N. Kirven, and B. J. Walton. 1989. California Peregrine Falcon monitoring and management effort in 1989 with a discussion of trend analysis. Ukiah District Office, U.S. Bureau of Land Management, Ukiah, CA.

Monk, J. G., and B. J. Walton. 1989. California Peregrine Falcon implementation plan-1989. U.S. Bureau of Land Management, Sacramento, CA.

Monneret, R. J. 1988. Changes in the Peregrine Falcon populations of France. Pages 201-213 in Peregrine Falcon Populations: Their Management and Recovery (T. J. Cade, J. H. Enderson, C. G. Thelander, and C. M. White, Eds.). The Peregrine Fund, Boise, ID.

Mooney, N., and N. Brothers. 1993. Dispersion, nest and pair fidelity of Peregrine Falcons Falco peregrinus in Tasmania. Pages 33-42 in Australian Raptor Studies (P. Olsen, Ed.). Australasian Raptor Association, Royal Australasian Ornithologists Union, Melbourne.

Moore, N. W. 1987. The Bird of Time: The Science and Politics of Nature Conservation. Cambridge University Press, Cambridge, U.K.

Moore, N. W., and D. A. Ratcliffe. 1962. Chlorinated hydrocarbon residues in the egg of a Peregrine Falcon Falco peregrinus from Perthshire. Bird Study 9:242-244.

Mueller, C. H., N. S. Mueller, D. D. Berger, G. Allez, W. Robichaud, and J. L. Kaspar. 2000. Age and sex differences in the timing of fall migration of hawks and falcons. Wilson Bulletin 112:214-224.

Murphy, R. 1963. The Peregrine Falcon. Houghton Mifflin, Boston.

Nelson, R. W. 1988. Do large natural broods increase mortality of parent Peregrine Falcons? Pages 719-728 in Peregrine Falcon Populations: Their Management and Recovery (T. J. Cade, J. H. Enderson, C. G. Thelander, and C. M. White, Eds.). The Peregrine Fund, Boise, ID.

Nelson, R. W. 1990. Status of the Peregrine Falcon Falco peregrinus pealei, on Langara Island, Queen Charlotte Islands, British Columbia, 1968-1989. Canadian Field-Naturalist 104:193-199.

Newton, I. 1979. Population ecology of raptors. T & A D Poyser, London.

Newton, I. 1986. The Sparrowhawk. T & A D Poyser, London.

Newton, I. 1988. Population regulation in Peregrines: an overview. Pages 761-770 in Peregrine Falcon Populations: Their Management and Recovery (T. J. Cade, J. H. Enderson, C. G. Thelander, and C. M. White, Eds.). The Peregrine Fund, Boise, ID.

Newton, I. 1991. Habitat variation and population regulation in Sparrowhawks. Ibis 133, supplemental 1:76-88.

Newton, I. 1992. Experiments on the limitation of bird numbers by territorial behaviour. Biological Reviews 67:129-173.

Newton, I. 1998. Population Limitation in Birds. Academic Press, London.

Newton, I., and R. M. Mearns. 1988. Population Ecology of Peregrines in South Scotland. Pages 651-665 in Peregrine Falcon Populations: Their Management and Recovery (T. J. Cade, J. H. Enderson, C. G. Thelander, and C. M. White, Eds.). The Peregrine Fund, Boise, ID.

Nye, A. G., Jr. 1942. American falconry. Journal of the Falconers Association of North America vol. 1:6-8.

Nye, A. G., Jr. 1986. Archives of American Falconry: Interview Series. Boise, ID.

Nye, A. G., Jr. 1990. Archives of American Falconry: Interview Series. Boise, ID.

O'Brien, D. 1988. The Rites of Autumn. Atlantic Monthly Press, New York.

Olendorff, R. R., D. D. Bibles, M. T. Dean, J. R. Haugh, and M. N. Kochert. 1989. Raptor habitat management under the U.S. Bureau of Land Management multiple-use mandate. Raptor Research Reports no. 8:1-80.

Olsen, P. D., and A. Cockburn. 1991. Female-biased sex allocation in Peregrine Falcons and other raptors. Behavioral Ecology and Sociology 28:417-423.

Olsen, P. D., and J. Olsen. 1988. Population trends, distribution, and status of the Peregrine Falcon in Australia. Pages 255-274 in Peregrine Falcon Populations: Their Management and Recovery (T. J. Cade, J. H. Enderson, C. G. Thelander, and C. M. White, Eds.). The Peregrine Fund, Boise, ID.

Olsen, P. D., and J. Olsen. 1989. Breeding of the Peregrine Falcon Falco peregrinus: III. Weather, nest quality and breeding success. Emu 89:6-14.

Orton, D. A. 1975. The speed of a Peregrine's dive. Field 25:9-75.

Pagel, J. E. 1991. Protocol for observing known and potential Peregrine Falcon eyries in the Pacific Northwest. Pages 83-96 in Proceedings, Symposium on Peregrine Falcons in the Pacific Northwest (J. E. Pagel, Ed.). Rouge River National Forest, Medford, OR.

Parrish, J. R., D. T. Rogers, Jr., and F. P. Ward. 1983. Identification of natal locales of Peregrine Falcons (Falco peregrinus) by trace element analysis of feathers. Auk 100:560-567.

Peakall, D. B., T. J. Cade, C. M. White, and J. R. Haugh. 1975. Organochlorine residues in Alaskan Peregrines. Pesticide Monitoring Journal 8:255-260.

Peakall, D. B., and L. F. Kiff. 1988. DDE contamination in Peregrines and American Kestrels and its effect on reproduction. Pages 337-350 in Peregrine Falcon Populations: Their Management and Recovery (T. J. Cade, J. H. Enderson, C. G. Thelander, and C. M. White, Eds.). The Peregrine Fund, Boise, ID.

Peakall, D. B., L. M. Reynolds, and M. C. French. 1976. DDE in eggs of the Peregrine Falcon. Bird Study 23:183-186.

Petersen, R. S. 1968. The domestic raising of the Peales Peregrine Falcon. Journal of the North American Falconers Association 7:64-68.

Peterson, R. T. 1948. Birds Over America. Dodd, Mead and Co., New York.

Peterson, R. T. 1988. Forward. Pages i-v in Peregrine Falcon Populations: Their Management and Recovery (T. J. Cade, J. H. Enderson, C. G. Thelander, and C. M. White, Eds.). The Peregrine Fund, Boise, ID.

Poole, K. G., and R. G. Bromley. 1988. Interrelationships within a raptor guild in the Central Canadian Arctic. Canadian Journal of Zoology 66:2275-2282.

Porter, R. D., and C. M. White. 1973. The Peregrine Falcon in Utah, emphasizing ecology and competition with the Prairie Falcon. Brigham Young University Science Bulletin. Biological Series. Provo, UT.

Porter, R. D., and S. N. Wiemeyer. 1969. Dieldrin and DDT effects on Sparrow Hawk eggshells and reproduction. Science 165:199-200.

Porter, R. D., and S. N. Wiemeyer. 1970. Propagation of captive American Kestrels. Journal of Wildlife Management 34:594-604.

Porter, R. D., and S. N. Wiemeyer. 1972. DDE at low dietary levels kills captive American Kestrels. Bulletin of Environmental Contamination and Toxicology 8:193-199.

Prestt, I. 1965. An enquiry into the recent breeding status of some of the smaller birds of prey and crows in Britain. Bird Study 12:196-221.

Rahn, H., and A. Ar. 1974. The avian egg: incubation time and water loss. Condor 76:147-152.

Ratcliffe, D. A. 1958. Broken eggs in Peregrine eyries. British Birds 51:23-26.

Ratcliffe, D. A. 1962. Breeding density in the Peregrine Falco peregrinus and Raven Corvus corax. Ibis 104:13-39.

Ratcliffe, D. A. 1963. The status of the Peregrine in Great Britain. Bird Study 10:56-90.

Ratcliffe, D. A. 1965. Organo-chlorine residues in some raptor and corvid eggs from northern Britain. British Birds 58:65-81.

Ratcliffe, D. A. 1967. Decrease in eggshell weight in certain birds of prey. Nature 215:208-210.

Ratcliffe, D. A. 1969. Population trends of the Peregrine Falcon in Great Britain. Pages 239-269 in Peregrine Falcon Populations: Their Biology and Decline (J. J. Hickey, Ed.). University of Wisconsin Press, Madison.

Ratcliffe, D. A. 1970. Changes attributable to pesticides in egg breakage frequency and eggshell thickness in some British birds. Journal of Applied Ecology 7:67-115.

Ratcliffe, D. 1980. The Peregrine Falcon. Buteo Books, Vermillion, SD.

Ratcliffe, D. A. 1993. The Peregrine Falcon. Second edition. T & A D Poyser, London.

Redig, P. T., and H. B. Tordoff. 1988. Peregrine Falcon reintroduction in the upper Mississippi valley and western Great Lakes region. Pages 559-563 in Peregrine Falcon Populations: Their Management and Recovery (T. J. Cade, J. H. Enderson, C. G. Thelander, and C. M. White, Eds.). The Peregrine Fund, Boise, ID.

Restani, M., and W. G. Mattox. 2000. Natal dispersal of Peregrine Falcons in Greenland. Auk 117:500-504.

Rice, J. N., Jr. 1960. The decline of the Peregrine population in Pennsylvania. Unpubl. manuscript, Archives of American Falconry, Boise, ID.

Rice, J. N., Jr. 1969. The decline of the Peregrine population in Pennsylvania. Pages 155-163 in Peregrine Falcon Populations: Their Biology and Decline (J. J. Hickey, Ed.). University of Wisconsin Press, Madison.

Ridgeway, R. 1889. The ornithology of Illinois. Natural History Survey of Illinois 1:282-284.

Risebrough, R. W. 2000. Historical and continuing effects on birds of the southern California islands of DDT wastes discharged by the Montrose Chemical Corporation. Expert witness report, Montrose case, submitted to U.S. Department of Justice and U.S. Fish and Wildlife Service.

Risebrough, R. W., R. J. Huggett, J. J. Griffin, and C. E. D. Goldberg. 1968a. Pesticides: transatlantic movements in the northeast trades. Science 159:1233-1235.

Risebrough, R. W., P. Reiche, D. B. Peakall, S. G. Herman, and M. N. Kirven. 1968b. Polychlorinated biphenyls in the global ecosystem. Nature 220:1098-1102.

Rochenbauch, D. 1998. Der Wanderfalke in Deutschland und umliegenden Gebieten. Band I. Verlag Christine Hölzinger, Auf der Schantz 23/2, D-71640 Ludwingsburg, Germany.

Romanoff, A. L., and A. J. Romanoff. 1949. The Avian Egg. John Wiley and Sons, New York.

Salomonsen, F. 1950-1951. Grønlands Fugle/The Birds of Greenland. Ejnar Munksgaards Forlag, Copenhagen.

Sargent, W. D. 1941. Egger destruction. Journal of the American Falconers Association 1(1):4.

Savage, C. 1992. Peregrine Falcons. Sierra Club Books, San Francisco, CA.

Schick, A. 1975. The Peregrine Falcons. Dial Press, New York.

Seegar, W. S., and M. A. Yates. 1994. Peregrine Falcon migration studies at Assateague Island, MD/VA. Unpubl. report, U.S. Army, Edgewood Research, Development and Engineering Center, Edgewood, MD.

Seegar, W. S., M. A. Yates, B. J. Dayton, and L. Schueck. 1998. Peregrine Falcon migration studies at Assateague Island, MD/VA. Unpubl. report, U.S. Army, Edgewood Research, Development and Engineering Center, Edgewood, MD.

Septon, G. A. 2000. Overwintering by urban-nesting Peregrine Falcons *Falco peregrinus* in midwestern North America. Pages 455-460 *in* Raptors at Risk: 5th World Conference on Birds of Prey (R. D. Chancellor and B.-U. Meyburg, Eds.). World Working Group on Birds of Prey, Berlin/Hancock House, Blaine, WA.

Septon, G. A., J. Bielefeldt, J. Ellstad, J. B. Marks, and R. N. Rosenfield. 1996. Peregrine Falcons: power plant nest structures and shoreline movements. Pages 145-153 *in* Raptors in Human Landscapes (D. M. Bird, D. E. Varland, and J. J. Negro, Eds.). Academic Press, London.

Sheail, J. 1985. Pesticides and nature conservation. The British Experience 1950-1975. Clarendon Press, Oxford, U.K.

Sherrod, S. K., W. R. Heinrich, W. A. Burnham, J. H. Barclay, and T. J. Cade. 1982. Hacking: A Method for Releasing Peregrine Falcons and Other Birds of Prey, 2nd edition. The Peregrine Fund, Boise, ID.

Shor, W. 1984. Operation falcon. Hawk Chalk 23:25-60.

Shor, W. 1988. "Operation Falcon" and the Peregrine. Pages 831-842 *in* Peregrine Falcon Populations: Their Management and Recovery (T. J. Cade, J. H. Enderson, C. G. Thelander, and C. M. White, Eds.). The Peregrine Fund, Boise, ID.

Soulé, M. E. 1987. History of the Society for Conservation Biology: how and why we got here. Conservation Biology 1:4-5.

Spofford, W. R. 1942. Nesting of the Peregrine Falcon in Tennessee. Migrant 13(2-3):29-31.

Spofford, W. R. 1943. Peregrines in a west Tennessee swamp. Migrant 14:56-58.

Spofford, W. R. 1945. Peregrine falcons in a west Tennessee swamp. Migrant 16:56-58.

Spofford, W. R. 1947. Another tree-nesting Peregrine Falcon record for Tennessee. Migrant 18:60.

Spofford, W. R. 1969a. The Peregrine decline in northern New England and New York. Pages 177-178 *in* Peregrine Falcon Populations: Their Biology and Decline (J. J. Hickey, Ed.). University of Wisconsin Press, Madison.

Spofford, W. R. 1969b. Peregrines in the southern and southeastern United States. Pages 181-182 *in* Peregrine Falcon Populations: Their Biology and Decline (J. J. Hickey, Ed.). University of Wisconsin Press, Madison.

Spuhler, E. H. 1968. A report of the first successful breeding of Peregrine Falcons in captivity written by Renz Waller. Journal of the North American Falconers Association 7:45-57.

Temple, S.A. 1972. Artificial insemination with imprinted birds of prey. Nature 237:287-288.

Temple, S. A., Ed. 1978. Endangered Birds: Management Techniques for Preserving Threatened Species. University of Wisconsin Press, Madison.

Temple, S. A. 1988. Future goals and needs for the management and conservation of the Peregrine Falcon. Pages 843-848 *in* Peregrine Falcon Populations: Their Management and Recovery (T. J. Cade, J. H. Enderson, C. G. Thelander, and C. M. White, Eds.). The Peregrine Fund, Boise, ID.

Thelander, C. G. 1973. Bald Eagle reproduction in California, 1972-1973. Wildlife Management Branch Administrative Report no. 73-5, California Department of Fish and Game, Sacramento, CA.

Thelander, C. G. 1974. Nesting territory utilization by Golden Eagles (*Aquila chrysaetos*) in California during 1974. Wildlife Management Branch Administrative Report no. 74-7, California Department Fish and Game, Sacramento, CA.

Thelander, C. G. 1975. Distribution and reproductive success of Peregrine Falcons in California during 1975. Wildlife Management Branch Administrative Report no. 75-6. California Department Fish and Game, Sacramento, CA.

Thelander, C. G. 1976. Distribution and reproductive success of Peregrine Falcons in California during 1975 and 1976. Administrative Report no.76-3, California Department Fish and Game, Sacramento, CA.

Thelander, C. G. 1977. The breeding status of Peregrine Falcons in California. Masters thesis, San Jose State University, San Jose, CA.

Thelander, C. G., and B. J. Walton. 1980. Evaluation of cliff-nesting raptor habitat, Angeles, San Bernadino, Los Padres National Forests in California. Los Padres National Forest, U.S. Forest Service, Los Padres, CA.

Thomasson, K. 1947. On the nesting sites of the Peregrine Falcon in the countries around the Baltic. Vår Fågelvårld 6:72-81.

Tomilson, R. E. 1968. Rewarding banding to determine reporting rates of recovered Mourning Dove bands. Journal of Wildlife Management 32:6-11.

Tordoff, H. B., J. S. Castrale, M. S. Martell, and P. T. Redig. 2000. Brood size and survival to breeding in Midwestern Peregrine Falcons. Journal of Field Ornithology 71:691-693.

Tordoff, H. B., M. S. Martell, and P. T. Redig. 1998a. Effect of fledge site on choice of nest site by midwestern Peregrine Falcons. Loon 70:127-129.

Tordoff, H. B., M. S. Martell, and P. T. Redig. 1998b. Midwest Peregrine Falcon restoration. Unpubl. report.

Tordoff, H. B., and P. T. Redig. 1997. Midwest Peregrine Falcon demography, 1982-1995. Journal of Raptor Research 31:339-346.

Tordoff, H. B., and P. T. Redig. 1999. Two fatal Peregrine Falcon territorial fights. Loon 71:182-186.

Tordoff, H. B., and P. T. Redig. 2001. Role of genetic background in success of reintroduced Peregrine Falcons. Conservation Biology 15:528-532.

Treleaven, R. B. 1977. Peregrine: The Private Life of the Peregrine Falcon. Headland Publications, Penzance, Cornwall, U.K.

Treleaven, R. B. 1998. In Pursuit of the Peregrine. Tiercel SB Publisher, Wheathampstead, Hertfordshire., U.K.

Tucker, V. A. 1995. An optical tracking device for recording the three-dimensional paths of flying birds. Review of Scientific Instruments 66:3042-3047.

Tucker, V. A., T. J. Cade, and A. E. Tucker. 1998. Diving speeds and angles of a Gyrfalcon. Journal of Experimental Biology 201:2061-2070.

U.S. Fish and Wildlife Service. 1982. Pacific States Recovery Plan. U.S. Department of Interior, Fish and Wildlife Service, Denver.

Van den Bosch, R. 1980. The Pesticide Conspiracy. Prism Press, Dorchester, U.K.

Village, A. 1990. The Kestrel. T & A D Poyser, London.

Wade, N. 1978. Bird lovers and bureaucrats at loggerheads over Peregrine Falcon. Science 199:1054-1055.

Walton, B. J. 1998. Natural history and restoration of Peregrine Falcons in California. Expert witness report, Montrose case, submitted to U.S. Department of Justice and U.S. Fish and Wildlife Service.

Walton, B. J. 2000. Natural history and restoration of Peregrine Falcon in California, 1998 and 1999 season update. Expert witness report, Montrose case, submitted to U.S. Department of Justice and U.S. Fish and Wildlife Service.

Ward, F. P. 1975. Colored and numbered tarsal bands as an aid to raptor demographic studies. Pages 98-102 in Proceedings of the North American Hawk Migration Conference (M. Harwood, Ed.). Hawk Migration Association of North America, Syracuse, NY.

Ward, F. P., and R. C. Laybourne. 1985. A difference in prey selection by adult and immature Peregrine Falcons during autumn migration. Pages 303-309 in Conservation Studies on Raptors (I. Newton and R. D. Chancellor, Eds.). International Council for Bird Preservation Technical Bulletin no. 5.

Ward, F. P., K. Titus, W. S. Seegar, M. A. Yates, and M. R. Fuller. 1988. Autumn migrations of Peregrine Falcons at Assateague Island, Maryland/Virginia, 1970-1984. Pages 485-495 in Peregrine Falcon Populations: Their Management and Recovery (T. J. Cade, J. H. Enderson, C. G. Thelander, and C. M. White, Eds.). The Peregrine Fund, Boise, ID.

Warkentin, I. G., P. C. James, and L. W. Oliphant. 1991. Influence of site fidelity on mate switching in urban-breeding Merlins (Falco columbarius). Auk 108:294-302.

Weaver, J. D., and T. J. Cade (Eds.). 1983. Falcon Propagation: a manual on captive breeding. The Peregrine Fund, Boise, ID.

White, C. M. 1968. Biosystematics of the North American Peregrine Falcons. Ph.D. dissertation, University of Utah, Salt Lake City.

White, C. M. 1975. Studies on Peregrine Falcons in the Aleutian Islands. Raptor Research Report 3:33-50.

White, C. M., and T. J. Cade. 1971. Cliff-nesting raptors and ravens along the Colville River in arctic Alaska. Living Bird 10:107-150.

White, C. M., N. J. Clum, T. J. Cade, and W. G. Hunt. 2002. Peregrine Falcon (Falco peregrinus) in The Birds of North America, no. 660 (A. Poole and F. Gill, Eds.). Academy of Natural Sciences, Philadelphia, PA, and American Ornithologists' Union, Washington, D.C.

White, C. M., and R. W. Nelson. 1991. Hunting ranges and strategies in a tundra breeding Peregrine and Gyrfalcon observed from a helicopter. Journal of Raptor Research 25:49-62.

Wiemeyer, S. N., and R. D. Porter. 1970. DDE thins eggshells of captive American Kestrels. Nature 227:737-738.

Wilcove. D. 1999. The Condor's Shadow: the Loss and Recovery of Wildlife in America. W. H. Freeman and Company, New York.

Willoughby, E. J., and T. J. Cade. 1964. Breeding behavior of the American Kestrel (Sparrow Hawk). Living Bird 3:75-96.

Wilson, U. W., A. McMillan, and F. C. Dobler. 2000. Nesting population trend and breeding success of Peregrine Falcons on the Washington outer coast, 1980-98. Journal of Raptor Research 34:67-74.

Wrege, P. H., and T. J. Cade. 1977. Courtship behavior of large falcons in captivity. Journal of Raptor Research 11:1-27.

Wynne, Edwards, V. C. 1962. Animal dispersion in relation to behaviour. Oliver and Boyd, London.

Yates, M. A., K. E. Riddle, and F. P. Ward. 1988. Recoveries of Peregrine Falcons migrating through the eastern and central United States 1955-1985. Pages 471-483 in Peregrine Falcon Populations: Their Management and Recovery (T. J. Cade, J. H. Enderson, C. G. Thelander, and C. M. White, Eds.). The Peregrine Fund, Boise, ID.

Young, H. F. 1969. Hypotheses of Peregrine population dynamics. Pages 513-519 in Peregrine Falcon Populations: Their Biology and Decline (J. J. Hickey, Ed.). University of Wisconsin Press, Madison.

Zimmerman, D. R. 1975. To Save a Bird in Peril. Coward, McCann and Geoghegan, New York.

Zollinger, R., and G. Müskens. 1994. Population dynamics and lifetime reproductive success in Sparrowhawks Accipiter nisus in a Dutch-German study area. Pages 77-85 in Raptor Conservation Today: 4th World Conference on Birds of Prey (B.-U. Meyburg and R. D. Chancellor, Eds.). World Working Group on Birds of Prey/Pica Press, Berlin/Robertsbridge, U.K.

Index

Aberdeen Proving Grounds, 77, 95, 235

Acadia National Park, 315

Adult survival, 175, 176, 179

Age-related variation, 342

Ahmanson Foundation, The, 157

Ahrens, Ron, 144

Aiken, Charles, 58

Alaska Department of Fish and Game, 191

Alaska Peregrine Falcon Recovery Plan, 197

Alaska Peregrine Falcon Recovery Team, 197

Alberta Fish and Wildlife Division, 110

Aldrich, John W., 15, 267

Aldrich, Tom, 144

Aldrin, 19, 24, 26, 106

Aleutian Islands, 336

Allaben-Confer, Karen, 328

Allen, Arthur A., 78, 86, 93

Allen, Harriet, 152

Allen, Joseph, 58

Allen, Tom, 333

Aller, Steve, 313

Alpine Lookout, 49

Alston, Joseph, 153, 248, 249

Alston, Judy, 248, 249

Amaral, Mike, 191

Ambrose, Michelle, 191

Ambrose, Robert (Skip), 189, 191, 193, 197, 210, 275

American Federation of Aviculturists, 269

American Museum of Natural History, 37, 53

American Ornithologists' Union, 267

Anderson, Bob, 178

Anderson, Bud, 206, 208, 209

Anderson, Dan, 31, 38, 39, 43

Anderson, David, 152, 310

Anderson, Ralph, 153

Andrus, Cecil, 144, 268, 269, 270

Anheuser-Busch Companies, Inc., 142, 143, 144

Ansell, Allen, 358

Appalachians, 6, 35-55, 57, 102, 103

Appel, J. C., 16, 17

Ar, A., 88

Archives of American Falconry, 37, 52, 54, 286, 288, 289

Arctic National Wildlife Refuge, 195

Arizona Department of Game and Fish, 293-294

Armbruster, Harry, 105, 115, 118

Armstrong, Ted, 120, 124

Arnett, G. Ray, 271

Aronian, John, 98, 329

Artificial insemination, 5, 60, 66, 74, 81, 85, 114, 118, 130, 139, 142, 150, 151, 290, 320, 324

Assateague Island, 16–18, 26, 59, 77, 86, 207, 213–217, 221, 223–225, 343

Atlantic City, 331

Atwood, E. L., 52

Aulman, D. Lee, 156, 159, 163, 165, 166

Aulman, Sheree, 159

Australia, 337–339

Babbitt, Bruce, 98, 195, 261, 276, 277, 353

Bailey, Alfred, 58, 190

Baird, Jim, 75, 78, 92

Baker, J. A., 317

Baltimore Peregrines, 321, 328

Baltimore Sun, The, 325, 328

Banasch, Ursula, 105, 115, 118, 122, 125

Banding, 201–205, 207–210, 237, 240, 306, 315, 321, 331, 337–340, 342–345

Baptiste, Steve, 156, 304

Barber, John, 321, 328

Barbour, Roger, 40

Barclay, Jack, 74, 78, 93, 94, 99, 102, 156, 231

Bartholomew, George A., 155

Basilli, Gianfranco, 60, 69

Bateman, Robert, 13, 105, 127, 173, 213

Batt, Phil, 277

Batten, M., 318

Bauer, Elizabeth, 69

Baumlin, John, 168

Bavin, Clark, 266, 268, 270, 271, 273

Bay of Fundy, 120

Baysinger, Earl, 16, 17, 77-78, 274

Bean, John, 70

Beauvais, Gary, 69

Beebe, Frank, 11, 58, 81, 86

Behavioral imprint, 85, 136, 144, 147, 151, 283, 290, 292, 320, 322, 326, 352

Behle, Dorothy, 192

Behle, William, 192

Belardo, Steve, 64, 70

Belke, Dave, 146

Bell Museum of Natural History, 186

Belli, Larry, 69

Bendire, Charles, 58

Benfield, Dan, 191

Bent, Arthur, 42, 51, 58

Bente, Peter, 191, 193

Berger, Daniel D., 27, 33, 40, 41, 43, 49–51, 57, 60–62, 67, 137, 153, 202, 249, 307–309

Berger, Max, 215

Berman, Mike, 69

Berner, Lou, 69

Berry, Barbara, 215

Berry, Carol, 215

Berry, Robert B., 35, 40, 43, 52, 54, 55, 63, 75, 85, 213–215, 224, 270, 282–284, 286–288, 357

Berthrong, Morgan, 66, 320

Big Bend National Park, 64, 69, 70

Big Horn Canyon National Recreation Area, 238

Biological diversity, 349–351

Bird Banding Laboratory, 209

Bird, David, 78, 112, 118–120

Bishop, Louis, 189

Blackwelder, Eliot, 190

Bloom, P., 158

Bodega Bay Institute, 168

Bohannon, Tom, 69

Boise Cascade Corporation, 129, 143, 144, 146, 152, 274

Boise State University, 143, 144

Bollengier, Rene, Jr., 78, 264, 314

Bond, Frank M., 35, 66, 75, 128, 132, 135, 155, 156, 195, 244, 268, 269, 279, 283, 291–293, 295, 310, 317, 324, 327, 335, 357

Bond, Frankel, 144

Bond, Richard M., 6, 42, 58, 127, 156, 160, 161

Booms, Travis, 208

Bowden, Elizabeth, 69

Bowen, Diana, 157

Boyce, Sandy, 156, 163

Boyd, Les, 66, 85, 136, 168, 290, 322

Boyd, Nicka, 168

Boynton, Allen, 77

Braker, Beth, 69

Branski, Brad, 69

Henderson, Carrol, 173

Henjum, Mark, 152

Henny, Charles, 33, 220

Henry, D. M., 317

Heptachlor, 24, 25, 26, 106

Herbert, Kathleen Green Skelton, 40, 41, 43, 44, 46, 47, 49, 51, 54

Herbert, Richard A., 41–47, 49, 51, 53, 54, 57, 359

Herbst, Robert, 268, 270, 272

Heritage Publication Series, 286

Herman, Steve, 156, 160, 163

Herrick, Jerry, 354

Hickel, Walter, 16, 18

Hickey, Joseph J., 6, 9, 13, 14, 18, 19, 26–31, 33, 38–42, 44–46, 49, 50, 52–55, 58, 59, 61, 62, 105, 119, 199, 267, 279, 288, 291, 335, 354, 359

Higby, Warren, 298

Hill, Burnell, 70

Hill, Laurie, 70

Hilliard, Mark, 129

Himmelwright, Craig, 156, 163, 165, 166

Hinckley, Dan, 153

Hines, Jane, 69

Hinkley, F. C., 189

Hitchcock, Mark, 70

Hodel, Donald, 274

Hodson, Keith, 108, 110

Hogan, Joel, 153

Holcomb, Dottie, 208

Hollister, Bob, 234, 304

Holroyd, Geoffrey L., 115, 117, 125

Hoover, J. Edgar, 268

Horn, William, 268

Houle, Marcy Cottrell, 67

Houle, Marey, 21

House Interior Subcommittee on Appropriations, 80

Howard, Rich, 153

Hubbard, John, 67

Huey, Bill, 129, 324

Hughes, Jeff, 191

Hummel, Monte, 120

Hunt, Alan, 23

Hunt, Grainger, 14, 64, 65, 70, 74, 157, 218, 219, 274, 293, 328, 339

Hunt, Philo, 64, 70

Hunter, Don, 14, 15, 58, 74, 145, 280, 291

IBM Corporation, 73

Iceland, 336

Idaho Department of Fish and Game, 143, 144, 152

Idaho Power Company, 143, 358

Imprinted falcons, (see Behavioral imprint)

Ince, Jim, 293

Incubation, 10, 83, 85, 87, 88, 91, 111, 132, 135, 137, 139, 142, 149, 150, 167, 284, 287, 308, 309, 342

International Association of Fish and Game Commissioners, 263

International Association of Fish and Wildlife Agencies, 80, 275, 294

International Council for Bird Preservation, 41

International Peregrine Conference, (see Madison International Peregrine Conference)

Ireland, 23, 29, 30

Isaac, Terry, 297

J.R. Simplot Company, 129

James, Fran, 75

Jamieson, Dave, 156

Jarman, Wally, 157, 168

Jayhawk Bluff, 182, 184

Jefferies, Don, 25, 26, 33

Jenkins, Alan, 202

Jenkins, Priscilla, 21, 328

Jennings, Douglas, 144, 145

Jenny, J. Peter, 229, 231, 232, 284

Johnson, Brenda, 70

Johnson, Lyndon, 14

Jones, F. M., 43

Jones, Marshall, 273

Jones, Zach, 59

Joseph, Ron, 153

Jump Mountain, 36, 43

Jurek, Ron, 156, 167

Jurs, Louis, 197

K-selected, 10, 11

Kaiman, Audrey, 40

Kaiman, Bernard, 40

Kaskey, Jack, 331

Kasten, Robert, 275

Katona, Robert, 168, 229

Kaufman, John, 21

Kay, Mike, 248

Keiser, John, 143, 144

Keith, Tony, 108, 119

Keller, Ken, 69

Kellogg, Peter Paul, 86

Kelly, Dan, 144

Kelly, Reid, 66

Kempthorne, Dirk, 277

Kendall, Henry, 63

Kerr, Gordon, 114, 118

Kessel, Brina, 194

Kestrel, American, 28, 31, 54, 57, 81, 82

Kestrel, Eurasian, 347

Kestrel, Mauritius, 10, 83, 92, 282, 287, 288, 351, 352, 355

Kestrel, Seychelles, 92

Kiff, Julie, 169

Kiff, Lloyd, 53, 156, 157, 163, 169, 229, 274

Kilpatrick, Chuck, 69

Kim, Dan, 69

Kimball, Thomas L., 265

Kimmel, Tim, 332

Kirven, Monte, 156, 163, 166

Kite, Red, 352

Klein, Lisa, 328

Kline, Rick, 168

Klots, Alex, 46

Knoder, Gene, 80, 129, 132, 310

Knowles, Don, 80

Knuckles, Penny, 191

Koch, Ed, 263

Kockert, Mike, 153

Kohlmoos, Dale, 69

Kola Peninsula, 344

Kolbe, Jay, 238

Konkel, Dan, 66, 137, 138, 140, 141, 156, 284

Konkel, Jeannie, 137, 139, 140

Kradolfer, Lyle, 146

Krahe, Diane, 238, 239, 241, 243, 245, 246

Krupa, Mary, 122

Kuhn, Ken, 40

Kussman, Joel, 132, 310

Lacey Act, 276

Lack, David, 346, 347

Laguna Atascosa National Wildlife Refuge, 220

Lake Superior Basin, 183

Lamm, Richard D., 143, 144

Langara Island, 7, 263, 336

Lanier, John, 77

Lanning, Dirk, 70

Lanting, Frans, 156

Larrabee, Jon, 59

Larsen, Howard, 264

Larson, Blair, 242

Larson, James, 197

Latta, Brian, 156, 163, 165, 166, 168

Laurion, Tom, 304

Lawson, Peter, 70

Laybourne, Roxy, 65

Leach, Rick D., 272

Lee, Julie, 328

Leopold, Starker, 288

Lepage, Michel, 120

Lepisto, Chris, 59

Lepori, Frank, 168

Leskosky, Steven, 197

Levine, Ed, 135, 137, 146, 149, 152, 229, 233, 254, 255, 300, 301, 304

Lewis, Cecil, 248

Lincer, Jeff, 28, 31, 63, 73, 78

Linthicum, Janet, 157, 164, 165, 166

Liotta, P. H., 21

Locke, Ross, 153

Lodge, George E., 199, 261

Long, Bill, 152

Long, Frank, 73

Long, Robin Hunter, 191

Longevity, 340

Loucks, Barbara Allen, 77, 99

Lovejoy, Thomas E., 75, 265

Lowery, Walt, 144, 145

Lujan, Manuel, Jr., 269

Lyle, Robert, 40

MacGowan, Jerry, 197

Mackenzie River, 62, 108

Mackenzie Valley, 117, 125

Madison International Peregrine Conference, 13, 14, 16, 27, 28, 41, 43, 74, 105, 163, 267, 294, 313

Maechtle, Tom, 59, 74, 93, 177, 204–207, 213, 219, 225, 227, 328

Maiden Rock, 182, 184

Mallette, Robert, 167

Marcus, Stanley, 280, 292

Mariani, Jina, 153

Martell, Mark S., 177, 186

Martin, Bob, 129, 136, 206, 293, 330

Martin, Chris, 77

Martin, Steve, 168, 320, 327

Massachusetts Audubon Society, 75, 78, 92, 263

Matagorda Island, 59, 218, 342

Mate attraction, 4

Mate fidelity, 346

Mattox, Joan, 129

Mattox, Tim, 206

Mattox, William G., 48, 129, 199, 202, 207, 209, 211, 215, 226, 343, 345

Mauer, Fran, 191

Maumenee, Niels, 69

Maxey, Hal, 143, 145

May, Cordelia Scaife, 75, 129

May, John B., 52, 267

Mayo Clinic, 174, 185

Mayr, Ernst, 37, 53, 264

McCaffrey, Eugene, 78

McCain, Emil, 69

McCallum, Bob, 327

McClure, Jim, 80

McDonagh, Jane, 193

McDonald, Brian, 37, 40, 41, 50, 54, 213, 215, 220, 225

McDonald, Joanne, 40

McEneaney, Terry, 153, 208, 304, 306

McFadden, Corny, 215

McFadden, Jerry, 215

McIntyre, Carol, 191

McKeating, Gerald, 125

McLain, Pete, 77, 78, 92, 100

McLaughlin, Ann Dore, 144

McLean, D. D., 160

McNamara Naturalists, 120

McNulty, Faith, 81

McPartlin, John Jeffrey, 270–272

McVean, Doug, 153

Mearns, Richard, 67, 339, 340

Meese, Bob, 208

Mellon, Prosser, 75

Melquist, Wayne, 135, 152, 299, 300

Meng, Heinz, 21, 40, 63, 74, 75, 78, 84, 86–88, 91, 97, 109, 263, 267, 282, 320

Mengel, Bob, 41

Meredith, Luff, 58, 59, 218

Mesa Verde, 60

Mesta, Robert, 156, 167, 275

Met Life Building, 98, 99

Metcalf, Burt, 60

Michell, E. B., 317

Midwest, 7, 40, 124, 173-187, 266, 270, 289, 337, 340, 341, 344, 345

Migration, 5, 59, 133, 176–178, 205, 207–210, 213-227, 321, 324, 343, 344, 347

Migratory Bird Conservation Act of 1917, 123

Migratory Bird Management Office, 268, 273, 275

Migratory Bird Treaty Act, 52, 262, 270, 276, 280

Millsap, Brian, 293, 294

Milwaukee Public Museum, 179, 186

Mindell, Dave, 191

Minnesota Department of Natural Resources, 173

Minnesota Falconers Association, 186

Mitchell, Kevin, 238

Moffat's equilibrium, 339

Møller, Søren, 209

Monahan, Hugh, 114

Monk, Geoff, 156, 163, 164, 166

Monks Wood Experimental Station, 25, 26

Montana Department of Fish, Wildlife, and Parks, 152

Moore, Norman, 25, 27, 33

Moran, John, 168

Morgan, Allen, 75

Morison, Bob, 73-103

Moritz, Teddy, 92

Morro Rock, 81, 155–158, 160, 168, 169, 300

Mossop, David, 272

Most, Ernie, 248

Mt. Tom, 230

Mueller, Helmut C., 49

Murie, Olaus, 189

Murphy, R., 317

Murphy, Bob, 206

Murray, Mike, 157

Mutch, Brian D., 59, 60, 137, 148, 231, 234–236, 238, 239, 241–243, 246, 247, 250, 255, 284, 300–302

Mutch, Dale, 146, 149, 152, 301–303

Mutch, Ruth, 149, 224

Myers, Norman, 350

Myshak, Richard, 144

Nadareski, Christopher A., 77, 96, 97, 99, 329

Naderman, Justin, 152

Natal dispersal, 343, 344, 345, 346, 347 (also see Dispersal and Breeding dispersal)

Natal nesting sites, 9

National Academy of Sciences, 351

National Audubon Society, 52, 63, 75, 77, 80, 128, 129, 185, 263, 265, 266, 267, 271, 272, 307, 310, 313

National Cattlemen's Association, 291

National Environmental Policy Act, 273

National Park Service, 16, 69, 77, 153, 186, 191, 215, 216, 276, 306, 310, 311, 314

National Science Foundation, 73, 75

National Wildlife Conference, 267

National Wildlife Federation, 144, 265

National Wildlife Health Center, 216

Nature Conservancy, The, 101, 186, 220

Naval Arctic Research Laboratory, 194

Naval Petroleum Reserve No. 4, 194

Nebraska Game and Fish Commission, 153

Neighbors, Cliff, 60, 68

Nelson, Alora, 168

Nelson, Gaylord, 19

Saturated populations, 340 (also see Carrying capacity)

Saunders, Aretas, 58

Savage, Candice, 21

Savell, Dewey, 156

Sayers, Mike, 129

Schaller, George, 194

Schempf, Phil, 191

Schick, Alice, 21

Schmitt, John, 155, 156, 160, 168, 349

Schneider, James, 208

Schommer, Tim, 153

Schoonmaker, Peter, 69

Schramm, Larry, 81, 282

Schreiner, Keith, 264

Schultz, Chris, 60, 68, 69, 206

Scotland, 23, 24, 25, 30-31, 336, 339, 340, 341, 342, 345, 346

Seal, Ulysses S., 350

Sealing, Clee, 280

Sears, Tom, 77

Sedge Island, 92, 100

Seegar, James, 226

Seegar, Janis, 226

Seegar, Tom, 226

Seegar, William H., 206, 226

Seegar, William S., 203, 206, 207, 210, 213, 214, 216, 219, 226, 227

Selander, Robert K., 265

Self-sustaining populations, 347

Semen donors, 320, 322, 323, 326 (also see Behavioral imprints)

Septon, Greg, 177, 178, 179

Sex difference, 345

Sex ratios, 341, 343

Sexual maturity, 10

Shank, Chris, 124

Sherrod, Steve, 73, 74, 78, 93, 94, 156, 193, 202, 206, 231, 288

Shinners, Bill, 215

Shippee, Jodi, 242

Shooting of raptors, 52, 124, 262

Shor, Will, 271

Shryer, Jeff, 191

Siegstad, Kâle, 206, 208

Sigmon, Neal, 80

Sigwald, Sidney, 37, 50

Silva, Jim, 191

Sindelar, Charles, 27, 40, 41, 61

Sipple, Jeff, 156

Sisk, Tom, 69

Site fidelity, (see Territory fidelity)

Site tenacity, (see Territorial behavior)

Skaggs, Roger, 70

Skyscrapers, (see Nest sites, manmade)

Sleeper, David, 64

Slowe, Daniel, 218

Smiley, Daniel, 97

Smith, Bruce, 153, 266

Smith, Norman, 89

Smith, Roger, 132

Smithsonian Institution, 65, 265, 351

Smokestacks, 96, 323, 337 (also see Nest sites, manmade)

Smylie, Cherie, 244

Smylie, Jamie, 244

Smylie, Tom, 58, 66, 92, 128, 135, 144, 206, 244, 245, 280, 291, 292, 293, 317, 324, 327

Snake River Birds of Prey National Conservation Area, 137, 138

Snelling, John, 60, 63, 73-103

Snowman, Thom, 202

Society for Conservation Biology, 350

Society for the Prevention of Cruelty to Animals, 46

Solensky, M., 177

Sorrow, Jim, 77

Soulé, Michael, 350

Sovalik, Pete, 195

Sparrowhawk, British, 33

Sparrowhawk, Eurasian, 344, 347

Sparrowhawks, European, 169

Spear, Mike, 275

Special Purpose Permit, (see Permitting)

Species Survival Commission, 350

Species, legal definition, 262

Spencer, Donald G., 37

Spitzer, Paul, 73, 195

Spofford, Walter R., 37, 40, 43, 47, 49, 50, 51, 53, 57, 58, 63, 195, 280, 354, 359

Spohn, Jim, 137

Springer, Alan, 191

Stabler, Robert, 54, 58, 287, 307

Stahr, Elvis J., 75

Stansell, Ken, 273, 274

Stepaneck, Patricia, 238, 239, 241, 243, 245

Sterner, Debbie, 144

Sterner, Ken, 144, 145

Stevens, Dave, 152, 153

Stevens, Ronald, 169, 244, 327

Stevens, Ward, 108

Stevenson, Dan, 152, 304

Stickel, Lucille, 31, 33, 61, 82

Stickel, William, 31, 33, 61, 82

Stiehl, Mike, 69

Stiles, Harry, 268

Stoddart, Jack, 59, 128, 146, 280

Stolzenburg, Kurt, 69

Stoop, 2, 3, 4

Strahl, Eric, 129

Stream, Lee, 152

Street, Philip, 45

Striegler, Thomas L., 273

Strzalkowska, Stefania, 237

Stuart, Lyman K., 75

Sumida, Clark, 163

Sumner, Jay, 303

Survival, 175, 338, 339, 340, 345, 346

Sutton, George M., 86

Swartz, Jerry, 63, 190

Swem, Ted, 190, 191, 193, 195, 275

Tanana River, 21, 189, 190, 192

Tappan Zee Bridge, 96, 97

Taubert, Bruce, 293, 294

Taughannock Falls, 40, 86, 92, 93

Taylor, Gary, 77

Tellico Dam, 261

Temple, Stanley A., 63, 66, 73, 78, 85, 92, 93, 95, 195, 322, 350, 351

Tennyson, Alfred Lord, 354

Territorial adults, 175, 176

Territorial behavior, 4, 8, 9, 11, 180, 181, 197, 338

Territories, 157, 158, 160, 161, 163, 164, 165, 167, 169, 170, 171, 181, 321, 335, 336, 338, 339, 340, 342, 345, 346, 358

Territory fidelity, 340, 346 (also see Occupancy)

Terteling Company, 143

Terteling, Joe, 145

Testa, John, 138, 146

Texas Department of Parks and Wildlife, 218

Thacker, Roger, 271, 280, 292

Thelander, Carl, 156, 158, 163, 168, 298

Theresa, Sherry, 69

Thiessen, Jerry, 144

Thomas, Alan, 129

Thomas, Hugh, 168

Thomas, Rex, 144

Thompson, Patty, 118, 120

Thorsell, Richard, 75, 357, 358

Throgs Neck Bridge, 90, 99

Tibbitts, Tim, 60, 69

Time-lapse cameras, 202, 204

Titus, Kim, 216

Todd, Charlie, 77

Todd, Chris, 191

Tomilson, R. E., 52

DATE DUE

GAYLORD			PRINTED IN U.S.A.